MW00787550

Reader Reviews of The Grand Illusion

I believe that your writing is even more important than your admirers realize because it can help to awaken the influential leaders who already know that we must begin immediately to build a new paradigm. That cannot happen without a revised understanding about the true nature of consciousness. I know of no one who is grappling with the problem at your level...I will be sharing your writing with others. —John Holum, M.S., B.A.

––––––––

This is a rare find. So seldom do we find a single publication that covers consciousness and the overlap between science and spirituality from so many angles. Humanity needs more publications like this. If *The Grand Illusion* was a text book in our education systems, then the world would be a better place! —Peter Smith, founder of the Institute for Quantum Consciousness, author of *Quantum Consciousness – Expanding your personal universe,*

––––––––

I will recommend [TGI 1] in my future newsletters...What a wonderful job of collating and integrating you have done! Every person in the field of "paranormal" psychology or related topics should have this book as a major reference. This is a wonderful book! It is 500 pages of well researched alternative scientific research on topics not covered by narrow traditional physics, chemistry, and biology.

It could well serve as a liberal scientific alternative course for one or perhaps two college semesters. It will really open the students' minds to what is going on in the world, not just the narrow worlds taught in college nowadays.

The book is clearly written, well organized, and thoroughly referenced. I read it twice taking a whole year to comprehend it all...Hooray for Brendan Murphy! —Dr. Buryl Payne, buryl.com

––––––––

Stunningly good. One of the best synthesis books on this sort of material I have ever read. Actually, no: it WAS the best. I've been re-reading it non-stop since finishing it the first time to soak more of it in. SO very well done. Can't wait for part 2. —Mark Jeffrey, Founder & CEO Guardian Circle, author of the *Max Quick Trilogy*

––––––––

Brendan Murphy has no doubt been synthesizing information for many lifetimes, and with *The Grand Illusion*, he knocks it out of the park. This is a brilliant compendium of evidence that unarguably demonstrates the existence of the implicate order - aka the aether, the source field, time-space, the zero point field, etc. - and how the (re)introduction of this aspect of reality into our cosmology presents a simple and elegant explanation of "paranormal" phenomenon such as remote viewing, distance and energy healing, and telepathy. Murphy arms the open-minded and disarms the skeptics, and goes a long way in the effort to erase the line in the sand of the science/spirit duality that in many ways defines (and contributes to the sickness of) our culture.
—Eileen McKusick, author of *Tuning the Human Biofield*, biofieldtuning.com

———

This book is outstanding, thorough, well researched information, bridging the gap between science, energy and the "ether" spiritual realm. Just brilliant. Quite the textbook! Thank you Brendan for this work! —Colleen Cheketri, holistic naturopath, colleencheketri.com.au

———

Brendan is the Chomsky of the spiritual movement. Such incredible quantities of research jam packed into a very readable format. Brendan synthesizes the work of several leading researchers all on one page, page after page. His research and knowledge is breathtaking, yet he is able to deliver it in a digestible way. His work wades into debates within quantum physics and succinctly follows the trail of academic discussion accurately and easily. He incorporates studies and experiments with academic writing to form a seamless discussion amongst the giants of the field. The train of thought delivered in his writing is both a history of discovery in the field of quantum *and* metaphysics, as well as a piece that clarifies and demonstrates the concepts in a clear and easy to read manner. It is 500 pages of quality. Not for the faint of heart, but a treasure trove for the intrepid. —Alistair Larmour, channel and medical intuitive, alistairlarmour.com

———

The Grand Illusion was a fascinating read, I couldn't put it down until I'd finished reading it. I love the combination of science, especially physics, with psychic experiments and suchlike. As someone who has degrees in engineering design but is also a Reiki Master-Teacher and training for lay Buddhist priesthood I appreciate open-minded scientific analysis. —Denise M.

———

Truly amazing. This is the book that all of us with highly developed psychic abilities have been longing for. Brendan methodically deals with each aspect of the paranormal and validates them all with extensive references to scientific research through the ages right up to current knowledge on quantum physics and string theory. He sets out to take the "para" out of paranormal and succeeds. A work of absolute genius and an essential reference book for anyone interested in the science of the (para)normal. This is a truly mind-stretching work. You will never look on this world through the same old eyes ever again. With the help of this book, we can break free of our false conceptions and liberate our souls. This book should be gifted by all world Governments as a manual of life to all children born into this world to educate them as to what "life" on this "planet" really is about. A must-read for any spiritual person. And anyone who isn't. —Roderick Shelton

———

This young man is genius quality. No doubt about it. Skimming was impossible. I wanted to get as much info from the book as I could. Others will too. —Alan Glassman, 2013, reviewer for *New Dawn* magazine (full *New Dawn* review at back)

———

THE GRAND ILLUSION

Book One

A Synthesis of Science and Spirituality

BRENDAN D. MURPHY

For all humankind, that you may remember
who and what you truly are.

The thing that we find today of opposition between science and spiritual knowledge is a plant of modern growth and does not come from the ancient world. —Annie Besant, *Self and its Sheaths* (1894)

Let the mind be enlarged . . . to the grandeur of the mysteries, and not the mysteries contracted to the narrowness of the mind.
—Francis Bacon

CONTENTS

LIST OF FIGURES

PREFACE

Condemnation without investigation is the height of ignorance. —Einstein

The purpose of Book One of *The Grand Illusion* (TGI) is essentially that of opening the mind and expanding consciousness, in order to remind the reader who and what he or she *really* is, beyond their persona. We will do this by exploring the deep interrelationship between science and what is popularly dubbed "spirituality." Aside from the fact that such an endeavour is intensely interesting and transformative on a personal level, there is a larger transpersonal imperative that compels us, for, when science and spirituality "are forcibly kept apart," as independent scholar John Major Jenkins observes, "the result is the crisis of the modern world." However, on the other hand, "when our consciousness allows them to integrate, the pathway through to a sustainable future opens."[1]

With the goal of raising consciousness and opening a path to a sustainable future in mind, I have used an eclectic array of sources from around the globe, and spanning thousands of years. Why limit ourselves to the last 200 years, or even just the last 2,000? Recorded human history goes back at least 5,000 years, and mythology and legend far, far further. The point is that the more information we take into account, the broader our context is for assessing information, and the more interesting, detailed and full a picture we can paint for ourselves.

In that sense, I don't care whether someone is a Christian mystic, yogi, Freemason, spiritualist, mediumistic Catholic priest, historian, atheist, theosophist, hands-on healer, doctor, lawyer, general, neurosurgeon, Tibetan Buddhist, hypnotherapist, psychiatrist, ufologist, journalist, police officer, kabbalist, biologist, reverend, child, quantum physicist, rabbi, archaeologist, black magician, porn star, or psychic ferret—if they have useful and/or insightful information, I will use it to illustrate a point.

This does not mean that we have to agree with every little thing any given individual said, believed, did, does (or was accused of doing) in their lifetime. Personal controversies do not interest us here. An exploration of consciousness and the nature of reality must be larger than any one persona it encounters, for is not the universe larger than a single man or woman? Ordinary human vision, thought and belief is limited. "Beware the man with a single book."

To clarify: quoting from, say, a theosophist doesn't *make* someone a theosophist any more than going to church makes someone a "true Christian" (or standing in a garage makes someone a car), as they say. But if a theosophist has perceptive and important metaphysical information that is also verifiable, then it would be ridiculous *not* to utilize it if our goal is to seek after truth, or to attain Reality. If our goal was merely to preserve a pre-existing belief structure, then partiality, prejudice, and selectivity would be acceptable, even commendable—but that is not the case here. Here there are no sacred cows, and personally, I therefore find the grass that little bit greener. I hope you do too.

Researching and writing this book (and its follow-ups) has been a large undertaking, a massive personal investment of my time and energy beginning at age 24 and continuing for about five years thereafter. In fact I initially produced such a behemoth of a book that it had to be divided into two parts due to its size. Hence Book One of TGI is actually the first half of what was originally written as a single book. While Book One can and does stand alone as a single book, TGI 2 (which I refer to now as TGI 2) builds upon the material covered here and expands it, adding new dimensions, penetrating to new depths. It provides an even larger context within which to view Book One, both continuing our synthesis of science and metaphysics and probing the spiritual destiny of humankind.

Acknowledgements

A book like this is always a sort of group effort, despite the fact that only one name will be formally attached to it. I am indebted to my generous parents for not attempting to force-fit me into one of society's prefabricated politically correct boxes (no matter how much they probably would have liked to!), and ultimately allowing me to be myself instead of the System's "vision" of what I "should" have become. I am also forever grateful to my grandmother Olive whose support and generosity over the years will never be forgotten. I was blessed to have her as my Nan.

My gratitude extends also to Deanna for her belief and moral support the whole way through the writing of TGI—and indeed for urging me to actually write such a book. My most sincere thanks go to Venetia Somerset, who has volunteered so much of her own time and energy at crucial stages to ensure the publication of this book—because she believes in what it says. It's a rare privilege to encounter someone who just "gets it," and I have been blessed she chose to so selflessly work on this. This book would not have been possible otherwise.

Thanks also to: the wonderful Isis Graywood for donating her artistic talents and design skills, both to this book and my Facebook pages (in the early days); Sol Luckman for being one of the good guys (and also for the Regenetics Method!); Dave Yurth for some valuable email exchanges and great quotes from *Seeing Past the Edge* (rock on!); Michael Talbot for waking me up with *The Holographic Universe*; my brother Dave for telling me about Talbot's book all those years ago!; David at *New Dawn* magazine for such generous support; Duncan at *Nexus* magazine—a great friend and ally; the amazing Lauretta Sela (and Amanda Jane) at *Mindscape* magazine; Kerrie Wearing at *inSpirit* magazine; the ever-hectic Nat at Barker Deane Publishing, Australia (who always found time to return my emails!); Josh Del Sol for being such a great guy and for

Take Back Your Power, Nick Sambrook, author of *IT: Blue Angel Knight*, who has probably saved me hundreds or even thousands of hours of thought and study for subsequent books (I'll explain in TGI 2), and whose friendship and support I'm truly grateful for (along with Jan's); the awesome Dylan Charles at wakingtimes.com; Dr Buryl Payne; Steve Bartlett at Nexus magazine (for typesetting and being generally useful as well as generous with his time); Ryan and Andy at wakeup-world.com; Phillip J. Watt for some cheeky social media help; the tireless Luke Lawless at Elegant Logic for being our IT Mr Fix It; the amazing and generous Michelle Stark for pro bono typesetting and meme work; every single reader whose testimonial features in these pages; my friends near and far who have helped "spread the word" to get this book into the hands of the people who will benefit most (such as the wonderful Tamara Dunn).

I'd also like to express my appreciation to those who have indirectly contributed to the construction of this book through the suggestion of excellent and valuable research materials. I might not have stumbled across them without you acting as extra pairs of eyes for me.

Lastly, though foremost, with the publishing of this new edition under the banner of GFM Press, it is only fitting that I pay tribute humbly to the most important woman and human being in my life: my amazing one-of-a-kind partner in thought-crime Aimee a.k.a. the Tiny Goddess. Everyone needs a "blue fairy" but few are so privileged as to have one. Thank you for being my Trinity.

ABBREVIATIONS

ALP	alkaline phosphatase
Anpsi	animal psi
CMS	closed-minded skeptics
CSE	cavity structural effect
CU	consciousness unit
D-space	direct space
DIA	Defense Intelligence Agency
DMILS	Distant Mental Influence of Living Systems
DMT	dimethyltryptamine
EEG	electroencephalogram
ELF	extremely low frequency
EM	electromagnetic
ESP	extrasensory perception
FFA	free fatty acid/s
GCP	Global Consciousness Project
GDV	gas discharge visualization
GR	general relativity
HEF	human energy field
Hz	Hertz
HSP	higher sense perception
IIED	intention-imprinted electronic device
LSD	lysergic acid diethylamide
Magma	magnetic plasma
MPA	micro-psi atom
NDE	near-death experience
OBE	out-of-body experience
PEAR	Princeton Engineering Anomalies Research

PIP	Polycontrast Interference Photography
PK	psychokinesis
R-space	reciprocal space
RNA	ribonucleic acid
RNG	random number generator
RV	remote viewing
SPR	Society for Psychical Research
SRI	Stanford Research Institute
SRV	scientific remote viewing
UED	unimprinted electronic device
UEF	universal energy field
UPA	ultimate physical atom (also *anu*)
ZPF	zero point field

INTRODUCTION

If we cannot openly challenge beliefs . . . we stand at risk of being enslaved by them, and manipulated by those who would impose them for sinister purposes. 2,400 years ago Socrates said that the unexamined life is not worth living. Equally so, it could be said that the unexamined belief is not worth holding.
—John Lamb Lash, <metahistory.org>

It is a great but terrible thing when doubt is born, terrible in that it destroys the old world, great in that it opens the way to a new and nobler one.
—J.J. van der Leeuw

What if . . . ?

Have you ever wondered what is actually real? Ever questioned whether there might be more to consciousness than solely electrochemical activity in the brain? Have you ever wondered if those strange experiences where your mind and awareness seemed to reach beyond the bounds of your cranium—or even breached the boundaries of space-time—might have been real? Do you believe that humans are capable of more than the reductionists would ask you to believe? Have you ever pondered what might happen when we die? Do you want to know the difference between believing and *knowing*?

What if I told you that within the pages of this book you can find a synthesis of science and spirituality that could leave you and your perception of yourself, consciousness and reality irrevocably altered in a way you never conceived to be possible? What if I told you that some of the best known occult/paranormal phenomena are now irrefutably scientifically proved? What if I went further and said that today there is such a confluence between science and the world's mystical and occult phenomena and traditions that there is no reason *not* to believe that you, that is, your consciousness, is actually . . . *immortal*, as these traditions hold?

Well guess what? That's exactly what I'm saying.

The Search for Reality

I started assembling this book (and its companion volumes) soon after turning 24. The writing had been on the wall for some time, clearly indicating the inevitability of this undertaking, though it took me a while to actually realize that I was always "destined" to write this book—anything to avoid a "real job"!

It all started one day when my younger brother came home from school having watched an address given to him and his peers by a young entrepreneurial type, a successful young man who was sharing some of his wisdom and experience. My brother was extremely impressed, not just by the accomplishments of this young man in his short life but also by his inspirational oratory, so when my brother got home the rest of the family heard all about it.

One point that stood out for him was the mention of a book called *The Holographic Universe* by the late physicist Michael Talbot. It sounded extremely provocative—the role that consciousness and belief play in creating our lives, perceptions, and sense of reality—and so I made a mental note to check this book out. It was several months before I got around to it, being something of a congenital procrastinator, but when I did, the information that confronted me was something I was totally unprepared for. My amorphous hybrid existential philosophy (if you could call it a philosophy) of "Christian materialism" that assumed the world of the five senses was the only reality (as per established scientific orthodoxy), but that also—paradoxically—held the possibility of some sort of vague Christian afterlife, was shattered overnight.

My ignorance of the nature of consciousness and reality was exposed sharply and my mind was blown wide open. Following this profound metanoia I was never the same again. Up to that point my vision of possibility had been the size of a pea. Having finished Talbot's book, it had expanded by many orders of magnitude. I believe I was 19 or 20 years of age at the time, about four years before I started *consciously* and deliberately assembling research material for any books.

Spellbound, I read and reread this amazing book, soaking it in like a thirsty sponge, and soon after, I started reading for "leisure" once more, though now virtually the only thing on my radar was from the non-fiction section, so to speak. I had to know more.

It was some time in the next 12 months that I started to notice and experience things I had never noticed or experienced before. It was almost as if the fabric of the universe had opened itself up to me in welcome—about time, Brendan. About time. And so I continued to pay close attention, as well as reading and taking notes as I read. I had gone from an almost casual Christian believer, to atheist, to agnostic, to . . . here, wherever that is.

It was the note-taking and the marking of pages that should have been the giveaway—most people don't abuse their books as I do, squeezing the information out as a sun-beaten and dehydrated man in the desert might wring a damp cloth for all the moisture it's got. The writing was on the wall, as I said. Sooner or later, I would attempt to take these notes and ponderings and arrange them into some humanly decipherable form.

This book is the result of over eight years of book research, experience of altered states of consciousness, meeting various interesting people, asking a lot of questions, watching a lot of documentaries and seminar presentations, and then reading some more.

Because Talbot's book had destroyed my own mental model of reality, and my sense of self to some extent, it freed me to simply investigate the nature of reality and consciousness without prejudice and without the fear of having cherished beliefs undermined by data or experiences that this model couldn't account for or incorporate—hence the contents of my Preface!

I quickly realized that for years, I (and almost everyone I had ever met) had all along been asking the wrong questions of mind, life, death, and reality itself. The real question, and the only one that really matters, is: what is consciousness? What are its capabilities? Its limitations—does it even have any? What are its experiential capacities? Where does it originate, so to speak? We must come to grips with these questions because the only way we can ever truly come to know anything about reality and our experiential capacity for it is through firsthand, conscious experience; without consciousness we can *know* nothing. Any knowledge of an "afterlife" or spiritual realities of any kind can only be known (as opposed to believed in) through direct conscious experience.

Rudolf Steiner made the same observation in 1913: "any human soul, by reflecting deeply, will in the long run be unable to disregard the fact that its most important questions concerning the meaning and significance of life must remain unanswered if there be no access to supersensible worlds."[1]

Belief or faith is not the same thing as knowledge or experience; it is investment in and identification with a mental construct, a conceptual matrix.

We must, I realized after my own consciousness paradigms were shattered, find a way to experience reality beyond our mental constructs. This book attempts, paradoxically, to explore consciousness and reality in the only way a book possibly can: via mental constructs, words, and the ideas, objects, and events they attempt to convey.

I hope the constructs I employ, whether just words and their syntax or linguistic devices such as analogy and metaphor, do not get too much in the way. Likewise, I hope the reader's own mental constructs, which include beliefs, assumptions, and preconceptions, do not get too much in the way and act as data filters that only allow the absorption of information that is aligned with the reader's own favorite mental constructs (models and their related beliefs). I hope the constructs contained in this book can assist the reader in improving their own, should they so desire. Here we must utilize constructs to go *beyond* constructs, for the world of the finite is only part of the story.

A genuinely talented psychic once told me I would "help a *lot* of people help themselves." Most of all, I hope she was right. On that note, let us begin . . .

Here is the history of occult science in a nutshell. (1) Once known. (2) Lost.
(3) Rediscovered. (4) Denied. (5) Reaffirmed, and by slow degrees,
under new names, victorious. —Reverend H.R. Haweis.

1

THE QUESTION OF CONSCIOUSNESS

Dogmatic belief systems, being innately biased, are the greatest of learning
contraceptives. Exploration systems, when truly impartial, are self-correcting and
produce knowledge rather than arbitrarily demanding faith. —Author

I shall not commit the fashionable stupidity of regarding everything
I cannot explain as fraud. —C.G. Jung

One must remember that historically logic and scientific methodology have not been
fixed and static systems but growing, dynamic processes.
—Raymond Moody

The Question of Consciousness

Etymologically, the word consciousness derives from the words *scire* (to know)
and *cum or con* (with). Consciousness is "to know with." So if you, the persona,
cognize (to know or be aware of), who are you cognizing with? Is there more to
consciousness than the Freudian ego and unconscious?

Mathematical physicist Roger Penrose has written:

> A scientific world-view which does not profoundly come to
> terms with the problem of conscious minds can have no serious

1

pretensions of [*sic*] completeness . . . I would maintain that there is yet no physical, biological, or computational theory that comes very close to explaining our consciousness or intelligence.[1]

Indeed, in the past (and even today?) some scientists had taken the absurd position that consciousness is an illusion. This, while providing a nonsensical reason to ignore the problem of consciousness, obviously fails to sate the curious inquirer's queries regarding how we got here and what we are doing here as conscious beings. Materialistic philosophy as we know it—derived from the mechanistic worldview—had, more or less since the dawning of the Age of Reason in the 1700s, steadfastly maintained that what we call experience arises solely as a by-product of the brain's internal workings. No brain, no consciousness. But is it really that simple? What about functions of consciousness that appear to transcend the cranial boundaries of our heads? The Age of Reason said that these forces had only ever existed in man's imagination; only reason could show man the truth about the universe. "The trouble was," according to Colin Wilson, "that man became a thinking pygmy, and the world of the rationalists was a daylight place in which boredom, triviality and ordinariness were ultimate truths."[2]

The Age of Reason glorified the rationalist, who, enamoured of his endless linear cogitations, was blinded to faculties of consciousness that actually transcended them: faculties that would have allowed him not to merely philosophize about deeper levels of reality, but actually access them. "This is the great tragedy of modern man," wrote occultist, philosopher, and composer Dane Rudhyar. "His much acclaimed scientific spirit frees him of the compulsions of subrational and subconscious states of mind, only to bind him to an empty rationalism and a quantitative analytical intellect, both of which actually entomb him in a sarcophagus filled with only the mimicry of life. This sarcophagus is the 'megalopolis'—the monstrous city."[3]

But something stirs in the bowels of the concrete jungle. An international online survey of paranormal experiences had met with an overwhelming response, according to Australian researchers in 2006. The survey, on phenomena that cannot be explained using the current "laws" of science, is by researchers at Monash University in Melbourne. A recent (for the time) Gallup poll revealed that 75% of Americans hold at least one paranormal belief, and a UK newspaper poll showed that 60% of Britons accept the existence of the paranormal, say the researchers. According to the researchers, the survey is not about beliefs or whether parapsychological phenomena exist, rather it is about what people have experienced and the impact it has had on their lives.

Some 2,000 people had made contact via the internet within six weeks of the survey beginning. A whopping 96% of respondents claim to have had at least one brush with the paranormal. The exercise seeks to gauge the frequency, effect, and age of onset of unexplained phenomena such as premonitions, out-of-body and near-death episodes, telepathy, and apparitions. Results as of 2006 showed that 70% of respondents believe an unexplained event changed their lives, mostly in a positive way. Some 70% also claim to have seen, heard, or been touched by an animal or person that wasn't there, 80% report having had a premonition, and almost 50% recalled a previous life.[4] In May 2000, the *New York Times Sunday Magazine* published results of a poll conducted by Blum & Weprin Associates; a huge 81% said they believed in life after death.[5]

Virtually all of these beliefs hint at (and require in order to be true) the existence of other realms—other realms in which consciousness can operate. A 2005 poll taken by the Scottish paranormal society showed that more people are likely to believe in ghosts and the paranormal than have faith in any organized religion. A Gallup survey taken in 2005 showed that about three in four Americans profess at least one paranormal belief.[6] This is a massive amount of "paranormal" experience and belief—all of it depending on the existence of other levels of reality, without which such experience can only be labeled as delusion and fantasy. While the fanatical skeptic would find such convenience irresistible, convenience and expedience are not our goals here.

Did you know that the American Psychiatric Association's *Diagnostic and Statistical Manual of Mental Disorders* (DSM) has now been amended so that genuinely psychic people are no longer considered "disordered"?[7]

Intuition and Creativity

Srinivasa Ramanujan (born in India, 1887–1920) has been called the strangest man in all of mathematics, probably in the entire history of science. Working in isolation from his peers, this genius was single-handedly able to re-derive a hundred years' worth of Western mathematics. As Michio Kaku reports in *Hyperspace*, the tragedy of his life is that much of his work was wasted rediscovering known mathematics.[8] Most interesting to us, Ramanujan said that the goddess Namakkal inspired him in his dreams; in other words, the source of his creative genius was this other realm within his sleep, rather than ordinary waking consciousness.

Is there a link between this other realm of sleep and paranormal phenomena? At a glance, such a presumption appears to be a stretch, but the reservation of judgment is highly recommended at this point. Carl Jung once said: "The images and ideas that dreams contain cannot possibly be explained solely in terms of memory. They express new thoughts that have never yet reached the threshold of consciousness."[9]

Ramanujan appears to provide an excellent example of the type of non-ordinary information access that the Russian paranormal researchers might call *hypercommunication*, and he isn't alone among specialists, pioneers, giants of science, and so-called regular people. In fact, pioneer psychiatrist and consciousness researcher Stanislav Grof found that during LSD experiences his own patients were capable of accessing the "collective unconscious," obtaining very specific, accurate, and detailed knowledge. In the LSD training program for scientists,

> relevant insights occurred in fields as diverse as cosmogenesis, the nature of space and time, subatomic physics, ethology, animal psychology, history, anthropology, sociology, politics, comparative religion, philosophy, genetics, obstetrics, psychosomatic medicine, psychology, psychopathology, and thanatology.[10]

Ramanujan, assuming he really did receive detailed formulas in his dreams via the subconscious, provides perhaps some indication of just how accurate and detailed this knowledge can be. As we will see, these insights that defy the Freudian and Newtonian-Cartesian (reductionist) worldview/s abound in the literature. In 1862 the chemist Friedrich August von Kekule famously arrived at the solution for the chemical formula for benzene in a dream wherein he saw the benzene ring in the form of a snake biting its tail—an archetypal symbol in itself—the Ouroburos. In a supreme historical irony, Descartes' principles of what ultimately became the mechanist philosophy originated from a dream on the eve of St. Martin's day of 1619 in which the "Angel of Truth" explained to him that mathematics was the key to unlocking the secrets of Nature![11] Similarly,

> Nikola Tesla constructed the electric generator . . . after the complete design of it appeared to him in great detail in a vision. The design for the experiment leading to the Nobel Prize–winning discovery of the chemical transmission of nerve impulses occurred to the physiologist Otto Leowi while he

was asleep. Albert Einstein discovered the basic principles of his special theory of relativity in an unusual state of mind; according to his description, most of the insights came to him in the form of kinaesthetic sensations.[12]

Einstein had said: "The supreme task of the physicist is to arrive at those universal elementary laws from which the cosmos can be built up by pure deduction. There is no logical path to these laws; only intuition, resting on sympathetic understanding of experience, can reach them."[13]

Many of the great scientists have said very similar things. From out of nowhere a revelatory vision or understanding hits them, as if suddenly downloaded into their minds from some esoteric conceptual repository. It is interesting that many people find in lucid dreams that they can learn skills that translate directly into real waking life or they can solve problems in the conscious dream state that in the physical world had stumped them, and moreover, these solutions *actually work*.[14] Francis Crick was under the influence of LSD in 1953 at the moment when he perceived the double helix shape and unraveled the structure of DNA.[15] The chemist D. I. Mendeleyev saw his entire periodic table of elements one night in a dream. And of course, many of history's greatest and most successful musical artists came up with their best material under the influence of one drug or another.

Oprah Winfrey says, "My business skills have come from being guided by my inner self—my intuition."[16] She's not alone among the financially abundant. Researchers have tested CEOs of successful corporations for their ability to see the future, such as by predicting a string of numbers they would be shown later. They found that the CEOs who are good at this are usually those who are also highly successful in running their corporations, while CEOs who did not have this ability tend to have mediocre success rates in their corporations. "In one study," says Dr. Larry Dossey, "experimenters were able to predict in advance the most successful corporate balance sheets by how well the CEOs did on tests that measured their ability to predict the future, such as a string of numbers they'd be shown later."[17]

In 1982 the *St. Louis Business Journal* tested how a psychic would fare against professional stockbrokers over a six-month period, and reported that the psychic, who had no formal training in stockmarket trading or analysis, outperformed 18 of 19 professional stockbrokers. During the testing period, the Dow Jones Industrial Average fell 8% but the psychic's stocks went up an average of 17.2%, while the sole broker who beat her achieved 17.4%.[18] Physicist and psi researcher Russel Targ's research group Delphi Associates succeeded in psychically forecasting for nine consecutive weeks the fluctuations in the silver commodity futures markets, earning them a tidy $120,000.[19] Psi* techniques are playing an increasingly important role on Wall Street, according to Dean Radin's sources.[20] In 1987 Richard S. Broughton, scientist and former president of the Parapsychological Association, pointed to the need-serving nature of psi and the competitive advantage it often provides in the struggle for survival—Darwinists rejoice.[21]

Many scientists have had profound interests in fields beyond the reach of the science of their day. For instance, Isaac Newton was an obsessive alchemist[22] and Freemason in search of the way to transform consciousness, Thomas Edison built machines to try to facilitate communication with the dead, and Marie Curie attended séances. The list of such eminent scientists with keen interests in the paranormal goes on and on. Is it a credible suggestion that they all were merely deluded into pursuing these areas by cunning charlatans or irrational, wishful thinking? We are about to see that there is clearly more to it than this. Even Freud, whose attitude towards the occult was originally negative, changed his tune as he matured and learned more about it, suggesting, in a 1949 paper called *Psychoanalysis and Telepathy*, a union between psychoanalysts and occultists: "[O]ne might expect a mutual sympathy between the two . . . [A]n alliance of, and collaboration between, psychoanalysis and occultists would seem to be both plausible and promising."[23]

What about those modern-day scientists and professionals who have experiences in the "paranormal" realm? Brian Weiss, psychiatrist, hypnotherapist, and author, wrote:

> The respected chairman of a major clinical department at my hospital is a man who is admired internationally for his expertise. He talks to his deceased father, who has several times protected him from serious danger. Another professor has dreams that provide the missing steps or solutions to his complex research experiments. The dreams are invariably correct. Another well-known doctor usually knows who is calling him on the phone before he answers it . . . [24]

---

* Psi (pronounced "sigh") is a term for parapsychological (occult) phenomena derived from the Greek, *psi*, twenty-third letter of the Greek alphabet; from the Greek *psyche*, "mind, soul." First used in a parapsychological context by biologist B.P. Wiesner, it was first used in print by British psychologist Robert Thouless in 1942.

If these insights come from only one man, imagine what else we might be missing out on.

No Sacred Cows

With so many people (many indeed being iconic historical figures) experiencing what they are supposedly not meant to, the reasonable individual might be forgiven for wondering if there is something more to consciousness than our materialistic paradigms would have us believe. Can we go further than questioning the assumed legitimacy of orthodox materialistic theories which reduce consciousness to a mere epiphenomenon (by-product) of physical matter (the brain) and even—heaven forbid—suggest that they are not merely incomplete, but actually types of *superstitions* in themselves? W. Heitler, a theoretical physicist at the University of Zurich, thinks so and says in his book *Man and Science*:

> Belief in a mechanistic universe is a modern superstition . . . based on a more or less extensive series of correct facts, facts which are subsequently generalized without warrant, and finally so distorted that they become grotesque . . . The "witch superstition" cost innumerable innocent women their lives, in the cruelest fashion. The mechanistic superstition is more dangerous . . . When once we have got to the stage of seeing in man merely a complex machine, what does it matter if we destroy him?[25]

The process of generalizing without warrant, as Heitler puts it, is essentially the process of inductive logic that is theoretical science's proverbial bread and butter, starting with particular data or concepts and then extrapolating out or deriving broader generalizations (that may or may not be accurate). As we shall see with the mechano-materialistic outlook, many of these broad generalizations are inaccurate. An example: scientists discover that brainwave states and neurochemical processes affect and alter states of consciousness and perception. From this, the materialistic scientist draws the conclusion (interprets) that consciousness is therefore entirely a brain-based phenomenon. Inductive logic is a great way to go drastically wrong while remaining entirely logical within a given framework.

Deductive logic works the other way: you start with broader conclusions/premises and try to draw more detailed facts. This too obviously has its limitations. You could make the complete opposite mistake; for example, someone has an "out-of-body experience" and concludes that, since they could still perceive while completely separate from brain and body, therefore the brain has *nothing* to do with human consciousness. This is a silly example, but may illustrate the point. Incidentally, the Tibetan word for body is *lü*, which means something you leave behind, like baggage.[26] Could the Tibetans know something we sophisticated Westerners don't?

I shall state confidently from the outset that consciousness does *not* arise from the brain; however, once *anchored* by the brain, the brain mediates conscious experience (unless consciousness is completely separated from the brain as in the "near-death experience" in particular, which we will deal with later). "Yes! says the quantum theorist, because changing the measurement apparatus does certainly change what can be measured, and therefore changes the event."[27]

Canadian brain researcher and specialist Dr. Michael Persinger, who discovered connections between electromagnetic (EM) fields and changes to the brain's temporal lobe, established that exposure to weak magnetic fields can induce altered states of awareness reminiscent of psychic and mystical experiences, the sensing of a "presence," experiences of "God," and other physical effects. The temporal lobe has been linked to out-of-body and mystical experiences, as well as to feelings of dissociation and hallucinations, by neuroscientist Peter Brugger.[28] Such studies in the nascent field of neurotheology do indeed show the mediation of conscious experience by the brain, but to infer from these facts that the brain actually generates consciousness where previously there was none is an unjustifiable and counterproductive leap of faith.

The brain acts, as authors such as Grof have put it, as a "reducing valve" for consciousness, tuning and altering it, acting as a conduit rather than the generator. Case in point: studies in near-death experiences (dealt with here but in even greater depth in TGI 2) reveal that transcendent states of awareness can be experienced by people who are clinically dead, with no brain function or signs of life at all. Offering validity to their claims, many have returned with true information gleaned while they were dead (sometimes from distant locations) that they—according to the brain-as-generator theory—should not have had awareness of, let alone access to. Similarly, respected computer engineer and author Bernardo Kastrup points out that, contrary to accepted wisdom, psychedelics produce "hallucinations" not by stimulating brain activity, but by *reducing* it. "Reduction of brain activity impairs the filter/localization mechanism, allowing one to temporarily and partially escape its entrapment and come closer to perceiving reality as it truly is."[29]

According to the eloquent metaphysicist and co-founder of theosophy Helena Petrovna Blavatsky, Professor George T. Ladd, a psychologist and philosopher, observed in the late 1800s that the "assumption that the mind is a real being, which can be acted upon by the brain, and which can act on the body through the brain, is the only one compatible with all the facts of experience."[30] Nothing has changed since then. More recently, physicist Amit Goswami's revelation was that he had vainly been seeking a description of consciousness within science, when "instead, what I and others have to look for is a description of science within consciousness."[31]

It was (and is) in fact the former approach that had gotten so much in the way of progressing our understanding of consciousness. Fellow physicist the late Evan Walker was more specific, commenting that "an understanding of psi phenomena and of consciousness must provide the basis of an improved understanding of [quantum mechanics]."[32]

Paradigm Shifts and Cognitive Dissonance

A paradigm is variously defined as

- distinct concepts[33]
- a set of assumptions, concepts, values, and practices that constitutes a way of viewing reality for the community that shares them[34]
- an example or pattern, especially an outstandingly clear or typical example or archetype.[35]

The information we are going to be discussing regarding what we will call the nonlocality of consciousness and its being the foundation of reality is not part of the dominant scientific paradigm. Collectively, the endless examples of the nonlocal action of consciousness constitutes, for the less open-minded scientists, little more than a nagging nuisance, or even a heretical blasphemy to diehard mechano-materialistic fanatics. But it won't go away. Like it or not, we are making the transition from one paradigm to the next—and doing so increasingly rapidly. Physics has not recognized the supposed objectivity of the world of "solid matter" for decades, and it cannot separate matter, space, energy, or time from one another. Mainstream physics has also run into the fact that quanta appear to have no definite existence when no one is looking, at least not as we understand existence in common terms. Physics has encountered consciousness. The hardest science of all suddenly went soft and spawned a generation of physicist-philosopher-mystics who have done their best to awaken somnambulant humanity.

Though philosophical and scientific pretenders assume the throne throughout time as we endlessly re-create our ontology (loosely, our sense of what is true or real), we can observe that throughout history the human race has experienced "paranormal" events and possessed "paranormal" abilities known in yogic philosophy as the *siddhis*, all of which continues to be the case today. The paranormal is not new, nor has it ever really gone away, but it is important to realize that only fairly recently in history was it considered as something *other* than normal, thanks to the transient construct known as philosophical materialism, whose view of reality was so narrow that anything outside the range of everyday banality was going to be consigned to the realm of the damned/paranormal.

The materialistic worldview is only the most recent of four overturned basal paradigms that humanity has moved through over the last 5,000 years. The previous three were animism, polytheism, and monotheism. What will the next paradigm be? Lipton and Bhaerman dub it simply "holism"—what will ultimately be a non-dualistic and integrated view of mind and "matter," one which places all beings in an interconnected and thus interdependent web of life which evolves fractally and also *purposively*.[36]

Today, scientists seriously research invisibility technology, anti-gravity technology, free energy, telepathy, psychokinesis, quantum biology, reincarnation, teleportation, precognition, mediumship, biocommunication, acausality, retrocognition, and more. The data from these pursuits accumulates at an impressive and even intimidating pace. It will not all be cast aside merely for the ideological convenience of the hardcore skeptics (what I refer to as "skeptics," in quotes). Rather, this research, manifesting such profound novelty as it does, is primarily what will cause the profound shift from one paradigm to the next, leaving the most dogged skeptics behind and "converting" the flexible remainder. In so doing, it will be mirroring the overall process of the evolution of the collective human psyche as it becomes more self-aware, knowledgeable, and perceptive. This is merely a function of the larger organism of which we are a part (the universe) becoming increasingly self-aware in its continued evolution. However, at the moment, it appears that very few people are aware that the stock skeptical arguments against psi have been addressed and dismantled in detail and are no longer valid.

Radin points out in the beginning of *The Conscious Universe* that new scientific discoveries tend to go through four predictable stages:

> In Stage 1, skeptics confidently proclaim that the idea is impossible because it violates the Laws of Science. This stage can last for years or for centuries, depending on how much the idea challenges conventional wisdom. In Stage 2, skeptics reluctantly concede that the idea is possible but that it is not very interesting and the claimed effects are extremely weak. Stage 3 begins when the mainstream realizes not only that the idea is important but that its effects are much stronger and more pervasive than previously imagined. Stage 4 is achieved when the same critics who previously disavowed any interest in the idea begin to proclaim that they thought of it first. Eventually, no one remembers that the idea was once considered a dangerous heresy.
>
> The idea discussed in this book is in the midst of the most important and the most difficult of the four transitions—from Stage 1 into Stage 2.[37]

The transition from the first stage to the second, Radin says, is the most difficult because the initial challenge to the mental-egoic level's sense of self/identity as defined by this 3-dimensional (3D) temporal realm (or 3-space) has not been overcome, or, indeed, fully comprehended by the critics. This initial phase of challenge is threatening to the ego, because it represents what would ultimately become an ego transcension, a reaching out beyond one's comfortable cognitive and conceptual limits, which the ego, of course, fearfully views as its own death. It whispers subtly that "it's a fraud," or "they are deluded," and offers all sorts of puerile attempts at distracting the rational intellect from factual information, in the hope that it can stave off its inevitable self-perceived doom.

Stage 1 is where the religiously anti-psi pseudo-skeptics and debunkers are the most vocal (and numerous): the data is least familiar at this stage, and thus at its most threatening. On some level they appear to realize that if they fail in their bid to prevent rational investigation into the phenomena in question, the end is nigh, at least in terms of their egoically based conception of the world and their place within it (not to mention the cosmos at large). Tibetan master Sogyal Rinpoche comments eloquently on the ego delusion, stating that ego is the absence of true self-awareness, along with the resultant clutching to a transient makeshift identity, "an inevitably chameleon charlatan self that keeps changing and has to, to keep alive the fiction of its existence."[38]

In Tibetan, ego is called *dak dzin*, meaning "grasping at a self." Ego is then defined as incessant movements of grasping at a delusory notion of "I" and "mine," self and other, and all the concepts, ideas, desires, and activity poured into preserving that construct.[39] Gate-keeping activity by organized skepticism is, then, the natural mammalian-reptilian ego defence and preservation mechanism against consciousness research and "the paranormal": "Nothing to see here, folks, the only experiential reality is the world of the ordinary senses. You don't want to be duped by those cunning charlatans, do you? Keep moving . . . Or else."

The idea Dean Radin discussed in his book is that "psychic phenomena are real," but we will be taking things a measure further, placing them in a larger context: a holistic view of life, consciousness, and all manifest facets of reality.

Trans*cience*

We must remember not to mistake the model of the universe that exists in our conditioned intellects for the Universe. The late professor of physics and astronomy at the university of Massachusetts, Edward Harrison (1919–2007), stated that a (personal) universe is a mask fitted on the face of the unknown Universe (capital "U").[40] In 1985 he had the humility to acknowledge the subjectivity inherent in each of the universes described throughout history, including the universe of contemporary science. Would that the average "skeptic" possessed Harrison's genuine and rather egalitarian skepticism (some of the more open-minded skeptics actually seem to). He wrote:

> The people in the past believed in their universes. Here is a fact we tend not to dwell upon because of its disconcerting implications. We see the people in the past believing in the truth of their universes, and because they were mistaken, might we not also be a little mistaken? And if a little, well then, why not a lot, like all the rest? We dismiss the thought on the grounds that the people in the past were ignorant. But . . . conceivably our modern beliefs are also greatly mistaken, and perhaps one day a new universe [paradigm] will arise, grander than the [current] universe. Those living in the future will look

back in history and see our twentieth-century universe as out-of-date and mistaken like all the rest.[41]

Alan Watts may have said it best of all: "Reality is only a Rorschach ink-blot, you know." Science finds one meaning in it in the 18th century, another in the 19th, a third in the 20th.[42] It is logically impossible to prove that our everyday experience isn't all fantasy, as Wilson observed in *Cosmic Trigger*.[43]

A brief study of history reveals that science has always authored the universe in the image of man and his limited knowledge, beliefs, imagination, and technical achievements. Throughout this process inventors and scientists who did not merely bow to conventional wisdom produced heretical ideas that were initially considered blasphemy against the "laws" of science or nature, but which ultimately become acknowledged as common sense. But since the laws that govern the most fundamental scientifically known levels of existence are now seen to be statistical or probabilistic, there are no longer any absolutes to be violated: in mainstream physical theory electrons can vanish and reappear elsewhere through discontinuous "jumps," and they can also be in many places at the same time.[44] This uncertainty applies to every other property: an atomic nucleus' north pole can be in a superposition state simultaneously pointing up and down.[45]

It is interesting to note just how little poise and intelligence actually prevail when a powerful new concept is born into the world. The human persona/ego, which for most people defines itself through the five primary human senses and the models of the universe the brain creates based on those five senses, is quick to counteract any threat to its perceived status and identity. If the ego were to build a shrine to itself in this modern age, that shrine might be called "organized skepticism," which is largely a faith-based religion (pseudo-skepticism) characterized by uncritical belief in the models of the universe that comprise the status quo. "Paradigms," Grosso states, "are cultural straitjackets."[46]

Sogyal Rinpoche is scathing about our modern conceptual prisons, and he bemoans our society's "brilliant selling of samsara and its barren distractions," along with its "celebration of all the things that lead away from the truth, make truth hard to live for, and discourage people from even believing that it exists."[47] Indeed, Blavatsky declared near the close of the 19th century: "Nature gives up her innermost secrets and imparts *true wisdom* only to him who seeks truth for its own sake, and who craves for knowledge in order to confer benefits on others, not on his own unimportant personality."[48]

13

As a primer, let's take note of some interesting sentiments regarding previously heretical ideas that ultimately redefined science and our place in the world by eventually becoming accepted as common sense.[49] This should help us to come to grips with just how wrong a given paradigm's "facts" can be and the way in which we author our personal universes, while the Universe itself merely waits for us to catch on to the Facts of Nature:

- "There is not the slightest indication that nuclear energy will ever be obtainable. It would mean that the atom would have to be shattered at will." —Albert Einstein, 1932.

- "A man has been arrested in New York for attempting to extort funds from *ignorant* and *superstitious* people by exhibiting a device which he says will convey the human voice any distance over metallic wires so that it will be heard by the listener at the other end. He calls this instrument a telephone. Well-informed people know that it is impossible to transmit the human voice over wires." —News item in a New York newspaper, 1868 (emphasis added). Is it not interesting how those whose vision is not quite so restricted as the majority's are painted by the less perceptive as ignorant and superstitious? In the intervening 140+ years, little regarding the psychology of the closed-minded (dis) believer has changed.

- "Heavier-than-air flying machines are impossible." —William Thomson. Even Thomas Edison believed the same.

- "I think there is a world market for maybe five computers." —Thomas Watson, chairman of IBM, 1943.

- "The horse is here to stay but the automobile is only a novelty—a fad." —The President of the Michigan Savings Bank advising Henry Ford's lawyer, Horace Rackham, not to invest in the Ford Motor Co., 1903.

- "X-rays will prove to be a hoax." —Lord Kelvin, President of the Royal Society, 1883.

- In 1915, German meteorologist Alfred Wegener published his "ludicrous" theory that the Earth's continents had once been a single contiguous piece. In 1930, he died an intellectual outcast, and yet, today this idea is standard textbook material.

- "Earth is the center of the universe. Aren't we special?" This geocentrism was the general consensus prior to the Copernican revolution (and an important aspect of the Christian worldview). Copernicus—a student of Hermeticism—lived from 1473 to 1543 but it took some 200 years for the heliocentric model to replace the geocentric model. Giordano

Bruno (1548–1600) was burned at the stake for supporting Copernicus. Old models die hard. Amusingly, it is recorded that the scientists of the time were as dogmatic and resistant to giving Copernicus a fair hearing as the Church was. (No surprises there then.)

- "Separate physical systems cannot influence one another unless via known physical mechanisms at no greater than the speed of light." Virtually everyone in the "developed" world (except occultists, mystics, psychics, and shamanic streams) believed this before quantum physics showed up and proved entanglement and nonlocality to be a reality.

Let us now, in lieu of the material to come, confidently immortalize the present-day psi and paranormal naysayers for all the wrong reasons with the modern equivalent to belief in a flat Earth:

> There is no such thing as psi or the "paranormal." Telepathy, precognition, psychokinesis, OBEs, NDEs, levitation, clairvoyance, bilocation, communication with the dead, and so on, are merely delusions and fantasies held aloft by superstitious, gullible and/or ignorant people, or the charlatans duping them. Consciousness is merely an epiphenomenon of the brain, its effects strictly limited to one's cranium.

This notion that "only matter matters," as Lipton and Bhaerman put it in *Spontaneous Evolution*, will be explored (and dismantled) in some depth in the pages to follow—along with other key elements of the mechano-materialistic paradigm, including reductionism, genetic primacy, determinism, and the belief in blind/random evolution. In a lecture he gave at the University of Southwestern Louisiana Lafayette, Louisiana in 1989, the late venerable biologist and reincarnation researcher Ian Stevenson said:

> What [history] has taught me is the transience . . . of our material accomplishments and, even more, of our ideas about the nature of man . . . Knowledge in science, as Whitehead said, keeps like fish . . . For me everything now believed by scientists is open to question, and I am always dismayed to find that many scientists accept current knowledge as forever fixed. They confuse the product with the process.[50]

There is a Tibetan saying: "Theories are like patches on a coat, one day they just wear off."[51] Harrison wrote in *Masks of the Universe* that we cling to the laws of the universe for as long as we possibly can, and yet, they "are as impermanent as [our contrived] universes. Where are the laws of 1,000 years ago? . . . [W]here can be found a single fundamental law of physics that has survived unscathed for the last 200 years?"[52]

Disturbing questions such as these are too often eschewed by some "skeptics" of "the paranormal," who act as if they prefer to believe they just happen to have been born into a civilization or society whose worldview represents the pinnacle of all possible scientific knowledge and philosophy, and that none of that knowledge or philosophy is dubious or open to questioning. The last thing the dogmatist wants to face is the historical trend of one dogma after another crumbling under the weight of its combined incorrect assumptions and inferences. And yet, all through the history of cosmology, observed Harrison, we find the concept or map of the contemporary universe mistaken for the Universe. He noted that this misidentification was as rife in the modern world as at any time in the past.[53] Harrison also noted that while materialists recognize the gods as elaborate anthropomorphisms and regard them as a hangover from the mythical intoxications of the past, they commit the error of mistaking *their* mechanistic universe for the Universe—despite the fact that the mechanistic universe occupies the same conceptual level as the gods.[54]

The menu is not the meal/the map is not the territory. This is what writers such as Watts, Capra, Wilson, and Harrison have been attempting to open our minds to, the simple fact that the intellect's perceptions and ideas about reality are not Reality itself. Daniel Pinchbeck asks: "Is it far fetched to suggest that the deities of our secular age include the super-strings, selfish genes, Black Holes, and Big Bangs described by our scientists, that define the limits of the materialist world view?"[55] The answer implicit in this book is a definite "no" (though super-strings fare far better in these pages than, say, the postulated "Big Bang"). As psychical researcher John Randall states: "It is a feature of the snobbery of our age to imagine that because we have a greater accumulated knowledge of natural phenomena than our forebears, we are therefore less gullible than they were."[56]

The point of bringing to awareness the limitations of our reality tunnels or paradigms is to enable us to consciously and purposefully step outside those conditioned constraints and recognize the value of information that doesn't fit them. It is novelty that produces paradigm change and growth after all. As much as many skeptics loathe the kind of novelty or anomaly produced in a field such as parapsychology, like it or not, the fact that these anomalies exist and are recurring in prolific numbers indicates that the idealized scientific spirit of research and discovery is alive and kicking. We can see, if we look, that *the scientific method of any period has within it the seeds of that paradigm's demise*, because "the method," as it is refined and also *expanded on*, causes anomalies to be of special interest because they lead to the asking of new questions, and these questions yield exotic new results. The unexpected results lead to new understandings, new ideas, and new universes/reality tunnels—which then lead to more questions, etc., etc.

Later in the book we will look at a card experiment that was performed to inquire into the nature of perception, where participants in the experiment viewed normal playing cards from a normal deck with some anomalous altered cards mixed in. As we will see, conditioned expectation prevented some participants from correctly identifying the altered cards as what they were. Such results, when extrapolated out into the macrocosm of science or even life experience in general, are not particularly unusual. We see this process in action all the time as new data creates conflict in people's minds by ramming up against old data (not to imply that all old data is invalid, just that it often creates internal conflict in clashing with the new).

> In science . . . novelty emerges only with difficulty, manifested by resistance, against a background provided by conditioned expectation. Initially, only the anticipated and usual are experienced even under circumstances where anomaly is later to be observed. Further acquaintance, however, does result in awareness of something wrong or does relate the effect to something that has gone wrong before. That awareness of anomaly opens a period in which conceptual categories are adjusted until the initially anomalous becomes the expected. At this point the discovery has been completed.[57]

These last two sentences of Kuhn's are particularly salient in terms of the content of this book, because we can observe that this is the transition in progress when it comes to the nature of consciousness and reality itself.

As we hurtle unknowingly through 2012 and beyond, we are observing Paradigmatic Revolution, or what philosopher, composer, occultist, and astrologer Dane Rudhyar would have referred to as *civilization*, in the dynamic sense. The adherents to the old paradigm/s will (and historically always do) for the most part die off rather than develop an understanding of the new paradigm's data/models, and the up-and-comers of science's youth brigade will take over and continue pushing the boundaries, ever bridging the shrinking perceived gap between mind and matter. It is becoming increasingly widely acknowledged scientific fact that you cannot meaningfully discuss the implications and findings of quantum mechanics without including the effects of consciousness on the functioning of quantum systems. Less than a hundred years ago, firmly entrenched in the mechano-materialistic paradigm, we "knew" such a situation was impossible. Imagine where we might be in another hundred years.

If you can take a step back from the paradigm/model that dominates your mind and shapes your primary assumptions about life, and realize that this process of authoring the universe that science engages in so authoritatively has been going on since humans first existed, you might find yourself less upset about scientific research that redefines the boundaries of science and causes paradigms to evolve and grow (or die outright). Why? Because we can then realize that science *never* described the Universe to begin with (at least not in totality); *it built models of it, approximations*—and aspects of some of these models can even be mutually exclusive (such as quantum physics versus aspects of Einstein's relativity). These models were/are abstracted by science's experimental and observational findings, and, importantly, by those findings they were or are *yet to make* (or acknowledge!). Physicist Harold Puthoff commented in the 1990s:

> The paradigm has shifted, especially for those people close to the data, who have done experiments and seen the results. They've seen there is something to it and this has changed their world view.
>
> The public, by and large, rightly rejects what they see in the tabloids as probably being mostly nonsense, and this is probably true. Not having access to firsthand scientific or other kinds of data, for them the paradigm hasn't shifted.[58]

Thus, there is a time delay between groups with differing data sets (models of reality). Those with the firsthand personal knowledge live in a different universe, one that has made a significant step towards defining Reality as it presumably is, rather than worshipping theories that obfuscate the simple truth; theories that the ardent believers have mistaken for Reality itself. A dichotomy will shortly arise pertaining to this paradigm-shift time delay between groups as we begin to see that a pre-existing scientific paradigm may tell us one thing, while cutting-edge scientific research may state the complete opposite. Hence, science can seem slightly contradictory to a casual observer. It has been a common assertion (or insinuation) by so-called skeptics that "the paranormal" somehow violates some unspecified "law" or rule of science. Meanwhile more up-to-date and progressive research has put such notions to rest well and truly.

However, because of the lag between scientific discovery and the general acceptance of new phenomena by the scientific community at large, those who only possess the data and assumptions belonging to the pre-established view/model can hold beliefs that are perfectly socially acceptable yet totally inaccurate. This is the case with psi research and its disbelievers, as things currently stand. Larry Dossey has observed: "Most skeptics are poorly informed. They simply ignore the experiments showing that people can sense the future, because these studies create huge holes in their arguments."[59] There are those who wish to learn (and create new models of reality), and those who are content with belief in their current model/s. When skepticism's traditional core tenets (reductionism, realism, mechanism, determinism, etc.) become factually outdated and the "skeptic" still clings to them—and insists that others should too—then skepticism has become religion of the worst sort. As Dr. Christopher Humphrey says: "To restrict science to the visible and tangible is to build assumptions about the nature of reality into science. If we do that, how is science any different from religion?"[60]

Max Planck (1858–1947) said that "a new scientific truth does not triumph by convincing its opponents and making them see the light, but rather because its opponents eventually die, and a new generation grows up that is familiar with it."[61] As Kuhn noted, these fresh-eyed newcomers, being less conditioned by the traditional rules of "normal" science, are very likely to discard those rules in order to conceive another more workable set to replace them.[62] Thus, the problem isn't availability of facts, it's human psychology. As more young scientists access their own insights as well as the literature pertaining to the new paradigm/s coming into view, they accelerate the transition between paradigms. They *are* accelerating this transition at an increasing rate. We are making the transition from a materialistic universe/paradigm to a holistic, non-dualist one in which spirituality and science will stand together, encompassing more of Nature's phenomena than any previous model of the universe ever has. The result will make the Copernican revolution look almost inconsequential.

So far, humanity has survived many catastrophic paradigm shifts. In our previous list (which could be much longer), we see a number of items that were once thought to be impossible within the bounds of the time's dominant paradigms/models. The majority of people evidently shared the consensus that nothing could ever come of these ideas, and still they unfolded into this reality anyway, with flagrant disregard for the beliefs of the majority. All it took was one or two heretics who would not bow to authority, but simply pursue information and innovation wherever it led them.

We can repeatedly see the error entire societies have fallen into by adopting the unconscious stance or attitude that what is familiar is necessarily "rational" or "objective," while the novel and unfamiliar is "quackery," "superstition," "pseudo-science," "fantasy," and just plain "impossible." Each such impossible item caused a paradigm shift on some scale in its own way; the discovery that the sun did not orbit the Earth shattered the amazingly naïve, self-aggrandizing, and anthropocentric Christian belief that Earth was the center of the universe, thus making humans the centerpiece and pinnacle of God's grand design; the flight of the Wright brothers destroyed the "nothing heavier than air can fly" paradigm; and more recently, quantum physics obliterated the notion of a separate and objective universe that exists independently of its observers (naïve realism). Just as there were those who denied the reality of flight, even as the Wright brothers' plane lifted off the ground, today there are still those who cling to the notion of their own objectified and observer-independent universes that are bereft of psi and the transpersonal effects of consciousness.

The difficulty experienced and controversy generated as the wheels of change creak into motion to crush or replace a paradigm says far more about human psychology than it does about evidence. We simply become addicted to belief through unconscious identification. The identification problem arises from our imperceptiveness; our lack of functional insight and intuition means we have to rely on the sensory cues interpreted by the brain as input by the five primary human senses, all of which offer little insight into the true nature of Reality. Thus, we identify and define ourselves solely through an illusion, a dream; a recipe for disaster if ever there was one, for how can a mind whose sense of self is totally tied up in the superficial, materialistic conception of the world ever honestly question the nature of reality without its very identity then being threatened?

Paradigms and Culture Minds

In a time of drastic change, it is the learners who inherit the future. The learned usually find themselves equipped to live in a world that no longer exists.
—Eric Hoffer

Kuhn states in *The Structure of Scientific Revolutions* that the actualization of a scientific paradigm is achieved by increasing the extent of the match between its facts and its predictions, and by further articulation of the paradigm itself: "mop-up work." Kuhn's candor is enlightening, as he explains that such work occupies most scientists right through their careers; it is "normal science," an enterprise attempting to force-fit nature into the preformed conceptual boxes supplied by the already existing paradigm. New sorts of phenomena are not sought, and those phenomena that won't be squeezed into pre-existing boxes tend to not even be seen at all. Scientists generally don't seek to invent new theories, and they don't always tolerate the theories of other scientists.[63]

Psychologically speaking, it makes sense that scientists imprinted by the culturally dominant paradigm they are born into will expend most of their energy attempting to understand it better and elaborate on it. Practically speaking, this has to be done because of the chasms that exist between science's theoretical understandings of the cosmos (from the Greek *Kosmos*, meaning "ordered whole") and what the cosmos actually has to offer—and every answer yields another ten questions. The average scientist is busy enough trying to test and validate aspects of the preformed paradigmatic box he or she has inherited without having to worry about various anomalies that challenge the basic parameters, theoretical underpinnings, or first principles of that box. Hence, anomalous data, such as that which we will deliberately focus on in this book, is typically unfavorable to those scientists imprinted by a theory or model of the universe that posits that such phenomena should not even exist. The presumption seemingly made by many scientists—like the child who naïvely sees his parents as being god-like in their knowledge and authority—is obviously that the paradigm *must* be right and that there's no point actually checking, or else why would it be the dominant paradigm? This, of course, creates unscientific institutionalized blind spots that do not harmonize with people whose conscious experience is not congruent with what the popular theory says they should or shouldn't be experiencing. If the facts of your waking experience are not encapsulated by the theory, and your experiences are being shared by millions of other people, then perhaps the theory needs some revision.

Importantly, Kuhn also stated that a paradigm defines what constitutes a valid scientific problem. Any pursuits venturing away from the confines of the paradigm therefore define themselves as being "unscientific" (and therefore the findings must be untrue) by default, and—to conventional thinking—this is where most of the information contained in this book lies: the scientific wilderness or no man's land. This briefly outlined "scientific" approach, needless to say, can institutionalize myopic and dogmatic gate-keeping activities that prevent novel research from occurring (or being published), ironically in the *name* of science if not the form, leading to a stagnation in the advancement of science to the extent that such activities succeed and prevail. However, history shows that such circumstances break down in the end, in line with the ultimate law of the world of form and relativity: the only constant is change.

The individuals who catalyze such breakdowns and revolutions of thought and encourage them to unfold towards what will ultimately be a state of greater order and understanding (whether they facilitate this consciously or otherwise) are what Rudhyar called *civilizers* (and what historian Arthur Toynbee referred to as *creative minorities*). These (relatively) independent and forward-thinking minds possess a differing vision from the majority of culturally conditioned minds, aptly designated as *culture minds*. For clarity, culture is defined by anthropologists as a collection of learned survival strategies passed on to our young through teaching and modeling.[64] The culture mind, which is essentially a reflection of the collective or group mind, is the one that imprints on and inherits a pre-existing paradigm, refines it, champions it, and, maybe above all, defends it against "attack" from unfamiliar and unexpected data—supposedly for the benefit of humankind, but in truth simply as a coping mechanism, perhaps a perversion of a biological survival drive. Such was the role of those who decried the invention of the light bulb, the radio, the telescope, and almost every other novel and important invention through our history.

Joseph C. Pearce refers to culture as "the collective embodiment of our survival ideation," and "a circular stalemate,"[65] and in this sense our narrow cultural tendencies are holding us back from transcending ourselves. The civilizer mind, on the other hand, is the lonely soul or minority of souls brave or silly enough to bring forth such unexpected and "ridiculous" creations as light bulbs, radios, quantum mechanics, or parapsychology, and pose the uncomfortable questions stemming from them that the culture mind's paradigm had failed to anticipate.

What if this new phenomenon is real? What if the universe doesn't work the precise way our paradigms led us to believe? What if *more* is possible? The civilizer will pursue a new line of inquiry in spite of its being politically incorrect or taboo, if he or she perceives that such a pursuit could benefit mankind in the long run. This will of course be done to the chagrin of the tribally oriented culture mind who perceives, however dimly, such investigation as a threat to his status and identity—his models of self and the universe. Eventually, when the civilizer has succeeded in gaining acceptance for his new concept or invention and it has become familiar and even commonplace, a new breed of culture mind will grow up taking this once dangerous heresy for granted as self-evident and obvious.

Thus, the genius civilizer and Hermeticist Isaac Newton's profound scientific output led to the formulation of new and unforeseen paradigms which would ultimately be inherited by culture mind minions who would dogmatically insist that those materialistic and reductionistic paradigms essentially described the Universe as it was and must necessarily be, refusing to acknowledge the validity of legitimate information that did not conform to the expectations induced by those (incomplete) paradigms. New data or refinements were permissible only insofar as they did not challenge the fundamental precepts of the Newtonian outlook, and thus the religion of Funda-Materialism (Fundamentalist Materialism) was born (which is ironic, since, as Newton matured he moved from a mechanistic view to an essentially "magical" one, being deeply involved in alchemical research, as well as being a Freemason and student of Biblical prophesy[66]).

The culture mind is typically bent on maintaining the status quo at any cost, for it lacks imagination and vision enough to see a potentially better way of operating, and more importantly, its identity is intimately tied to said status quo, so challenging the latter threatens the former by default. It might reluctantly agree to consider making some small changes, however, if a "credible" and familiar cultural authority figure can induce it into perceiving some kind of self-benefit for such an action. As Joseph Chilton Pearce observes, "Culture is the fundamental deviancy of intellect from intelligence, and because of its massively unnatural and arbitrary, and illogical nature, it requires an equally massive energy to sustain it."[67]

Inspection reveals that for the most part—within the context of paranormal research—that energy is the emotion known as *fear*, and it is usually repressed/ subliminal, lurking in the background, tacitly guiding our processes of logic (and sabotaging our capacity to learn). Culture, as Pearce points out, feeds the ancient survival modes of our brain and keeps us locked into them.[68] This means that information challenging the culture mind's paradigm and sense of self evokes a fight-or-flight biological sort of response—about the lowest level of intelligence available to us. Having only those two ways of responding to "threatening" data is profoundly limiting to intelligence. It leaves one with only the option of perpetually debunking ("fighting") information through a pseudo-intellectual veneer, or simply fleeing from the most challenging facts altogether. More intelligent responses could be forthcoming if our sense of self was not based on such flimsy ground and so easily "undermined"—*expanded on*, in truth—by the "unexplainable."

Self-interest is a strong motive for the biospherically oriented culture mind, while the civilizer's motive is typically something more transpersonal, something vaster and more far-reaching. The civilizer seeks to drag the possible future into the manifest present. In Rudhyar's estimation, the steps to preparing for the role as a civilizer include "having a deep-seated dissatisfaction with the forms and institutions that the culture has built . . . and the development of a mind able to relentlessly question the intellectual and/or moral validity of the essential premises (paradigms) constituting the framework of the collective mentality of a society having already passed its maturity."[69]

Gautama the Buddha, Pythagoras, Newton, Bacon, Tesla and many researchers, mystics, and occultists who will be mentioned in the following pages have been cast in the mould of the civilizer mind, pioneers and trailblazers that they are (or were). The consciousness of these individuals no longer imbues the familiar cultural beliefs, assumptions, values, behavioral patterns, and concepts, with the importance and/or meaning they have for the average human being/ culture mind. In some cases, Rudhyar observed, these people have actually "transferred the center of their consciousness and therefore their sense of identity from the biopsychic level to a spiritual-mental level."[70] This is exactly what we seek to facilitate here.

What the creative minds are able to communicate to others in their culture "becomes a mutating ideologic seed that, sooner or later, will germinate and affect other minds."[71] Thus, culture is the carrier wave, as Rudhyar termed it, of civilization. The process of civilization cannot occur without cultures and culture minds to evolve and transform, to "civilize." "*Culture forms. Civilization transforms.*"[72]

The process of transformation implies a sort of *crisis* (from a Greek root, meaning "to decide"), and it is indeed a crisis/decision point that humanity currently finds itself at. This is especially so for our dominant scientific paradigms, placed under siege and laid waste by inconvenient facts that have been swept under the proverbial rug for so long now that the rug looks as if it's hiding a jittery woolly mammoth. This hulking mass now appears ready to topple over into collective awareness with an almighty crash. Our cherished materialistic-reductionist paradigms of life and consciousness are crumbling under the weight of their own obfuscations and omissions. Such is the saturation of inconvenient facts that perceptive scientists such as Radin can legitimately state that we are indeed making the step from Phase 1 of outright institutional denial to Phase 2 of reluctant acceptance and further, more mainstream investigation. This very fact signifies a philosophical crisis occurring in the hallowed halls of science, as the growing realization dawns on more and more minds that our dominant politically correct scientifically induced (and *scientistically* preserved) metaphysical assumptions about our existence are simply unable to cope with the questions being asked of them.

New paradigms are in the making—culture is being civilized (transformed) in a way that few generations on this Earth have ever had the opportunity to witness. With the capability to "nuke" or simply pollute and contaminate ourselves out of existence, there has probably not been a better time in our recorded history to embrace the dynamic of civilization and choose to consciously transform ourselves and our cultures (and by that I don't mean throwing in with a totalitarian World Government agenda run by psychopathic unelected financial oligarchs). The creations of civilizer minds, as opposed to culture minds, induce sociocultural transformation rather than fulfilment, or what we might often refer to as the preservation of the status quo. Such humans are *transpersonal* beings, according to Rudhyar. "Space, life, God, *act through them*, even if they are not aware of this fact."[73] The civilization process pertains to the activity of "spirit" as spirit acts through the mind. While spirit creates, culture merely reproduces.[74] Finally, Rudhyar tells us: "The way of transformation is what occultists call 'The Path.' The real civilizer is the man of relationship. He relates the as-yet-unknown to the known, the greater to the lesser."[75]

This book, as the reader has no doubt gathered by now, is the kind of dangerous and subversive text that can potentially play a civilizing or transformative role—as long as one's mind is receptive, curious, and open. The time is ripe for such outlandish material to be circulated en masse, because perhaps never in our known history have the masses of mankind been so beaten down, worn out, and disillusioned with the status quo (just look at the "Occupy" movement!). More to the point is the fact that never before have we known the collective mind to be undertaking the kind of mass awakening that now appears to be happening and gathering pace, even as I type these words.

What makes this book dangerous to the conditioned culture mind is the author's refusal to allow his perceptions to be utterly dictated and shaped by his own culture's customs, taboos, and metaphysical assumptions. This book challenges dogma, culturally ingrained assumptions, and beliefs, rather than arbitrarily selecting one particular "culturized" viewpoint (say, materialism, Freudianism, or Christian fundamentalism) and espousing it at the expense of all other viewpoints merely out of fear or pride. Culture seizes the new ideas civilization creates and erects them into systems and truths endowed with permanent value, leading to tradition and also dogmatism. The civilizer "plays with" ideas and his mind "sees," while the culture-man's mind cogitates and endlessly argues pros and cons.[76] The purpose of this book is not to merely argue pros and cons, but to expand one's vision: to civilize/transform.

It is interesting to note that one cannot spell *culture* without *cult*. What is a cult best at? Rigidly and fiercely maintaining its own cognitive status quo, its ontology, in spite of any and all evidence to the contrary—indefinitely. Extreme data filtration and streamlining. Model fanaticism courtesy of what I dub "paradigmatic fanatics." No cult member ever really realizes the depths of stupidity he or she, as a believer, sinks to until they leave the cult, dis-identify with its models of reality and the world, and stand on the outside looking in. We want to transcend the *cult*ure mind. A change in perspective (data reception and meaning creation) is a powerful thing. The product of any profound and positive change in perspective is transformation/civilization. At this point in our history, can we aim for anything less?

2

SCIENCE AIN'T ALWAYS SCIENTIFIC

Real scientific endeavour does not dictate what *"should"* be. Ideally, it designs a
sound protocol through which nature can reveal what *is.* —Author

It is not a question of belief; the scientific attitude one should take on any subject is
whether it is true. The Law of Gravitation worked as efficiently before Newton as
after him. The cosmos would be fairly chaotic if its laws could not operate without
the sanction of human belief. —Sri Yukteswar

The Myth of Objectivity and Impartiality

Doesn't science state that paranormal occurrences are impossible?
Philosophically, science can no longer maintain that position—not if it wants
to appeal to today's evidence. Evidentially speaking, many so-called paranormal
phenomena have been irrefutably scientifically proved. The body of mainstream
science has a history of becoming quite hysterical in the face of information
seemingly competing for its "target demographic," or even just information
that doesn't conform to the dominant paradigm in operation at the time. As
such, it is organized science that has often proved and continues to prove to
be the biggest adversary to impartial discussion and consideration of novel
data—an alien concept to many people due to the way science, particularly in
the mainstream, has been mythologized as a totally dispassionate and objective

enterprise that only cares for so-called truth (though the anthropogenic global warming scandal no doubt helped undermine that myth!). We think of the man in the lab coat as impartial and analytical, but he is just as motivated by emotion and self-interest as the next person. Degrees and Ph.D.s don't suddenly make someone utterly impartial and free of emotional or intellectual prejudice, or immune to other forms of corruption for that matter.

Consider the Nazi-like book-burning and the persecution of pioneering scientist Wilhelm Reich in America—an allegedly free country—in the 1950s. Had Reich hate-mongered? Had he called for the torture and killing of baby seals? Had he conducted Satanic rituals and conjured hordes of demons? Taken candy from a baby? Voted Republican? No. He merely published his research into an energy he called "orgone," which challenged scientists' indoctrinated preconceptions and psychological imprinting about the nature of reality. Therefore, the only logical course of action was a book burning and jail for this dangerous lunatic.[1] Of course. While the book burning was sanctioned by the government, it was supported by various scientists who were not capable of approaching his material logically and open-mindedly. Had Reich made his discoveries today his material might have received a fairer treatment (might!).

Author, philosopher, and playwright the late Robert Anton Wilson—also a man ahead of his time—expressed his "horror and considerable indignation" at Reich's politically, ideologically, and corporately inspired persecution in 1957: "I was astounded and flabbergasted that the US government was imitating its former [Nazi] enemy to the extent of actually burning scientific papers it found heretical."[2] The Catholic Church of yore would have been proud. The great Indian physicist J.C. Bose had himself noted the presence of an "unconscious theological bias" operating within the institution of science.[3] This is a theme that may be returned to repeatedly, for science provides many examples of the worst kind of *religious thought* when it follows in the "arrogant and authoritarian footsteps of the Papacy," as Wilson put it. He would further quip that "someone who knew only recent history and was unaware of the past might come to the conclusion that Science, not Theology, is the main enemy of free thought and free enquiry."[4]

Science tends to be a more diverse area than orthodox religion and it is not as easy to generalize, but they certainly have their similarities. Kuhn wrote that an education in normal science is probably more narrow and rigid than any other except perhaps one in orthodox theology.[5] It is noteworthy that "heresy" derives from the Greek *hairesis*, "choice." "To be a heretic means to have choices, to opt for another way of believing, another kind of knowing, another channel of perceiving, another course of experience. Heresy is about having options."[6] One thing any good dictator loathes is competition. More

28

disturbing is "official" corporate science's aversion to it when such competition takes the form of psychical and consciousness research—a widely lamented theme—though the situation is even worse in other areas (such as alternative health or overunity technology/free energy).

Here we will not be getting into the story of just how badly organized "skepticism" has lost its way—that's a story for another book. Suffice it to say that the term "skeptic" comes from the Greek *skepsis*, which means *examination and doubt*, and not knee-jerk denial. Somewhere then, organized skepticism and enthusiastic debunkers went wrong. Somewhere along the way, some people began to unconsciously mistake closed-minded cynicism and arrogance for skepticism—and the one thing the best known "skeptics" never seem to doubt, of course, is their own set of ontological or existential assumptions.

When someone provides a meticulously researched, quantitative challenge to conventional materialistic dogma, there is often a frenzied and juvenile response from many scientists and "skeptical" laypeople who hide behind the authority of science rather than utilizing its methods or spirit of inquiry to seek understanding. Kuhn explained that, because novelties are subversive of mainline science's commitment to the status quo, normal science suppresses them.[7] Despite this, and as Kuhn noted, as long as the status quo viewpoint contains an element of the arbitrary, novelty cannot be suppressed for very long. As Wilson observed, "Science achieves, or approximates, objectivity not because the individual scientist is immune from the psychological laws that govern the rest of us, but because scientific method—a group creation— eventually overrides individual prejudices, in the long run."[8]

We are not going to focus here on the corruption in the world of science that too often prevents scientific progress from occurring and serves to mire civilization in destructive beliefs and behavioral patterns; we merely wish to observe that the decrees of science, in particular "mainstream" and/or corporate science, cannot always be taken at face value, particularly science's traditional pronouncements on so-called paranormal phenomena.

Letting Emotion Steer the Ship

[Opening the mind] will orient you to the possibility that you can be redefined continuously. In other words, *give your allegiance to transformation rather than defending the status quo.* Now you are ready to disassemble your worldview. You are ready to stop having a stake in the world limited to the narrow confines of I, me, and mine. —Deepak Chopra

Like non-scientists, scientists themselves often fall prey to emotions and attitudinal biases. The image of the detached, indifferent, and "objective" scientist just earnestly doing his research for the good of mankind without need of thanks or reward is largely a fiction that less and less has a place in the world of corporate science. Even when money or politics don't pressure a scientist, he or she may still fall prey to unconscious prejudices induced by childhood conditioning, emotional experiences from adult life, or any variety of events, that will skew the results of his or her research, perceptions, or commentary on a given topic. As physicist Brian D. Josephson points out, "Some scientists are especially prone to whip up emotion 'in the cause of science' (or so they believe)."[9]

When was the last time that emotion helped you reach a rational and impartial conclusion? Ray Hyman, a career disbeliever in psi, has gone so far to admit that "[t]he level of the debate [about psi] during the past 130 years has been an embarrassment for anyone who would like to believe that scholars and scientists adhere to standards of rationality and fair play."[10] Scientific truth, particularly in the context of psi, is determined primarily by *non*scientific factors such as cultural conditioning, propaganda, rhetoric, *ad hominem* attack, politics, and competition for limited funding.

In fact, it is widely observed that the Scientific Priesthood or "elite" are driven to not perceive psi. Their egos have too much at stake, too much invested in an overarching paradigm that ruled that psi is an impossibility, and too much attachment to pet theories and beliefs that depend on it not existing. This tendency towards rigid dogmatism is incompatible with the fundamental spirit and basic methods of scientific inquiry, and has led many scientists to defend moribund worldviews and theories. What is the point of further research if you think you already know what is possible and what is not? While hardcore "skeptics" think that the widespread beliefs in psi and paranormal experiences and events indicates the public's decreasing capacity for rational thought, I will demonstrate here that the increasing belief in psi actually reflects just the opposite, but more to the point, it also represents the maturation of science and a fundamental evolutionary trend towards the greater advancement of the human race.

Veteran parapsychologist Stephen Braude has seen the ways emotion can subvert intellectual honesty and ethics:

> Since dipping into the data of parapsychology, I have encountered more examples of intellectual cowardice and dishonesty than I had previously thought possible. I have seen how prominent scholars marshal their considerable intellectual gifts and skills to avoid honest inquiry. I have seen how intelligence . . .

30

sometimes affords little more than complicated ways of making mistakes, entrenching people in views or opinions they are afraid to scrutinize or abandon.[11]

While many people think the basic issue is fear of the unknown (part of Rudhyar's cultural provincialism), the reality that will emerge here is that every "skeptic" knows the truth at a subconscious level. Their hostility and closed-mindedness, I believe, arise from the internal conflict or cognitive dissonance resulting from the clash between the hidden subconscious knowledge that is in conflict with their consciously held belief structures (often these are imprinted very early in life and remain relatively intact thereafter). "Skeptics" loathe it when portions of their repressed knowledge are presented to them at a conscious level—it is an uncomfortable experience.

As someone who isn't afraid of playing devil's advocate occasionally, I have found that many people tend to react like addicts when their beliefs are challenged, even if politely enough. Rather than the mature, thoughtful response along the lines of "That's interesting, how/where did you learn that?" many people will go into defence mode and act as if their entire world is under siege—"That's not possible, science says so! What you're talking about is pseudo-science!" Of course, such pronouncements are almost invariably preceded and followed with zero devoted, determined, and open-minded research.

Most of these knee-jerk reactions are nothing more than the acting out of ingrained mental habits. Some people are all too happy to rehash all the hearsay and assumptions they have gathered and lived by throughout their lives, as if that constitutes a valid argument. It doesn't, but it maintains the apparent safety of a limited *weltbild*. Their opinions are almost always somebody else's but they mistake these opinions as self-evident truth, apparently by sheer force of the number of other people who happen to agree with them. "Our thoughts, opinions, prejudices, and predilections are part of our mental possessions, children of our mind, and that is why we feel and show such tender regard for them."[12]

Raymond Moody has written that "'explanations' are not just abstract intellectual systems. They are also in some respects projects of the egos of the persons who hold them. People become emotionally wedded, as it were, to the canons of scientific explanation which they devise or adopt."[13] After dedicating a lifetime of research to an area, it would understandably be threatening to have your facts challenged, and yet this is the response of the pride-filled ego, not of the analytical intellect. Science can only perform its role properly when the ego is removed (or at least tempered) and replaced with an unprejudiced, impartial search for truth, *whatever* it turns out to be.

Miseducation

One reason so many people make it through life with a fairly closed mind to "paranormal" information in particular is that they never have an experience that forces a catastrophic psychological upheaval upon them, leaving them to reassess everything they have ever assumed to be true. One of the key problems for people who have had these upheavals is that much of the population have not had them and thus have no experience/s of their own with which they can compare them. Their "information grids" are bereft of any relevant or analogous information.

Sadly, much of the closed-mindedness in the world is engendered by the one entity that is supposed to achieve the opposite effect: the education system. I was at a friend's rented house in Sydney one day (some time in the year 2007, if my memory serves me), when his girlfriend's friend dropped by. She was studying medicine at one of Sydney's universities. I was just making small talk with her, trying to strike up a bit of a conversation, when there developed an opening for me to mention a friend of mine and her impressive intuitive abilities. For a reason I was unaware of at that moment, I noticed my voice catching in my throat, and a strange reluctance to say what I was about to. In spite of this I forged ahead, saying something like, "My friend is very intuitive . . ." at which point she suddenly cut me off and blurted out, "I believe in science!"

I was stunned. She did not even let me finish my sentence, and yet I had already offended her scientific sensibilities. Notice that I wasn't telling her what I *believed in*; I was just making an honest disclosure based on my own repeated personal experiences, research, and observation of fact. She apparently heard me say something completely different to what I remember myself saying. In hindsight, I could see that my own intuitive faculties had kicked in and were subtly indicating that this person was not going to be receptive to what I was going to say; hence my initial hesitation. I have noticed this on many occasions. I sometimes have an inner knowing about the response I will get that I couldn't possibly have without some kind of psychic (intuitive) functioning.

The girl was an unwitting believer not in *science* per se (her attitude and reaction was anything but scientific), but *scientism*. Scientism is generally defined as the collection of attitudes and practices considered typical of scientists. In theory, this sounds fine, even admirable, but when you look at official science's track record, one marred by bias, intellectual snobbery, prejudice, and in many instances lies, corruption, and corporate manipulation, a different meaning of scientism emerges. At this point, Raymond Moody's description of scientism is apt: "a value judgement that other disciplines . . . are worthwhile only insofar as they conform their techniques of investigation to those of the physical and biological sciences."[14]

If these other disciplines don't conform, they are "unscientific" by default. Since when does scientific research require isomorphism? This girl had obviously been well versed in what are considered appropriate or credible sources of information in the eyes of the educational establishment, and had, like so many obedient students of science, begun to develop a suitably scientistic attitude towards anything unfamiliar to her, such as psi phenomena. That is to say she was prepared to derogate before investigate. William Tiller, a "hard scientist" and pioneering psi researcher, has succinctly stated that scientism is a corruption of the science craft.[15]

As Kuhn noted in the late 1960s, "Science students accept theories on the authority of teacher and text, not because of evidence."[16] The same goes for all students. Accepting official doctrine is always an act of faith to some degree, but to precisely *what* degree most of the indoctrinated never think to check. As for psi research, just as in Galileo's day, the Scientific Priesthood still refuses to look through the telescope.

The history of science and human psychology shows clearly even into the present day that when the aspiring (or practicing) scientist is met with another person's experiences that do not conform to the doctrine provided by teacher and text, the vast majority of the time the conscious firsthand experience being related is all too readily discarded in favor of the scientist's pet theory—usually backed by their own *absence* of experience. Kuhn asks of the science student how they could be expected to know any better, since the doctrines and applications laid out in textbooks are not there as evidence, but simply because learning them is part and parcel of inheriting the paradigm that dictates current scientific practices.[17]

It is such a loaded statement, "I believe in science." Which branch of science? What period's science? How are you defining "science"? Too often, because people are taught something at school or college, they make the assumption that it *must* be true—after all, "they wouldn't teach us that if it wasn't true!" Officially recognized scientific dogma may be based at least partly in truth, and indeed in some form of logic, but some people mistakenly and unconsciously leap to the conclusion that they have been given the *whole truth and nothing but the truth*, and that anything that does not fit within their academically defined scientific parameters is simply invalid or nonexistent. (Questioning the logic involved is also something of a no-no.)

Take parapsychology, a field of scientific research into psi that is over a hundred years old, yet many introductory psychology textbooks, despite the incredible abundance of verifiable psi research available, have presented flawed descriptions of psi experiments and the field in general. Here we have a prime example (from a large pool of potential samples) of the education system miseducating through both distortion and omission.

In 1991 64 psychology textbooks published between 1980 and 1989 were surveyed for their references and content pertaining to parapsychology. Only 43 included some meaningful mention of it, meaning that a third ignored it completely. The authors concluded that overall these publications— intended for unassuming psychology students—presented a misleading and misrepresentative view of parapsychological research. A follow-up review of texts from 1990 to 1999 showed the situation had improved little, and a review of 2002 psychology texts found that even a notorious career denialist— infamous for a near-pathological inability to report fairly and accurately on parapsychological and psychical research—was cited in *15* of the texts that mentioned parapsychology (a whopping 45% of that year's introductory texts). Overall, skeptical coverage was roughly twice as extensive as that in favor of parapsychology and the situation appeared to have worsened from the 1990s overall, with factual errors and misleading coverage persisting. The authors suggested that the poor coverage could partly be attributed to the unfamiliarity of authors with the field of parapsychology and also a continued overreliance on secondary sources written by "skeptical nonparapsychologists."[18]

Unfortunately, because the assumption with which most students enter into college education is that they are going to be properly informed, it never occurs to many to question what they are presented with in a given field of study. Thus, the education system can in fact be responsible for the perpetuation of myths and lies, at times serving the propagation of ignorance instead of enlightenment. Such myths usually die hard in the minds of the "educated," regardless of the field of study.

The established scientific worldview is based on centuries-old Newtonian-Cartesian philosophical underpinnings (or perhaps it would be more accurate to say that the body of "accepted" data in science, and its interpretations, have actually led to this reductionistic outlook—along with science's preferred exploratory methods). The officially accepted philosophical credo basically amounts to this: "The world/universe is a gigantic clockwork machine (at least at our macro scale/s) with independent parts or building blocks. It is deterministic and predictable using known maths and science (quantum scales notwithstanding). The body is also a machine with different individual parts. If the body parts break down, you 'fix,' medicate, or replace them, as you would with a car. When you die, since your consciousness arose solely as an epiphenomenon of your brain, you cease to think, feel, experience, or exist in any capacity. Your life and existence at large is therefore innately meaningless (at least until you imbue it with your own personal meaning). Our collective existence as a species is merely a lucky Darwinian accident."

I propose that this mechano-materialistic outlook (itself, more or less an 18th-century scientific ontology only slightly modified by 20th century physics) is in itself a faith-based belief system that is maintained by the calculated and/or unconscious omission of massive tracts of factual data. The definition of materialism, for our purposes, runs as follows: "The only reality is 'matter,' usually as perceived by the five primary human sense organs (or 'credible' scientific procedure and equipment); the universe is not governed by intelligence or purpose but only randomly by mechanical localized cause and effect (quantum physics notwithstanding once more). There is no possibility of independence between mind and body, since the mind only exists as a result of the brain that houses it."

It could legitimately be pointed out that many materialists have no doubt begun to realize some of the limitations of this viewpoint as I represent it here, but the point is that, within the context of mysticism, psi, and occult phenomena in general (the "paranormal"), this is the sort of "scientific" attitude one is often met with.

As something of a former materialist (non-dogmatic, thankfully), I reserve the right to point out its inherent silliness. As the noted theosophist J.J. van der Leeuw said,

> to conclude . . . that . . . the living individual is but a byproduct of the body and to exclaim with a triumphant and unholy joy that . . . we have proved that the body is primary and man in his aspirations and creative effort is but secondary, is as unthinking and unfounded as it would be to say that the artist is but a by-product of his violin since, when a string is missing, the possibilities of his artistic expression are changed forthwith.[19]

There is no room in this Newtonian-Cartesian worldview for "paranormal" communication between two people, no room for interactive bioenergetic fields, no room for mind-to-mind contact, no room for an afterlife, and no room for virtually all other occult phenomena. In short, the traditional scientific conception of reality and mind allows almost no room for consciousness (and has no way of explaining its existence), unless it is merely a product of electro-chemical processes in the brain. Yet we need to remember, this is just a belief system. Never in an experiment has consciousness been created from inert matter.

Unfortunately, even today, when it comes to "mind," students of science are, without realizing it, indoctrinated into an incredibly narrow vision of possibility. They then mistake this narrow-mindedness for a common-sense view of reality. They are not encouraged to have any sense of subtlety or mental flexibility—such traits largely arise, when in fact they do, in *spite* of their education, not because of it. This is largely why debunkers and pseudo-skeptics continue to be taken seriously, or worse, as gospel on these matters—because the education system keeps churning out devotees of the mechano-reductionist theology.

Writing in the late 1980s in *Many Lives, Many Masters*, Brian Weiss, a prominent psychiatrist and pioneer in past life regression and consciousness research, noted the closed-mindedness of many of his peers, saying that they refuse to examine and evaluate the considerable evidence being gathered about survival after bodily death and about past-life memories. "Their eyes stay tightly shut."[20] What about yours?

Funding, Image, and Prestige

Prestige (pecking order status), a concern of the mammalian ego, has a nasty way of blocking progress and important scientific research in areas of profound importance to humanity. For instance, what could be more important than the question "What happens when we die?" And yet, funds for afterlife research, practically speaking, don't exist. By contrast, untold wealth is spent on defending, maintaining, and expanding economic and military power. More than 70% of all scientific research is either funded by or geared towards applications of new technologies for weapons of mass destruction and related military uses.[21] Even in the late 1800s, H.P. Blavatsky lamented that England alone already harboured 21,268 firms fabricating and selling explosive substances.[22] Something is drastically wrong. America's bogus "War on Terror" and unlawful invasions of Iraq and Afghanistan (resulting in massive civilian casualties and catastrophic damage to basic infrastructure) have sucked up enough financial resources to feed the planet—yet still millions starve and go without potable water. Soon perhaps we will realize we cannot drink crude oil or eat bullets.

According to near-death researcher P.M.H. Atwater, universities across America are now "taking steps to phase out departments and professors who pursue the 'embarrassing' activity of near-death research—because it delves into 'questionable' phenomena. Grant monies have dried up."[23] And yet, people live lives deprived of ultimate purpose and meaning without possession of genuine knowledge of or belief in an "afterlife."[24] Overall, the total human and financial resources devoted to parapsychology since 1882 might at best, it has been estimated, equal the expenditures for *two months* of conventional psychological research in the USA in the year 1983.[25] Though psi research in parts of Eastern Europe once boomed prior to the fall of the Soviet Union, there are now fewer than 50 conventionally trained doctoral-level scientists around the world engaged in full-time psi research (though this does not take into account private research centers and classified government projects).[26] In Sogyal Rinpoche's view, the great deception and source of the world's materialism is humanity's monocular focus on our current lives, and *only* our current lives.[27]

Psychical studies are not only inherently interesting on different levels, but also essential if we hope to comprehend what it means to be human.[28] They can change the way we view and define ourselves and interact with each other, and have done for many of those familiar with the data. As Schoch and Yonavjak state, the implications of psychical research are profound and paradigm-shifting.[29] A shift of worldview is long overdue: we are destroying ourselves. A former Brazilian Minister for the Environment has remonstrated that unless the "fanatical religion" of modern industrialized society undergoes a radical change of heart, mind, and vision, our planet will wind up dead like Venus.[30]

As seasoned scientist, multiple patent holder, and co-founder of the Nova Institute of Technology David G. Yurth asks in his very highly recommended book *Seeing Past the Edge*, "Do we have to suffer the ravages of near-extinction before we wake up and move in another direction?" I have noticed that the more metaphysically/spiritually aware people I have encountered tend to think and act in ways more congruous with our collective desire to survive in the long term than is the case with their materialist counterparts. Not coincidentally, they are, on average, also more comfortable outside the proverbial box. My view is that the fundamental issue underlying the world's ills is our overall lack of spirituality; not religion, but spirituality, meaning self-awareness. I speak of that sense of self that transcends the culture-bound constructs of both scientific and exoteric religious thought.

"It Can't Be Real . . ."

"Though modern science grew out of a counter-cultural response to the Christian Church," DeGracia writes, "it adopted the unconscious metaphysical orientation of Christianity: that of perceiving an organizing force that somehow or another exists outside of our actual everyday lives . . . [Science] replaced the idea of God with mathematical formulas and abstract principles . . ."[31] As Joseph

Chilton Pearce observes, "Science supposedly supplanted religion, but simply became a new religious form, an even more powerful cultural support, and an equal source of restraint on our spirit."[32]

Despite the fact that some of science's best known names in years past were avid researchers into the occult (to say nothing of the genius scientist-hermeticists who developed science as we know it today), since the mid- to late 1800s at least, it has been fashionable for scientists to treat the occult, mysticism, and the paranormal with a smug and condescending contempt, and yet, if one looks, one can see that the objectors are barely familiar with these topics. For the past roughly 400 years, writes Tiller, the unstated assumption of establishment science has been that "no human qualities of consciousness, intention, emotion, mind or spirit can significantly influence a well-designed target experiment in physical reality."[33]

Another assumption seems to be that "nothing lying beyond the bounds of my formal education or sphere of experiential familiarity could possibly be true"—an unusual attitude that seems to be inculcated almost wholly subliminally in almost all students during their years in the education system. Though science is regarded widely by conservative types as being an objective exercise in dispassionate, rational thought, in the mainstream it has not been any of these things towards the paranormal (and other out-of-the-box subject matter) for many years. As Trevor James Constable astutely observes: "The . . . 'problem' lies . . . in the orientation of [psychologically] armored man away from anything that leads to the roots of his own existence."[34]

Because mainstream science has viewed the paranormal largely with contempt (borne of fear), it has not seen fit to study it. Given that it has not seen fit to study it, science in the mainstream has learned next to nothing about it. Can one logically dismiss a topic that one has refused to study and thus knows nothing about? This double-think appears to escape many "rational" scientists, in particular those who subscribe to some sort of materialistic theology.

The combination of what Ingo Swann refers to as "real or assumed scientific knowledge"[35] could be loosely referred to as a paradigm. The paradigm's general principles and tenets, that is, things that are deduced or postulated as being possible, and those that are deemed *not* to be possible—usually given the status of "laws"—are imprinted into the psyche of virtually all scientists, because these tenets are used to define what constitutes science and "valid" areas of scientific research. The paradigm constitutes a map of sorts; a cartography that the scientist uses as a reference point to decide what areas of inquiry are the most important, the most urgent, and the most "scientific." The scientist checks where he is, in relation to where the paradigm tells him he should be.

If scientists stray too far into the world of parapsychology or the occult, they become pseudo-scientists by default; not because of their methods or their results—these things are immaterial—but because they are no longer operating within the parameters of what is defined as being politically correct and socially acceptable science. Thus, they must be quacks or crackpots, worthy only of ridicule. Given the staunch philosophical materialism that has for so many years been the map-maker and boundary-marker of "science proper," we can see that the continued maligning of parapsychology and occult phenomena is a hangover from the turf deal Descartes struck with the Roman Catholic church, which arbitrarily split mind and matter: science would deal with matter, while the church would deal with "spirit stuff."[36] The wholesale dismissal of uncomfortable observable facts as "pseudo-science" is, as David Yurth points out, "cult-speak for 'stuff we can see but cannot explain.'"[37]

There is a saying: it only takes one white crow to prove that all crows aren't black. This book is full of white crows, as you are about to see. Unfortunately, with human psychology being as frail as it is, the Funda-Materialists entrenched in established science, who had inherited this reductionist paradigmatic outlook, developed a proud tradition of learning to look quickly the other way whenever a white crow flew into view. They learned quickly to remind those who saw the white crows, and even managed to produce them within highly controlled and replicable laboratory experiments that, since they (the Funda-Materialists) had never seen any, or managed to produce any in their own experiments, such white crows could not possibly exist. What the Funda-Materialists neglected to note is that you aren't likely to spot any white crows if your eyes are tightly shut.

The obvious error that the materialistic paradigm's most ardent supporters made was in defining the limits of science's modest knowledge as being the limits of Nature itself—the same error as mistaking the universe for the Universe. This error is slowly being corrected as we learn to distinguish between the paradigmatic "map" science draws up for us, and the actual territory (Nature) itself that it seeks to model or represent. We are seemingly only just now learning that *the map is not the territory*. We are gradually becoming more conceptual and less Aristotelian in our thinking. By Aristotelian logic, we mean "category logic, excluded-middle logic, on/off logic, either/or logic. No greys—only black and white. This false logic lies at the heart of authoritarianism, conflict, and a great deal of inadequate science."[38] It is this logic that cannot resolve opposites or apparent paradoxes, whereas four-law logic can and does. (See Chapter 5 where we detail a mystical experience of mine.)

According to three-law logic, you are either "with us or with the terrorists," as per George W. Bush's political dictum for dummies. You can imagine how this kind of simplistic thought must have wrought havoc on many a mind when quantum physicists stumbled upon the wave/particle conundrum. For us humans, the problem isn't simply absorbing new facts, it's trying to make sense of them while filtering them through ontological assumptions that are almost wholly unconscious, and often badly flawed. Our systems of logic often lead us, quite logically, to grossly erroneous conclusions or just dead ends.

Although it has not been of primary concern to us here, we have nonetheless now covered a few different factors contributing to the biases operating in science, and I would like to bring to light one final point from Kuhn's *Structure of Scientific Revolutions*. He explains that increased scientific specialization and professionalization leads to increased restriction of the scientist's vision, as well as building in resistance to paradigm change—ultimately making the science more rigid.[39]

Ironically, it is this specialization and refinement of technique which leads to the (eventual) demise of the paradigm that a given scientist is operating within, because it becomes excellent at identifying legitimate anomalies, a.k.a. unexpected results that do not fit the dominant theory's expectations. Thus we might wonder how it is that so many scientists could be so rigidly closed-minded when it comes to new information they do not understand (as a result of having no frame of reference for it, or simple conditioning against it).

Obviously, the first factor is the incomprehension that makes it easy, even preferable, to dismiss something. Then the "fear of the unknown" leads us away from what we do not understand, and that avoidance perpetuates the lack of understanding, which leads to continued fear which leads to more avoidance, and so on. I have noted in my research numerous examples of individual "skeptics" or groups of "skeptics" staunchly refusing to even look at freely offered research data from the paranormal or parapsychology field/s. They don't want to know. And yet, the beauty of science's maps is that they can be *updated and adjusted*.

Importantly, from the psychological viewpoint, Kuhn stated that scientists will not abandon a paradigm/map because of its flaws or limitations unless there is another valid candidate for a paradigm ready and waiting. But if, as Kuhn also observed, the puzzles and problems facing "normal science" exist simply because no single paradigm ever successfully *solves* all of its problems,[40] then why would we take a hostile stance towards the unfamiliar or unresolved? Why fear the development of a new paradigm? Do we really need to derive that much of our self-identity from science's officially (or implicitly) condoned paradigms? Science is consistently illuminating anomalies and gradually explaining them, despite the protestations of the adherents of the old paradigm that failed to anticipate those anomalies, and who were not equipped by said paradigm to make sense of such unexpected discoveries. As Isaac Asimov (1920–92) said, "the most exciting phrase to hear in science, the one that heralds new discoveries, is not 'Eureka!,' but 'That's funny.'"

We can witness the inevitable shift occurring and observe the larger context in which it occurs, or we can try to rationalize it away and preserve the old moribund paradigm/s. I have chosen the former option. It is inevitable that humanity's awareness will continue to shift and expand at a rapid rate, causing the mutations (or abandonments) of its most treasured paradigms; that is what happens as novelty accumulates, and we are reaching (or perhaps have reached) a critical mass of novelty, causing scientist and layman alike to reconsider some of their core assumptions. Such is life in the world of relative truth.

A comment from renowned independent scientist and Director of the Association of Distinguished American Scientists Lieutenant Colonel Tom Bearden is apt before we proceed:

> [P]resently scientists have not the foggiest notion what mind, being, life, death, time, etc. are. For that matter, they don't really know what matter and energy and charge are either . . . [O]ur modern "science" is only about three hundred years old, and that's a snap of the finger in even just the existence of this world. Much of modern science still considers the mind as a "meat computer" . . . Materialism has not died, even though quantum mechanics essentially wiped it out decades ago, and the old concept of "mass" as something hard, permanent, and "material" has also long since vanished.[41]

Larry Dossey concurs: "[O]ur common-sense ideas about time, space, matter and our own minds are flawed. The universe works differently than we supposed."[42] Precisely how differently is hard to convey, but we will make more than a passing attempt, because, at this increasingly unstable point in our known history—with novelty piling upon uncertainty, piling upon ecological disasters, piling upon increasingly deranged activities by the global ruling elite, piling upon (orchestrated) economic meltdowns, piling upon increased military activities, and adding the continued starvation and subjugation of countless masses, there has never been a more urgent time to recover our identities and know who and what we really are, and thereby outgrow and move beyond the very attachment to various paradigms (and the false identities tied up in them) that are actually destroying us.

41

Paradigms cast spells on the brain; they make some things appear and
other things disappear. —Michael Grosso

Belief in the traditional sense, or certitude, or dogma, amounts to the grandiose
delusion, "My current model"—or grid, or map, or reality-tunnel—"contains the
whole universe and will never need to be revised." . . . I am perpetually astonished
that so many people still manage to live with such a medieval attitude.
—R.A. Wilson

The word fact comes from the Latin *factum* which means "having been made."
Man builds the facts of which he speaks when he develops the concept of empirical
knowledge. Empirical knowledge, built on facts not only perceived by man's senses,
but reified by man's conceptual and cultured mind, is only one type of knowledge,
resulting from one type of "knowingness." To say that it is the only valid mode,
or even the most basic and valid mode is a form of mental myopia or cultural
provincialism. —Dane Rudhyar

3

A DIFFERENT VIEWPOINT

I think the "educated" people have been so thoroughly conditioned . . . into . . . definitions of what is and is not real, that they are incapable of seeing something that is right in front of their face unless it fits into standard definitions. This is quite an ironic situation. The myths of the peasants turn out to be real; what could be a worse nightmare to the university professor? —Donald DeGracia

There was a time when the opposition between the "natural" and the "supernatural" had a meaning of some importance, but it has none any more. The conception of the "natural" has so changed that it either includes all that had formerly been denominated by the "supernatural" or it does not prevent the "supernatural" from existing alongside of it. —James Hyslop, *Life After Death* (1918)

Semantic Pedantics

In this brief chapter I would like to make a few suggestions here to help clear away some old baggage. First, there is no such thing as "paranormal," and nor is there an "abnormal" or "normal." These are just constructs of the mind; concepts with which we have attempted to navigate our way through our existence and make sense of our experience as humans. These arbitrary intellectual constructs actually indicate our perceptual and psychological biases and limits. These terms and their abuse by factions of the scientific establishment and interested

43

(if not well-informed) laypeople have created bias against those aspects of our experience that are less common and consequently often less understood. The term "paranormal" was created to designate phenomena *beyond* (para) the norm, and which had thus far escaped scientific explanations. The fact that paranormal phenomena provably exist, thanks in part to modern technology and research techniques, simply indicates how limited our traditional scientific conceptual and ontological matrices have been.

G.N.M. Tyrrell, writing in *Time and Tide* of November 20, 1943, stated: "The 'natural' and 'supernatural' must both be swept away. A new conception must replace them, that of a unitary reality, undivided in its essence, and divided only in appearance."[1] Tyrrell recognized the fundamentally arbitrary nature of these designations and the dualistic schism they needlessly create in the mind. How does one best decide whether to categorize something as normal or otherwise? The process is fundamentally arbitrary.

Because of the misuse of terms like paranormal, concepts such as altered states of consciousness, telepathy, mediumship, and even UFO sightings and abductions have been dismissed time and time again as delusion or hallucination by closed or complacent minds that have allowed themselves to be conditioned into believing that these things are abnormal and unnatural, and therefore not possible, let alone provable realities. As a result, some of these minds seek to disprove their reality by knowingly or unknowingly being highly selective with the information they choose to acknowledge and analyze (outright dishonesty being set aside for now), building a belief system (model) tantamount to a metaphorical house of cards that comes crashing to the ground under the slightest impartial scrutiny.

The paranormal vernacular is highly charged and there is no point discussing any related topics without de-charging and clarifying the language to some extent. Let us take note that there is no such thing as an entirely objective definition of "paranormal" or even of "normal." We use different terms to relate information about ideas and experiences, new concepts and such, and those terms generally have an implied meaning that is largely shaped by cultural context. Each person then assigns a personalized, idiosyncratic meaning to each term in the vernacular, a meaning based upon the unique and personal combination of information they have and the information they *don't* have pertaining to those terms. Thus there is, in less understood spheres of information, vast potential for misunderstanding and misconception of ideas, since the terms used to convey those ideas will mean different things to different people.

Really, when we use terms like "psi," we are referring mainly to "anomalous" (comparatively rarer and less well understood) functions of consciousness that have been misconceived and unduly maligned, mainly by those with no understanding, insight, or experience of their own. I hope this book will, along with others like it, go some small way to correcting this situation.

In *The Last Laugh*, Raymond Moody elaborates on the language barrier that has prevented further understanding of the nature of consciousness and anomalous phenomena in general. He observes that "the paranormal is not simply an unknown, but an unknown that is already draped seductively in its own distinctive array of emotional trappings . . . It becomes increasingly difficult to talk about something—much less really come to know about it—when the people dominating the public dialogue are using loaded language, each bringing their particular bias to the considerations at hand."[2] We must eliminate the biases innate within ideas of normality, abnormality, or paranormality. These words merely point to concepts that vary in meaning from person to person.

Most people, if you were to ask them what constitutes "paranormal," would perhaps give some examples of phenomena they *perceive* as such: ghosts, levitation, telepathy, and so on. If you asked them about "normal" things, most people would probably rattle off a list of familiar items, concepts or behaviors: sunlight, gravity, a comfortable armchair, catching up over a coffee, computers, working nine to five, picking your nose when you think no one is looking, and so on. But if you were to ask people about their concept of normality versus *para*normality and how they actually defined those concepts into being such that they could go about using them with apparent adroitness, and making the necessary distinctions, I am willing to bet that most people would be at a loss to explain precisely the process of logic they used such that they could ultimately view one thing as being normal and another as something other than normal.

Most of the time when we look at these concepts, what we will find is that we usually designate the familiar as being "normal" and the unfamiliar or comparatively less familiar as being abnormal, strange, or even paranormal. This is Rhudyar's "cultural provincialism." Something usually becomes familiar to us not through a process of logical deduction but by repeated experience with it, or perhaps vicarious experience. That is ultimately the bulk of the basis of our distinction between "normal" and "paranormal"; it is merely a perceptual one, not an objective or quantifiable one. As the famous Russian psychic Wolf Messing once said: "There is nothing strange. Only what is not yet commonplace."[3]

Now, a point that appears to be lost on most hardcore soi-disant skeptics is that our experiential capacities exist on a vast continuum. What we need to realize, and what I will illustrate, is that not everyone has the same perceptual or experiential capacities; these vary from person to person at any given moment, for reasons I will elaborate on later. Thus, when we combine the different scenarios and circumstances life can throw at us with the fact that no two people experience the universe in exactly the same way, you have a truly prodigious potential for varied and unique experiences along the continuum among the people of this planet. We fail to take cognizance of this fact at our peril. What all of this means is that our concept of "normality" is actually highly subjective, while the same is true for "paranormality."

These terms elucidate the innate biases and experiential (and conceptual) limitations of the user more than they actually communicate anything about reality itself.

When we make the mistake of assuming that our ordinary conscious experience, even if shared by many, is fundamentally and indisputably indicative of the limits of all possible "legitimate" experience within Nature or reality, the terms normal or paranormal begin to take on the presumptuous and dogmatic tone that the words themselves imply. In many ways, *normal* is just one person's way of saying they *believe in it* (whatever "it" is). *Paranormal*, for the cognitively rigidified psi "skeptic," is simply stating the opposite prejudice: they disbelieve (because for them it connotes *impossibility*). Neither of these things, of course, constitutes *knowing*. All we can truly *know* is our own internal conscious experience, and although much of the content of this book is not based within the realm of the subjectivity of internal experience, much of it is, and for good reason. Of special significance to us here, because of its mind- and paradigm-changing quality, is when such internal subjective experience is augmented by credible external verification. This is when we can find that the supposedly paranormal is not so strange after all, and this is when we begin to realize the narrow and myopic nature of our concepts of normality versus paranormality.

Contrary to popular misconception, the word "paranormal" does not necessarily connote an absence of objectivity, or the presence of a supposed impossibility. As we will see, much paranormal data is highly objective, and many "strange" experiences can be verified. I therefore ask readers to divest themselves of any preconceptions they have regarding some of the terminology that will be used in this book. For instance, I will use the word "paranormal" as a rough point of reference but not a literal term, because in order to have a paranormal, you have to have defined into existence a normal against which to contrast it (which I am not going to do), creating a false dichotomy. This immediately loads any discussion with built-in prejudices and immediately makes anyone who appears to be "pro-paranormal" by definition *not* normal or *ab*normal—not a helpful way to go about discussing the nature of consciousness or reality, since it immediately creates a duality or polemic wherein one party is automatically one-up on the other right from the start, and we do not want to encourage such mammalian-reptilian thought.

You cannot go and buy a can of Normal at the supermarket and likewise you cannot buy a bag of Paranormal. These are merely *concepts*: *categories*. "All categories are arbitrary; categories do not exist 'out there.' Once your mind is ruled by category, you are in a mind-trap; you are unable to think with clarity or independence."[4] Take, for example, the term "anomalous"; it is merely a red flag of unknowing, an admission that one or more thresholds of understanding have been breached and little-understood territory has been entered. In short, terms like "miracle" or "supernatural" are simply indicators of our current ignorance. Amit Goswami points out that we are already making good models for the understanding of the paranormal within more general laws,[5] so what is anomalous or miraculous within one theory, construct, or outlook may be entirely predictable within another.

When it comes to discussing the apparent nature of reality we must recognize the arbitrariness and relativity of abstract concepts defined into existence through arbitrary standards and qualifiers derived from limited data. It is much easier to recognize the reality of something if it has not been predefined as abnormal or impossible and programmed into our minds as nonexistent. It's harder to recognize something you expect never to see.

Aristotelian thought, being ruled by abstract category, has tended to inhibit creative and realistic thinking.[6] R.A. Wilson insisted that both in psychology and physics, we have outgrown the medieval Aristotelian notions of "objective reality" and entered a non-Aristotelian realm.[7] Here, for the most part, we do not desire to definitely force-fit data into one category/model or another; we will utilize models and play with concepts in order to expand our vision of possibility. Perhaps the truth is a combination of many things rather than simply being of one category or the other, so to speak. Please consider the words I use here as guides, tools, and maps of sorts, and remember that the map is not the territory (Alfred Korzybski), even if sometimes my arrangement of words creates the impression that I might have momentarily forgotten that fact. What I am really alluding to and attempting to point at is the nature of reality and consciousness, not the words and concepts we use in attempts at defining or describing it.

Dogmatic belief in abstract concepts—whether established scientific theories or theological systems—is unworthy of the truth-seeker. Of course, to be a *dis*believer in something, you have to believe in something else, some kind of conflicting but seemingly superior ideology, and here I insist on belief in no particular doctrine or world model, drawing instead on an eclectic array of sources and fields. "Beware the man with one book," as the Arab proverb goes. Observe the most dogged "skeptics"; while they profess (or pretend) caution and measured doubt regarding the so-called paranormal, their strong disbelief is paralleled by an equally strong credulity regarding a *different world model*. As R.A. Wilson has pointed out, the participant in organized, activistic, or evangelical "skepticism" of paranormality is only skeptical about anything that lies beyond his own contrived existential reality tunnel.

Belief or disbelief is what one achieves when one has to make speculations, deductions, inferences, or assumptions in order to draw a conclusion; it is necessarily the product of a certain degree of ignorance. Belief or disbelief is an attitude, an emotional investment, a stance, a posture, an information filter. Far more constructive and healthy is open-minded consideration and investigation.

Now, I make no claim to being omniscient, but when it comes to consciousness and the nature of reality I no longer have the luxury of being able to choose between belief or disbelief because my mental filters and old world models have been shredded (see Chapter 5). Please do not take my word for anything, or anybody else's. Be your own skeptic and be your own authority—don't fall for group-think.

A note on terminology: for the purposes of our discussion I generally use the more passive terms such as "higher sense perception" (HSP), extrasensory perception (ESP), psychic perception, and intuition interchangeably. Psi distinguishes itself from these as a term inclusive of mind-over-matter phenomena, and is thus more generalized. ESP I will define here as being *the act of perceiving, knowing, or sensing information without the rational mind, and beyond the means normally attributed to the commonly acknowledged five primary human sense faculties, in ways that ostensibly transcend the bounds of known space-time.* ("ESP" dates back to the late 1800s when Dr. Paul Joire first used it in reference to the ability of tranced or hypnotized subjects to sense things external to them without the ordinary five senses).

Now let's get "paranormal"!

One's own lack of experience with or understanding of something does not necessarily demand a lack of experience or insight on the part of another. That is to say that we cannot realistically expect one person's partial and approximate model of the universe to be faithfully replicated by every other individual and idiosyncratic mind. —Author

4

QUANTUM WEIRDNESS AND COSMIC ONENESS

The bottom line is that ideas will control you to the degree that you blindly accept them. The alternative is for you to control ideas and use them as *you* see fit.—Donald DeGracia

Probably whatever is true will in fact be crazy, because historically the truth in physics always seems to be more far-out than anything you could have imagined.—John Baez, physicist

I don't see the soul and consciousness as an epiphenomenon, or product, of matter. It's just the other way around: I see matter as an epiphenomenon of soul and consciousness. The material world has evolved from the absolute vacuum of space—the home of the soul.[1]—Fred Alan Wolf, physicist

Physics within Consciousness

The world of physics at large is still divided on how exactly to interpret the experimental findings of investigations into the theories and mathematical predictions of quantum mechanics. Of the many interpretations, an incomplete list includes the Copenhagen interpretation, the many-worlds interpretation, the transactional interpretation, David Bohm's interpretation and various others. These different interpretations imply different things about our reality and our place within it, though in the context given here, Amit Goswami's monistic idealism makes a lot of sense and affords the acknowledgment of much otherwise awkward data.[2] Monistic idealism is the antithesis of material realism, and supposes that it is not matter but consciousness that is fundamental, thus allowing for the study of all of quantum physics' phenomena with fresh eyes, not to mention data from the world of parapsychology, occultism, and mysticism. We will also consider equivalent concepts such as Bohm's implicate versus explicate order idea, and Dewey Larson's time-space versus space-time dichotomy.

The Double-Slit Experiment:
Physics Encounters Consciousness

Laboratory experiments by Geoffrey Ingram Taylor in the early 1900s (based on Thomas Young's experiments from the first decade of the 1800s) have shown that a single photon (or electron), when fired at two extremely narrow slits in a photographic plate, will, when no one is observing it directly, behave as if it is a wave of light, passing through *both* slits, interacting with itself, creating an interference pattern on the plate (when waves are superposed/overlap or cross over one another, interference patterns result).

Thomas Young had already shown that photons had wave properties which created interference patterns when passed through the double slits, but improved technology allowed Taylor to fire just *one photon at a time*, unexpectedly leading to this photonic self-interference within the solitary wave/particle ("wavicle"). This phenomenon has been metaphorically referred to as the sound of one hand clapping and proves the wave nature of quanta. On the other hand, when someone observes the photon, it will (almost) always behave as if it is a singular entity, seemingly choosing one of the two slits to pass through, instead of passing, apparently miraculously, through both. This bizarre yet undeniable reality suggests that the act of observation is fundamentally creative or perturbative with regard to the system being observed. When physicists try to measure the particle, the particle "knows" and decides to pick one slit, but when not measured, it plays silly and passes through *both*, according to most physicists, as a *wave of possibility/probability, not an actual wave in space-time.*

It's as if the act of observation instantaneously selects a singular outcome out of a virtually infinite number of possible outcomes. Some physicists refer to this phenomenon as "wave function collapse," whereby, for instance, the cloud-like miasma that electrons are conceived to exist in around an atom, pre-observation, will appear to collapse upon measurement/observation into a singular particle, yielding a "classical" state of reality where things don't exist in a haze of probability waves (also known as a wave packet). The quantum wave function indicates only the chance of finding a particle at any place and time. In other words, *the probability of finding that particle is given by Schrödinger's wave* (Schrödinger won the 1933 Nobel Prize for his wave equation, building on de Broglie's wave concept).

Prior to "collapse," the electron exists not at our space-time level of reality, but in potential, in the "transcendent domain," as Goswami puts it. To some, it's almost as if the quantum realm is telling us that when we aren't looking, everything that *can* exist *does* exist, yet when we seek to observe what is *happening* to see for ourselves, we make a singular selection from an infinite array of possibilities and ultimately witness one event, one possible outcome, out of all that could have occurred (and perhaps *has* occurred in some other dimension or universe).

Non-observation preserves the wave-potential reality, allowing, for instance, the aforementioned interference patterns to occur in the double-slit experiment. However, this dualism has been challenged by novel experiments (which we will look at shortly) that have shown that both the particle and wave reality can be made manifest *simultaneously*, indicating that there may in fact be no wave "collapse" at all, that the wave may occupy its own "parallel" or "inverted" reality alongside the particle. Late American engineer Dewey Larson's Reciprocal System theory accounts for this by assigning the quantum waves to "reciprocal space," which is not a spatial reference frame, but a temporal one: time-space. Information and energy flow between each of these complementary realities.[3]

The concept of superposition is evinced by Thomas Young's double-slit experiment (1802), which proves that light has a wave aspect. In 1926 Heisenberg's previous advisor, Max Born, apparently discovered why no one had found a physical interpretation for Schrödinger's wave function. They are not physical waves in space-time at all; rather, the wave function includes all the possible states of a system; it is an information wave (also referred to as a de Broglie[*] wave). Before a measurement those states exist in *superposition*, in

---

[*] French aristocrat Prince Louis de Broglie proposed this wave in 1923 and used it to calculate the orbits of atoms, each orbit determined by the standing waves of the de Broglie vibration. Movement of these standing waves indicates movement of the associated particle. De Broglie won the 1929 Nobel Prize for his work, stating in his acceptance speech that "the existence of corpuscles accompanied by waves has to be assumed in all cases." (Source: Aspden, 1972, 64.)

which every possible outcome is described at the same time. Superposition is one of the defining qualities of quantum mechanics and implies that individual events cannot be predicted with certainty; only the *probability* of an experimental outcome can be derived.[4] In terms of Larson's model, this is because we and our scientific equipment do not have direct access to the temporal reference frame (time-space) that quantum waves are operating in. Therefore, the results of their operations are, to us, not certain but statistical.[5]

As noted, Taylor's experiments showed that the mere act of observation affected the way the quantum entities were behaving. In 1998, scientists at Israel's Weizmann Institute of Science repeated Taylor's experiment and found that the observer's influence on what happened increased as the amount of "watching" did.[6] This in itself is a massive clue that not only has parapsychology *not* been wasting its time researching interactions between the human mind and surrounding matter and the environment, but that existing effects recorded in such research can be amplified through the focused attention of increased numbers of participants.

Indeed, there is plenty of evidence to support such notions, and the Global Consciousness Project, based at Princeton University, has produced irrefutable data that further proves that the more watchers there are, the greater indeed is the effect upon the quantum realm globally, further proving the interaction between consciousness and the energy matrix we are immersed in. This suggests interesting possibilities with regard to mind–matter interactions and how we create our personal perceptual and experiential "bubbles." We might also infer that psi-negative effects could be created as a function of focus or even belief— how many skeptics ever experience the paranormal firsthand? I will elaborate on these ideas later.

Quantum mechanics predicts that wherever the wave energy or impulse is strongest is where you are most likely to "find" the particle, although, in view of the concept of superposition, the particle could theoretically manifest anywhere, even the next galaxy. According to Amit Goswami (and earlier, Ludwig Bass), what prevents this from happening is a common ground of unified consciousness.[7] Consciousness, as we will see more clearly as we go, seems to have the ability to impress upon "external" things a certain order. It selects one experiential reality from a multitude of possible ones. Consciousness seems to ensure that if you look away and then look back at your quantum wave, the particle form will be exactly where it "should" be: a sign of an innately intelligent and integrated subject/object universe, although this subject/object dualism is actually a clever perceptual deception and a duality we can ultimately discard. Capra elaborates for us in *The Tao of Physics*:

52

At the sub-atomic level, matter does not exist with certainty at definite places, but rather, shows "tendencies to exist," and atomic events do not occur with certainty at definite times and in definite ways, but rather show "tendencies to occur" [Heisenberg's uncertainty principle] . . . [T]hese tendencies are expressed as probabilities and are associated with mathematical quantities which take the form of waves . . . which are related to the probabilities of finding the particles at particular points in space and at particular times . . . Quantum theory has thus demolished the classical concepts of strictly solid objects and of strictly deterministic* laws of nature. At the subatomic level, the solid material objects of classical physics dissolve into wave-like patterns of probabilities, and these patterns, ultimately, represent not probabilities of things, but probabilities of interconnections . . . [T]he subatomic particles have no meaning as isolated entities, but can only be understood as interconnections between the preparation of an experiment and the subsequent measurement. Quantum theory thus reveals a basic oneness of the universe . . . The human observer constitutes the final link in the chain of observational processes, and the properties of any atomic object can only be understood in terms of the object's interaction with the observer. This means that the classical ideal of an objective description of nature is no longer valid . . . In atomic physics we can never speak about nature, without at the same time speaking about ourselves.[8]

As David Yurth puts it: "The most fundamental tenet of the ancient book of Hindu verses known as the Vedas has now been unarguably demonstrated. The act of observation and the means of observation cannot be separated from that which is being observed."[9] So the way that we tend to perceive Nature via our human sense receptors and brain is drastically different to the way that quantum physics reveals it to be. Standard human perception primarily identifies the

---

* Determinism, being a corollary of materialism, is the view that every event, including human cognition, behavior, decision and action, is causally determined by an unbroken sequence of prior events and that all motion can be predicted exactly given the laws of motion and the initial conditions on the objects. This is a major aspect of the Newtonian outlook.

apparent "separateness" of things, while quantum physics begins to reveal their vital underlying interconnectedness. Interestingly, research psychologist Lawrence LeShan identified this same reversal occurring in mystics and psychics when they obtain information via non-ordinary or "paranormal" means: "It is the *unity* of all things that is seen as most important, their *relationships* rather than their individual and unique characteristics that are seen as crucial."[10]

Quantum physicists Anton Zeilinger and Markus Aspelmeyer told us more recently that electrons, neutrons, and atoms have been shown to exhibit interference effects when passing through a double slit, thus proving that these "massive" systems did not pass through only one or the other slit.[11] Similar behavior was observed in 1999 by Zeilinger and colleagues at Vienna for relatively large carbon-60 and carbon-70 fullerene molecules (a.k.a. Buckyballs), and ongoing research has demonstrated interference with even heavier and larger systems. One of the main goals of this research is to realize quantum interference for small viruses or maybe even nanobacteria.[12] Here the Hermetic axiom "as above, so below"—a major philosophical underpinning of occultism—starts to play on one's mind. As well as fluorinated carbon, interference in double-slit experiments has been demonstrated with tetraphenylporphyrin, both of which are composed of over a hundred atoms each.[13] Each molecular system existed in a state of superposition or uncertainty, its atom's "waves of probability" mingling with each other as they passed through the slits. Zeilinger was awarded the inaugural Isaac Newton medal in October 2007 for this work, which essentially shows molecular systems operate according to holographic principles.

One wonders: what is the limit? Is there one? According to Zeilinger it's only budget.[14] In other words, all macro systems studied under appropriate conditions should demonstrate this quantum interference, given enough time and know-how. This will indicate that the wave information of 3-dimensional objects is smeared in an apparently indeterminate state of superposition in the transcendent domain ("hyperspace" or "time-space"), rather than being definitely identifiable at a particular location in space-time. In principle, as far as quantum mechanics is concerned, what applies at the quantum level also applies at the macroscopic level. "Truly macroscopic superpositions containing many billions of electrons have been demonstrated where each electron is simultaneously moving in two directions," Rosenblum and Kuttner tell us. "Bose-Einstein condensates have been created in which each of several thousand atoms is spread over several millimeters. A recent American Institute of Physics news bulletin bore the headline '3600 Atoms in Two Places at Once.'"[15]

All of this indicates that the macro world perceptible to the human senses may be susceptible to the influence of directed human intention—if intention can influence the de Broglie/probability waves of "matter" by functioning in their hyperspace domain.

The Wave Function "Collapse"

Chris Humphrey states that if we accept the reality of the de Broglie wave and that it does not collapse but coexists with its particle, then we can resolve the apparent wave/particle paradox in physics.[16] William Tiller has said that if we assume the simultaneous existence of matter as both particle and wave and that the de Broglie wave reality exists in a sort of parallel frequency domain outside our standard space-time reference frame we can resolve some of the quantum weirdness.[17] We will elaborate on this shortly because it is vital in understanding "paranormal" phenomena and the nature of consciousness.

Regardless, physics has long since arrived at a place where strict determinism can no longer be sustained; the quantum (and subquantum) worlds are fundamentally indeterminate, random, and unpredictable to us here in ordinary space-time. The wave-like quantum information fields outside our space-time reference frame are the codes for the physical universe. Fred Alan Wolf tells us that in all of the major or most widely employed wave-particle interpretations, "the quantum wave function includes many parallel branches [of information or possibility]. But what happens to these branches changes according to the interpretation."[18]

In the Bohm and Everett parallel universes postulates, the quantum wave function is real and includes many parallel branches that do *not* disappear/collapse upon observation. In the Everett parallel universes or many-worlds theory, our universe is made from all of the overlapping parallel universes' branches.[19] If we hypothesize the existence of a 4-spatial reality, then we can have 3-space universes existing side by side unaware of each other, interconnected by the extra spatial dimension. Alternatively, we can postulate a "parallel" 3-dimensional reciprocal time domain which complements our 3D space-time (as Larson did, similarly to Bohm).

Goswami points out that the ability of consciousness to affect the quantum wave is a paradox only if consciousness is made of atoms. If, on the other hand, consciousness itself possesses a wave nature and inhabits (even if only transiently) the de Broglie wave's domain, then logically it could influence what we see as matter. Goswami postulates that the ground of all existence is actually consciousness, and that therefore we should not find it particularly odd that the observer can seemingly cause a particle to manifest as a point ("wave collapse") in space-time reality where previously there was only a probability wave (in parallel time-space).[20]

It is important to realize that the principle of reductionism as an explanation of consciousness (or even existence in general) is not an experimental proof, and as such is increasingly under siege. On locality, Goswami adds that the instantaneous collapse of quantum waves spread over vast distances means that the influence of our measurement is not travelling locally: locality is ruled out. Building on this, Goswami asks how consciousness, as a supposedly localized epiphenomenon of matter (the brain) can "collapse" the nonlocalized wave of a quantum object when it takes a quantum measurement?[21] Logically, a consciousness that can "collapse the wave function" of a quantum entity at a distance instantly must itself be nonlocal, or "transcendent," as Goswami puts it. As we are beginning to see, this "transcendent domain" has many names, facets and conceptualizations; Carl Jung called one facet the collective unconscious.

Many Worlds, Double Slits, and Paranormal Phenomena

Proposed by Hugh Everett in 1957, the many-worlds interpretation is one of the most occult-sounding interpretations of quantum physics' compelling findings. As far as the double-slit experiment is concerned, the many-worlds interpretation runs something along the following lines. When a photon is fired at the screen with the two slits cut into it and no one attempts to observe/ measure it, it will pass through both slits and interfere with itself as if it were a wave. Yet, when someone attempts to measure/observe the process, the photon will "select" a single slit to pass through and not interfere with itself, as if it is corpuscular. The wave function "collapses" and a single outcome/path has been selected out of an infinitude of possible outcomes. The many-worlds interpretation postulates that although in our reality the photon has selected one single path, it has actually traveled every possible path—somewhere! (From an extradimensional perspective this might be true enough, since a 3D reality would be completely enfolded within a 4D reality.) In other words, for every possible path the electron could have taken, there is another world/reality in which it actually *did* take that path. As author Marie D. Jones put it, the many-worlds interpretation "holds that *everything* is real, even when you don't look at it."[22] Perhaps every possibility *is* real—in the time domain/time-space.

Occultism has always concerned itself with describing other planes/worlds of existence; worlds that are, according to occult doctrine, part of our greater spiritual heritage. Occultism has always been firmly rooted in the perceptions and experiences of clairvoyants/seers who have been able to actually access these other planes of reality and return to tell the tale. It is thus not an abstract thought system arbitrarily created; it is grounded in empiricism, in direct personal apprehension of realities beyond the ordinary waking perceptual abilities of the average person. Interestingly, string theory has, in its various forms, postulated the existence of as many as 36 dimensions of existence. Occultism acknowledges seven primary planes of existence, although these are all subdivided into further lots of seven, which are also all subdivided into further lots of seven, ad infinitum. It is a fundamentally fractal/self-similar paradigm, which fits perfectly with the modern notion of a holographic universe (see Chapter 7).

"[W]here a complex, open, self-organizing system exists anywhere in our space-time continuum, it is self-similar at all scales."[23] The occult universe is a self-referencing fractal universe, the term "fractal" being coined by mathematician Benoit Mandelbrot following his ten-year study of supposedly unrelated systems such as the fluctuations in stock market prices and the irregular shapes of coastlines, which revealed to him self-similar patterns repeating at ever larger and smaller scales across a range of such disparate phenomena. The fragmented geometrical shapes yielded by the mathematical equations he dubbed fractals[*], and these were the first sign that beneath the apparent chaos of complex systems there is a profound harmonic order,[24] a clue to a hidden intelligence tacitly guiding cosmic processes at all scales. In fact, physicist Max Planck said back in 1944:

> As a man who has devoted his whole life to . . . the study of matter, I can tell you as a result of my research about atoms this much: There is no matter as such. All matter originates and exists only by virtue of a force which brings the particle of an atom to vibration and holds [it] together. We must assume behind this force the existence of a conscious and intelligent mind. This mind is the matrix of all matter.[25]

The many-worlds interpretation of quantum mechanics is used by some to circumvent or nullify the "grandfather paradox," first proposed by Russian physicist Igor Novikov. This basically refers to the idea of what would happen

---

[*] From the Latin, *fractus*, from the verb *frangere*, "to break." Above all, fractal meant self-similar: self-similarity is symmetry across scale and implies recursion pattern inside pattern. Source: Gleick, 1988.

if you traveled back in time to shoot your grandfather so that he never sires any progeny. Would you cease to exist? According to the old view of linear time, if you killed Gramps and continued to exist, there would be a paradox because you should not still exist if you went "back" and eliminated him. According to the many-worlds interpretation, when you go back in time, you are not merely traveling "backwards" along the arrow of time in your dimension, you actually end up in a "parallel world" where you *can* shoot Gramps in his youth (a tad macabre, isn't it) and thus prevent your parents from meeting and producing offspring. In this scenario, you (the time-traveling you) do not cease to exist. Rather, you merely prevent another version or copy of you from being born in this other parallel reality.

From the occult or mystical perspective this works perfectly well. The many-worlds interpretation of the grandfather paradox renders any would-be paradox null and void, because it preserves free will but also preserves your existence once you pull the trigger. From this perspective, this action simply prevents your doppelganger in this other reality from entering that particular world. Your own mind continues on regardless—there is no paradox. You can exist without (that particular version of) your grandfather existing in that alternative reality, because the grandfather from your own reality/timewave has not been harmed in any way.

Those physicists who are not comfortable with the many-worlds viewpoint are forced to construct other hypothetical scenarios for what might happen once you stepped out of the time machine and aimed the gun at Gramps, in order to maintain and preserve the principle of "self-consistency" (in this instance, meaning that the fact of your existence has to remain rationally and *linearly* explicable). The gun inexplicably jams, for instance, or some other intervention mysteriously occurs no matter what you try to do, and thus your plan is foiled every time by some chance unforeseen occurrence you could not avoid. Thus, in this contrived view, Gramps lives to meet your grandmother and produces your parents, who in turn produce you—you "had" to be produced, because there you are. This keeps the so-called law of self-consistency intact, but I struggle to imagine many occultists or mystics falling prey to this theory, which rests on an outdated linear view of time.

As something of a mystic, and a student of the occult, I perceive the many-worlds view as possessing intrinsic validity, and know that it goes some way to describing reality, reality being infinite potential infinitely realized* (even if we

---

* String theorists refer to this as the "Populated Landscape," meaning every possible universe is made manifest somewhere in the theoretical "Landscape." (Source:

can't prove it). To believe there is a Grandfather Paradox is to impose limits upon Nature that do not exist. If you travel back in time, you encounter an entirely different 3-space reality and "timeline" from the one you left: there can be no paradox.

The eminent physicist and co-founder of string theory, Michio Kaku, has actually said:

> [I]f you have a radio in your living room . . . and you have all frequencies in your living room; BBC, Radio Moscow, ABC, but your radio is tuned to one frequency—you're decohered from all the other frequencies. You're only coherent [wave phase and amplitude in alignment; either exactly or in whole number ratios] with one frequency. We now believe that the universe is vibrating and that there are vibrations of other universes right in this room. There are the universes of dinosaurs because the comet didn't hit 65 million years ago; the wave function of aliens from outer space looking at the rubble of an earth that already was destroyed—all in your living room, except we have decohered from them. We're no longer in tune with them, we don't vibrate with them . . . [P]robably there are other parallel universes in your living room and believe it or not this is called modern physics . . . get used to it. This is the modern interpretation of the quantum theory, that many worlds represents reality.[26]

Not long ago, almost anyone who uttered such a sentiment would have been dismissed by many as "New Age-y," "flaky," and so on, but it is no longer feasible to use such convenient rationalizations with physicists of Kaku's credibility speaking as a clairvoyant or mystic might. In fact, identical sentiments have been put forth by theosophists a century and more ago in describing the astral plane, which interpenetrates the physical plane without either realm's inhabitants being aware of the other, "whose senses are normally capable of responding to the undulations of their world only."[27]

In 1953, Aldous Huxley, having experimented with ingesting hallucinogens such as mescaline, psilocybin, and LSD, suggested that the function of the brain, nervous system, and sense organs is primarily eliminative rather than productive, operating as a "reducing valve" that protects us from being overwhelmed and

---

Susskind, 2006, 294.)

confused by a mass of useless and irrelevant knowledge, leaving only the tiny selection likely to be practically useful.[28] The eminent psychiatrist Stanislav Grof, who has researched the effects of LSD on consciousness extensively, has expressed agreement with this "reducing valve" way of looking at the brain.[29] By the time of publication of his book *The Holotropic Mind* in 1993, Grof had completed some 24,000 altered state sessions with clients and patients—no small body of evidence to substantiate his view. In 1983, Swiss scientist Albert Hoffman, who first synthesized LSD (and experimented with it on himself), expressed the view that LSD, by altering the brain's chemistry, tunes it to other wavelengths from its usual one, thus allowing other realities to enter into one's awareness.[30]

Intuitives have long used the terms *vibration* and *frequency* to describe what they see and feel, but only now is it becoming quite apparent how prescient their vernacular actually was even before the advent of quantum physics. This is the dialect of modern physics, not the old physics that described a "dead," meaningless world of inert, "solid" matter with only empty space in between, and that featured merely epiphenomenal consciousness. Cybernetician David Foster wrote in a letter to Colin Wilson that the universe is a structure of waves and vibrations, the inner content of which is "meaning," with man being a micro-system of the same essential vibratory nature within the meaningful universal wave system. He went on to add that the mind is a radio set that can "tune in" to thousands of different vibrations in the aether.[31]

Such "tuning in" yields what we myopically call ESP. Think of it this way: two people with the same quantum phase have a phase difference of zero, and are therefore completely real to each other. To be able to shake hands or interact solidly, we must have the same quantum phase, the same "time-dependent phase factor," meaning we share the same moment in time. If our quantum phases are altered with respect to each other, our interaction will be less tangible.[32] One of us may perceive the other as being "ghostly"; the interaction may appear to be "paranormal"—get the idea?

In Bearden's model, the "only difference between any two entities in the various worlds is a matter of orthogonal rotation," rotation at right angles to the original reference frame/reality. One orthorotation away, the first "hyperspace" in this schema, is the electromagnetic field. Another 90 degree rotation away is the hyperspace occupied by the de Broglie waves. Following this, one more rotation away is a purely mental/virtual world in which 3D objects would be points to us here if seen from our reference frame. According to Bearden, any hyperspace beyond this is only ever three rotational turns away from our frame. Physical phenomena in these frames are mental phenomena with respect to ours—but they are still very real.[33] This would effectively make the contents of all parallel worlds aspects of our collective unconscious, part of our own psyche.

Intriguingly, Rick Strassman, psychiatrist and researcher into dimethyltryptamine (DMT), following his research into the effects of DMT on human consciousness and the anomalous experiences it produced in test subjects, speculated that parallel universes might be familiar to us, even if the organisms and technologies therein developed along drastically different lines. He believes that reptilian and insect-like beings, and unrecognizable shapes imbued with intelligence should not be unexpected, and nor should highly advanced forms of technology—all of which were reported by his DMT test subjects.[34]

Holding all of the above firmly in mind, we note those bizarre instances—of which there are documented cases—wherein people have inexplicably found themselves witnessing or even participating in a scene from a "parallel" reality, sometimes what they perceive as the "past."

For instance, on August 10, 1901, two Oxford professors, Anne Moberly, the principal of St. Hugh's College, and Eleanor Jourdain, the vice-principal, were wandering, lost, through the garden of the Petit Trianon at Versailles when they were both overcome with sudden feelings of gloom, depression, and unease, though they said nothing of it to one another at the time. Suddenly the scenery seemed somehow abnormal, lifeless, and unreal. Two men in "long greyish-green coats with small three-cornered hats" suddenly appeared and directed the women to the Petit Trianon. They strolled past an isolated cottage where a woman and a 12- or 13-year-old girl were standing at the doorway, both wearing white kerchiefs fastened under their bodices. Jourdain would later write that "both seemed to pause for an instant, as in a motion picture."

The two continued on their way and soon reached a pavilion that stood in the middle of an enclosure. A sinister-looking man was sitting outside the pavilion, his face repulsively disfigured by smallpox, wearing a black cloak around his shoulders and a slouch hat—bizarre dress for the period and the weather. He turned to look in their direction though seemed almost to stare through them, not responding to their presence. Still, it was enough to make them feel extremely uncomfortable and the two professors walked on in silent unease until they reached a small terraced country house. A lady was sitting in full view on the lawn with her back to the house, though bizarrely, only one of the pair saw her despite both being keenly on the lookout for someone to ask for directions. The woman, oddly dressed for the period in a summer dress with a long bodice and a very full but short skirt, held a large sheet of paper or cardboard in her hand and seemed to be working at a drawing. She had a pale green fichu or kerchief draped around her shoulders, and a large white hat covered her fair hair. As Moberly and Jourdain continued on, a young man, again oddly dressed, ran up to them and urgently offered them directions towards the Petit Trianon which they eventually located and entered, finding themselves in the midst of a wedding party wherein the participants were dressed in the garb of 1901, their time.

On subsequent trips to the Petit Trianon gardens the women found to their bafflement that a path they had walked down on their initial visit was now blocked by an old stone wall and had been for some time, evidently. Others no longer existed at all. Overall, the layout and dimensions of the grounds and buildings was completely and yet unaccountably different. The kiosk where the disfigured man sat, for instance, was no longer there.

Home in England searching through historical records, the women concluded that they had perhaps been transported into Queen Marie Antoinette's actual memory of the day (August 10, 1972) in which the sacking of the Tuileries and the massacre of the Swiss Guards had taken place—which accounted for the agitated manner of the people in the garden and general sense of oppressive gloom—and that the woman seated in the garden was none other than the Queen herself. Moberly later came across a picture of Antoinette drawn by the artist Wertmüller and was able to identify her as the same sketching woman she had seen near the Petit Trianon—even the clothes were the same. The pockmarked and "evil"-looking man by the pavilion, the records suggested, may have been the Queen's betrayer, Comte de Vaudreuil.[35] Moberly and Jourdain's descriptions of the layout of the gardens and the outbuildings were unknown by Versailles historians at the time but were later verified by painstaking search and scrutiny of obscure records of Louis XVI's court, including wages he paid to gardeners and carpenters for specific projects.[36]

String theorists and cyberneticians rejoice. Probably the most compelling element of this particular report is that people from the scene/period approached the two women and addressed them specifically, demonstrating that they were not merely invisible bystanders, but very much real and perceptible. Thus, the women had essentially been transported back in time; they weren't just witnessing a scene as outside observers, they were there in the "past." In a 1957 paper on how the focus of our awareness creates our reality, Hugh Everett described "simple moments in time when it becomes possible to jump from one reality to another by creating a quantum bridge between two already existing possibilities." One wonders if he had intended to include such possibilities as this time-warping one. Everett called these windows of opportunity "choice points."[37] He was, evidently, very much aware of the pluralistic nature of "reality."

Events such as Moberly and Jourdain's are familiar even to government-employed remote viewers. As we have seen and will see further, in quantum physics the past, present, and future are not clearly distinguishable from one another and research is ongoing into the effects the future has on the present (you read that correctly). In short, past, present, and future—all of them—exist *now*. In the words of physicist and string theory exponent Brian Greene, "If you were having a great time at the stroke of midnight on New Year's Eve, 1999, you still are." (We will return to this comment again soon.)

From the many-worlds perspective, there is nothing particularly unusual about this event. The occultist might suggest that the women had essentially stepped into an Akashic record of the past. So, were these two women of the 20th century *actually* there in the 1700s? Taking the view of the many-worlds interpretation, in at least one version, they were (and still are), and perhaps somewhere in that "parallel reality" there exists a record in some long since departed soul's tattered old diary of the two "oddly dressed" women who seemed out of place in the garden of the Petit Trianon that day as everyone bustled about hastily and on edge. There is no "separate time period," simply a larger hyperdimensional reality that enfolds all time. If we could step into a hyperframe and see all instants through history frozen in time, we could choose a different one to step into and experience.

Novikov applied the "principle of least action" to time travel, and, in what Strieber refers to as a "brilliant feat of mathematics" showed that the only movements through time satisfying this principle must be those in which the grandfather paradox cannot apply: "time travel will never cause a situation in which one of these paradoxes could take place."[38] If we were to access a particle stream moving faster than light, we could theoretically time-travel. As Einstein's relativity showed, the faster something moves, the slower its subjective time passes, and if it were to break the light speed threshold, it would then be traveling backwards in time (time would "reverse"). Author Whitley Strieber asked in 1997 if the mind could somehow enable time travel.[39] Strieber has had his own Versailles-like experiences, so he already knew the answer. It is "yes." Government-backed research has validated this notion, as we will see.

Nobel laureate Frank Wilczek says, "We are haunted by the awareness that infinitely many slightly variant copies of ourselves are living out their parallel lives and that every moment more duplicates spring into existence and take up our many alternative futures."[40] Max Tegmark of MIT has expressed a virtually identical view.[41]

Kaku mentioned in his description of reality something called *decoherence*, a theory stating that though all these infinite parallel universes are possibilities, our universe's wave function has decohered from them: it no longer vibrates in unison/in phase with them. It therefore no longer interacts with them. The result is that though we might coexist simultaneously with the wave function of inhabitants of other universes, we are no longer "in tune" with them.[42] Nobel laureate Steve Weinberg has also used the radio station in the living room analogy to describe our situation.[43] This is a very apt analogy for the reality we find ourselves in. The decoherence interpretation of quantum mechanics leads to multiple universes/many worlds and avoids the postulation of a wave function collapse. For the time being we note that these parallel worlds postulated by the many-worlds interpretation of quantum mechanics, or "decohered universes" actually do, in rare circumstances, spill over into this world, so to speak.

Goswami puts a slightly different spin on the many-worlds interpretation of the quantum wave function collapse, stating that the many-worlds idea can be incorporated easily into monistic idealism. Rather than each observation splitting off a branch of the material universe, he postulates that "each observation makes a causal pathway in the fabric of possibilities in the transcendental domain of reality. Once the choice is made, all except one of the pathways are excluded from the world of manifestation."[44] This interpretation does not require us humans to be in some way the center of the quantum universe, literally generating separate parallel branches of reality with each observation made—a ludicrous scenario somewhat reminiscent of Christian geocentrism. We merely manifest outcomes in our universe from a state of infinite possibilities in the transcendent or implicate domain (or time-space). Some physicists think that one way of getting to parallel universes is via wormholes, otherwise known as black holes or Einstein-Rosen bridges. For author Marie Jones, the most exciting kind of (theoretical) wormhole is a Lorentzian wormhole, which may allow for such traversable shortcuts through space and time.[45]

Matter and Anti-Matter

By the 1950s physicists had begun to realize that for every particle there is a twin with an opposite charge. The first such anti-particle to be discovered was the anti-electron (called the positron), which has a positive charge, in 1932. The positron is identical to the electron in every way except that it carries the opposite charge. In 1955 the particle accelerator at the University of California at Berkeley, the Bevatron, produced the first anti-proton, identical to the proton except with a negative charge. This means that, in principle, one can create anti-atoms (with positrons circulating around anti-protons). Kaku states that entire anti-universes with "anti" inhabitants are theoretically allowable.[46] According to him, if we reversed the charges of particles that have charge (electrons and photons for instance), reversed the parity (reverse the left–right relationship as happens when looking in a mirror), *and the march of time*, then the resulting universe would obey all the laws of physics. The CPT (charge-parity-time)–reversed universe is theoretically allowed by current laws of physics.[47] Some occult and clairvoyant experiences actually support the notion of parity-reversed realities, as we will see later.

String Theory and Superstring Theory

String theory's mathematics—in its current form in the mainstream—demands the existence of at least 11 dimensions: 10 of space and one of time. Superstring theory is an approach that many scientists believe successfully merges general relativity and quantum mechanics. "Strings" are incredibly small, some 100 billion billion times smaller than a single atomic nucleus, and though they appear to be points even when examined with our most advanced atom smashers, they are really 1-dimensional oscillating lines.

According to string theory (a general term that includes superstring theory), there is only one fundamental ingredient, the string—and the abundance of different types of particles simply reflects the different vibrational patterns that a string can execute. The different vibrational patterns in string theory correspond to different kinds of particles. The key point is that the detailed pattern of vibration executed by a string produces a specific mass, a specific electric charge, a specific spin, and so on—the specific list of properties, that is, which distinguish one kind of particle from another. A string vibrating in one particular pattern might have the properties of an electron, while a string vibrating in a different pattern might share the properties of an up-quark, a down-quark, and so on. Thus, a single species of string can account for a great variety of particles because the string can execute a great variety of vibrational patterns. Metaphorically, the different notes that can be played by a single species of string would account for all of the different particles that have been detected. "At the ultra-microscopic level, the universe would be akin to a string symphony vibrating matter into existence," as Greene puts it. The *mass* of a particle in string theory is nothing but the *energy* of its vibrating string.[48]

Ultimately, M-Theory, a progression of string theory that ties all five incarnations of string theory together and reveals that they are all basically different interpretations of the same thing, concluded that the universe (within this framework at least) has the 11 dimensions mentioned above. Still, string theory is just in its infancy. In this schema, the Standard Model simply represents the lowest vibration of the superstring. In addition to higher dimensions, string theory predicts the "multiverse,"[49] this term being coined in 1895 by the psychologist and philosopher William James.[50] (Some string theorists, Leonard Susskind for instance, prefer "megaverse," which contains all the different kinds of universes along with our own.)

In the eleventh dimension a new mathematical object called a "membrane" (like the surface of a sphere, for instance) can exist. According to researchers, if one dropped from 11 dimensions down to 10 dimensions, all five string theories would emerge, starting from a single membrane or *brane*. Hence all five string theories were just different ways of moving a membrane down from 11 to 10 dimensions.[51] A brane (short for membrane) is thus a multidimensional object to which strings are linked, and within which strings oscillate.[52] In terms of branes, Goswami believes that Einstein's theory that space is curved "can be interpreted with the concept that we live on the 3-dimensional (hyper-)surface of a 4-dimensional volume."[53]

The eleventh dimension gave string specialists a new picture and also meant that the universe itself might be a membrane floating in an 11-dimensional space-time. Moreover, not all these dimensions had to be small. In fact, some of them might actually be infinite, and as Greene points out, "we don't see them because of the way we see."[54] Thus, our universe might exist in a multiverse/megaverse of other universes, each universe floating in a vast 11-dimensional hyperspace. Individual universes might join with others, split apart, spontaneously burst into existence, or disappear. We may inhabit the membrane of such a universe.[55] Infinite universes, according to Susskind in *The Cosmic Landscape*, are the inevitable consequences of established conventional principles of general relativity and quantum mechanics.

The dimensional mathematics of string theory is based on the work done by the Hindu genius Srinivasa Ramanujan who believed he acquired his equations from the goddess Namakkal. David Wilcock qualifies the theoretical and mathematical speculations of string theory by referring to the geometry of the platonic solids and how Ramanujan's work fits in with the harmonics of aether theory* (to be discussed later). He explains that the physicists believed strings

---

*   *Aether* is spelt with an "a" to distinguish between the chemical *ether* and the occultist's etheric plane and personal etheric field, though the universal *aether* (or implicate order) can be conceived as encompassing all of these occult realms in their different densities.

could only vibrate if they were symmetrical, and symmetry required the addition of two extra dimensions. However, he believes this addition was unnecessary since, a) the missing symmetry is probably accounted for by the "zero point energy" existing between the strings, and b) "the Superstring physicists were not aware of the basic geometries that are formed when the aether vibrates."[56]

String theory postulates trillions upon trillions of possible universes, each one compatible with relativity and the quantum theory. Kaku explains that everything in our electromagnetic space-time domain is the lowest vibration of the superstring, while "dark matter" might be the next higher set of superstring vibrations.[57] These might correspond with the occultist's etheric particles, which we will discuss later. Superstring theories postulate that each known particle in our reality has a massive and more energetic shadow "super" particle.

The theoretical requirement for more dimensions than five has been established, but I would remind the reader that mathematical constructs and scientific concepts should not be confused with experiential reality. For example, shamans and occultists are familiar with the other planes of existence not because of elaborate theoretical constructs, but because of the possibility of their own direct conscious access to these realms. These other realities are not merely conceptual but experiential, and can theoretically be accessed by any human and verified through firsthand experience, and sometimes corroborating evidence. In that sense it is interesting that "super string (M) theory and the verses of the ancient . . . [Hindu] Vedas describe the processes of creation and annihilation, with equal symmetry and precision, in terms which are precisely equivalent."[58]

> [T]he structure, harmonic resonances and constructions of the . . . Vedas define exactly the same dynamics as super string theory. The Vedas were constructed as the result of disciplined introspection, metaphysics in its highest and best sense. This is a phenomenon which we are finding replicated in other areas long thought to be the exclusive domain of science.[59]

Hence the earlier statement that metaphysics both includes and transcends physics. "How is it," asks Yurth rhetorically, "that super string theory, the most sophisticated predictive model ever developed by modern science, describes the processes of creation in terms which are fundamentally consistent with those embodied in the construction of the Vedas?"[60] Though string theory has been touted as a 21st-century theory that fell into the 20th century, Jay Alfred points out that metaphysicists such as Charles Hinton had, as early as the 19th century, been conceptualizing atoms as 3D cross-sections of 4D threads—preempting physicists (such as Kaku) who explain now that the cross-sections of superstrings can appear to us as particles,[61] suggesting they are an orthorotation or two away from our reference frame. The *Seth Material* channelled by the psychic Jane Roberts from the 1960s to the 1980s also comports nicely with fundamental aspects of string theory (which didn't even exist in the 1960s and 1970s), as David Wilcock emphasizes in his ground-breaking *Convergence* series. In Chapter 6 we will examine the results of occult investigations into subatomic matter that began in 1895, and were ultimately validated through string theory and modern physics in general.

Einstein, Podolsky, and Rosen (EPR)

In 1935 a paper by Albert Einstein and his colleagues Boris Podolsky and Nathan Rosen was published in which they proposed the now infamous EPR experiment, designed in such as way as to demolish the introduction of probability into physics. The paper was titled *Can Quantum-Mechanical Description of Physical Reality Be Considered Complete?* EPR believed that particles had real attributes prior to measurement (realism) and that "spooky" actions at a distance somehow transcending ordinary local causal factors could be better explained in more common-sense terms that didn't violate the speed of light (locality). Ironically, actual experimentation on the theory merely proved the validity of quantum theory. Local realism was dealt a powerful blow and has never recovered. As noted, we now know that twin-state particles fired in opposite directions are still bound by their invisible Schrödinger/de Broglie wave connecting both of them in hyperspace/time-space/aether. If something happens to one particle, a corresponding change is immediately registered in the other. This phenomenon is known now, thanks to Schrödinger, as "entanglement," the concept that particles separated in space have a connection linking them together beyond the constraints of a local-realistic worldview (where light is regarded as the uppermost speed limit).

According to Michio Kaku, this means that what happens to us has instantaneous effects in far corners of the universe, that a "web of entanglement" connects everything in the universe.[62] As I will detail shortly, I know from both direct, conscious insight and my research into science and consciousness that this is the case.

Because entanglement appeared to contravene the notion that light speed was the fastest speed possible,* and that particles have real measurable traits before measurement, Einstein set about mustering all his intellectual muscle towards disproving this finding and removing probability from quantum physics (which basically means the death of quantum physics). Einstein believed in a local-realistic universe.

Unfortunately for EPR, however . . .

Bell's Theorem and Nonlocality Arrive

In 1964, physicist John Bell (1928–90) took a sabbatical and spent some time pondering the mysteries of quantum mechanics. The result was that he showed in theory that nonlocal effects were real and not a result of "hidden variables" as Einstein had proposed in his attempt to explain what he called "spooky action at a distance"—the apparent connection distant particles displayed when traveling away from each other. This work became known as Bell's theorem. Bell's theorem basically states that there are no isolated or separate systems; every particle is theoretically in instantaneous contact or communication with every other particle in existence, or at least with every other particle it has ever come into contact with. For this to be true, there must be an underlying and totally integrated holographic information field "behind" our space-time reference frame—an "implicate order."

Kuttner and Rosenblum put it this way: "In principle . . . any two objects that have ever interacted are forever entangled. The behavior of one instantaneously influences the other. An entanglement exists even if the interaction is through each of the objects having interacted with a third object. In principle, our world has a universal connectedness."[63] Bell's theorem was labeled "the most profound discovery of science" by physicist Henry Stapp.[64]

This is all the more so if you believe that the universe began with a Big Bang (the term was coined by Fred Hoyle in 1951), a postulated (and now increasingly discredited) common point of origin for all particles/energy, which would presumably entangle all life-forms within the universe with one another nonlocally forever. We know that we are all made of the same quantum energy/ matter, or as Carl Sagan put it, "We're made of star stuff"—the same cosmic

---

* Einstein's relativity does not specifically forbid speeds greater than light, but only precludes that any known particle with rest mass can be accelerated to light speed or beyond, according to some observers.

"star stuff" that is universally interconnected (entangled). High-precision experiments performed repeatedly have, contrary to initial expectation, shown that two photons fired from the same source in opposite directions are fundamentally interdependent in accordance with the predictions of quantum theory. Any attempt to measure the spin of one of the photons automatically and *instantaneously* decides the spin of the other, meaning there is a connection between them that transcends the so-called light speed limit and destroys the philosophical assumption of "locality"—the idea that influences between all material objects must travel through space-time one bit at a time with a finite velocity no greater than C (light speed), and that what happens over "here" cannot influence things over "there" more quickly than C allows. Distance between the particles in these experiments is not a factor. They act virtually as one, despite being, at least ostensibly, two distinct entities. To Einstein, this was spooky because the particles were somehow linked but, apparently, not *causally* linked, in the sense that we would normally think.

There was, to mainstream scientists, no discernible cause for this interconnection, but David Wilcock has pointed out that the hidden connection (or "hidden variable") appears to be geometry: the particles are linked by a higher-dimensional unseen tetrahedral geometry which expands as the photons move away from each other. Geometry plays a crucially important role in quantum processes in general; tetrahedral geometry has apparently been discovered and rediscovered over the decades by several researchers, only to be obscured and forgotten yet again.[65] It is this piece of the puzzle that the string theorists seem to be missing. It is an object of fascination for some physicists that entangled photons essentially comprise a singular object. The geometry of such an object, however, is embedded in a more fundamental, unseen "level" of reality, an "implicate order." There seems to be no other way to explain how the two oppositely travelling photons can be reflected off separate *differently angled* mirrors and yet both turn in the *same* angular direction, meaning one of the pair is violating all known laws of mirror reflection while displaying this nonlocal connection! "Both of these mysteries are explained when we see that these 'particles' are, in fact, little harmonic packets of geometry—and if you stretch them apart, the geometry will get larger—and comparably weaker—but the 'particle' still acts as a whole," states Wilcock.[66]

It was initially John Clauser who set out to challenge the foundation of quantum mechanics by investigating Bell's theorem using twin-state photons. Working with graduate student Stuart J. Freeman in 1972, he found that, exactly as quantum theory predicted, Bell's inequality* was violated, confirming the legitimacy of quantum mechanics again. Nonlocal entanglement was real. Measurement of one particle instantly determines the spin or position of the other so that it has either the same or exact opposite trait to its partner. Clauser's experiments were interpreted as ruling out either "local reality" or "local hidden variables." The experiments showed that the properties of objects in our world have an observation-created reality *or* that there exists a universal interconnectedness, or both. Confirming quantum theory's predicted violation of Bell's inequality, he showed instead that a "reasonable" description of our world, with *both* separability and reality, would never be possible.[67] Rosenblum and Kuttner explain that the violation of Bell's inequality would indicate "a lack of reality or separability for everything such photons could possibly interact with. That is *everything*."[68]

Experiments done on Bell's theorem in 1982 by Alain Aspect with improved electronics further proved this interconnection. When Aspect used detectors placed 13 m apart, where the two photons' spins correlated perfectly to one another, Bell's inequality was violated by exactly the amount predicted by quantum theory. In 1997, Nicholas Gisin and his team at the University of Geneva carried out a version of the Aspect experiment in which the two detectors were placed 11 km apart. The results were unchanged.[69] In 1999 over a distance of over 100 km the instantaneous connection was again demonstrated. High-precision cesium clocks yield zero time difference between each quantum's polarity change—across nine digits.[70] Entanglement is real. As Jan Wicherink observes in his excellent *Souls of Distortion Awakening*, the reality of non-local effects means that either there must be other hyperspace dimensions facilitating this non-local communication, or Einstein's assumption that no local effect in our universe can surpass the speed of light is false.[71]

As it turns out, we now know that superluminal speeds exist and that there *are* other planes of existence that connect the superficial or manifest ("explicate") aspects of reality that we perceive. String theory specialists tell us that the mathematics of string theory dictates that there must be other dimensions of existence, and as we shall see, some such of these planes have been explored by history's intrepid occultists and mystics. Moreover, Gisin et al. showed that in their experiments the velocity of the information exchange occurred at least one order of magnitude (ten times) faster than the speed of light. The speed of light "has been exceeded by a factor of at least 10^9 (1,000,000,000) times in

---

* Bell's inequality is the expectation that measurements of the two quanta should yield different data ("inequalities"), thus demonstrating their independence from one another.

carefully controlled, impeccably documented experiments by scientists whose credentials are utterly above reproach."[72]

Yurth reports that "extensive astronomical studies performed by teams of Russian scientists, directly sponsored by the Russian Academy of Sciences during the 1980s and 1990s, document numerous instances of superluminal trajectories exhibited by massive stellar objects and entire galactic systems."[73] Superluminal speeds exist. Wang and colleagues at Princeton have verified that under properly engineered conditions, information can be transported in a local/linear way at least 300 times faster than C. Light has even been slowed to less than 40 miles per hour under carefully controlled conditions, showing it is not necessarily a constant (which should give fans of the Doppler effect interpretation of redshift pause for thought). Yurth observes: "None of the long held notions about the fundamental nature of light have survived the onslaught of recent advanced scientific investigation."[74] In recent repeated experiments, even the humble neutrino appears to have possibly violated the speed of light "limit," albeit slightly.[75]

Physicist Paul A. LaViolette has explained that we can hold on to causality and resist adopting logical positivism ("observation creates reality") if we interpret the results of EPR experiments with entanglement in terms of superluminal velocities. Information is conveyed not mysteriously or spookily, but much faster than light speed. This view is one of causal nonlocality. This interpretation can be sustained within aether physics models, which we have hinted at with our references to the role of geometry in twin-photon experiments, and which we look at in relation to the occult in Chapter 6. In quantum theory, nonlocality doesn't allow for the transmission of any *electromagnetically* detectable signals in space-time, but rather, simultaneous correlations. Torsion energy, on the other hand, allows for superluminal and instantaneous *information* transfer *without* EM energy transfer, which is interesting given that the physicist Roy Frieden postulates that *conscious observation of a system injects information into it.*[76] (This book contains much evidence in support of Frieden's idea.) Is the spiraling torsion energy of hyperspace the unseen energy facilitating this? As we will see, some researchers think so, and again, this ties back into geometry, since torsion fields can apparently possess geometrical aspects that influence the formation and operations of systems in space-time.

In 1998 Anton Zeilinger and colleagues, then at the University of Innsbruck, closed the locality loophole by using two fully independent quantum random-number generators to set the directions of the photon measurements. This meant that the direction along which the polarization of each photon was measured was decided at the last instant, such that no detectable or already known signal would be able to transfer information to the other side before that photon was registered—at least not without superluminal speeds. Bell's inequality was violated once again (meaning that the photons' polarizations were negatively correlated over distance beyond light speed).[77]

In 1987 Greenberger, Horne and Zeilinger (collectively GHZ) realized that the entanglement of three or more particles would more definitively challenge local realism than two-particle entanglement. While two entangled particles conflict with local realism only in their statistical properties (the essence of Bell's theorem), three entangled particles can produce an immediate conflict in a single measurement result because measurements on two of the particles allow definite prediction of the property of the third particle. The first experiments on three entangled photons were performed in late 1999 by Zeilinger and his colleagues, and accorded with quantum theory. So far, all tests of both Bell's inequalities and on three entangled particles (known as GHZ experiments) confirm the predictions of quantum theory, and hence are in conflict with local realism. No local-realistic theory can explain quantum entanglement.[78]

We will see in Chapter 6 that quantum indeterminacy or randomness actually arises out of a subquantum matrix, a fluid-like "aetheric" medium (also referred to as gravity) that is innately indeterminate in its perpetual flux. Such aetheric models posit indeterminate causality rather than the indeterminate acausality promoted by the Copenhagen school of thought which states that particles have no traits prior to measurement.

It is interesting to note that entanglement experiments involving two *pairs* of photons originating from *different* sources have shown that entanglement can effectively be "transmitted" between particles in the different pairs, meaning that each entity need not share a common origin for entanglement to be demonstrated.[79] David Bohm had suggested that the two particles in twin-photon experiments are merely different facets of the one transcendent unifying reality: the mystical-sounding "implicate order." He stated that "the various particles have to be taken literally as projections of a higher-dimensional reality which cannot be accounted for in terms of any force of interaction between them."[80]

In Goswami's and others' view, these experiments have confirmed the idea of transcendence in quantum physics because the invisible connections between the Bellian particles must exist in "the transcendent domain of reality," that is, hyperspatially. According to Goswami's fellow physicist Henry Stapp, the message of quantum nonlocality is that events located in space-time are fundamentally generated by processes outside of it.[81] We will see that there are multiple domains beyond our space-time, incorporating both extra spatial dimensions, higher frequencies and non-electromagnetic energy.

Bohm called our everyday world of space, time, and causality the *explicate order*. He proposed that underlying this everyday world is the *implicate order*, from which our manifest reality is projected (literally, unfolds). A hidden order was required to explain how the entanglement in the twin photon experiments could exist—it is here that the imperceptible superluminal energies and the holographic field responsible for nonlocality reside. Well-known theosophists have stated in the past (many years ago now), that physics had begun to impinge upon the "astral plane," only the physicists obviously had no idea. Actually, we can look at Bohm's implicate order (or Larson's time-space) as an all-encompassing hidden/unmanifest reality that includes the occultist's astral plane (a.k.a. the fourth dimension), as well as the other "planes" of reality hidden from view. Alternatively, the astral plane could be the explicate expression of an altogether different implicate order of its own. In point of fact, the physicist F. David Peat (Bohm's co-author) has observed that "there may be a whole hierarchy of implicate orders, each more subtle than the other."[82] What occultist would argue? Bohm himself suggested that

> the quantum potential is itself organized and guided by a superquantum potential, representing a second implicate order, or superimplicate order. Indeed he proposes that there may be an infinite series, and perhaps hierarchies, of implicate (or "generative") orders . . . Higher implicate orders organize the lower ones, which in turn influence the higher.[83]

The work of researchers such as Rod Johnson, Buckminster Fuller, and David Wilcock (see Wilcock's *Convergence* books) has shown that Bohm's implicate order is one of (latent) geometric relations ("hidden variables"). Others refer to it (or aspects of it) as hyperspace, time-space, or the "time domain"—time encompassing and suffusing all of space, thereby providing a subtle realm of pure nonlocality or interconnectedness for our enveloped 3D level.

To mystics and occultists alike, the suggestion that particles can be fundamentally interconnected over vast distances, or "entangled," will be about as shocking as pointing out that a clear sky is blue, but to physicists stumbling upon these completely unexpected phenomena that ran contrary to the Newtonian-Cartesian worldview, these were earth-shattering revelations. Indirect experimental support for those "airy-fairy and loopy mystical ideas" about the oneness of all things was probably the last thing any educated person was expecting. However, as Capra observed, mysticism, or the Perennial

Philosophy, offers the philosophical background most consistent with the new scientific paradigm.[84]

The Perennial Philosophy is the result of distilling the wisdom that remains after all transient/illusory realities have been subtracted. "This subtraction process is called in ancient Sanskrit *niti-niti*, meaning 'not this, not this.'"[85] In other words, according to the Perennial Philosophy (and the body of contemporary consciousness research involving altered states of mind, drug-free and otherwise), what remains after you subtract state, time, and culture-dependent realities, which are all transient "inventions," is the unbroken, unified, and eternal consciousness that creates and pervades all. This realization is at the core of all the major religions (behind the exoteric dogmas), and, incidentally, is also the view of various "spiritual" physicists, who see what quantum physics is pointing us towards.

Other Observer Effects

While quantum physics has run headlong into the problem of choice and the observer in the quantum realm, Zeilinger's work hints that consciousness can also "intervene" in the macro world perceptible to the human senses. In fact, as far back as July of 1921 it was reported by the *New York Times* that Dr. Charles Russ had shown the Ophthalmological Congress at Oxford that with a properly designed apparatus a person could cause a solenoid to move by just gazing at it.[86]

Page 222 of the July 30, 1921 issue of the British medical journal *The Lancet* featured an article by Russ entitled "An Instrument which is Set in Motion by Vision or by Proximity of the Human Body." The device he called a "sthenometer." It consisted of a balanced needle suspended by a thread inside a surrounding transparent shield, preferably made of quartz (although glass worked too). A horizontal dial marked off in degrees was placed below the horizontally suspended needle. Russ stated that it would respond instantly to a gaze or the proximity of a human body.[87]

Many experiments have shown the presence of a non-magnetic spin field around the body, including over 1,000 conducted and recently reported on by Dr. Buryl Payne.[88] Apparently the earliest known such experiments were conducted by Dr. Hippolyte Baraduc, who evidently passed away in the early 1900s. The force field around the body that he identified he dubbed the "vital current."[89] Reichenbach and Mesmer found it and called it "animal magnetism." Baraduc's work showed that its flow could be modified through focused intent.

As a result of years of experiments, Russ believed that there was a transmission of power and force between people when one person looked at another, attributable to a ray emanating from the eye.[90] This idea is not original to him, but apparently goes back at least as far as Rudolf Steiner. Ernst Lerhs, one of Steiner's students, deals with the visual ray—a ray of biological energy which "carries consciousness outside the body"—in his book *Man or Matter* (1958). Trevor James Constable develops this notion in his seminal book *Sky Critters* (1978), where he identifies this "ray" as Reich's orgone energy, equivalent to *prana** or the energy of one's "etheric double."[91]

This non-electromagnetic "ray" is an extension of the occultist's etheric field, or "vital body," an energetic duplicate of the physical body which is still considered physical itself. (See Chapter 9.) Reich, as noted, referred to this energy as orgone, which floats freely in the atmosphere (as we will see later). You can think of this visual ray as a beam of force and also information—inseparable from consciousness—which transacts with objects it contacts, exchanging information and thereby affecting other systems. This is an interesting angle, considering that Frieden postulates that conscious observation of a system injects *information* into it, which thereby interacts with the energy and matter within the object, and between this and other objects, flowing from one space-time object to another.[92]

I established for myself years ago, through informal tests with a talented clairvoyant, that this beam of mental energy really exists. She could easily see and identify where I directed this beam despite the physical impossibility of her being able to observe where I was facing, or where my eyes were pointing. Observing mental energy appeared, for her, to be as easy as reading the words off a page in a book. (See my article *How We Sense When We Are Being Stared At*, <brendandmurphy.com>.)

Numerous studies into the sense of being stared at reinforce the idea that the act of looking at someone or something can actually affect the system being observed. According to biologist and paranormal researcher Rupert Sheldrake, many tests have been conducted in schools. This research has been popularized through *New Scientist* magazine, BBC TV, and Discovery Channel TV, and test procedures have been published on these organizations' websites, as well as on Sheldrake's own (www.sheldrake.org), allowing many people to participate in the research. Overall, there have been tens of thousands of trials, and several student projects on staring experiments have won prizes at science

---

* *Prana* is a Sanskrit word, derived from *pra*, forth, and *an*, to breathe, move, live. Thus the nearest English equivalents to *pra-an*, prana, is breathing forth life-breath or life-energy. It can be inhaled with the breath.

fairs, according to Sheldrake.[93] He states that the results are very consistent, with about 55% of the guesses being right, as opposed to the 50% expected by chance—a statistically astronomically significant result when obtained over thousands of trials.

> In experiments in which the same subjects were tested repeatedly and given trial-by-trial feedback, there was a striking learning effect, with a significant (p=0.003) improvement in scores with practice (Colwell *et al.*, 2000). In a German school, with repeated testing, some 8 to 9 year-old children achieved accuracies as high as 90%.[94]

The sense of being stared at effect appears to be widely replicable, with many studies yielding positive results. In Russia, the well-known psychic Mikhail Kuni found by working with hundreds of people that the deaf and dumb were particularly good at sensing an unseen person's glance.[95] Dr. Bernard B. Kajinsky worked with the psychic Vladimir Durov and reportedly almost all those subjected to Durov's gaze could tell when he stared hard.[96] In a student project in Ireland, Susan and Jennifer Brodigan compared pairs of twins as lookers and starers with pairs of untwinned siblings and people who were unrelated (subjects/starees were blindfolded and not given feedback). Twins scored significantly higher than untwinned siblings or unrelated people,[97] suggesting stronger psi between twins (not uncommonly noted).

Dean Radin analysed the results of variations of staring experiments, constituting 33,357 trials over 60 experiments from publications cited by Sheldrake and others. The overall success rate was 54.5% as opposed to the 50% expected by chance, registering odds against chance of 202 octodecillion (that's 2×10^{59}) to one. Even accounting for an estimated "file drawer" of six unreported "negative" studies, the odds against chance remained absurdly high at 10^{46} to one.[98] There is an observer effect on living systems, in other words, and we can, under certain circumstances, attribute it to the "visual ray." (We return to the visual ray idea later.)

Probably the most telling finding from this research is that success in looking trials did *not* depend on a minority of especially sensitive subjects, but instead represents a general tendency for subjects to score better when they are being looked at than when they are not. The results indicate that the intuitive faculties are innate in our species. "More than 100,000 trials have now been carried out, and the results are overwhelmingly positive and hugely significant statistically, with odds against chance of quadrillions to one."[99]

There is other good, if indirect, empirical evidence for a non-EM ray of energy which can be directed from our bodies to a selected target. Enter Russian researcher Dr. Konstantin Korotkov of St Petersburg. In 1996 Korotkov developed a range of instruments for stimulation, recording, and processing of electro-photonic images and called his technique Gas Discharge Visualization (GDV). This technique allowed quantification of the human energy field for the first time (most likely the etheric layer of the field).

One of many fascinating GDV experiments of Korotkov's is one he did on water. A 1 ml sample of de-ionized water in a test tube was subjected to an intense concentration exercise by Allan Chumak (known to be skilled in these areas), who focused on imagining the water as part of himself. There was no physical contact between Chumak and the equipment housing the water sample, and yet, after ten minutes of "conscious and coherent information transfer," the electro-photonic glow of the water had intensified by almost *30 times* its original amount.[100]

Korotkov suggests that the increase in the electro-photonic glow around a drop of water cannot be explained without considering the energy and information transfer from our consciousness. If consciousness creates these electro-photonic effects, then we can infer that consciousness arises (and operates) from an even more fundamental level: the "vacuum," "aether," "time-space," or "implicate order." Further tests showed that the new "conscious" state of water is not only long-lasting but can spread to a separate sample, which will acquire the new state when left close by for a few days. It seems that water shares its new informational state from one container to another. (Similar "contagiousness" has been discovered by others, including Dr. Masaru Emoto, whose work we look at later.) It was found that many people could modify the electro-photonic properties of water by conscious concentration, although their effects were much less spectacular than Chumak's.[101]

"The fact that consciousness is inextricably infused in the fabric of our being at the primary level of complexity means that the exercise of 'seeing' exerts a demonstrable effect on whatever we observe because everything is equally and similarly infused with 'consciousness' that operates in the non-local holographic field [implicate order] as well."[102]

Delayed Choice and Retroactivity

Observation/measurement can do more than "just" influence a system in space. Experiments with quantum mechanics suggest that we can essentially determine the path that a photon takes in an experiment even if we make the measurement after the fact. Such a delayed choice experiment was actually carried out in 1985 by three physicists: Carroll Alley, Oleg Jakubowicz, and William Wickes of the university of Maryland.

> The Alley, Jakubowicz, and Wickes experiment was literally all done with mirrors. By electronically inserting mirror surfaces in strategic locations in their setup they were able to manipulate a single photon emitted from a source into their apparatus so that it would pass into two well-separated channels. After passing through the channels, the photon would be observed in two different ways. By inserting the mirror just before the observation point, the photon could be made to interfere with itself. By leaving the mirror out, the photon would not undergo any such interference. With the mirror present, their data confirmed that the photon had to pass through both channels simultaneously. With the mirror out, the photon would pass through one channel or the other. Even more bizarre, the decision to insert or not to insert the mirror wasn't made until *after* the photon had entered the setup. They indeed showed that their last nanosecond decision did choose by which means a photon traveled, either by both paths or by one of the two paths.[103]

So we now have causal retroactivity—effects acting backwards through time. In Wheeler's words, there is no fixed past "out there": "The traditional model of the past does not serve us if we wish to understand the non-local correlation. Thus, we need a model in which the present can influence the past."[104] Larson's Reciprocal System, with its three dimensions of time comprising time-space offers such a model, because here, rather than events fading into nothingness as the one-dimensional "arrow" of time points to the next moment on an imaginary timeline, there can be a simultaneity of points in time and events. Not only could the present influence the past, and vice-versa, but the "future" could also influence the present.

Goswami states that since an object's motion is not determined solely by initial conditions, but that each observation creates a new beginning, this means the universe—of which we are an integral part—is fundamentally creative.[105] Erwin Schrödinger told his now famous cat story to illustrate that since the quantum theory applies to the large as well as the small, the theory is seemingly saying something absurd. Schrödinger's cat, according to quantum theory, could be simultaneously dead and alive—until our observation *causes* it to be either dead or alive. Moreover, finding the cat dead would create a history of its developing rigor mortis; finding it alive would create a history of its developing hunger—*backward in time*.[106]

Kaku explains that to account for the simultaneously dead and alive states postulated by quantum mechanics, physicists have been forced to entertain the possibility of an all-pervasive cosmic consciousness, or that there is an infinite number of quantum universes.[107] I believe that both are true: a cosmic consciousness spawned the infinite universes as an expression of its own infinite nature (more on this in Chapter 5) in order to experience and evolve itself in an infinitude of ways. Kaku reports that Wheeler actually toyed with an alternative explanation for the cat paradox which assumed that information is at the root of all existence, and it sprang into being when the universe observed itself. This he calls the "participatory universe."

If observation itself is creative, then what about active intention? Let's look at some more examples. In 1988 Helmut Schmidt and Marilyn Schlitz presented some of their research into retroactive psychokinesis (PK), illustrating that retroactivity is more than just a quantum-level effect and that it can produce macro-level effects more readily observable to us—as a result of human intention. In one study Schmidt and Schlitz used a computerized randomization process to record 1,000 different sequences of sound. Each sequence consisted of 100 tones of varying duration, some of them pleasing to the ear and some just bursts of noise. Because the selection process was random, each sequence should contain roughly 50% pleasing sounds and 50% noise. Cassette recordings of the sequences were then mailed to volunteers who were directed to try to psychokinetically increase the duration of the pleasing sounds and decrease the durations of the noise.

The results showed that the recordings the subjects listened to contained significantly longer stretches of pleasing sounds than noise. In other words, it appeared that the subjects had psychokinetically reached back through time and had an effect on the randomized process from which their *prerecorded* cassettes had been made. In another test Schmidt and Schlitz programmed the computer to produce 100-tone sequences randomly composed of four different notes, and subjects were instructed to try to psychokinetically cause more high notes to appear on the tapes than low, again with similar results. Clearly this suggests that consciousness can operate in—and is native to—the "quantum wave domain"; time-space/implicate order. Schmidt and Schlitz also discovered that volunteers who meditated regularly created stronger PK effects than non-meditators,[108] supporting the notion that consistent contact with time-space is crucial for exerting PK effects.

Interestingly, Schmidt's results indicated it was important that the person attempting to influence his tapes be the very first listener. Evidently, the first listener would crystallize a manifest reality out of the realm of quantum uncertainty, thus "collapsing" the other infinite possibilities for manipulation by subsequent would-be listeners, thereby rendering their attempts at retro-PK less effective; the possibilities presented by time-space were squelched. An outcome had already been "observed" or selected from the esoteric realm of potential and actualized in our space-time. Schmidt's positive combined results for five separate highly controlled experiments had achieved statistical odds against chance of 8,000 to one.[109]

At PEAR (Princeton Engineering Anomalies Research), Robert Jahn and Brendan Dunne had discovered this retrocausality when they investigated time displacement in their REG (random event generator) trials. In some 87,000 of these experiments, volunteers were asked to attempt to mentally influence the random output of the REGs in a specific direction anywhere from three days to two weeks after the machines had run. As a whole, these "time-displaced" experiments achieved even greater effects than the standard ones,[110] suggesting that thoughts may be even more powerful when they transcend linear causation (though I suspect this could possibly be put down to the higher level of novelty involved in such tests, at least when the subject is aware beforehand of the nature of the task).

Conventional science accepts odds against chance of only 20 to one as being significant. Research centers working on psi have obtained results billions of times more significant than this. In four studies of an adaptation of Swedish psychologist Holger Klintman's Stroop Test (including three of his own performed with Edwin May), Dean Radin found that the time it took to carry out a *second* mental task was affecting the time it took to carry out the *first* one (this effect had already been dubbed "time reversed interference" by Klintman). Radin concluded that his studies offered evidence of time displacement in the nervous system at respectable odds of 125 to one.[111] A 1996 statistical analysis of the best studies of time displacement produced odds against chance in favor of time displacement of 630 billion to one.[112]

A similarly mind-warping quantum retrocausality experiment to John Wheeler's delayed choice experiments was carried out by Vlatko Vedral and Caslav Brukner to test Bell's inequality as it applies to plural measurements taken of one particle in serialized time, one after the other. Vedral and Brukner calculated a lone photon's polarization and then measured it again moments later. They discovered that between the two points of time, Bell's inequality had been violated: the measurement of the first polarization had changed the second time around. The second measurement had apparently altered the first polarization—time had become entangled.[113] (Again, these results suggest there can be no real wave "collapse.")

More recently, Professor Daryl Bem at Cornell University published the results of a five-year study featuring a series of nine precognition experiments in which over 1,000 Cornell students took part. To statistically significant levels, and with combined odds of *over a billion to one against chance*, the students' choices in the present were ostensibly influenced by data they were yet to receive in the future, meaning that present and future had an immediacy regarding each another; they were entangled.[114] Linear time takes yet another blow. Time doesn't "pass" in a uni-directional manner like water in a flowing river—we are immersed in three dimensions of it according to Larson's Reciprocal System. "Today linearity is viewed as a special case of non-linearity that holds only under certain limiting conditions," states Peat.[115]

Perhaps then, today's world is the result of future knowledge being reflected backward in time, meaning that our universe acts like a cosmic feedback loop—with the lessons of the present also altering the past.[116] If so, I tend to think we must be slow learners in the future!

The Double-Slit Experiment—Reprise

In 2004, physicist Shahriar Afshar undertook an experiment that challenged quantum theory and Bohr's contention that the wave and particle properties of matter could not be perceived at the same time. Afshar devised a variation of the double-slit experiment, repeated in 2006, that enables both the particle and wave aspects of light to be perceived together, as it measures the path of photons, while at the same time showing their wavelike interference patterns. Until then, quantum physicists had mostly thought (and apparently still do) that the action of an observer "collapsed" the quantum wave probabilities into an actualized or particular state. But what Afshar has apparently accomplished, according to Lazslo and Currivan, is to show that the wave function is both more fundamental than the manifest particle and that essentially, instead of collapsing, the wave function becomes *coherent* by the act of observation.[117]

This result does not really change anything that we have previously discussed, for example with regard to the many-worlds interpretation of quantum mechanics. In fact, it can be interpreted as supporting the notion that, yes, there are these other realities and that, no, they are not merely created by observation—everything that can exist *does* exist *somewhere in time*, regardless of observation.

What observation achieves is the ordering of one person's own subjective reality in space-time: a 3D corpuscular subject–object awareness. Observation does not collapse higher or parallel realities into nothingness, and nor does it create them. Other levels of reality continue to be, but, as Greene said, "we don't see them because of the *way* we see." *How* we observe the universe determines the facets of the cosmos that reveal themselves to us. The tools we use to perceive or experience determine the nature of our perceptions.

Having said that, William Tiller's duplex-space perspective where our electromagnetic reality (D-space) interacts with an inverted magnetoelectric wave level of reality (R-space) can possibly explain results like Afshar's quite succinctly: the slit structure itself, without the light waves, *already has an R-space substance interference pattern* existing around the slit regions of the D-space structure. The R-space pattern guides the light into its high—and low-intensity bands behind the slits. Both levels of reality exist and neither "collapse" or vanish upon measurement or observation.[118] This extra, inverted dimension can perhaps resolve the quantum weirdness, much as Larson's Reciprocal System does with its time-space antithesis to our space-time.

Bearden rightly points out that the two-slit experiment is itself a "paranormal manifestation experiment" (as is the "delayed choice" style of experiment). When we invoke the photon interaction through observation, a classical object and behavior result, but when we *don't* observe—and therefore don't invoke the photon interaction—the wave nature and behavior[119] of R-space/time-space manifests. (As we will see increasingly, consciousness can operate not only in the realm where the quantum wave function resides, which explains a lot of ostensible "mind-matter" interactions, but consciousness comprises the most *fundamental* level/s of reality.) In Bearden's model, the photon interaction "quenches" or "squelches" time or the time channel, it "invokes a time-differentiating operation, stripping away or suppressing the time dimension, resulting in a spatial reality or objective reality being perceived or observed . . . [Therefore] we do not see time or the mind in our ordinary physical observation."[120]

Bell Meets Jung

Jungian synchronicity—accepted not just by Jungians but by a lot of other psychologists—also involves nonlocal and "noncausal" correlation, except that instead of the correlation merely appearing between two subatomic particles, it occurs between our mind and what we perceive as our external reality; the two synchronize so that our "external" presents us with entities and processes relating to the contents of the subconscious, which is generally the instigator.

Jung specified that synchronicity ("meaningful coincidence") could not fit into any purely causal (local, realistic) theory of the universe. He defined it as an acausal ordering principle. The phenomenon is fundamentally hyperspatial, as with quantum entanglement.

Jung has a story that is famous for its amazing meaningful coincidence. In it, he was in a therapy session with a female client who was trying, largely unsuccessfully, to work through some psychological issues, but Jung felt the progress was slow going because of the woman's stubbornness and near-refusal to consider a different point of view. As is so often the case, her Cartesian rationalism was the root of her closed-mindedness and lack of perception. Jung lamented that she thought she always knew better about everything, and used her Cartesian rationalism—provided by her "excellent" education—as a weapon against the truth that needed facing.

She told Jung of a dream she had in which she was given a golden scarab beetle. Jung recognized that in Egyptian mythology the scarab represented rebirth and he "wondered if the woman's subconscious mind was symbolically announcing that she was about to undergo some kind of psychological rebirth." He was just about to tell her this when something tapped on the window, and he looked up to see a gold-green scarab on the other side of the glass—for the first and only time ever, we might add. He opened the window and the scarab flew into the room, allowing him to apprehend it and present it to the woman—"Here is your scarab"—providing sufficient shock to the woman's rigidly rationalistic tendencies for her to become more psychologically flexible, improving her response to therapy from then on. In Jung's words, it "broke the ice of her intellectual resistance."[121]

It just goes to show that the conscious rational mind is only useful and knowledgeable to a point—insofar as its semantic maps and models of reality can be put to use constructively in healthy and life-affirming ways (guided by healthy subconscious belief structures).

The first time I encountered Jung's scarab story, I was reading Talbot's *Holographic Universe*, which provided me with my own "Holographic Universe synchronicity," while I was immersed in it. I was reading a section where Talbot was speaking about Rosa Parks, an African-American woman who rose to prominence by refusing to obey bus driver James Blake's order that she give up her seat on the bus to make room for a white passenger. She became a prominent equal rights activist and her admirable refusal of the bus driver's order ultimately sparked the "Montgomery Bus Boycott"—an action protesting the marginalization of blacks.

As I was reading this brief section, where Talbot lamented that perhaps science needed its own equivalent of a Rosa Parks, someone on the radio, which was on in the background, mentioned "Rosa Parks." Perhaps not the most earth-shattering event ever, but it is interesting nonetheless how your internal reality can "sync up" with your "external" reality (though these terms are meaningless in a nonlocal, holographic universe). What made it even *more* synchronistic was that I was at the time reading a book that dealt with synchronicity and how our internal reality is indeed connected to our seemingly external reality. Essentially, I was reading a book about the holographic nature of the universe, when suddenly my own universe began acting rather holographically as well, revealing its self-referencing nature. I have had numerous things like this happen over the years, but, admittedly, I tend to forget them because they are just not that memorable when compared to some of the other things I have experienced, which outstrip it in weirdness by several orders of magnitude.

Clearly, meaningfulness is central to the notion of synchronicity and hints at the link between our own psychological processes and the happenings around us. In a holographic universe, all information, all thoughts, all feelings, images, etc. effectively exist everywhere and are potentially accessible to everyone with even latent psi faculties (which is everyone).

One reason so many people resist acknowledging such meaningful and seemingly impossible sequences of events is that it is always a potential first step to recognizing the fundamental interconnectedness of your mind and consciousness with your "external reality"—the persona or personal ego in its little self-contained reality bubble has its sense of identity and reality challenged. Synchronicity has a way of presenting the individual with elements of their internal and subconscious processes that they might prefer not to face (but my need to in order to effect a personal transformation or some sort of psycho-emotional healing), but more to the point, it leads the way to the ultimate realization that the individual's cherished persona is in fact only a tiny fragment of what they are. Grof tells us in *The Holotropic Mind* that he has repeatedly noted extremely unlikely strings of mishaps and accidents "coincidentally" happening to people who were psychologically nearing an ego death. The dangers ceased almost magically as the process was completed and they were spiritually "reborn."[122]

In his work with "naturally occurring" alien encounters, John Mack refers to how often these "alien" encounter experiences occur at times of personal crisis, trauma, and loss.[123] It appears that many alien abductions, along with synchronicity experiences, are facets or manifestations of the collective unconscious (I elaborate on the alien link in detail in TGI 2). It is not that they are not "real"; they are part of a greater underlying archetypal reality of which we are all a part, an "imaginal" reality, as Corbin dubbed it. Interestingly, some "near-death experiencers" find the incident to be induced by extreme emotional or psychospiritual crisis; perhaps elevated DMT levels are sometimes responsible for NDEs—another kind of voyage into hyperspace—in times of unusual distress. It is worth noting that DMT is found in traditional shamanic potions such as yopo and ayahuasca; the shamanic stream has for millennia been using these types of "entheogens" because they expand one's awareness into the spiritual/imaginal domain, and can facilitate the OBE and/or shamanic initiatory voyages (although at least some ayahuasqueros themselves apparently consider *Banisteriopsis caapi*, which contains the beta-carbolines, as the main ingredient—and *Psychotria viridis*, which contains the DMT, as merely the additive).

To Jung it was crucial for psychology to recognize that the individual human experience is produced by the development of archaic and transpersonal instinctive structures which he termed "archetypes." The total collection of these structures he dubbed the "collective unconscious." Supposedly, these unconscious (from our perspective) archetypal structures lie behind and generate the symbolism of all mythological and religious systems and are therefore responsible for the similarities among these. For instance: the crucified saviour god that appears so widely before Christianity ever employed such imagery; the patriarchal deity; the virgin birth of the saviour, etc., etc. The archetypes also produce such distinctive and universal motifs as the King, the Goddess, the Hero, and so on. Their emergence into human consciousness is generally accompanied by a sense of profundity and numinosity.[124] "They are in a sense the deposits of all our ancestral experiences," said Jung.[125]

Jung was once asked if there was one case in particular that led him to part ways with Freud in terms of his clinical thinking, something that constituted a turning point in his thought. He replied that he had had quite a number of such experiences that ultimately led him to hypothesize that there is an "impersonal stratum in our psyche."* He cited one such example, involving a patient who had been diagnosed as "completely dissociated, a schizophrenic," a man who had been institutionalized for 20 years.

---

* It's a little-known fact that Freud too was forced to the conclusion that there is "a collective mind in which mental processes occur just as they do in the mind of the individual." (Source: Sheldrake, *The Presence of the Past*, 247.)

[O]nce I came into the ward and he was obviously excited and called to me, took me by the lapel of my coat, and led me to the window, and said:

"Doctor! Now! Now you will see. Now look at it. Look up at the sun and see how it moves. See, you must move your head, too, like this, and then you will see the phallus of the sun, and you know, that's the origin of the wind. And you see how the sun moves as you move your head, from one side to the other!"

Of course, I did not understand it at all . . . But that case remained in my mind, and four years later I came across a paper written by the German historian, Dieterich, who had dealt with the so-called Mithras Liturgy, a part of the Great Parisian Magic Papyrus. And there he produced part of the so-called Mithras Liturgy. Namely it had said there: "After the second prayer you will see how the disc of the sun unfolds, and you will see hanging down from it the tube, the origin of the wind, and when you move your face to the regions of the east it will move there, and if you move your face to the regions of the west it will follow you." And instantly I knew—now this is it! This is the vision of my patient![126]

Jung's patient was somehow perceiving an archetype from the collective unconscious, a virtual/hyperspatial reality. Jung was next asked how he could be sure the patient was not recalling something somebody had told him. His response: "Oh, no. Quite out of the question, because that thing was not known. It was in a magic papyrus in Paris, and it wasn't even published. It was only published four years later . . ."[127]

The research of Nelson, Radin and colleagues with the Global Consciousness Project has yielded irrefutable proof of the link between the quantum sea/ vacuum and processes occurring within the collective unconscious on earth. The GCP has set up all around the globe, some 65 (as at 2007[128]) random number generators (RNGs)—shielded from EM fields and temperature changes—that spew noise constantly, which is then digitized and fed into the internet and linked back to Princeton. The team looks for correlations in the data between the RNGs.

For instance, in data from four hours *before* the September 11 terrorist attacks (which, according to the FBI and Dick Cheney, curiously enough, cannot be evidentially linked to Osama Bin Laden), they found an enormous level of coherence between the RNGs, indicating a hyperdimensional "forewarning" of a large impending event and collective focusing of consciousness on this event. The period immediately surrounding the event shows a huge spike in coherence as humanity's collective mind was focused on events as they unfolded. The same results occurred before the Asian tsunami of 2004 and during the funeral service of Princess Diana,[129] and overall, the 185 events analysed between August 1998 and April 2005 showed odds against chance of 36,400 to one. The September 11 RNGs' deviations from chance represented *the largest of 2001*, while the ongoing analysis of our collective responses so far has shown a cumulative probability above chance of a million to one.[130]

In Nelson's words: "The largest or most reliable effects seem to involve ritual or some other influence that is designed to bring people to a shared state of mind." As of 2008, the GCP had selected 250 "rigorously vetted, pre-specified events" in advance so that predictions of departure from statistical chance by the RNGs could be made—rather than simply looking for spikes in the data after the fact. These events included tragedies, large celebrations, natural disasters, and spontaneous gatherings of large numbers. In every case, the collective RNG network registered anomalous data output—at combined odds of 10 million to one.[131]

Paradoxically, while there was a collective forewarning of impending disaster at subconscious levels on 9/11, data collected from online precognition trials between September 2, 2000, and June 30, 2003 indicated to Radin that as 9/11 approached, *conscious* psi abilities and premonitions had actually decreased and indicated a *significant collective subconscious avoidance of related topics/material* (collective "psi-missing"). Online card-guessing tests at www.GotPsi.org also showed a drop in psi scores just prior to 9/11.[132] We were avoiding contact with the traumatic contents of our subconscious awareness *of the future.*

One particularly interesting chapter in the GCP story is that the two geostationary operational environmental satellites (GOES-8 and GOES-10) orbiting about 22,000 miles above the Earth detected a surge in geomagnetic levels on 9/11. The first surge was detected by GOES-8 and it preceded an increase in the readings that plateaued at almost 50 units (nanoteslas) higher than usual—it was 15 minutes after the first plane impact and about 15 minutes before the second impact.[133]

Braden explains in *Fractal Time* that the satellites had recorded analagous surges during previous events of mass focus, such as the death of Princess Diana, and that the factor responsible had to be the human heart, which is known to possess a toroidal magnetic field—the strongest in the body— nearly 5,000 times stronger than that of the brain. The heart's magnetic field appears to respond to the quality of emotion we experience. Moreover, some of the frequencies in the Earth's atmosphere overlap those created by the heart in its communication with the brain, indicating that we are energetically tuned into and resonate with the planet's atmosphere and the global energy information network. Therefore we can expect strong collective emotion to create measurable effects in the geomagnetic field.[134]

Three days after 9/11, worldwide prayers for peace and periods of silence were held and broadcast around the world, with millions of people participating. The GCP data output "shows a marginally significant *decrease* in the deviations of the [RNG] data . . . The trend is steadily opposite to the specified direction."[135] The collective consciousness created the opposite effect this time to what it had done three days earlier when billions of people had responded in horror.

Building on all of this, a study was done collating the data from 20 years' worth of ESP experiments done all over the world where the data was compared against the sidereal day (the time it takes for Earth to spin once relative to the stars: 23 hours, 56 minutes). The chart shows a tremendous peak of "anomalous cognition" (an increase of some 500%), followed soon after by an obvious valley where a prominent drop-off in anomalous cognition occurred in the experiments overall (in the experiments done globally). What Radin wanted to know was why this was the case, which is where his friend Richard Hoagland comes in. Hoagland is a former museum space science curator, a former NASA consultant, and during the Apollo Missions to the Moon was science advisor to Walter Cronkite and CBS News. In 1992, he was awarded the International Angstrom Medal for Excellence in Science by the Angstrom Foundation in Stockholm Sweden.

What Hoagland identified was that this large peak was occurring at 60° to the galactic center, or *60° before a particular experimental location actually lined up with galactic center*. In Hoagland's words, "If you carry out an ESP trial at that location on Earth four hours before the Galactic center passes the meridian, you will have peak success . . . When it's aligned with the galactic centre is when the lowest success rate in ESP trials occurs . . . because sixty degrees is a hyperdimensional angle . . ."[136] May (2001) and Spottiswood (1997) have reported that at 13:30 local sidereal time (LST), plus or minus about an hour, ESP scores increase *threefold* above their average.[137] On the other hand, Spottiswood found, after analysing 61 psi studies conducted from 1976 to 1996, that increased solar activity corresponded with decreased psi performance.[138]

So, not only is ESP/psi very real, but the likelihood of its manifestation is actually strongly linked to the geometrical relationships between planets and the galactic center, as well as solar activity. In other words, there is, as Hoagland and

Wilcock would say, a matrix of hyperdimensional ("torsion") energy connecting all planets and galaxies that, in part, mediates the expressions and functions of consciousness on Earth (astrologers rejoice). Welcome to what Hoagland refers to as "hyperdimensional astrology": the basis for and explanation of why aspects of astrology work and why certain positive results within scientific studies of astrology are irrefutable. This explanation of Hoagland's demonstrates the powerful cyclic influence of hyperdimensional energy, and astrology is partly about the identification and prediction of cycles and patterns within our lives and human behavior.

Even the election results and lead-up to the results from Barack Obama's 2008 election campaign showed clear patterns of coherence between the RNGs scattered around the globe, illustrating the link between human consciousness and coherence in the RNG data. This link is established via hyperdimensional energetic transactions occurring perhaps in what the occultist might call the mental, astral, and etheric planes, which then influence quantum probabilities, revealing higher levels of quantum coherence as measured through the RNGs. Hoagland argues that this increasing coherence in the collective consciousness is occurring in an increasingly coherent hyperdimensional environment. The Global Consciousness Project further proves Jung's collective unconscious concept, at least to the extent that it is a clear-cut proof of a unified sea of consciousness in which we are all immersed. One inference we can make from the GCP data is that consciousness exists in the same aetheric/transcendent/ wave or hyperspatial domain that shapes quantum outcomes.

Interestingly, a large number of ESP experiments have shown that fluctuations in the earth's magnetic field have a negative correlation with psi results.[139] The quieter the geomagnetic field, the better, although the reverse appears to be the case for psychokinesis, which seems to be augmented when the Earth's GM field is agitated. These meaningful patterns strongly support that the overall data set for spontaneous psi cases is genuine. Intriguingly, William Tiller had devised experiments in which psychics performed better than usual when enclosed in Faraday cages, and worse when placed in a magnetically shielded room. In experiments with healers, Gary Schwartz and Melinda Connor had shown that directed intention manifests itself as both electrostatic and magnetic energy.[140] These energies and forces are the EM expressions of the hyperdimensional torsion energy of consciousness: they are derivative secondary effects, not the fundamental energy responsible for instigating psi.

In offering a possible explanation for the role we play in creating synchronicities (and presumably other "paranormal" phenomena as well), Charles D. Loughlin (1996) suggests that

[i]n a sense, neural networks may be "prepared" to operate as transducers of patterned activity in the quantum sea. Transformations of neural activity may produce transformations in the structure of the sea, and vice versa. Thus local causation based upon biochemical interaction among neural cells may be transformed into non-local causation based upon biophysical activity between cells and the sea.[141]

We are "coupled" to the quantum sea, in other words, via our cellular proteins, DNA, and energy fields, and this facilitates various psi phenomena and perception. As a nonlocal phenomenon, synchronicity's processes may be considered hyperdimensional (and holographic); they transcend the linear cause and effect of our 3D space-time realm. Rather than one facet of a synchronicity *causing* the other, we conceive that each facet draws the other to it simultaneously in some sort of coherent and resonant process, creating the baffling coincidences we see. "Coherence" refers to events correlated over space or time: in a coherent system, activity at one place in the system is directly connected to activity in another place in the system. Thus, synchronicity manifests through a nonlocal, coherent, and conscious system that is holographic at base.

Another possible example is the phenomenon of parallel inventions: Newton and Leibniz, for instance, both independently discovered differential calculus while unaware of the other man's work. There are many such cases of something totally novel being born into the world in a parallel process by distinct parties working in isolation from each other. Evidently, these inventors are simultaneously extracting their concepts from time-space.

Is There a Parallel Reality Where Space and Time "Flip"?

"The answer is yes," according to independent aether and consciousness researcher David Wilcock, who states that this solves all the basic quantum physics problems.[142] We can conceptualize this idea in different ways, as noted. William Tiller refers to this inverted "parallel" reality as reciprocal space (R-space) in his model, the domain occupied by the de Broglie pilot waves that accompany particles/matter. We will refer to it as time-space (as opposed to space-time), R-space, aether, hyperspace, zero point field, vacuum, and so forth. For us, these are all equivalent terms. Talbot referred to a "frequency domain" or Bohmian implicate order typified by waves, which was more fundamental than our manifest space-time and its observable particles.

Wilcock refers us back to the double-slit experiments evincing apparent wave/particle duality. The idea as he puts it, is that a particle here in space-time is fixed in time but can move around in space, while in the inverted world it's spread out in *time*. "So, it's still the same thing, it's just that it's now flipped over into another domain, and in that other domain it spaces [spreads] out in time and thus, you get this . . . wave-form," he explains.[143] This is essentially the Reciprocal System model developed by Larson. Wilcock then draws our attention once more to the Buckyball (a Carbon-60 molecule, composed of 60 carbon atoms bound together), named after American architect R. Buckminister Fuller. Buckyballs were discovered in 1985—the product of an experiment on carbon molecules in space. Each face is the shape of a hexagon.

In 1999, Olaf Nairz, Zeilinger and colleagues took carbon-60 (C-60) molecules and fired them at a diffraction grating consisting of a series of 50 nm-wide slits spaced 100 nm apart and obtained an interference pattern. The Buckyballs were "flipping" or inverting themselves somehow, becoming wave-like as they passed through the slit.[144] In a presentation in Austria in 2003, Zeilinger's colleague, A.C. Elitzur, cautioned the audience that unless someone stops Zeilinger, he will eventually try to have an innocent human thrown at a wall with two distant windows.[145] Who said science was dull? In fact, in 2001, Nairz et al. discovered that they didn't need to fire the Buckyballs at a diffraction grating to produce the wave pattern, they could simply use laser light (coherent light) to transform these large molecular structures into waves.[146]

What we have here, according to the reciprocal model, is a situation where the physical, particle-like structure of matter existing in space-time is mirrored or flipped back into a "parallel" reality—time-space, the reciprocal of space-time—in which it exists nonlocally "encoded" *as a wave frequency in the past, present and future*, effectively rendering the concept of space from our perspective here in 3D null and void. This also appears to be the nature of the realm(s) that clairvoyants access in perceiving likely future events; they access time-space where they can theoretically look forwards and backwards through time, rather than looking forwards and backwards through space as we do in space-time. When you move around in time-space, you move through time—you time-travel, so to speak.

In Talbot's brilliant book *The Holographic Universe*, he references this situation through David Bohm's concepts of the implicate and explicate orders and illustrates the principles by employing the hologram analogy (which we look at in Chapter 7). We could consider that this time-space reality is the frequency domain of the superconscious mind as well as the collective unconscious, while the space-time reality is the realm of the conscious personality level we experience in 3D, where we perceive the (convincing) illusion known as "discrete matter" and the material world.

Tom Bearden compares the conscious mind to a periscope put up from the subconscious and withdrawn back into it. It is this parallel reality or consciousness field that facilitates what we call "psi" or, in general, "the paranormal," which is not actually paranormal at all. The recognition of this parallel time-space reality is thus crucially important. From the point of view of 3D discrete matter, the delayed choice experiments, teleportation, and the double-slit experiments appear to make no rational sense. However, looking at teleportation in particular, we can see that it no longer appears to be so mysterious or inexplicable. The entity being teleported already exists at the target site because its quantum wave information is spread out in time/time-space; it exists everywhere, embedded in the holographic implicate order. It isn't so much a matter of *sending* the entity, but knowing how to manifest or decode its information into being detectable at the target site in the explicate order. All the while, the wave state of potential still exists in time-space (or the implicate order), but is not normally perceptible. All of the above leads to the view that time itself is holographic in the sense that present, past, and future are simultaneously present at any point in space.

What might a taste of time-space feel like, you ask? There would be many ways to experience it. As one woman recalled of a hallucinogenically induced altered state shared with friends: "[W]hilst others were . . . conversing with small talk and jokes, I was interrupting them with their future sentences and joke punch lines. To this day they still talk about the day I spent a night reading their mind[s], whereas I remember the day that I was in another realm, flitting forwards into the future and back to the Now."[147]

A Bridge to the Mystical?

While pre-quantum/Newtonian physics is typically a good approximation for objects much larger than molecules, we know that this worldview is fatally flawed. In fact, where initially it was supposed that nonlocal entanglement could not be evinced by anything other than quanta in specially controlled circumstances, we now know it is a fundamental aspect of reality. To illustrate the point, the entanglement of holmium atoms in a tiny chip of magnetic salt has been unexpectedly observed in the laboratory, showing that "big" things like atoms, and not just photons and electrons (individual quanta), can be entangled.[148] More recently (December 2011), it was announced by a group of physicists that two diamonds approximately 3 mm in size and separated by about 6 inches were successfully entangled at room temperature.[149]

Previously, it was believed that once things got to the level of atoms and molecules, the universe started acting strictly deterministically again, according to predictable Newtonian laws. This is no longer a scientifically viable view. A review of developments on entanglement research in March 2004 by *New Scientist* writer Michael Brooks concluded that "Physicists now believe that entanglement between particles exists everywhere, all the time."[150]

Wide-scale or "nonspecific entanglement" has been experimentally validated in many ways. For example, around 1956 Pavel Naumov conducted animal biocommunication studies between a submerged Soviet Navy submarine and a shore research station. These tests involved a mother rabbit and her newborn litter. According to Naumov, scientists put the baby rabbits on board the submarine, but kept the mother rabbit in a laboratory on shore where they implanted electrodes in her brain. When the submarine was submerged, assistants killed the babies one by one. At each precise moment of death, the mother's brain produced detectable and recordable reactions.[151] Many examples can be found in Soviet literature dealing with dogs, bears, birds, insects, and fish in conjunction with basic psychotronic (psi) research. The Pavlov Institute in Moscow may have been involved in animal telepathy until 1970.[152] Researchers such as David Wilcock and Richard Hoagland posit that these nonlocal interactions are facilitated by the hyperdimensional torsion/spin waves of the unified field/aether (or gravity, as Wilcock emphasizes in *The Source Field Investigations*) we are all immersed in. We will look further at torsion and nonlocality between sentient beings soon.

Once, the esteemed physicist Eugene Wigner remarked to Karl Pribram, a board-certified neurosurgeon and professor of psychiatry and psychology, that in quantum physics we no longer have observables (invariants) but only *observations*. Tongue in cheek, Pribram asked whether that meant that quantum physics is really psychology, at which Wigner beamed and replied, "yes, yes, that's exactly correct." "If indeed one wants to take the reductive path, one ends up with psychology, not particles," says Pribram. "In fact, it is a psychological process, mathematics, that describes the relationships that organize matter. In a non-trivial sense current physics is rooted in both matter and mind."[153]

Indeed, one of the main points R.A. Wilson made in *Quantum Psychology* was that "the laws of the subatomic world and the laws of the human 'mind' parallel each other precisely, exquisitely, and elegantly, down to minute details."[154]

Wigner, as a physicist, had said that "it was not possible to formulate the laws of quantum mechanics in a fully consistent way without reference to the consciousness . . . [I]t will remain remarkable in whatever way our future concepts develop, that the very study of the external world led to the conclusion that the content of the consciousness is an ultimate reality."[155] Sir Arthur Eddington said that the lesson from physics and especially from quantum mechanics is that insofar as we can describe the world at all we are necessarily describing the structure of our own minds. By collating various forms of scientific thought generated over time, "we obtain the structure known as the physical universe."[156]

Wilson further said: "We have found a strange foot-print on the shores of the unknown. We have devised profound theories, one after another, to account for its origin. At last, we have succeeded in reconstructing the creature that made the foot-print. And Lo! It is our own."[157] Similarly, Goswami has puzzled that according to the new physics, the particle tracks left in cloud chambers are simply extensions of ourselves. The objectified, absolute, Newtonian linear-mechanistic view of the universe is dead. Quantum physics—as per ancient mystical perspectives—simply does not allow the luxury of the concept of the separate observer, because it is meaningless to conceive of the scientist as being separate from his equipment, or anything else. Wheeler has wondered: "May the universe in some sense be brought into being by the participation of those who participate?"[158]

We are no longer dealing with interactions between two dissimilar entities—"mind" and "matter"—but with a single unified, conscious, holographic entity. Mind is "physical" too if you can rotate into phase with its contents/energies. "From science then, if it must be so," wrote Paramahansa Yogananda, "let man learn the philosophic truth that there is no material universe; its warp and woof is *maya*, illusion."[159]

Consider what it tells us that a hard science like physics, which set out to investigate the so-called physical world, ended up running headlong into the nonphysical—consciousness. The mystics already knew why this would be so: consciousness is the ultimate reality and the foundation of all existence. It is the *sine qua non* of the cosmos. It is curious that some "scientifically-minded" types become irate at the mere suggestion that a mystic or occultist could have known something before the venerable institution of science found it out. They seem to forget that scientific research is an implicit acknowledgment of ignorance. If scientists already knew all the answers, scientific research would not exist, because science is, fundamentally, an *inquiry*; it is not an a priori presumption of omniscience. Science builds models of reality based on what the knowledge of reality it possesses—it does not build reality itself. We need to remember again not to confuse the map with the territory. A scientific theory of something is not the same as the tangible or experiential reality it attempts to describe.

In an interview about his theory of monistic idealism, the interviewer commented to Amit Goswami that "science's current findings seem to be parallel to the essence of the perennial spiritual teaching." Goswami responded succinctly: "It *is* the spiritual teaching. It is not just parallel."[160] Renee Weber, a philosopher at Rutgers University, actually raised the possibility that mysticism may, in a sense, be more committed to the spirit of scientific exploration than science itself.[161] In fact, mystics have been described as "the most thoroughgoing empiricists in the history of philosophy."[162]

What identifies a mystic then? The true mystic is not a believer or a disbeliever—he or she *knows the existential fundamentals*, and in getting to the point of knowing, has discarded belief altogether. The mystic has *direct insight* into the nature of things, as opposed to having to rely on laboratory equipment, equations, theories, speculation, or educated guesses. For the mystic, as far as the fundamental nature of consciousness goes, *there is no mystery*. For millennia, mystics have known via direct cognition what Bell's theorem has only fairly recently revealed to the world of science. The mystic experiences the nonlocal, interconnected/entangled nature of consciousness and reality *directly*, and in doing so, understands it (in a holistic, existential sense).

The mystic knows that human consciousness and our infinitely complex and elegant self-organizing universe did not come into existence through the random interactions of inert matter. This idea has been likened by Stanislav Grof to a tornado blowing through a junkyard and accidentally assembling a 747 jet.[163] Noted occultist J.J. van der Leeuw pre-empted Grof almost a century ago, commenting that we might as well believe a heap of bricks could randomly form themselves into a building, if we are going to believe that the blind chance of "natural selection" is responsible for biological life and consciousness.[164] It is a ludicrous proposition, in other words. Writing in the 1980s, Francis Crick, the co-(re)discoverer of the DNA molecule, showed the total mathematical implausibility of even a single protein emerging by chance.[165] Van der Leeuw added that the data of science are not in any way incompatible with the belief in a creative Intelligence, directing and guiding evolution from *within* (as opposed to the external "man behind the curtain" scenario advocated by creationists). More than 90 years later this is overwhelmingly the case, as, for example, Yurth's Self-Organizing Criticality model shows.

A growing point of view among physicists is that there must be a cosmic consciousness pervading the universe. Objects seem to spring into being when measurements are made, and measurements are made by conscious beings. Hence, there must be cosmic consciousness that pervades the universe determining which state we are in. Some, like Nobel laureate Eugene Wigner, have argued that this proves the existence of "God" or some cosmic consciousness. Wigner not surprisingly expressed an interest in the Vedanta philosophy of Hinduism, in which the universe is pervaded by an all-embracing consciousness.[166] This type of sentiment is becoming increasingly widely held by physicists who are realizing the implications of what quantum mechanics and other fields of research such as parapsychology are telling us.

In order to truly understand what mysticism is and the spirit of it, one has to have encountered a drastically expanded sense of perception or awareness that completely transcends the ordinary waking state of mind and its associated perceptual limitations. If one steps beyond the bounds of permitted thoughts allowed by the materialistic paradigm, one learns an awful lot about just how limited and myopic this reductionist view of life actually is, and how much fact it must ignore and deny in order to maintain its own survival. Please note: I used to be something of a materialist myself (philosophically). The problem is that *this belief structure can only survive within very narrow experiential and investigative parameters that not every human life can (or will) facilitate.* If it could, everyone in the so-called developed world would be a materialist, or would have been, were it not for the advent of quantum mechanics. So, is any talk of or related to mysticism "pseudo-science" by definition? Categorically, no. Grof (for one) agrees, stating that the "pedestrian consciousness and world-view" have simply not caught up with mysticism or modern physics.[167]

Another common misconception is that mysticism is analogous or related to Western conceptions of religion or religious zeal and/or faith. But the mystical experience is not a moment of intense faith; it is a moment of intensely deep experience beyond this ordinary world and/or its normal sense impressions. Do you have *faith* in the existence of the chair you are sitting on? No, you simply observe and sense that the chair exists, otherwise you would have landed rather sharply on the floor! By your experience you *know* it exists and can leave it at that. In contrast, simply *believing* in the chair would probably not be enough to hold you up off the floor, no matter how lovely and detailed a 2D schematic of it you might have drawn up! Thus, mysticism is based first and foremost on direct and lucid experience of expanded and altered states of awareness/consciousness and *thus asks no blind faith.* (A mystic also knows not to confuse the map with the territory.) In this sense, we can see that mysticism does not consist in believing in some abstract faith-based dogma.

Donald DeGracia is a biochemical researcher in the field of cerebral ischemia and reperfusion. In his excellent book *Beyond the Physical,* he wrote:

> Mysticism is the true spiritual approach, it is the true way to religion, [which] in the West [today] is but a watered-down, overly rigid, dogmatic and institutionalized vestige of ancient expressions of the mystical experience. The true mystical experience defies the mind at all of its levels . . . and brings into direct comprehension the . . . living unity of all existence.[168]

Mysticism expands consciousness, deepens awareness, and develops wisdom, whereas organized religion—having been "de-mysticized"—has a tendency towards often (though not always) achieving the complete opposite effect, especially in its literalistic fundamentalist and extremist forms. This applies much less to its more progressive streams, which appear to be moving in a more experiential and enlightened direction, such as is the way in mysticism and true occultism. In other words, even that most intellectually rigid and stagnant of institutions, mainstream religion, is very gradually creating new models of "God" and reality. It still has not really realized its mystical roots though, still suffering institutionalized amnesia.

Science's childish attitude towards what it conceives to be mysticism has in many ways been as bad as religion's attitude towards it. To both institutions, mysticism has traditionally been "the devil." "Yet the mocking presumptuousness of modern science and philosophy towards occultism and mysticism is only an admission of their ignorance and insecurity in the light of knowledge and wisdom that neither possesses."[169]

In the late 1970s, Fritjof Capra said this, in simplifying and reconciling the different approaches taken by mystics and scientists: "Mystics understand the roots but not the branches, scientists understand the branches but not the roots."[170] Evelyn Underhill put it this way: "even the report of the greatest contemplative saint is much like that of the wise shepherd, who can tell us much about the weather, but nothing about meteorology."[171] What mystics understand the roots of is this: the fundamental nature of reality itself and the fundamental nature of consciousness (same thing). Mystics are actually much more inclined towards understanding areas of inquiry such as quantum physics than many otherwise intelligent people are. They have an experiential advantage with nonlocality, for a start. There is nothing airy-fairy or flaky about a mystic. It is an awareness characterized by deep insight and *clarity* of thought, not a lack of it. In fact, Capra wrote an entire book on the similarities between mysticism and physics. In *The Tao of Physics* he explained that, while the mystic begins his exploration from the inner realm and the physicist begins from the outer, they both ultimately reach the same destination: awareness of the fundamental unity between all things and events.[172]

Modern science tells us that the world of supposedly solid matter, as presented to us by the standard five senses, is an illusion. This is, of course, the view taken by mystics ever since there was such a thing as a mystic. How else is it that the deeper we attempt to peer into supposedly solid matter, the more empty space we find? Seemingly inert matter proves, upon closer inspection, to be very much alive and in constant motion; Larson's proposition—and he was not alone—was that the only thing that really exists in our space-time is motion. Apparent solidity is merely a function of a particular mode of perception, not an absolute truth.

The mystic's outlook encompasses the materialist's perspective and *extends beyond*, much as metaphysics both includes and transcends physics. As Taimni said in *The Science of Yoga*, the higher viewpoint includes and enhances the lower, while placing the lower in its proper perspective. "Expansion of consciousness means inclusion of more and more and exclusion of nothing."[173] Thus, the mystic's sense of reality places the world of appearances in its proper context, giving one the awareness of the difference between illusion and reality/truth.

The Medium, the Mystic, and the Physicist

One of our major themes so far—one shared by physics and mysticism—has been unity: the fundamental unity of consciousness and all of existence. In his compelling book *The Medium, the Mystic and the Physicist* (first published in 1974), Lawrence LeShan highlights the similarities between the worldviews and philosophies of these three diverse groups, demonstrating that they are all essentially describing the same interconnected, harmonious conception of reality as one another, while having arrived at these perspectives via very different paths.

In general, we mere mortals tend to perceive from the perspective of the serializing intellect, in that we identify things as being discrete, separate, and distinct from one another. We notice the differences between things and classify and categorize them. Our perspective is one of fragmentation and apparent separation. We usually tend to consider that the most important aspects are the ones clustering around the unique and individual end of the spectrum,[174] the things that allow the analytical mind to discern between one thing and the next.

What LeShan found, and amply demonstrated, was that mediums and clairvoyants or "sensitives," during moments of higher sense perception (as clairvoyant Barbara Brennan refers to it), would completely reverse this state of being and perception. Likewise, the perception of time is altered. In ordinary states of awareness, time appears to flow one-dimensionally, with events occurring one after the other, linearly. In the clairvoyant state (in time-space), all events exist simultaneously. All events *are*, they do not happen,[175] and they are thus accessible to the clairvoyant's perception. Hence, "predictions" that mysteriously and unexpectedly come true are merely a matter of observation in the clairvoyant reality.

This view of time is of course compatible with contemporary physics, which has revealed our perception of time to be little more than a figment of the imagination. Utilizing the time-space concept we can see, for instance, that delayed choice–style experiments—or those done by Vlatko Vedral and others—are not as baffling as they seem. In time-space the initial quantum/wave state of a system still exists to be modified, even if in space-time we have "moved on" and left initial conditions "behind" and made more measurements. A 3D time-space affords the ability to modify what we think of as the past by acting on its ever-present wave state in time-space. This is why a second measurement on a particle can influence its original measurement traits; the wave function in time-space never goes away or "collapses." From the perspective of relativistic physics, events, regardless of when they happen from any particular perspective, just *are*. They all exist. They eternally occupy their particular point in space-time. There is no flow. "If you were having a great time at the stroke of midnight on New Year's Eve, 1999, you still are, since that is just one immutable location in space-time."[176]

Bearden says that "mass" is a "frozen 3-spatial [3-dimensional] intersection of the space-time entity. It is exactly comparable to a frozen frame in a movie film. The individual frame never has any existence except at a frozen moment in the slide projector."[177]

The metaphor Brian Greene employs in explaining the illusion of time-flow is that each moment in time is a "slice" of the whole space-time "loaf."[178] Each slice (moment) exists for all time, much as it does in the occultist's Akashic record, though it is only "lit up" or animated by the activity or projection of consciousness for an instant, as the intellect serializes the unbroken whole of existence into "linearized" moments, using its purpose-designed faculties.

To really illustrate his point about the similar fundamental outlook shared by mystics and physicists, LeShan listed 62 statements from both groups (31 from each group) without assigning ownership to them. The sentiments expressed by the two groups in their descriptions of reality proved to observers (which included mystics and physicists) to be virtually indistinguishable, with mystics faring slightly better in distinguishing (perhaps as a result of more developed intuitive capabilities).[179] The point to remember here would be that the mystical experience is not a conceptual one, it is a direct immersion in what might be considered the ultimate reality. As Einstein noted, "Pure logical thinking cannot yield us any knowledge of the empirical world; all knowledge of reality starts from experience and ends in it. Propositions arrived at by pure logical means are completely empty as regards reality."[180] In this sense, to a mystic, those without personal experience or insight have no firsthand knowledge of Reality. This is not a matter of condescending judgment, merely honest observation.

LeShan discovered in his research that Bertrand Russel had researched the mystic's conception of reality in his own time and found that during the "mystical experience," four characteristics were present that all mystics agreed upon:

1. There is a better way of gaining information than through the [physical] senses.
2. There is a fundamental unity to all things.
3. Time is an illusion.
4. All evil is mere appearance.[181]

What struck LeShan was that he had found Russel's analysis of mystics after completing his own analysis of the Clairvoyant Reality as described by clairvoyants, and that the two groups were talking about the same thing. He said the identical nature of the two perspectives was overwhelming; they had each concluded that there was an ordinary way of looking at reality and this *other* way, "and they agreed completely on the nature of this other."[182]

The one major difference LeShan found between the mystic and the medium was their respective attitudes towards "paranormal" abilities (the siddhis). LeShan observed that mystics—particularly Eastern mystics—report that the psi faculties naturally emerge as a result of their merging increasingly with the underlying unified Reality. However, fascination with these abilities ultimately leads away from the most desired psychological changes (liberation from attachment, desire, and repulsion, primarily).[183]

All mystics would surely agree that a compulsive preoccupation or complete fixation on the siddhis rather than one-pointed seeking of pure truth and transcension of the illusion of "separation consciousness" (tightly bound up in the human ego) is counterproductive for anyone, but especially for the aspiring mystic.

101

Occultism Versus Mysticism

References to the occult that one finds in scientifically oriented literature are usually based on little more than hearsay and misconception, DeGracia grouses in *Beyond the Physical*: "There is indeed a vast literature and tradition of occultism stemming from the depths of antiquity, and most scientists . . . are simply unfamiliar with this fact." Attempting to understand occultism is harder than most would presume. Once one finds the real thing "it turns out to be vastly complex, and not a simple topic in the least."[184]

The occult tends to get lumped in with mysticism, or at least, *confused* with it, which is somewhat forgivable since the two overlap in both spirit and content. Still, it is important to distinguish between these two approaches. The difference between a mystic and an occultist, we might say, is basically the same difference between a mystic and a medium, as outlined by LeShan.

The word "occult" comes from the Latin *occultus*, meaning hidden. Mysticism and occultism both recognize that the sensory world we humans appear to inhabit and take for granted as being "real" is in fact an illusion, or merely one kind of temporary reality among an infinitude of others. Occultism, like mysticism, recognizes that there is more to existence than merely the physical level we are so familiar with and that seems so real. Occultists seek to explore aspects of the greater reality by expanding and altering their awareness, usually through specific meditative and other training techniques. The primary tool for the occultist in their exploration of the different densities or planes of reality is the siddhis (a Sanskrit term). These exist in two categories: the mundane (*laukika*) and the supermundane. The first category usually comprises clairvoyance, magnification (micro-psi), clairaudience, telepathy, invisibility, everlasting youth, levitation, and other marvels. The supermundane category is enlightenment itself. Further, regular occultism is not to be foolishly confused with Satanism and black magic—although for many religious fundamentalists, all occult explorations and pursuits are necessarily "Satanic"—a belief that does not withstand even modest scrutiny. In fact, occultism (of the noble variety) offers a refined value system premised on the idea of *service to others*.

"To think," wrote Aldous Huxley, that the Siddhis "have anything to do with liberation is, [as the Hindus] say, a dangerous illusion. These things are either irrelevant to the main issue of life, or, if too much prized and attended to, an obstacle in the way of spiritual advance."[185] However, these occult powers are very real as we have already begun to see, and it is acknowledged by yogis that they will naturally arise within the individual as their training progresses. Nonetheless, the aspiring mystic is to recognize that these too are ultimately distractions in the world/s of ephemera, and they too are to be transcended in kind.

Occultism probably has more to do *directly* with much of the data we will be looking at than mysticism does because most of that data pertains to exploration of the sensory illusion and some of its infinite facets. However, the occult and scientific information derived from analyzing the illusion and our subjective experiences within various "levels" of it will be used to point the way back towards the all-encompassing unified reality of infinite awareness with which the mystic is familiar. Theosophist Annie Besant clarified precisely what occultism is and is not in a speech delivered to the Blavatsky lodge in London in 1898. The input of a dedicated, serious and knowledgeable occultist (albeit heavily influenced by Eastern mysticism) is desirable here. She said:

> H.P. Blavatsky once defined [occultism] as the study of mind in nature, [or] the study of the Universal Mind [*Alaya-Akasa*], the Divine Mind, the . . . workings of God in the Universe . . . It is the study of the life side of the Universe, the side from which everything proceeds and from which everything is moulded, the looking through the illusory form to the reality which animates it . . . [I]t is the piercing through the veil of maya and perceiving the reality, the one Self, the one Life, the one Force, that which is in everything and all things in it.[186]

From there—no longer a slave to illusion—the occultist seeks to use his or her awareness and developing abilities in the capacity of service to others. In fact, it's extremely important to note the significance of the way in which high morality and the path of service is esteemed in true occultism. According to Besant, "There is no true spiritual life, there is no real occultism, until the man at least recognizes that the goal of his living is to become a force for good . . . There is only one thing left within him, the longing to be of service."[187] In few social institutions besides occultism are *active* morality and ethics so utterly paramount, and, maybe more importantly, in few institutions besides occultism can these things be so actively and truly developed. Without a developed moral compass, occult knowledge and powers, it has long been warned, will lead one to employ such for one's own selfish ends. These lower expressions are sorcery and black magic. Blavatsky advised that it is *Atma-Vidya*, or "knowledge of the Soul," that is the form of occultism any theosophist who would be wise and unselfish ought to strive after, because to her as the co-founder of theosophy, real occultism or theosophy is "the Great renunciation of SELF . . . It is altruism."[188]

Regarding what occultism is *not*, Besant said:

> Geomancy, palmistry, the use of the tarot, etc . . . are not occultism and their professors are not occultists . . . A man may be past-master of all these arts, and yet be further away from occultism than is a pure and selfless woman seeking only to love and to serve . . . [189]

Through the late 1970s and 1980s, the "science/mysticism debate" brought attention to a range of scientific data, primarily from the world of quantum physics, that had obvious spiritual implications. But as DeGracia points out, it completely omitted reference to the occult. "The point . . . is that the current science/mysticism debate is right on the verge of realizing that: *It is not science and mysticism that are intimately related but science and occultism.*"[190]

Decades earlier, Steiner stated laconically in *An Outline of Occult Science* that the occultist "desires to speak about the non-sensory in the same way natural science speaks about the sensory." DeGracia adds that, while linking science to mysticism was the first step, the next is "understanding the relevance of occult thinking to modern science, and particularly to theories of human psychology and theories of physics."[191] As Radin shows in *Entangled Minds*, we now know that the Newtonian-Cartesian worldview is wrong in just the ways needed to support the reality of psi phenomena and paranormal abilities/siddhis.[192]

There is something that I have missed in all this discussion of mysticism and occultism, however, and I was very pleased to find that J.J. van der Leeuw enunciated it with eloquence in *The Conquest of Illusion* (1928).[193] He explained the roles of mysticism and occultism in relation to philosophy and science, pointing out that the former are, respectively, extensions of the latter.

> [Occultism] teaches that there are worlds of subtler matter which can be explored scientifically by those who have developed the faculties of perception in those worlds . . . [A]s ordinary science explores the physical world-image so does occultism attempt to explore an etheric, astral or mental world-image.
>
> It, therefore, has the same possibilities and limitations which science has, it leads to knowledge of the how not of the why of things, it leads to knowledge and control of the outer worlds, not to knowledge of ultimate principles . . . [E]ssentially it is not the task of either science or occultism to answer final

questions ... Just as in modern theosophy* we find occultism or psychism presented as an extension of science so do we find a philosophical mysticism presented as an extension of philosophy. The fundamental doctrine of theosophy, that of the unity of all life, belongs to this domain of philosophical mysticism; no clairvoyant [or scientific] investigation at whatsoever level can ever *observe* the unity of life.

[P]hilosophical mysticism goes one step further [than intellectual philosophy] and claims that it is possible for man to enter the world of reality and *experience* living truth ... Thus, *where philosophy [including religion] believes, philosophical mysticism experiences, it transcends belief in being* [emphasis added]. In this way philosophical mysticism is as legitimate an extension of ordinary philosophy as occultism ... is of ordinary science.[194]

These are the crucial differences between mysticism and occultism as summarized by someone who knew them very, very well. As the experiential extension of philosophy, mysticism concerns itself more with the *why* and direct experience of the answer to that question, while occultism, as the extension of science, concerns itself with the *what* and, equally importantly, *how*. The mystical experience can immerse you in a oneness that utterly transcends the phenomenal world and that no words can capture, while an occult experience may peel back a layer or two of the illusion to show you the deeper workings of the phenomenal world(s)—a psi experience. That is why you might find that you meet clairvoyants who are as clueless as to the *meaning* and fundamental nature of life and creation as the next person with no overt extrasensory abilities whatsoever. Clairvoyance and other psi phenomena relate very much to the world of occultism, even though many such people would not consider themselves occultists per se. Experiential mysticism goes beyond what can be measured, and is therefore, in that sense, perhaps not as much a scientific pursuit as occultism is.

---

* The co-founder of theosophy, H.P. Blavatsky, was emphatic in pointing out that theosophy is not a religion but a science. The meaning of the term is "Divine Wisdom." See *The Key to Theosophy*, 1–2.

Where Does Parapsychology Fit?

> If I had to live my life over again, I should devote myself to psychical
> research rather than to psychoanalysis.
> —Freud

Parapsychology—the more "credible" term for psychical research coined by Max Dessoir in 1889, and popularized by J.B. Rhine—explicitly studies the interactions between consciousness and the physical world. It is essentially the pursuit of understanding occult ideas and phenomena ("the paranormal") by attempting to research it within a scientific framework and methodology, all the while, however, shunning occultism itself—a lessening trend, thankfully. This has robbed parapsychology of some much-needed insight over the years, but despite this, it has yielded an impressive and truly vast body of positive evidence.

DeGracia has actually referred to occultism as "the true science of the phenomena [parapsychologists] purport to study."[195] In fact, the famous Freemason and royally commissioned editor of the King James (also a Freemason) Bible, Francis Bacon, suggested back in 1627 that various occult phenomena might be amenable to investigation, and even suggested some methods (such as PK tests using the throwing of dice, and card guessing tests for telepathy) that were indeed employed some 300 years later by pioneering parapsychologists.[196] Thus—as Radin observes—among some of science's earliest proposed uses was the idea to test psi phenomena,[197] and these particular ideas (of Bacon's) come from a man now largely considered as a "proto-reductionist"!

Not only has occultism shown that the psi phenomena parapsychology seeks to prove have already been proved and repeatedly demonstrated (goal no. 1 of parapsychology achieved), but it also goes further than any other science has so far in *explaining* these phenomena (goal no. 2 achieved), albeit within its own framework/s. Furthermore, it provides ways of developing psi ability and mastering it, bringing it under conscious control. There is nothing mystical or paranormal about psi phenomena when seen through the eyes of occultism. It has been the prejudice against occultism and "unusual" phenomena of fashionable modern belief systems (not least those maintained by scientists who had/have no idea what occultism actually is) that has led to this unnecessary and childish mystification (and marginalization) of the occult.

Having said all of this, parapsychology still, as noted, offers a very impressive body of extremely compelling evidence for occult phenomena, as sincere researchers will recognize. The geologist and geophysicist Robert Schoch, who, to the chagrin of conventionalist historians, has dated the Sphinx back to at least 7,000 BC and possibly further back than 9,000 bc on the basis of water erosion, undertook a comprehensive study of the serious scientific "paranormal" literature at the prodding of one of his standout students, Logan Yonavjak. The result of his collaboration with Yonavjak is *The Parapsychology Revolution*, in which he concedes that there is still definitely something to the paranormal once the dross is cleared away.[198] Schoch says he agrees with the statement made by David Fontana, professor of transpersonal psychology at Liverpool John Moores University: "Psychic abilities are a matter of fact not of belief . . . one cannot dismiss them as fiction and yet retain credibility as an unbiased observer."[199]

Well-informed, intelligent, credible, non-dogmatic, and relatively impartial observers such as Schoch and Fontana increase in number by the day. It does not take a clairvoyant or mystic (or Nobel laureate) to see the validity of the parapsychological data, it merely requires someone who is not compulsively attached to their psi-negative preconceptions. In fact, such was the persuasiveness of the American J.B. Rhine's parapsychology research that Edward Naumov, formerly Chief of Technical Parapsychology at a laboratory connected with the State Instrument Engineering College of Moscow, once said that, as a result of Rhine's proof of psi, researchers there were no longer trying to prove it exists, but *how* and *why* it worked.[200] This has become the case for most psi researchers today: they seek not to show the best established phenomena's existence but rather to begin understanding their dynamics.

As we will see, Dean Radin has shown that the answer to the question of replication has been soundly provided in the affirmative, and that there are vast amounts of empirical evidence proving the reality of psi. To underscore the legitimacy of parapsychology and the phenomena it studies, parapsychology was formally recognized by the mainstream as a legitimate scientific discipline on December 30, 1969 when the Parapsychological Association, an international scientific society, was accepted as an affiliate member of the American Association for the Advancement of Science (AAAS).[201] Religious sects and "skeptical" groups are *not* affiliates of the AAAS.

Meta-Analysis

Meta-analysis is a research method (and term) developed by University of Colorado psychologist Gene Glass in 1976 to describe a statistical technique of obtaining an overview of a subject by combining separate experiments into one: "Meta-analysis refers to the analysis of analyses. I use it to refer to the statistical analysis of a large collection of results from individual studies for the purpose of integrating the findings."[202]

In a meta-analysis, the raw data points are the results of *whole separate experiments*, as opposed to a typical psi study in which a single data point might be a single individual's response in a particular psi experiment. Though this technique has its own limitations (not accounting for qualitative effects, for instance), meta-analysis has allowed the hardcore skeptics' assertion that better controlled studies would show *smaller* psi effects—implying that all psi effects are due to poorly controlled experiments—to be thoroughly invalidated, by examining how study quality is related to the actual results of each experiment.

This technique provides a much more objective assessment of a body of research than the traditional descriptive or narrative literature review which can be influenced subtly by many variables, including publication and reviewer biases. Traditional narrative literature review can actually allow a reviewer to reach conclusions that are contrary to what the data actually reveal.[203] This has long been a problem with vocal psi pseudo-skeptics insisting, based on their own cursory (and typically very selective) examinations, that the evidence for psi doesn't exist. With meta-analysis there is an aggregate quantitative measurement of the effect of interest, and, as noted, most of the problems related to reviewer bias and selective study publication can be counteracted or prevented.

Meta-analysis afforded a new level of statistical power and objectivity in psychical research, and has perhaps been the final nail in the pseudo-skeptic's coffin—there is no way to hide from the numbers. We will reference meta-analytical data where appropriate as we go. Of course, one major thrust of this book and its companion volume is to find out what happens when we go beyond all the meta-analyses, theories, arguments, debates, and so on, and simply explore consciousness firsthand with our own minds, thus negating the need for any belief at all.

It is ultimately counterproductive to appeal endlessly to science for approval or permission to think our own thoughts and have our own personal insight. Science can give us data but not direct, conscious experience; that occurs within our personal consciousness alone. —Author

When it comes to consciousness and its myriad capacities and functions, science is still playing "catchup." Its job is to *learn* the rules, not *invent* them. —Author

5

The Mystical Experience: Transcending the Persona and its Beliefs

Belief is the death of intelligence. —R.A. Wilson

It is through the mystical experience that one learns the difference
between *belief* and *knowledge*.—Author

Scientists would do well to remember that they have not made the facts and laws,
the discovery of which has enabled them to do so many marvellous things.
They have merely discovered those facts.—I.K. Taimni

Transcending the Intellect

Is the human's linear reductionistic intellect the highest possible advancement
of consciousness available to us? Is it the best the mechanisms of evolution
could call forth? As Bertrand Russel's research determined many years ago,
mystics uniformly agree there is a better way to perceive than only through the
mind based in the ordinary five-sense mode. Writes Ken Wilber in *The Atman
Project*: "The individual ego is a marvelously high-order unity, but compared
with the Unity of the cosmos at large, it is a pitiful slice of holistic reality. Has
nature labored these billions of years just to bring forth this egoic mouse?"

Wilber goes on to observe that the few rare individuals to have taken the problem seriously have advanced the idea that our great mystics and sages "represent some of the very highest, if not the highest, of all stages of human development."[1] For the purposes of his own thesis, Wilber worked from the assumption that such people did indeed occupy the highest stages of human development, virtually making "normal" humanity appear ape-like in comparison.[2]

John Violette has referred to mystics as "evolutionary prodigies"[3] whose messages were so badly misunderstood and distorted that the religions they spawned actually ended up leading people away from the intended message. Violette views the mystical experience as essential to the survival of the human race, as well as being history's most important natural phenomenon.[4]

Interestingly, Andrew Greeley, a sociologist at the University of Arizona, tested people reporting profound mystical experiences with the Affect Balance Scale of psychological wellbeing, a standardized psychological test used to measure healthy personality. Guess what? People who had mystical experiences achieved top scores. Norman Bradburn, the University of Chicago psychologist who developed the scale, said no other factor has ever been found to correlate so highly with psychological balance as mystical experience.[5] Is this alone not reason enough to seriously pursue psi and consciousness research—if only for the betterment of our collective mental health? Prior belief in the paranormal or mystical, as well as religious involvement, have not, on average, been found to be significant factors in terms of such mystical experiences. Itzhak Bentov noted the irony that advanced evolutionary mutants of humankind "are institutionalized as subnormal by their 'normal' peers."[6] Based on discussions with psychiatrist friends, he estimated that possibly 25–30% of schizophrenics belonged to this category.

Plato, a student of the enigmatic philosopher Socrates, compared our human condition to that of slaves enchained in a cave where they can only see the two-dimensional shadows of themselves cast on the surface of a wall. Eventually we, like Plato's hypothetical slaves, came to accept these shadows as reality itself, while the *source* of the shadows went ignored. This author realized around the age of 19 or 20, for better or worse, that the shadows on the wall were not reality itself, but merely the projections of a greater all-encompassing unity, and moreover, he set about leaving the cave to enter into and explore that greater unity directly—not systematically in the way a dedicated true mystic or occultist would, but in his own haphazard and inquisitive way, which yielded mystic insights nonetheless. In order to continue the process, I had to simply pursue information in the most honest and credible direction that it led me. C.G. Jung wrote in *On Death and Immortality*:

Prejudice cripples and injures the full phenomenon of psychic life . . . Critical rationalism has apparently eliminated . . . the idea of life after death. This could only have happened because nowadays most people identify themselves almost exclusively with their [ordinary] consciousness, and imagine that they are only what they know about themselves . . . Rationalism and doctrinairism are the disease of our time; they pretend to have all the answers. [However,] I lend an attentive ear to the strange myths of the psyche, and take a careful look at the varied events that come my way, regardless of whether or not they fit in with my theoretical postulates.[7]

Stanislav Grof is a psychiatrist with over 50 years' experience of research into non-ordinary states of consciousness (induced by psychedelic substances and various non-drug techniques) and one of the founders and pioneers of transpersonal psychology (the study and/or treatment of consciousness beyond the restrictions of the body, ego, and space-time). He was born in Prague, where he also received his scientific training—an M.D. degree from the Charles University School of Medicine and a Ph.D. from the Czechoslovakian Academy of Sciences. In his insightful book *The Holotropic Mind* (1993), he wrote that although he started out as a materialist and atheist, he eventually had to consider the "spiritual dimension" as crucial to the human psyche and the cosmos at large, assessing that it might even be essential to our survival on this planet.[8]

It was 1991 when, in writing his book, he revealed that the previous three decades of research in consciousness had convinced him of the inadequacy of established scientific models of the human psyche in the face of much data that they could not account for. He described these models collectively as a "conceptual straitjacket" which was hampering attainment of deeper understanding. Grof exhorted his fellow scientists not to dictate what reality "should" be, but to let go of preconceived ideas about the psyche so that it could be allowed to reveal its nature on its own terms.[9]

During the course of his career, Grof and his wife Christina developed their Holotropic Breathwork technique to allow people to access non-ordinary states of consciousness that transcended the limits of the physical world, invariably resulting in profound and near-spontaneous emotional (and even physical) healing that, early on, was totally unexpected. This discovery has been mirrored by other qualified psychiatrists using hypnotic techniques to achieve the type of non-ordinary states of consciousness that generate such amazing healing. If it all sounds a bit much, or too good to be true, we should note that

Grof's material is drawn from over 20,000 Holotropic Breathwork sessions with people from different countries and from all walks of life, as well as 4,000 psychedelic sessions that he conducted in the earlier phases of his research. His systematic study of non-ordinary consciousness states revealed irrevocably just how "painfully narrow and superficial" the traditional view of the human psyche actually was.[10]

Grof's research forced him to acknowledge the existence of a transpersonal realm which reaches far beyond the ordinary limits of our minds, connecting individual psyches with the Jungian collective unconscious, and the universe at large.[11] Years earlier, Jung's research into the human psyche also forced him to go beyond Freudian psychology and acknowledge the "collective unconscious" that unites all of humankind, laying the groundwork for those who would follow. When Grof first became aware of these territories in his researches, he thought he was creating a new map of the psyche that was made possible by the discovery of a revolutionary tool, LSD. But as this work continued, he realized that he was *rediscovering* ancient knowledge of human consciousness possibly going back millennia, which was embodied in various esoteric (and exoteric) traditions, and which had been wrongly rejected by an immature and conceptually crippled Western science. It is interesting to note, as an aside, that the esoteric streams of the "great" religions actually pre-empt the findings of modern consciousness research such as Grof's, while the more mainstream versions have had those elements removed and have fallen prey to endless abstractions and misinterpretations, spawning useless dogmas and superstitions.

The view of human consciousness as a mere epiphenomenon of the brain seems valid enough where everyday states of consciousness are concerned, but it fails to account for what happens when we enter non-ordinary consciousness states, particularly those in which we access veridical information not available to the rational mind. "Modern consciousness research reveals that our psyches have no real and absolute boundaries; on the contrary, we are part of an infinite field of consciousness that encompasses all there is," states Grof.[12] We first hear this revelation from the authors of the Upanishads (the final portion of the Hindu Vedas), who lived over 3,000 years ago: "I have known that spirit," said Svetasvatara, "who is infinite and in all, who is ever-one, beyond time."[13]

One of the fathers of modern brain research, neurosurgeon Wilder Penfield, believed towards the end of his life that consciousness is something more than neurochemistry alone could account for, saying, "the mind has energy . . . different from that of neuronal potentials that travel the axon pathways. There I must leave it."[14] Psychologist and "paranormal" researcher Gary E. Schwartz has stated that "all of the findings in contemporary neuroscience are actually consistent with the hypothesis that the brain serves as an 'antenna-receiver' for consciousness rather than being the 'creator' of consciousness."[15] Consciousness is not limited in the ways that the brain and sensory organs are. Clearly this view stands in stark contrast to the picture of reality we tend to be conditioned into as children.

Jung had earlier said that the most important question for man is whether or not he is "related" to something infinite or not.[16] This is indeed the primary concern of this book, and this chapter in particular. Why should we concern ourselves with such a question? Because, as Jung explained, knowing that we have a link with the infinite causes desires and attitudes to change—we are transformed by the knowledge.

> In the final analysis, we count for something only because of the essential we embody, and if we do not embody that, life is wasted . . . The greatest limitation for man is the "self" [human ego-persona]; it is manifested in the experience: "I am *only* that!"[17]

Our age has shifted all emphasis to the here and now, and thus brought about a "daemonization of man and his world," according to Jung. For him, the miseries wrought on the world by dictators, tyrants, and the like was the result of the shortsightedness of the "super-intellectuals" robbing mankind of transcendence. Like them, we too have fallen victim to unconsciousness. Jung viewed man's task or destiny as being to create more and more consciousness, to become increasingly aware, and thus "kindle a light in the darkness of mere being."[18]

This then, is our mission: to become conscious of the infinite world of interconnectedness that quantum physics and parapsychology present us with and which shamans, mystics, seers, and modern transpersonal psychologists have explored and mapped over the millennia right up to the present day.

That there are "levels" of consciousness that transcend space and time is not some nebulous New Age invention, but a fact of Reality that can be proved to oneself—*but only for oneself.* Anything less than the direct experience is a mere conceptual approximation. Not only is the concept of transcending space and time not the product of some frivolous or fanciful New Age fad, it is something that military forces around the world—particularly in the USA, Russia, and China—have been systematically exploring—and exploiting— for decades. Former US Army Captain David Morehouse found this out for himself after revealing to one of his superiors, Ennis Cole*—a psychologist with serious rank and credentials—that one night on a camping trip he had spontaneously experienced a state of consciousness removed from his body; an out-of-body experience, or OBE. Rather than dismissing him as delusional, Morehouse's superior officer reassured him that not only was the psychological literature replete with such accounts, but that under lab conditions, the army's test subjects were able to induce OBEs and obtain data not available to the ordinary senses.[19]

A small, select group of soldiers were having OBEs, going to distant targets, and successfully describing them, in a process they called remote viewing, the colonel explained.[20] This enterprise is what you might call the systematic exploration and utilization of the grand tapestry of consciousness that unites all of existence. Accessing it allows the transcension of ordinary space-time. It also changes the individual experient irrevocably. Morehouse, before starting his duties as a "psi-spy" in his new department, was actually warned of the profound psychological changes that would result from his professional involvement in the military's remote viewing (RV) program. Fern Gauvin, who assessed Morehouse's suitability for the project, earnestly warned Morehouse that if he participated in the project he and his worldview would never be the same again, "because you'll know too much."[21]

All of this from military men. I ask the reader: are we to suppose that the military would take such occult pursuits so seriously as to actually classify thousands of pages of documents relating to these research projects if it was all merely a load of empty New Age hokum?

The Mystical Experience: Nonlocality of Consciousness

The human being can deceive himself. He can yield to the belief that there is no hidden world, that what appears to his senses and his intellect contains everything that can possibly exist. But this deception is only possible, not for the deeper, but for the surface consciousness. —Rudolf Steiner

If I have been speaking something like a mystic thus far, it's only because I am. Or something like that. Allow me to explain. Sometime around the age of 20 I experienced this "mystical" oneness that we are talking about. I was lying on my back in bed, waiting to go to sleep, but having trouble stopping the mental

---

* This was a pseudonym used to protect anonymity.

chatter, as usual. I was completely lucid and not particularly sleepy or tired when a momentary cessation of the chatter occurred, and without any intent or expectation whatsoever, I suddenly and inexplicably found that I was, well . . . an infinite field of consciousness. I experienced infinite consciousness. Not a goal I had ever set just before trying to get to sleep. Flossed? Check. Brushed teeth? Check. Experienced infinite consciousness? Check. Nighty-night.

I should elaborate. I did not experience a gradual shifting of consciousness. One second, I was awake on my back waiting to get tired and fall asleep, and the next second, my brainwave state having slowed and my rate of breath having decreased subconsciously, I was experiencing myself as the *universe in its entirety*. I could feel planets and galaxies, in the field of consciousness that I was. I was simultaneously everywhere and nowhere. I touched the farthest reaches of infinity and went on forever more. I didn't have a beginning or an end. I just was—completely beyond 3D space-time and yet encompassing all of it. Infinite.

I knew (as opposed to believed) then that the perceptive quantum physicist was right: everything truly is interconnected in ways we cannot directly perceive through the ordinary human senses. Essentially and literally, all is One. This is no mere metaphor but an observation gleaned from firsthand, conscious experience. *Gnosis*. Reality and consciousness are infinite and infinitely entwined—it was true long before John Alexander Bell showed up, and it will remain true until the end of time (ignoring momentarily that time as a one-dimensional "flow" is an illusion). As William Blake said: "If the doors of perception were cleansed every thing would appear to man as it is, infinite. For man has closed himself up till he sees all things through narrow chinks of his cavern."

The only way to convey this archetypal mystical experience is through analogy and/or metaphor. The mystic must try to relate the supra-conceptual via the conceptual, the supra-mental at the mental level. This does not for good understanding make. Regardless, I will offer one analogy here. This infinite awareness was not completely unlike what it might be like to be a hydrogen bomb exploding, with a couple of major differences. First, there is no end to the explosion (and there is also no starting point). The reaches of your exploding consciousness encounter no boundaries, only more of itself. Second, there is no real "unfolding" or "expanding" outwards because there is *nowhere to go that you are not already*. Swami Rama Tirtha expressed his own realization:

> *It is all One*. There is neither me nor He. Everything is lost in One . . . The dolls of ego and intellect have both been burnt down today . . . Run, if you can. Run away. But, where to? If you

> hide in the sky, I am already present there . . . I am all absorbed
> in My own sublimity . . . I am Love personified . . . Time and
> space have disappeared. There is no distance, inner or outer. *It
> is all One. It is all One.*[22]

And thus we meet with the gross inadequacy of language when we attempt to harness it to capture a reality or awareness far "beyond" our terrestrial conceptualizations. Further attempts at describing the indescribable will merely yield circuitous babbling. The inability of the mystic to convincingly convey the mystical reality underlying all of creation is a notorious fact, for he or she attempts the impossible. The Infinite cannot be expressed with such finite things as words—unless it be poetry perhaps, for here words can go a long way to expressing the inexpressible.

As the *Tao Te Ching* says, "The way [Tao] that can be spoken of is not the constant way. The name that can be named is not the constant name."[23] To paraphrase Swami Abhayananda, who nevertheless uses words to sum up the ultimate mystical experience quite effectively, "the consciousness of the individual suddenly becomes the consciousness of the entire vast universe."[24] It doesn't get much more succinct than that.

It is important to note here that I was not dreaming, day-dreaming, imagining, or *thinking* any of this. In a state of consciousness like that, thinking, or *trying* to think, is likely to "snap you out of it" because it is a left-brain function binding you to space-time. During the mystical experience you are quite literally out of your ordinary mind—the analytical, rationalizing intellect and its endless chattering has subsided. You have, as Neale Donald Walsch might phrase it, "taken leave of your mind."[25]

We are so ill familiar with these sorts of transcendent, hyperdimensional realms that we cannot, for the most part, conceptualize them or process them in intellectual terms as they occur. Finite or Aristotelian three-law logic cannot comprehend ideas like "all is One," or "past, present and future all exist now"— it cannot reconcile opposites (how can you be everywhere and nowhere?)—they simply present an insoluble paradox to it. Four-law logic or transfinite logic (as Violette calls it) is what is needed to comprehend that the whole exists in every part.[26] Only this latter form of logic (also known as transrational) can comprehend the seemingly paradoxical accounts of higher consciousness operating in higher dimensions.

I was not imagining this experience and this I know because you cannot *experience infinity* by trying to *imagine* it. Try. You always fall short, and yet it *can be directly experienced*—no imagination necessary. I had no lapse in consciousness and have had no lapse in memory of this experience. I was completely awake and lucid before, during, and after. During it, the only thing I was aware of was that I was everything.

An awareness entered my consciousness that translated to "I am the universe and the universe is me." (Again, the paradox of the whole in every part, incomprehensible to Aristotelian logic.) As soon as the human analytical part of my mind (left brain) tried to process this awareness by thinking about it, the experience ended, almost as suddenly as it had begun. This realm of infinite consciousness is beyond the mentations of the human mind. Thinking only pulls you away from it—it cannot take you there. When I had returned from the transcendental world of formlessness to the hallucinatory world of multiplicity, I had, for the first time, encountered an experiential reality that showed me the difference between Reality and illusion, the difference between *believing* and *knowing*. What if . . .

the Truth is not a concept, but an experiential reality?
the Truth is not words on a page, but a state of being?
the Truth is not an idea, but an awareness?
the Truth is not of this world or even of this dimension or "level" of reality?
the Truth is not a belief and does not require one's faith or credulity to remain so?

Here we might consider some of the dubiousness of religious symbolism: being of the earthly conceptual realm, it is open to our idiosyncratic interpretations, literalism (particularly in the case of the Judeo-Christian systems) being a particularly sketchy proposition. Concepts are not Reality itself, they are signposts. As the Hindu sage Lahiri Mahasaya told us, "words are only shells"—if you want to know "God" exists, find out in meditation.[27]

To describe how this infinite consciousness *felt* is not easy. I was an infinite field of awareness with no beginning and no end. I did not experience the "passage of time," because as infinite awareness, you are everywhere and everything (omnipresent), and a sense of serialized time therefore cannot exist for you. This sense of time is an illusion that arises from the perception of space and multiplicity—relativity, in other words. Such relativity, we might hypothesize, only arose from the Infinite as a result of the collective consciousness creating ripples or oscillations within itself, ultimately leading to self-perpetuating phenomena/entities that we call mind, energy, and matter (and eventually sentient physical organisms). All such form is vibration; a conjuring of the One cosmic mind that it dreamed up to subjectively experience itself with.

In the beginning was the "Word," and the Word was . . . vibration, "sound," in point of fact, and sound is apparently more fundamental than light. That is why first there was the Word, and *then* followed the command "let there be light," the creation of space-time and electromagnetism from time-space/Void/aether/implicate order. (Incidentally, whoever wrote those Bible passages clearly appropriated them from the ancient Hindu Vedas: "In the beginning was Brahman, with whom was the Word. And the Word is Brahman."[28])

As well as being everywhere at once, I also had my own apparent point of individuality (*Atman*) within this infinite oneness (*Brahman**). It felt spectacularly puny, like a single molecule of water in the Pacific Ocean. The difference was that I could feel that I was simultaneously and instantaneously interconnected with everything else, which made me decidedly expansive at the same time (hence the paradoxical nature of the Zen koan which attempts to convey the unconveyable nature of reality). I was completely nonlocal and "self-entangled," to put it in the increasingly fashionable quasi-physics parlance. All was (is) Self. I was (am) the micro and the macro, the Alpha and the Omega, if you will. Ralph Waldo Emerson once said: "I hate quotes. Tell me what you know." Well, this one's for you, Ralph—this much I *know*.

Since this awareness is a timeless one, I do not really know how long it lasted. It could have been just a few seconds, but it was (is), in essence, *eternal*, beyond the neurotic tick-tock of the clock's compulsive arms. From this insight, I realized with a certainty beyond belief that serial time is not a literal thing, but a sensory delusion; there is, in the absolute sense, no such thing as time "passing"—all actuality, history, and potential exists in the now.

In 1967, John Wheeler and Bryce DeWitt published the Wheeler-DeWitt equation; a reputedly successful attempt to merge the quantum and classical ways of thinking about the world. The catch was that to solve the equation, time had to be eliminated: it simply disappears. This seems to be where studies at Germany's Max Planck Institute of Quantum Optics are leading to, as physicists are telling us that at scales smaller than the ultra-tiny Planck scale

---

* "*Upanishadic* awareness uses the terms *Atman, Brahman, Sat* (Being), *Chit* (Pure Consciousness), *[and] Ananda* (Bliss)" synonymously. (Source: Dr Varanasi Ramabrahmam, *The Upanishads from a Scientific Perspective*. <http://venetiaansell. wordpress.com/2009/01/12/the-upanishads-from-a-scientific-perspective-dr-varanasi-ramabrahmam/>.) Here I am using the term Atman in this way, more or less how Wilber employs it in *The Atman Project* (p 10): "ultimate Unity Consciousness in only God."

of time (a trillionth of a trillionth of an attosecond), time disappears. Physicist Carlo Rovelli suggests that it "may be that the best way to think about quantum reality is to give up the notion of time—that the fundamental description of the universe must be timeless."[29] I couldn't agree more. Wheeler has said, "there is no before, there is no after."[30] In a state of infinite existence where you occupy all space, there can be no experience of the "passage of time." Where does time or consciousness "pass" or "flow" when it is everywhere to begin with? Einstein had stated decades ago that "time is not at all what it seems. It does not flow in only one direction, and the future exists simultaneously with the past." It is interesting that such insights into the nature of reality can also be gleaned from lucid dreams[31] and near-death experiences, which can both open our awareness up to the information of the so-called collective unconscious.

Following this experience of mine, as my consciousness returned to "normal," I lay awake for a few minutes processing it. Somehow it failed to shock or surprise me. I will repeat that: experiencing infinite consciousness for the first time did not surprise or shock me in the least. On some level I had already known it to be true and I was merely experiencing that which my larger or "higher" consciousness already knew. How could you not be surprised to discover you are infinite unless you were *already* aware of it at some level, even if only subconsciously? This was not the only "mystical experience" I have had, but the first of several. This one in particular may have had the greatest impact of all, since it was the first. Lawrence LeShan wrote of the perception of yourself as being a part of the whole and the whole itself, expressing how he then knew why he had blocked perceiving it for so long: "I understood something of the meaning of the statement in the Zohar: 'God is not nice. He is not an uncle. He is an earthquake.' One can be, as I was, pretty shattered by this."[32]

Rick Strassman on the mystical experience:

> There no longer is any separation between the self and what is not the self. Personal identity and all of existence become one and the same [and] we understand at the most basic level the underlying unity and interdependence of all existence. Past, present, and future merge together into . . . the now of eternity . . . [S]pace becomes vast. Like time, space is no longer here or there but everywhere, limitless, without edges. It is all here.[33]

For Strassman, "there is a searing sense of the sacred and holy [and] we know we have met the fundamental bedrock and fountainhead of existence, one that emanates love, wisdom, and power on an unimaginable scale." For him—like

Violette, Grof, and others—it is the most important event that will ever happen to anyone, and could take the remainder of one's life to process the insights obtained.[34]

Such transcendent experience is more disturbing or shattering to the human ego/personality level the more rigidly certain beliefs are held in one's mind (i.e., the more one has invested in the dualistic perception of the space-time–bound human persona). On confronting the infinite, one's ego seems to explode into pieces. The fundamentalist materialist and fundamentalist religionist endure a common delusion: they both think they are *only* their human ego/persona and they both use finite/serial logic to process "reality," even when something subtler ("holographic logic") is demanded. The belief in separation that the ego constructs is completely demolished as you realize that the appearance of spatial separation arises purely from our own particular human mode of being "in" and perceiving the universe, which is actually nothing more than millions of energy frequencies vibrating in a complex, conscious matrix. Such ego identification begins to be dismantled through the mystical experience of the Infinite. We then know that we are not a body, but a formless, concept-less, and beginningless consciousness.

From the type of experience I am describing here, you begin, gradually, to recognize this physical realm we inhabit as being scarcely more real than the dream worlds we create in our sleep. In fact, they are thought or virtual worlds and possess their own reality—they are just vibrating mental energy, as is our cosmos, in a manner of speaking. When Idries Shah, the preeminent Sufi teacher, was asked to name "a fundamental mistake of man's," he replied, "To think that he is alive, when he has merely fallen asleep in life's waiting room."[35]

I wonder how people would perceive this life, if, instead of sleeping for roughly eight hours a day and spending the remaining 16 awake (or so people like to think), they slept for 23 hours and spent one hour conscious in the "real world," with full memory of what they experienced while sleeping and dreaming. Imagine if those 23 hours were spent dreaming *lucidly*. Upon awakening into our material realm, you would be constantly frustrated by the concrete-like limbs attached to your leaden body, your gravity-bound frame, and the slow and restrictive process of moving to and fro using only the primitive propulsion of your legs, or, slightly less time-consuming, your car. It would all seem so *unreal*: so many restrictions and limitations, not to mention the strange feeling of disconnection from other people and the ambient environment. As the psychologist Havelock Ellis said, "Dreams are real while they last, can we say more of life?"

I put it to you now that this reality of ours is just another form of dream, much like those we have in the privacy of our own beds. This notion has been expressed by yogis ever since there were yogis to penetrate beyond the five-sense models of reality we create with the brain. Australian Aborigines have long taken the same view. It is certainly interesting to note that we are informed by Stephen LaBerge that, in physiological terms, lucid dreams are real to the dreamer and things such as respiration rate and eye movements in lucid dreams correspond to actions in the dreamer's physical body. To the brain, the lucid dream is just as real as waking life.[36] More than this, Tibetan teacher Tarthang Tulku has said that through continued practice at the art of lucid dreaming, the difference between the waking and the dream state begins to fade. The increasingly refined awareness makes for a more vivid waking life.[37]

As odd or inexplicable as this may sound to some people, I had no choice but to accept this experience and the expanded awareness it left me with—not least because of my occasional meditations. I have, on a couple of occasions now well in the past, experienced a more physical, tangible sense of this infinite oneness and interconnectedness over a more controlled and sustained period. I achieved an incredible tactile sense of oneness with what felt like the entire cosmos. These experiences were different to my first mystical experience. Aside from being sustained for much longer in a controlled trance state, these were physically tangible and totally sublime. I was feeling this oneness bodily—not something you forget easily. To physically feel distant galaxies flow through you is not something you can easily put into words. "Nearby" galaxies are tens of thousands of light years away, and yet you can be sitting there in the comfort of your own home and feel these distant entities "flowing" through you. Bell's theorem is right. Everything is fundamentally "entangled." Period.

In principle, quantum uncertainty according to the Copenhagen school allows for the theoretical possibility that the atoms that compose your body may spontaneously and without warning disappear and reappear on a distant planet for no apparent reason, though the likelihood of this happening is minuscule because of the quantum averaging that occurs throughout the trillions of atoms in your body, reducing the chance to little more than zero, or so the explanation goes.[38] Remember Kaku's comments from Chapter 4 that, "what happens to us automatically affects things instantaneously in distant corners of the universe . . . In some sense there is a web of entanglement that connects distant corners of the universe, including us."[39]

Biologist Mae Wan Ho states that we each have the waves of all other organisms entangled within us,[40] though the resolution fidelity of this information is considered to decrease with distance,[41] not unlike the way that a tiny fragment

121

of a holographic image has lower resolution than the original whole. Yet, we are not merely *connected* to other organisms or distant corners of the universe ("entangled"), we *are* these things at a most fundamental level. Every mystic knows this, though they may express it in different ways.

Combining the other experiences I have had with the research I have been doing for years has left me with no choice but to accept my new expanded reality. I hope it is clear that these transcendent experiences are the result of heightened awareness/perception, not an impaired or hallucinatory awareness, though some people who are unfamiliar with such things would try to argue this, merely because they are operating on the assumption that consciousness is simply generated by the brain. The simple truth is that this belief is false, as the mystical experience clearly reveals to the individual who has it. You need not take my word for this, however, because we are going to demolish the myth of brain-generated consciousness in quite some depth through both TGI 1 and 2.

Grof expressed what I am attempting to convey of my own insight here in poignant terms in *LSD Psychotherapy*, when he wrote of the high-dose LSD session (which was used largely to generate transpersonal experiences):

> The insights emerging . . . are of a global, intuitive and holographic nature. The transcendental "aha!" experience of this kind cannot be dissected easily by the Western analytical mind, nor can it be exploited in a pragmatic sense. It is an illuminating insight into the very essence of existence. The experient does not gain rational understanding of the cosmic process, but reaches instant comprehension by losing his or her separate identity and literally *becoming* the process [through] a transcendence of phenomena, space, time and causality.[42]

The same sentiment is expressed by many near-death experiencers who have actually experienced the death process and pierced the veil between this world and the next, though typically they encounter a subtler realm of form and multiplicity than the transcendent Infinite Oneness we speak of. One such woman said:

> I began receiving "all knowledge," or at least that is what it felt like . . . This didn't come to me as words [but] more as complete thoughts, [as] complete words and pictures in my mind. As I could form a question in my mind I had the answer. Not just

the answer to that question, but the why and how and the answer to every other question the answer would bring up. EVERYTHING in the entire universe fit together like a jigsaw puzzle. EVERYTHING MADE SENSE.[43]

Another NDEer said, "I came to see that reality is everywhere. That it is not simply the earthly life but the infinite life. Everything is not only connected together, everything is also one. So I felt a wholeness with the light, a sense that all is right with me and the universe. I could be anywhere instantly, really there."[44] This sentiment is from a man who had previously been a typical scientific materialist, convinced that consciousness is extinguished when one dies. Afterwards he got a second Ph.D. in the psychology of religion, moved from Russia to the USA, and became a minister, although his view of spirituality—rather than being sectarian/denominational—was more universalistic and expansive. His view of "God" united the opposites of dark and light, acknowledging that "God" is everything that exists.[45]

Evelyn Underhill wrote that "[t]he Christian formula, which declares that His creative Word 'was made flesh and dwelt among us' simply expresses this loving revelation of the Infinite in terms of the finite."[46] Therefore in light of the foregoing (and the still to come), we are forced to abide by the conclusion that perhaps the most constructive way to interpret the proclamation of the biblical character of Jesus that "I and the Father are one" is as an allegorical depiction of man's awareness of his transcendental identity/consciousness ("godhood"). If only each Christian could see this statement in this way, they too would realize, at least hypothetically, that they and the "Father" are also one, and that such "divinity" is not the province of merely one man who stars in a book written largely by authors unknown to us.

Even some alien abduction experiences have deep and obvious parallels with mystical experiences. Abductee Betty Andreasson was induced into an out-of-body experience by her "alien" captors, and then ushered into a "world of light" where she experienced an overwhelming and ineffable sense of joy and "Oneness." They told her that this was her real "home," where the "One was," and that everyone would experience this for themselves one day.[47] "Love is the greatest of all," the beings' leader informed her,[48] just as so many mystics have informed humanity for so long.

Following my first mystical experience, I had wondered to myself if we were all really "God," and that this entity had "divided" itself in order to experience subjectivity and allow its composite parts to evolve along individual timelines. "Unless It becomes two, the One has no experience, no universe of forms," as Abhayananda notes.[49] Remote viewer and author Courtney Brown had an experience during a remote viewing session that illustrates this idea beautifully. It showed him a representation of the essence of the beginning of the universe (note the reference to a vortex!):

> There was a shape of light that somewhat resembled a spinning cloud or vortex . . . The vortex was alive. There was the sense of a huge consciousness, and as I extended my mind across this consciousness, I felt stretched like the skin of a balloon, although not uncomfortably so. It had spent an eternity by itself, slowly evolving . . . Then, in one sudden burst, I experienced this being's solution. The being essentially blew itself up, or at least much of itself. As I followed the outwards rush of the being's fragmenting expansion, I perceived that it experienced a new joy that nearly overwhelmed me . . . At first the bits and pieces of the larger being were too small and immature to even be aware of themselves . . . From this point began the most profound evolution of the original being. It had become a parent to the fragments of itself. The fragmented parts began to experience existence in a way that seemed independent of the parent. Initially they did not understand that they were literally part of a single larger being. Yet as they continued to grow in experience, they matured and developed an intense need to know how they came to exist, and indeed, the reason for their existence. This led them to eventually seek and discover the reality of their parent, their loving creator. It was at this moment of realisation that they understood that they were their parent, and that their own growth and evolution was also the growth and evolution of their parent. The parent had created a way to look back at itself through a mirror of a multitude of individual consciousnesses.[50]

Lucid dreamers have had similar insights, as LaBerge and Rheingold have documented.[51] In terms of Yurth's Y-Bias and Angularity Theory, the Source is referred to as the Physical Vacuum.[52] Elsewhere in physics, the One is referred to by Maxwell and Whittaker as the primary field of infinite scalar potential. This is the causal plane from which undifferentiated information emerges from scalar potentials to create matter and energy.[53]

Tibetan Buddhists explain that the formless Infinite mind, *Rigpa*, generates or radiates all that we perceive to be as other than ourselves, that all we that experience or cognize is the "self-radiance" of this singular consciousness. "Samsara is your mind, and nirvana is also your mind; all pleasure and pain, and all delusions exist nowhere apart from your mind."[54]

Colin Wilson has offered the hypothesis that "the force of life began its conquest of matter by somehow splitting itself into units, each of which felt 'separate' from the rest of the universe."[55] The direct experience of thousands of individuals across time bears this inference out. First there was the Void, or Infinite Oneness, and it created a ripple (vibration or "Word") within itself in an attempt at generating what would ultimately be the vibrational world of energy and form. This is essentially why synchronicity exists. This is essentially why fractality exists. This is why we constantly (if we pay attention) encounter shadows and reflections of ourselves wherever we go—because all that exists is the One. I. Ramakrishna said, "The Universe is nothing but the Divine uttering his own name to himself." An NDE had by one of Kenneth Ring's personal friends illustrates the point well:

[S]he felt that she was "rocketing through layers upon layers of realities, seemingly to the heart of the universe itself," and she was terrified. She thought she had gone too far and would be lost forever. Then: Oh my God. I was "picked up" as if by an ENORMOUS pair of hands, and as I looked up I found myself looking into a gigantic EYE, out of which flowed a tear of all consuming, profound ineffable love and compassion, and I KNEW without a doubt, that I was looking into the heart of my self, who is all selves, whatever it is that God is. And I was brought into the EYE, and was home.[56]

The 8th-century Hindu mystic Shankara exuberantly expressed his realization: "I am reality without beginning, without equal . . . I dwell within all beings as the Self, the pure consciousness, the ground of all phenomena, internal and external. I am both the enjoyer and that which is enjoyed . . . Now I know that I am all."[57]

Descriptions of reality by mystics are typically holographic, laden with prose hinting at the "whole within each part" nature of existence that the poet Blake wrote about. LSD subjects also often arrive at the conclusion that no real boundaries exist between themselves and the rest of the universe. Everything appears to be part of a unified field of cosmic energy, and the boundaries of the individual are those of existence itself. "The universe is seen as an ever-unfolding drama of endless adventures in consciousness, very much in the sense of the Hindu *lila*, or divine play. Against the background of this infinitely complex and eternal cosmic drama, the fact of impending individual destruction seems to lose its tragic significance."[58]

In speaking of his own mystical experience and the records and legacies left by other mystics, Swami Abhayananda said, "their experience is my experience; for all who have realized the Truth have known that same eternal Self."[59] This certainty is a hallmark of those psychonauts who have pierced the veil of illusion and accessed hyperdimensional awareness. "Ask of those who have attained God; all speak the same word . . . All the enlightened have left one message . . . it is only those in the midst of their journey who hold diverse opinions," wrote the 15th-century Islamic saint Dadu.[60]

"Until we reach enlightenment," writes Sogyal Rinpoche, "there will inevitably be doubts, because doubt is a fundamental activity of the unenlightened mind."[61] The culture mind is moulded by its cultural milieu into doubting everything except the prosaic and familiar, the primary and transient ego identifiers sanctioned for belief by prevailing paradigms.

The consistency from one mystic's report to the next demands we pay attention, for they reveal that mystics the world over and through time have been accessing similar facets of the same unitive reality—different shades of the Infinite within. These perceptions are not mere neurological aberrations; these are portals beyond space-time to underlying Reality.

In kabbalistic doctrine, the creative "godhead" had a thought, and the thought became the origin of all creation.[62] The mystic realizes that he and the "godhead" (the source of all creation) are one and the same. My own mystical experiences confirm and validate all of the preceding insights. The mystic cannot prove to anyone that his own experience of the Infinite even happened, let alone that it was "real," and nor is he interested in attempting to do so. Neither can the insight be disproved, because we have well and truly left the world of the scientifically testable in the proverbial dust.

As I made clear in the first three chapters, to believe that the limits of scientific knowledge are the limits of all possible knowledge would be extremely foolish.[63] Instead I invite you to consider that what is true for me regarding "my own" infinite consciousness and the oneness of all things, must, if true, also apply to absolutely everyone else. After all, mystics all experience "in different ways and degrees *one and the same sublime reality*,"[64] and not everyone is a practicing mystic before they experience it—they are often just "regular" people whose nonlocal cosmic consciousness smashes its way from the subconscious awareness into conscious awareness with a sledgehammer, often when they least expect it: "Men and women of spiritual genius all come before us, not as the painstaking discoverers of something, but as the astonished receivers of something."[65] For them, "there is no more relationship, but only the eternal and all-inclusive I AM."[66]

The term "relationship" implies *relativity*, duality. How can you have a relationship with yourself if you are Infinite, the Absolute? There is only Self. There is only One. We have moved consciously beyond the delusory realm of duality inhabited by imaginary deities and their subjects and believers into complete, *conscious* unity. All beliefs get left at the door. All faith is exchanged for something so much rarer: conscious awareness of the Infinite, which translates in the mental realm as *knowledge* or Gnosis.

All the transient cultural constructs, beliefs, images, and edicts arising in space-time that are familiar to the individual experient, no matter from which part of the globe he or she hails, need to be either suddenly discarded or rearranged and re-prioritized in light of the Eternal. Suddenly the world of relative knowledge is seen for what it is, and the decrees of governments, priests, scriptures, politicians, doctors, lawyers, and professors need no longer occupy the prestigious seat of supposed ontological preeminence. There is a new ontology, based on direct insight into Infinity. The resulting doctrine has been known as the Perennial Wisdom/Philosophy because of its unchanging nature, transcending the culture mind as it so spectacularly does.

It is worth noting the difference between the Perennial Wisdom and the "truths" conveyed to us by science and religion over the centuries: notice how the "facts" of these latter institutions are constantly mutating, shifting with new discoveries or social pressures. Various scholars and researchers have pointed out, for instance, that much of what comprises the "essential" aspects of present-day Christianity did not feature at all in earlier versions of the Gospels. Recently the Pope abolished the concept (was it ever anything else?) of limbo for the unbaptised babies of Catholics (what about non-Catholics?). "The decision was taken after Pope Benedict XVI was presented with Vatican studies that said there were 'serious' grounds that such souls could go to heaven . . ."[67] Phew, that's a relief then! (Maybe budget cuts were required by the holy administrators in heaven when the GFC hit, as limbo was no longer deemed cost-effective.)

Yet, the mystics of the ages—and "Christ" fits the description—reveal one fact over and over: that we are Infinite and Eternal consciousness, beyond space and time. This fact has never been subject to the whims of any cultural constructs, despite being greatly obscured by them.

I am, in a sense, asking for trouble by inviting your intellect to understand something that is not of the intellect but beyond it completely; this invites distortions and misunderstandings, which is why I have covered this from so many angles. As Colin Wilson noted, lower states of consciousness do not understand the higher.[68] Yogi Ramacharaka was succinct when he said in 1904 that "none may understand the Absolute fully, unless he be the Absolute himself."[69]

"That higher state," wrote van der Leeuw's fellow theosophist Arthur E. Powell in the early 1920s, "is to be realized only when the activities of consciousness are carried . . . beyond the groping cave-life in which they normally dwell. That higher consciousness will come to all men sooner or later; and when it comes all life will suddenly appear changed."[70]

Other Names for Truth

This unitive state of awareness, or being, this absolute reality, has been called Brahman in Hinduism (and more intense experiences of it referred to as the "Brahmic Splendor"[71]), *Nirvikalpa Samadhi* (a drawn-out but still temporary experience of this infinite peace),[72] *al haqq* (islam, meaning the Truth [cap T] or the Reality [cap R]), God by Judeo-Christians, the Absolute and other such lofty things. The Chinese sages simply called it the *Tao*. Taoism is therefore the Chinese name for the Perennial Philosophy.[73] Tibetan Buddhism calls consciousness beyond form, emotion, and conceptualization: *Rigpa*, a primordial, pure, pristine awareness that is at once intelligent, cognizant, radiant, and always awake. "[T]o realize the nature of mind is to realize the nature of all things," states Sogyal Rinpoche in *The Tibetan Book of Living and Dying*.[74]

The Hindu Vedas, which may date back as far as 7,000 years, speak of a unified field of "pure consciousness" that sustains, bathes, and permeates all of creation: Brahman. The individual "soul spark" or "self" within this infinite reality is Atman. In *Samkhya*, one school of Hindu philosophy, *Purusha* is another term for this pure consciousness, our true identity—in contrast with *Prakrti*, the material world.[75]

Sounding like a description of the unified zero point field or "aether" of cutting-edge physics, the Zohar (a revered Jewish mystical text) states that "Everything shall return to its Jesod, or foundation, from which it has proceeded. All marrow, seed and energy are gathered in this place. Hence, all of the potentialities which exist go out through this." Hebrew mysticism refers to the unmanifest as *Ain Soph*—the unconditioned fundamental ground of existence.

Aether researcher Ron Pearson says his research "shows the [a]ether having a complex structure, intelligence and [consciousness as] the core ingredient."[76] Science is winding its way, via multiple different paths, to the primacy of consciousness. Pearson refers to the aether also as "i-ther" and "nuether," and states that "the i-theric structure can be arranged to look like replicas of the neural networks of our brains and might have arisen by a form of evolution by such self-organization. So, background intelligence might exist that is able to organise energy to create what we see as matter."[77] This is physics in the 21st century.

In Chapter 13 of the Hindu *Bhagavad Gita* (part of the ancient Sanskrit epic the *Mahabharata*), Krishna (representing the Infinite) states: "Whatever is born in this world comes from the union of the Field and the Knower of the Field." Abhayananda clarifies: "But when a man knows that he is the eternal Knower, the experiencer of the Field, and not the Field alone, he knows his eternal freedom."[78]

The event of experiencing and accessing this awareness is sometimes referred to as enlightenment or *satori* (Buddhism),[79] but the truly enlightened bathe in an awareness of connection to Source from moment to moment, being more than just intellectually aware of it. The term for this is God-realization or God-consciousness. Jones commented in *PSIence* that access to, and bonding with the field represents "the Holy Grail of spirituality."[80] Conscious experience of the Unchanging Infinite and the transient manifest as a union is referred to as *Paramatman*: the Supreme Self (or Supreme Soul).[81] It is from this timeless, spaceless metaphysical bedrock that the illusion of the manifest sensory universe we inhabit is hewn.

Before proceeding to the next sub-heading, I want to note that I absolutely do not consider my own unitive experiences to be the "highest" that are possible, or even the highest available to humanity as things currently stand.

Ego Death, Transcendence, and Transformation

Graduation from identifying solely with the world of the five senses represents a massive step in personal evolution. As Evelyn Underhill so succinctly pointed out, the true mystical experience never leaves the human subject at the level at which it found him, compelling him to form new standards for himself and to reach beyond his comfort zone.[82] These experiences "which spiritual genius reports to us":

(a) have a vocational character,

(b) introduce the self into a life which is more and more fully controlled by man's characteristic spiritual activity, prayer, [which is no longer comprised of petitioning some distant deity]

(c) effect a fundamental transformation of personality.[83]

All this precisely mirrors the trends observed in near-death experiencers who have physically died, experienced something of an "afterlife" (time-space), and returned to tell the tale. They thirst for greater knowledge, develop interests in areas of no previous interest to them (such as physics and philosophy), see everything and everyone as part of themselves, develop higher empathy and compassion, become less fixated on status and self-image, more charitably-minded, and cease to fear the specter of physical death, knowing that consciousness is not generated by their brain, but is in fact eternal.

One thing left off the above list, however, is the fact that NDEers—like many who have profound mystical awakenings—also have a tendency to become much more psychic after "crossing over." Some people become notorious for causing electronic equipment or lights in their vicinity to fail—by their mere presence.[84] Others find that the mental content of those around them spills unbidden into their awareness.[85] Still others find themselves with incredible healing abilities—even to the extent that this becomes a new career path![86] Intelligence and self-acceptance increase, following immersion in a realm of total and blissful love and acceptance. Concern about what others think of them diminishes, and materialistic thinking evaporates.[87] Overwhelmingly, the aftermath of the NDE and the mystical experience is profoundly positive (in a way that hallucinations, for instance, cannot account for). Kenneth Ring established in his study *The Omega Project* that this applies also to UFO abductees and "close encounter" experients, despite the often traumatic nature of these latter types of encounters as they unfold in the moment.

To account for the psychospiritual and physiological changes that these groups undergo, Ring postulated that somehow kundalini energy was being activated in these people through these "extraordinary encounters." The result was "a radical, biologically based transformation of the human personality."[88] Other serious researchers have also linked kundalini with NDEs, including Margot Grey and Bruce Greyson.[89] This makes sense of the electrical disturbances caused by some NDEers and abductees. Kundalini—linked intimately to the body's etheric field—is antagonistic to electricity, and Trevor Constable has shown in *Sky Creatures* that the etheric/orgone energy that many

UFOs are composed of does indeed cause the failure of electrical systems in close proximity.

In short, the increasing numbers of people having NDEs, close encounters of the fourth kind, mystical experiences, and awakenings in general (including kundalini awakenings and DNA activations), points to humanity taking a major evolutionary leap. We are becoming something more—and we need to if we want to survive.

The extraordinary experiences discussed above clearly qualify as profound evolutionary triggers. They raise consciousness as no intellectual or religious doctrine could ever hope to do. From the new awareness and thought systems that blossom following such insights, one's choices and actions obviously change accordingly—not on a moralistic basis, but on the basis of a better understanding of what is real, what actually matters and is important in this realm in light of the Eternal that the experient (particularly the mystic) once touched and realizes that they *are*. Realizing you are more than just your ego-persona frees you to change it. No more can you then mistake the map for the territory.[90]

As LaBerge and Rheingold point out, the less we identify with who we *think* we are, the more likely we are to discover who we *really* are. The Sufi master Tariqavi wrote: "When you have found yourself you can have knowledge. Until then you can only have opinions."[91] Goswami states that monistic idealism can be experientially proven through mysticism.[92] We might say: let those who would believe, believe. Let those who would know, *experience*.

To summarize, modern physics combined with psi research, occultism, and mysticism presents us with an infinitely interconnected multiverse, the fundament of which is pure consciousness. As a result of consciousness existing everywhere, all information also exists everywhere simultaneously, so therefore psi experiences don't necessarily require a transfer of information, but a calling forth from the subconscious to the conscious level of pre-existing and omnipresent data in the "field of scalar potentials." Remember: this is the causal* plane consisting of "pure, undifferentiated information" from which emerge matter and energy.[93] Here, concepts like distance, direction, and duality are meaningless. In fact, from the perspective held during my own mystical experiences, even the concept of undifferentiated information doesn't seem very useful; there is only a vast and conscious beingness.

---

* This is not intended in the theosophical sense.

Clarification

There are systematized methods for producing and reproducing such transcendent mystical states. They include, among others, yogic training, various forms of meditation and bio-feedback techniques, psychedelic therapy (which we will look at later), and systems such as Grof's trademarked Holotropic Breathwork (which he developed on the back of years of work in psychedelic therapy), as well as systems like Genpo Roshi's Big Mind Big Heart Zen-based techniques for increasing awareness and even experiencing the universe's infinite oneness.

South American shamans ingested the plant hallucinogen known in the Quecha language of the Incas as *ayahuasca* (a composite word meaning "Vine of the Dead" or the "Vine of Souls"). It contains DMT, an extremely potent and fast-acting hallucinogen that is known to catapult the user into powerful shamanic visions and mystical experiences, and which psychiatrist Rick Strassman calls the Spirit Molecule. (Ayahuasca also contains the alkaloid harmaline, which lengthens the "trip"—something absent in pure DMT, which yields far shorter trips.) A number of plants in the Amazon contain DMT, all of which have long been known to shamans there and utilized to transcend the ordinary sense world.[94]

Under the influence of ayahuasca in South America, researcher and author David Icke found himself—in a state of cosmic consciousness—repeating out loud in a voice not his own: "I am everything and everything is me, I am infinite possibility."[95] Sound familiar? This was accompanied by spontaneous electrical malfunctions in the room: overhead lights turned on of their own accord and a stereo playing music switched off and came back on ten minutes later.

Graham Hancock, a sober and determined independent scholar not intimidated by cultural taboos and customs, had his own sessions with ayahuasca and other hallucinogens that he details in *Supernatural*, knowing that scholarship without personal experience in these areas is empty scholarship. The morning after another ayahuasca session, he confirmed the Hermetic axiom (as above, so below) in a notebook, comparing the worlds of spirit to that of matter. He stated that from the ayahuasca perspective the material world is revealed as being merely a part of a larger multidimensional pattern containing other realities that interpenetrate our own. Due to this interdimensional interpenetration, observable *effects* in our world may be *caused* by factors in other worlds.[96]

Anthropologist Jeremy Narby has shown in his excellent book *The Cosmic Serpent* that for thousands of years, shamans around the world have symbolically depicted DNA helixes in their hallucinogenically inspired art—suggesting that their specially formulated hallucinogenic brews (often ayahuasca, with tobacco used separately) have the effect of reducing their conscious perception to the molecular level where they can gain veracious biological information. A friend of Narby's with a background in molecular biology inspected a painting depicting a hallucinogenic experience by modern Peruvian shaman Pablo Amaringo and identified within it, among other things: triple helixes of collagen; DNA from afar; chromosomes at a specific phase; DNA spools in their nucleosome structure. Other shamans shown Amaringo's work recognised some identical elements within their own visions.[97]

Shamanic substances aside, fasting and detoxification are facets of various disciplines designed to induce heightened states of awareness, not least in the yogic disciplines. I know from experience that severe detoxification can help to awaken latent psychic faculties, such as the ability to see through one's own skin and into one's body (etheric vision). Even Catholicism features a (now much shortened) fast before receiving the Eucharist—a vestige of its mystic and shamanic roots long since forgotten. It has been shown that in all likelihood, the Great Pyramid of Giza was actually used as an initiation chamber designed to induce cosmic consciousness in initiations,[98] among other things.[99] Certain Freemasonic initiatory rituals are also designed to do exactly that (and they do),[100] thus continuing the legacy of the ancient Mystery Schools (and no, not all Freemasons are "Illuminati").

Hancock writes that at the heart of the Upper Paleolithic religion lay a major "shamanic quest." Persisting for over 25,000 years, this massive project systematically, and in controlled settings, employed non-ordinary consciousness states, "to explore and chart the antipodes of the mind."[101] Indeed, it may well have been shamanic exploration of virtual/hyperspatial realms (and even microbiological realms) during this time which precipitated the extraction "of our ancestors from the 5-million-year torpor of the hominid line . . . and set them on a dramatically new course of evolution."[102]

Moreover, in making an observation that will no doubt rankle with amnesic ivory tower academics today, John Major Jenkins has pointed out that in more recent history, "the Eleusinian Mysteries clearly show that something akin to psychedelic shamanism informed the founders of Western science and philosophy."[103] Researchers and co-authors Picknett and Prince go further and state that the scientific revolution was directly inspired by a collection of magical works known as the Hermetica, which were attributed to the legendary Hermes Trismegistus, and believed to preserve the wisdom of the ancient Egyptian pyramid-building civilization. As case in point, they show that *"All [of] Copernicus' radical notions can be found in the Hermetica."*[104]

Saints, mystics, and sages throughout the millennia have variously experienced their own transtemporal and transspatial states such as the ones we have described, giving them insight into the most profound of truths, that we are "god" itself, or as Australian author Aletha Warton put it, "We are a story god tells itself." If we are "god," and we must be, for there is no one and no thing outside of the Infinite, then we are telling *ourselves* that story. "What is this universe?" asks Pinchbeck rhetorically in *2012: The Return of Quetzalcoatl*. "It is a poem that writes itself. It is a song that sings itself into being. This universe has no origin and no end."[105] It is a self-reference cosmology. Or, as the Kalahari Bushmen told Laurens van der Post, "There is a dream dreaming us."[106]

Tripartite Truth

Rupert Sheldrake, in seeking for an answer to the ultimate origins of our universe (and the "morphic fields" which shape its phenomena and processes), turned to David Bohm's concepts of the implicate order, explicate order, and the fundamental unifying ground enveloping them both—a sort of dynamic hologram from which they both emerge, which Bohm termed the "holomovement."

For our purposes, the implicate order is equivalent to the "aether" concept, or Larson's time-space from which the explicate order (our space-time) unfolds or emerges. It is characterized by a "nonlocal flavour," an unbroken wholeness. The concept of objective spatial orientation or distance here is more or less meaningless, since Larson's thesis has it that you now exist in a temporal reference frame, not dissimilarly to Bohm's model, wherein "all places and all times are, we might say, merged, so that what happens in one place will interpenetrate what happens in another place."[107] As noted, this is the realm of "mind": "the actual structure, function, and activity of thought" are here.[108]

The "holomovement," the unitive ground underlying and enfolding both of these relative reciprocal (explicate/implicate) realities, is, as noted, known by yogis and other mystics as Brahman, the Absolute, God, and so on. In this model, any event or entity from our relative world of form in space-time (explicate order) is "an abstraction from an unknown and undefinable totality of flowing movement"—the universal flux dubbed the "holomovement."[109]

This fundamental ground is primary, self-existent, eternal, infinite, beginningless, and changeless (at least insofar as we think of change), and it "carries" within it both relative realities of time-space (implicate order) and manifest space-time (explicate order). My own major non-dualistic mystical

134

experiences seem to match reasonably well with Bohm's concept of the holomovement (they certainly don't match the time-space idea, wherein sense reception and therefore subject-object awareness—duality—can still exist, albeit in modified form).

Thus (momentarily setting aside the notion of multiple implicate orders, for the purpose of simplicity), we now have a three-tiered holistic view of ourselves and reality at large. Luckman provides a useful schema for visualising this idea.[110] In the top tier is primary non-dualistic consciousness/the Absolute/Brahman/God/the Infinite/holomovement; in the second tier emerging from this is the aether/zero point field/Larson's "time-space"/Bohm's "implicate order." Luckman also refers to this as the "sound domain", where, in his compelling model, "sonic" torsion/spin fields operate to ultimately create light and matter in the explicate order/light domain of our space-time (third tier)—sound being more fundamental than light.

If the reports of mystics and shamans through the ages are any indication, the truth about what R.A. Wilson reluctantly referred to as "deep reality"—though we may conceptualize it in different ways—clearly does not need a defence; it does not require someone to shelter and protect it through threats of eternal damnation, excommunication, debunking, the loss of one's job, prestige, reputation, or research grants. Truth does not alter its constitution to bend to the transient whims of our faiths, dogmas, fashionable scientific paradigms, and idle assumptions. Rather, our awareness of truth morphs according to the extent to which our "spiritual awareness" has unfolded from within. Besides this, there is always information available that hints at the greater "spiritual reality" and the power of the Perennial Wisdom. We ignore it to our own detriment.

The noted 20th-century logician Ludwig Wittgenstein, in his last book *On Certainty*, gave primacy to experience over theory, finally conceding that, "The solution to the riddle of life in space and time lies outside space and time."[111] Is this not what the mystic has always said?

I cannot be awake,
For nothing looks to me as it did before,
Or else I am awake for the first time,
And all before has been a mean sleep. —Walt Whitman

A mystic is a man who has partly "come to." —Colin Wilson (1979)

6

THE OCCULT AETHER

The reality is that physical existence arose from non-material existence, as the
physics of the Aether Physics Model clearly reveals. —David Thomson

There is nothing that smacks of incorrectness quite so much as the concept of
"political correctness" itself. Taboos are the culture mind's way of hiding from itself
and they have no place in science. —Author

Occult Chemistry: Leadbeater and Besant

From 1895 to 1933, Annie Besant (1847–1933) and Charles Leadbeater (1847–
1934) conducted clairvoyant investigations into all the known elements and
certain compounds to observe the "fundamental building blocks" that composed
them as well as their general structure. This involved the apprehension of visual
information at micro levels (subquantum in fact), far beyond the ability of the
eyes to perceive. The term for this kind of clairvoyant perception today is "micro-
psi" (Besant and Leadbeater referred to it as "magnifying clairvoyance"), and
it rendered accessible to the clairvoyant investigators a world that physics had
yet to discover. Their clairvoyant observations of the elements bore spectacular
and compelling results, as we will see. The initial investigations were collected
and published in the first edition of *Occult Chemistry* in 1908. A reprint of the
1908 material was issued in 1919 as the second edition of *Occult Chemistry*. The

sum total of Besant and Leadbeater's clairvoyant observations of the chemical elements were collected and published posthumously in a third edition of *Occult Chemistry* in 1951.

An article entitled "Occult Chemistry" appeared in *Lucifer* in 1895 (the year Leadbeater and Besant began their collaboration) and was reprinted as a separate pamphlet in 1905. In it, three chemical elements, hydrogen, nitrogen, and oxygen, were clairvoyantly examined and their analyses presented tentatively to the public by Besant and Leadbeater. Hydrogen, the first chemical atom selected for analysis, and possessing the lowest atomic weight, was found to be composed of a total of 18 smaller entities. Clairvoyantly, it was seen to consist of six small bodies, contained in an egg-like form (Figure 6.1). According to Leadbeater/Besant, it rotated with great rapidity on its own axis, vibrating at the same time, and the internal bodies performed similar gyrations. "The whole atom spins and quivers, and has to be steadied before exact observation is possible," they wrote. The six little bodies are arranged in two sets of three, forming two triangles that are not interchangeable. Further, the six bodies are not all alike; they each contain three smaller bodies—each of these being an ultimate physical atom—but in two of them the three atoms are arranged in a line, while in the remaining four they are arranged in a triangle.[1]

Figure 6.1 The hydrogen micro-psi atom, as observed by Besant and Leadbeater

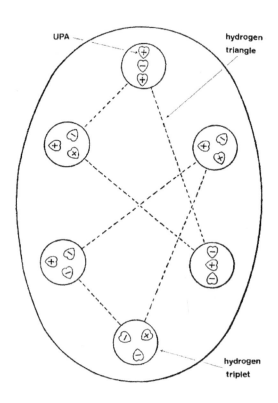

The UPAs are the heart-shaped objects designated a plus or minus sign denoting either an inflow (–) or outflow (+) of energy.

Source: *Occult Chemistry* by Annie Besant and C.W. Leadbeater.
© The Theosophical Publishing House, Adyar, Chennai-600 020. India http://www.ts-adyar.org & http://www.adyarbooks.com.

The Ultimate Physical Atom

As noted, in 1895 when physical atoms were still thought to be the most basic unit of matter, in the early stages of their investigation Leadbeater and Besant observed that hydrogen was not a unity but was composed of 18 smaller units. These smaller units they dubbed an "ultimate physical atom" (UPA), and later took to referring to them as *anu* (singular and plural)—the Sanskrit term for this new entity. They had no way to determine the exact size of the UPA but they found that it existed in two varieties: positive and negative (or Yin and Yang). The positive and negative aspects wound around each other in opposite directions (somewhat like the snakes on the caduceus, or the helical structure of DNA), forming the UPA.[2]

According to Besant and Leadbeater, the UPA was a very complex entity, with only its main characteristics provided in the diagram. "It is composed entirely of spirals, the spiral being in its turn composed of spirillae, and these again of minuter spirillae."[3] In addition to this reference to the subatomic fractality of "matter," they correctly declared that the Anu was definitely *not the electron*. The spirals composing the UPA, if unwound, would actually be found to be circles or strings—twisted around on themselves many times to create the helical form depicted.

Oxygen was found to consist of 290 minor atoms and nitrogen of 261. This is where it gets even more interesting. When Besant and Leadbeater divided the number of UPAs in oxygen by the number of UPAs comprising hydrogen (18), they arrived at 16.11, almost exactly the atomic weight of the oxygen atom (16). This procedure yielded the same precision with nitrogen, an even more complex structure than oxygen, and therefore that much more challenging to apprehend clairvoyantly for the occultists. In fact, this uncanny precision continued right through the entire table of known elements of the time (minor human counting errors notwithstanding).

Although science had not identified such a thing as the ultimate physical atom, Besant and Leadbeater had identified this tiny entity as composing physical atoms. Moreover, by using hydrogen as the standard (being the first element in the periodic table—itself being composed of 18 UPA), they were able to ascertain the atomic weight of the elements by dividing the number of UPA they observed by 18. Should Besant and Leadbeater have been merely "delusional cranks," we should not expect this kind of amazing result. Their "ability to deduce the accepted atomic weights of the elements from the number of UPAs they observed was the only thing *Occult Chemistry* had in common with the chemistry of 1895."[4]

Noteworthy is the way the UPA was depicted by Leadbeater/Besant as being created by an upwelling of force from a higher-dimensional source—just as in the hyperdimensional physics advocated by Wilcock, Hoagland, and others researching aether physics. The models of physics on the cutting edge have been left with no choice but to incorporate other dimensions or "levels" of reality to account for today's scientifically observable phenomena. Furthermore, Leadbeater and Besant's clairvoyant analysis provides intimate and detailed verification of the hyperdimensional spin forces embedded in the "aether." They vividly validated the centuries-old yogic teaching that a UPA is a "little whirlpool" in the aether, the ancient Sanskrit word *Vritta* meaning whirlpool, and being used to indicate waves or vibrations of mind, forming "thought."[5]

How They Arrived at the UPA

Leadbeater and Besant explained:

> Any gaseous chemical atom may be dissociated into less complicated bodies; these, again, into still less complicated . . . [T]he fourth dissociation gives the ultimate physical atom. *This may vanish from the physical plane*, but it can undergo no further dissociation on it.[6] (emphasis added)

Note that in their description of the UPA is a hint of multidimensional behaviour (this becomes relevant shortly). Interestingly, in 1888, the co-founder of theosophy (it was founded in 1875), Helena P. Blavatsky, pre-empting Leadbeater and Besant by at least seven years, explained in *The Secret Doctrine* that, even just on the next higher plane (etheric), what then-current science considered an undecomposable unity would—to higher perception—prove to be very complex. Water, for example, would feature "many other constituents" besides just hydrogen and oxygen.[7]

Thus, as theosophists, Leadbeater and Besant would have expected the composition of the elements they clairvoyantly inspected (having obtained some hard-to-get samples via Sir William Crookes) to have been much more complex than the scientists of their time believed. They were right. Believe it or not, there appears to have been another clairvoyant ahead of the game. At a time when Newton (himself a Hermeticist, though not clairvoyant) was arguing that matter was composed of impenetrable atoms given motion by outside forces, Emmanuel Swedenborg taught that matter was made up of a series of particles in ascending order of size, each of which was composed of a closed vortex of energy which spiraled at "infinite" speeds to give the appearance of solidity.[8] The sub-atomic structure of matter was supposedly also well known even to the ancient Hindus.[9]

Two types of UPAs were observed by Besant and Leadbeater (Figure 6.2), and they were identical in every way except "the direction of their whorls and of the force which pours through them. In the one case force pours in from the 'outside,' from fourth-dimensional space [aether], and passing through the atom, pours into the physical world ['male']. In the second, it pours in from the physical world, and out through the atom into the 'outside' again, i.e., vanishes from the physical world."[10] (This was the "female" UPA.)

Figure 6.2 The two forms of the UPA

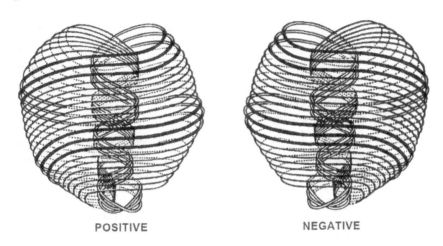

POSITIVE   NEGATIVE

Source: *Occult Chemistry* by Annie Besant and C.W. Leadbeater.
© The Theosophical Publishing House, Adyar, Chennai-600 020. India http://www.ts-adyar.org & http://www.adyarbooks.com.

In agreement with present-day aether researcher Paul LaViolette, Yurth states in *Seeing Past the Edge* that these two opposite or mirror image particles constitute what we now refer to as matter and anti-matter states,[11] which makes sense in light of Leadbeater and Besant's comments that the positive/male UPA flows its creative energy outwards into our reality while the negative/female (anti-matter) counterpart transmutes energy from our reality back into the aether. Leadbeater and Besant said that if the higher-dimensional energy flow was stopped even momentarily, the whole manifest universe would disappear, "as a cloud melts away in the empyrean. It is only the persistence of that flow which maintains the physical basis of the universe."[12]

LaViolette (among many others) has vindicated our two eminent occultists on this point, agreeing that without this constant flow the subatomic particles and energy waves composing our physical universe would gradually dissipate, disolving [*sic*] into a state of uniformity. What would remain would be the ever-present, vast, and unfathomable multi-dimensional consciousness, of which we are a part, and whose now featureless calm "surface" had once generated our beautiful physical universe.[13]

Physicist Nassim Haramein also supports this view, stating that "without spin, none of reality can come to exist. All things spin!" Haramein agrees that "spin is fundamental to creation and objects that appear to be inanimate exist solely because spinning atoms within allow the objects to radiate, and hence, appear in our reality."[14] Yurth adds: "The fields that operate to organize atomic structures are the products of spin vortices—it is the spinning dynamic that creates polarity in all its aspects."[15]

How did Leadbeater and Besant (and Swedenborg) know with such certainty so far in advance of science that our "physical" universe's source of origin are the nonphysical dimensions which have only recently begun to be accepted as existing in mainstream science? How could they have understood back then that aetheric spin dynamics and angular momentum—which they referred to as *Fohat*, the "life force" being "breathed" by the Logos—whirl matter (vortices in the aether/koilon) into existence? (Even if we grant the possibility that Leadbeater and Besant gleaned their information from obscure ancient Hindu sources, the question remains: how did the Hindus know all this?) Fohat, the theosophists said, "digs holes" (or vortices) in space, and those holes, being the absence of the aetheric medium, are what we imagine to be solid matter.

Summing things up rather succinctly, Lipton and Bhaerman state that the quantum physicists' invisible energy field that shapes matter has the same characteristics as the formative fields metaphysicians refer to as "spirit."[16]

The ultimate physical atom Besant and Leadbeater described as a sphere, slightly flattened, with a depression at the point where the force flows in, causing a "heart-like" form. "Each atom is surrounded by a field," they wrote, "formed of the atoms of the four higher planes, which surround and interpenetrate it."[17] If this is accurate, then etheric, astral and mental particles are of increasingly large size (physicists are searching for these "super particles" without realising they have already been unofficially discovered), though at the same time, the two occultists explained that further subdivision of UPAs themselves would reveal even tinier astral components on the astral plane.

Besant and Leadbeater's depiction of the UPA was fundamentally toroidal and way ahead of their time: "It turns incessantly upon its own axis, spinning like a top; it describes a small circle with its axis, as though the axis of the spinning top moved in a small circle; it has a regular pulsation, a contraction and expansion, like the pulsation of the heart."[18]

Spin was first proposed in physics 30 years later by Goudsmit and Uhlenbeck in 1925 and was confirmed in electrons by Phipps and Taylor in 1927. The circular precessional motion described by the axis of the spinning UPA would later become known in physics as Larmor precession. Though the expansion and contraction (radial pulsation) described by Leadbeater and Besant is still unknown to physicists today, LaViolette points out that this description is quite plausible in the context of ancient aether physics.[19] The UPA's spinning motion is common to globules in complex plasmas,[20] and as we will see in Chapter 9, many of Leadbeater and other metaphysicists' clairvoyant observations can be accounted for in light of plasma dynamics. For instance, when exposed to an electric current the UPAs as depicted by Besant and Leadbeater in 1919 arranged themselves in parallel rows of "particle chains"—just like globules in complex plasma, as illustrated by A. Piel et al.[21] In this UPA formation the depression of one UPA received the etheric flow of its neighboring particle and then passed it out through its own apex, and so on.

In *Occult Chemistry* Leadbeater refers to the UPA as having a certain level of apparent consciousness. Wilcock's model states that the aether is comprised of a "vast sea of [toroidal] energy 'units'" unbound by the constraints of space and time as we think of them, which he refers to as Consciousness Units. Their size can vary from ultra-subatomic to cosmic; the universe could have a toroidal form.[22] This was an idea also advocated by Bentov. The UPA, therefore, would be an example of a small-scale consciousness unit, and our best occultists and mystics all seem to agree that the universe is indeed conscious at all levels. It is interesting that David Bohm's research into plasmas yielded the observation that electrons in a plasma configuration began to act as if they were part of a larger, interconnected whole, so much so that he frequently had the impression that the electron sea was alive in some sense.[23] At "deeper" levels of reality the presence of conscious intelligence becomes even more obvious.

While Wilcock states that the aether's substance naturally forms itself into a spherical formation because of the near-uniformity of the aetheric pressure on all sides, as well as the fact that it is the most "harmonic" topology, he acknowledges that changing energy densities in the aether can cause these spheres to warp to some extent. For instance, they may stretch and flatten to create a donut-like shape, otherwise known as the torus, a model employed by Wilcock and Haramein[24] and in string theory.[25]

In the human body, we find the toroidal structures of the *chakras* (Sanskrit for "wheel") to be nested within one another. The "wheel" effect of a chakra is apparently given by the fact that the seer is looking down the "barrel" of a torus' central tube—an area of intense energy. (We look at the irrefutable proof of the human energy field and chakras in Chapter 9.) It is interesting to note briefly at this point that one of the higher-order structures DNA can shape itself into is the toroid. Glen Rein has proposed that this allows it to sense subtle energies in the environment, suggesting that "toroidal DNA acts as a transducer converting subtle [torsion or scalar] energy into conventional EM energy which is then radiated from the DNA to produce a variety of intracellular events at the biochemical level."[26]

Other examples of consciousness units (CUs) within Wilcock's model include ball lightning, vacuum domains, all subatomic "particles," planets, and much more. There is also extensive evidence in ancient shamanic and spiritual literature that people in altered states of consciousness, or participating in shamanic initiatory rites, or having OBEs, have experienced these massive CUs in other densities of existence. They obviously did not use the term "consciousness unit" but most often employed the metaphor of the tree. Thus, the observed tube became the "trunk" and the outstreaming energy flowing from the top of the torus became "foliage." The downward outstreaming energy became "roots." The cosmic tree or universal tree (among other metaphors, including "egg") became widely used terminology and part of many cultures' cosmologies (such as the Norse cosmology with *Yggdrasil*[27]—an image employed in the recent Thor movie in scenes inside the "Bifrost," the vortex/Einstein-Rosen bridge generator the Asgardians use for teleportation). There are even clear indications in Hindu art that the artists are depicting—in anthropomorphized terms—the torus/CU.[28]

On top of this, contemporary authors such as near-death experience researcher P.M.H. Atwater have encountered the torus in their own NDEs. Atwater described her vision as two colossal, rapidly spinning cyclonic vortices, one inverted over the other in an hourglass shape. The one on top spun clockwise and the one below counterclockwise. This very much captures the form of the toroidal structure. Inside the top cyclone Atwater saw herself— with all her past and future selves superimposed over it, all living their lives simultaneously. Each entity was connected to all others by "bubbly threads of brilliant light that formed a fabric netting or web."[29] The bottom cyclone perfectly mirrored the top.

It is of interest that Atwater perceived that alterations made to the overall "pattern" of a personal scenario would instantly affect past and future selves— as well as those of other people; this is a view of time and causality accepted by many physicists. From her "outer-dimensional" perspective, Atwater could look at all of her many timelines at once as they occupied the same space (almost as if her perception of time became infinite). But from *inside* a cyclone/torus, one's perception would return to that of a singular lifetime—and the cosmos would become seemingly infinite in space once more. Viewed from outside, our space-time reality appears finite. Thus it is valid to say that our universe is both finite and infinite—depending on your frame of reference.

Vindication via Stephen Phillips

In the late 1970s Dr. Stephen Phillips, then a physics graduate student at the University of California, happened across some of the diagrams from *Occult Chemistry*. Contrary to what we might expect of most physicists, he took a serious interest in the material, and the end result was a major technical validation of the data obtained by Leadbeater and Besant. Phillips discovered that "Besant and Leadbeater's clairvoyant descriptions of the chemical elements are completely consistent with the Quark, Quantum Chromodynamic and Super-String theories of modern subatomic physics."[30] This he details in depth in his 1980 book *The Extra-Sensory Perception of Quarks*, in which Phillips reconciles *Occult Chemistry* with modern physics. Because of his work, "*Occult Chemistry* now stands as a glittering testimony to the validity of Besant and Leadbeater's claims."[31]

To clarify, a UPA's "whorls" *are* the strings of modern string theory. Phillips suggests, based on comparisons between the occultists' whorls and the "strings" of string theory, that a whorl "is a closed, 26-dimensional, *bosonic** string (the reported presence of *spherical* 'bubbles in koilon' in 7th-order spirillae imply that whorls extend *beyond* the sixth, compactified dimension, so that they *must* be 26-, not 10-, dimensional strings)," and also that "[t]he UPA is a subquark state of a superstring composed of ten strings, i.e. the superstring is itself a composite object."[32]

So, Stephen Phillips has reinterpreted Besant and Leadbeater's observation to be not those of atoms, but of subquarks and quarks. The notion of quarks was only introduced into modern physics in 1964, decades after these pioneers, by Gell-Mann and Zweig.[33] Quarks are the building blocks of so-called "elementary" particles, and are generally accepted as existing by the scientific community today.

---

* Bosons are massless or non-substantial particles: photons, gluons, and gravitons, for instance.

However, Phillips' model is actually a *sub*quark (or composite quark) model. In it subquarks make up quarks, quarks make up elementary particles (protons, etc.), elementary particles make up atoms, and so on. Thus, Phillips has identified the UPAs as subquarks, and, as DeGracia reports in *Beyond the Physical*, he calls his subquarks "omegons" to indicate that they are the final and smallest form of physical matter (omega is the final letter of the Greek alphabet). Thus, Phillips has shown, through rigorous quantitative procedures, that *"the sub-quark combinations predicted by his model are almost in exact agreement with the detailed structures presented by Besant and Leadbeater."*[34] He has successfully correlated the structure of the UPA with "superstring" models: the UPA itself is the "superstring" of modern subatomic physics.

However, please note: the only way in which Phillips could get the numbers generated by his theory to match the actual observations of Besant and Leadbeater was to infer that when they were observing the subquark structure of an atom, they were not observing one atom but *two* atoms that had somehow fused together—as a result of their interference with and observations of these entities—to create a diatomic arrangement. For Phillips, this might have resulted from the spreading of the particles' wave packets/de Broglie waves caused by the mental stabilization of the particles exerted by the theosophists, removing the uncertainty in their momentum, therefore increasing the uncertainty of their spatial locations, so they might interact. From a slightly different angle, the procedure, in effect, may have "teased out" some of the inherent nonlocality of the particles' de Broglie waves/wave packets so as to influence their locations in space-time, causing this interaction.

> [E]ach particle would become so delocalized that there would now be just as much chance of finding it near an adjacent atomic nucleus as there was in finding it in the much smaller space occupied by the nucleus prior to its coming under observation . . . The coupling of highly delocalized particles in neighboring nuclei and their aggregation into larger bound states would lead to the formation of a quasi-nuclear system of multi-subquark and multi-quark bound states—precisely what analysis of MPAs reveals.[35]

The clairvoyantly observed structure of micro-psi atoms (MPAs) consisted of two overlapping triangular formations, with each triangle containing nine UPAs, while the contemporary view of hydrogen is of a lone electron orbiting a nucleus of one proton. However, from the viewpoint of modern quark theory, that lone proton is actually an arrangement consisting of three quarks. Phillips further claims that each quark is in turn made up of three subquarks, meaning the hydrogen atom consists of nine subquarks. Because in Besant and Leadbeater's hydrogen there were two triangles each of nine UPAs, Phillips' conclusion is that each triangle must correspond to an atom of hydrogen as understood by modern science, meaning that the hydrogen structure observed by Besant and Leadbeater was actually made up of two atoms of hydrogen.

In the end there are far too many correspondences between what Besant and Leadbeater observed and what is now scientifically known about subatomic behaviour to dismiss their work. "The shapes they described, the fact that they observed isotopes of elements before isotopes were widely recognized in science* . . . and a host of other relevant observations—*all of these are ideas that were completely unknown to the science of their day.*"[36]

---

* For example, Leadbeater and Besant discovered something they called meta-neon in 1907 (reported in 1908) which was confirmed in 1912 by Professor Francis W. Aston, inventor of the mass spectrograph, who gave it the same name, perhaps in homage to the theosophists, and he even made direct reference to their work in *Occult Chemistry* in his 1913 address to the British Association. This "new" gas was ultimately deemed an isotope of neon, initially by radio-chemist Frederick Soddy. In 1922 Aston won the Nobel Prize for his work and in his acceptance speech neglected to mention who originally observed the isotope of meta-neon, as well as removing all references to *Occult Chemistry* in his 1922 textbook, *Isotopes*. The history of neon-22 and isotopes was sanitized. (Jeff Hughes, *Occultism and the Atom.*) Curiously, when Aston was informed in 1943 that Besant and Leadbeater had beaten science to the discovery of meta-neon by five years by their colleague C. Jinarajadasa, he suspiciously replied that he wasn't interested in theosophy! (Phillips, *Extrasensory Perception of Subatomic Particles.*)

Table 6.1 provides a partial overview of Leadbeater and Besant's clairvoyant observations as compared with subsequent scientific discoveries.

Table 6.1. Some micro-psi anticipations of scientific discoveries and ideas

Micro-psi	Science
1895: positive and negative hydrogen triplets observed in MPAs (micro-psi atoms). *[Matter and antimatter sub-quarks ostensibly discovered and named by occultists UPAs. Antimatter unheard of as yet.]*	*[1928: Dirac predicts existence of antimatter; 1932: Carl Anderson discovers anti-matter (the positron) experimentally.]* 1964: quark model proposes nuclei are made up of positive u quarks and negative d quarks. *[1990s: 450 scientists confirm the existence of sub-quarks.]*
1908: meta neon (number weight = 22.33); axes of UPAs aligned by electric field;	1912: neon-22 discovered; 1933: magnetic monopoles discussed by Dirac;
UPAs depicted as joined by "lines of force" of "a magnetic nature";	string model of hadrons;
some UPAs shown as endpoints of single lines of force;	quarks regarded as ends of strings or flux tubes;
Y-shaped configurations of lines of force ending on UPAs; UPA consists of closed curves; 1st-order spirillae wind about six successively smaller circles;	1975: baryons regarded as Y-shaped strings with quarks at their ends; 1982: closed superstrings considered; 6-d torus studied as model of compactified space;
1909: "illinium" (number weight = 146.66); "masurium" (number weight = 100.11);	1945: promethium- 147 discovered; 1937: technetium-99 discovered;
1924: precessional motion of "hydrogen triangles" (protons);	1924: spin of nuclei suggested;
1932: "element 85" (number weight = 221.00); "element 87" (number weight = 222.55);	1940: astatine-219 discovered; 1939: francium-223 discovered.

My comments are in italicized brackets. Source: Stephen M. Phillips, Extrasensory Perception of Subatomic Particles. *Journal of Scientific Exploration,* 9(4), pp 489–525, 1995.

Thanks to Phillips we know that to comprehend the finer points of *Occult Chemistry* one requires an advanced understanding of modern physics. Besant and Leadbeater described the quantum nature of physical matter in 1895, exactly as science would 30 years later and more. Even conceding that Besant and Leadbeater erroneously thought they were observing regular atoms, we still must ask how they were able to document the form, structure, and interplay of quarks and subquarks so far in advance of modern physics.

To gain some comprehension of how controversial a terrain we tread here, the existence of subquarks was only recently scientifically accepted, and even then not unanimously. Yurth reports that in the 1990s an armada of 450 scientists confirmed the existence of subquarks with an "unprecedented" level of scrutiny, and still "physicists at the American Physical Society, MIT, Princeton, and Columbia University succeeded in suppressing the publication of the research data in such mainstream publications as *Scientific American, Physics Letters, Physics Review* and *Nature*."[37]

Regardless, Besant and Leadbeater were obviously capable of perceiving the fundamental nature of matter using the siddhis. According to Leadbeater, there is a tube-like structure that protrudes from the Ajna, or third-eye chakra of the etheric body and it is by means of using this tube as an organ of vision that one can exercise micro-psi. As we can see, there is good reason to believe him. This psi faculty/ability is one of the siddhis Patanjali wrote about in his *Yoga Sutras* circa 400 BC

Another interesting thing about subquarks highly pertinent to our occult leitmotif: the subquark's track looks the way it does because in our space-time continuum the particle exists and then does not exist, exists and then does not exist.

> With the discovery of the sub-quark, we observed for the very first time a scientifically verified instance of multi-dimensional behavior in a measurable physical component. The behavior of the sub-quark is uniquely profound—in the rarified environment of the particle accelerator, the sub-quark exists-disappears-exists-disappears with a consistent, repeated, predictable frequency pattern . . . [38]

Leadbeater and Besant had stated that the UPA—like the subquark today—could vanish from its plane but could undergo no further subdivision. This is truly the most fundamental aspect of physical matter at our density level. The scientific verification of Leadbeater and Besant's observations clearly indicates the human ability to peer into domains "non-existent" to our ordinary senses and science's conventional equipment—domains our most fundamental known "particles" venture rhythmically in and out of. Yurth comments that this brings us "literally to the Edge of creation."[39] Do pause and let all of that sink in for a moment.

It is, as DeGracia notes, very interesting to observe the following statement found in the first chapter of the second edition of *Occult Chemistry* (1919): "Many physicists, though not all, will resent the idea of treating the ether of space as atomic."

> [At the time] physicists generally thought that matter, space, and time formed a continuum, this being the [inert and mechanical lumeniferous ether] of nineteenth-century physics. It was the

quantum revolution that occurred after 1925 that overthrew this notion in science. Today, matter is thought of as discrete (or "atomic" as used in the quote above). The [Leadbeater and Besant] quote above clearly shows that Theosophical occultists held that matter was fundamentally discrete, and that they knew via direct clairvoyant observation.[40]

We should emphasize, however, that while mainstream particle physics conceives of atoms and quanta as isolated entities floating in the zero point field/vacuum, Leadbeater and Besant's depictions of UPAs rightly specify the structure of the UPA as being a toroidal "extension" of the aether itself. Leadbeater said that it cannot really be said to have a "wall" of its own. Its "wall" is the pressed back "space" (which they called "koilon," a Greek word meaning hollow). The force of the UPA "clears itself a space, pressing back the undifferentiated matter of the plane, and making to itself a whirling wall of this matter."[41]

On his website, Paul LaViolette references Leadbeater and Besant's UPA and says: "The whirling ether flux, which they saw flowing into and out from the center of the particle, matches the predictions of subquantum kinetics."[42] He further says: "Both in the psychically 'observed' Anu and in the dissipative structures described in ancient mythology and modern systems physics, two particle polarities and [a]ether flow directions are possible."[43] This is something Wilcock writes of (and supports with extensive evidence) in the Convergence series; the notion of two nested, counter-rotating spherical torus fields.

The UPA, then, is more a flow pattern, a structure of standing waves, than a particle. Subatomic particles have become standing waves visualized as "vortices of energy resembling nano-tornadoes."[44] Vortical structures similar to those depicted by Leadbeater and Besant have been observed at larger scales in plasma physics experiments. For example, the plasma focus device produces spherical plasma vortices measuring about .5 mm across, composed of eight or 10 electric current plasma filaments twisted into a helical donut-shaped structure closely resembling the UPA.[45]

Einstein and Koilon

Einstein advocated rejecting the concept of an aether in 1910, and thousands of scientists subsequently did so—often vehemently and without looking at the notion rationally. Some still think that Einstein's relativity theories "disprove" the aether idea. But in 1920 Einstein acknowledged that the existence of the aether would not contradict the special theory of relativity. And in 1924 he wrote: "[I]n theoretical physics, we cannot get along without the ether, i.e., a continuum assigned physical properties, because the general theory of relativity . . . excludes direct long-range action; and each theory of short-range action assumes the presence of continuous fields and, consequently, the existence of the 'ether.'"[46]

He further stated that space without (a)ether would be "unthinkable; for in such space there not only would be no propagation of light, but also no possibility of existence for standards of space and time."[47] Put simply, Einstein's space-time "fabric" in his theory of general relativity is the aetheric medium, and its flow/movement produces what relativity somewhat misleadingly calls the "curvature" of space.

Leadbeater and Besant actually preempted Einstein in speaking of the aether and the "substance" they named koilon—an extraordinarily dense substance that appeared (they stressed it was probably just an appearance) to be homogeneous. This koilon filled all of what was typically regarded as empty space. In other words, Besant and Leadbeater had apparently identified clairvoyantly the aetheric medium (known previously under a different guise as the "lumeniferous ether") and given it the rather obscure name of koilon, which Leadbeater refers to as "the true aether of space."[48]

Space to Leadbeater and Besant was a plenum—the view adopted by contemporary physics. They said (and this is where Einstein comes in): "[W]hat we call matter is not koilon but the absence of koilon . . . [T]o comprehend the real conditions we must modify our ideas of matter and space—modify them almost to the extent of reversing our terminology. Emptiness has become solidity and solidity emptiness."[49]

Einstein would famously proclaim that "form is condensed emptiness." In *The Tao of Physics* Capra described particles as "local condensations of the [quantum] field; concentrations of energy that come and go . . ." A Buddhist principle stated over 2,500 years ago in *The Heart Sutra* says that "Form is none other than emptiness and emptiness is none other than form," thus pre-empting Einstein and subsequent physics by two and a half millennia.[50] Leadbeater and Besant were using the word "koilon" instead of zero point field, vacuum, or aether. We now see that the most cutting-edge information available demands we acknowledge the aether model of reality as being fundamental and undeniable, as well as challenging us to consider that "solidity" is actually emptiness: standing waves in the aetheric medium generating enough force to pierce the aetheric veil and enter the third dimension/density.

The analogy Leadbeater and Besant employed was that matter is like bubbles in water. The bubbles force the water back in a spherical shape to produce a region of pressurized emptiness. The bubbles are not water, but the absence of it, and so too is "matter" not the aetheric medium, but the absence of it. The UPA, then, is composed of millions upon millions of "bubbles" in the aether/ koilon. We all know that matter is actually composed of atomic energy that is at least 99% empty space. The less than 1% left is not solid, but rather "arises from the aetheric 'zero-point energy' of consciousness."[51]

It is also interesting to note the apparently enormous pressure that the omnipresent koilon exerted according to our star occultists, who described it as "infinitely dense." In modern science, the Casimir Effect demonstrates that the ZPF/aether/koilon can cause two parallel plates to be pushed towards each other by the aetheric energies with such power that, if they are allowed to touch, they apparently have to be broken to be separated again. (Interestingly, lab experiments have also shown that the Casimir force can be a repulsive force.[52] If held at a tiny distance apart and perfectly parallel, the plates are capable of siphoning small amounts of energy from the aether/ZPF indefinitely. In general, the Casimir energy is proportional to the inverse fourth power of the distance of separation between the plates. This means that the smaller the distance of separation, the larger the energy drawn out of "thin air.")

The Casimir effect was measured precisely in 1996 by Steven Lamoreaux at the Los Alamos National Laboratory, and the attractive force is 1/30,000th the weight of an ant.[53] This does not sound like much pressure, until you consider this force is being generated by so-called "empty space," something that is recognized in science now as a fiction, but which was realized to be so much earlier by occultists and mystics. In an ancient occult treatise, we read of a "colorless spiritual fluid" which

> exists everywhere and forms the first foundation on which our solar system is built . . . As its substance is of a different kind from that known on earth, the inhabitants of the latter, seeing "through it," believe, in their illusion and ignorance, that it is empty space. There is not one finger's breadth of void space in the whole boundless universe.[54]

As former nuclear weapons technician in the US Air Force Henry C. Warren states, "the Casimir effect screams out . . . that a reality still exists to which we are electromagnetically blind. This reality underpins the physics we can 'see.'"[55]

P.M.H. Atwater has had several opportunities to perceive the aetheric medium in altered states of consciousness. As she observed it, the aether varies in contour, being thinner near objects of mass, and thicker farther away.[56] This is totally congruent with the scientific aether models of today and how they account for the ill-conceived "curvature" of space. It is actually a thinning of the spatial fabric itself as it—in the form of what we know as gravity—streams into the center of a body in space to create matter in our EM reality. (And the flow of gravity/aether is the flow of time.[57])

In 1900, in his book *The Astral Plane*, Leadbeater said that, though undetectable to our senses, there is an aetheric pressure, roughly analogous to, but far greater than, the atmospheric pressure. "[I]f science were able to exhaust the [a]ether from a given space, as it can exhaust the air, the one could be proved as readily as the other."[58] Casimir's experiment is the modern experiment demonstrating the very real physical effects of the aether on matter, something along the lines of which Leadbeater had apparently envisioned over a hundred years ago. The technology to conduct Casimir's experiment precisely and also to detect an attractive force 1/30,000th the weight of an ant did not exist until nine decades after Leadbeater lamented the then-unprovable reality of the aether/koilon.

Today it is increasingly well recognized that so-called "physical matter" is actually standing waves, "congealed light," or as David Bohm referred to it, "frozen light" moving in patterns back and forth at less than the speed of light. This is the conclusion reached by Dr. Richard Gerber in *Vibrational Medicine*— that matter is "frozen light"—and Dr. Len Horowitz reaches precisely the same conclusion, stating that humans are "crystallized or precipitated light."[59]

In *The Science of Oneness*, we read that light in the aether "naturally assumes a spherical form [see Figure 6.1 above]. When the form is in motion, it becomes visible to us as a 'photon,' but . . . as a 'standing wave' it can form matter particles, ball lightning and possibly much larger bodies of energy as well."[60]

Leadbeater and Besant had actually stated that a UPA appears initially to micro-psi as a point of light. This may be the kind of light emitted by an individual's etheric body (no "a" to distinguish between personal etheric field and universal aetheric medium/koilon/zero point field) accessible to clairvoyant etheric vision. Einstein once remarked, "we have been all wrong. What we have called matter is energy, whose vibration has been so lowered as to be perceptible to the senses. There is no matter." We can therefore see where comedian Bill Hicks' LSD insight that "all matter is merely energy condensed to a slow vibration" comes from.

Physicist and wave structure of matter (WSM) researcher Milo Wolff wrote: "The Wave Structure of Matter is itself a new exciting forefront of science which displays the *inter-dependence of all matter in the universe* and restores some of the original adventurous spirit of natural philosophy" (emphasis added). In an aetheric model, all matter is interdependent because it all springs from the unified aetheric field. Gabriel LaFreniere is another proponent of the WSM doctrine. He says plainly: "Matter is made of waves. Nothing else exists but the aether." He adds that the notion of "solid" particles is "no longer needed to explain matter. It is even excluded. An electron isn't a metal marble covered in chrome. An electron cannot be made of matter."[61]

Wilcock, in Chapter 2 of his incredible *Shift of the Ages*, listed some facts regarding the aether as it is increasingly known to cutting-edge science. I have included some points of his that highlight and reinforce the research done by Leadbeater and Besant many years ago, validating and confirming their own clairvoyant observations:

- What we have is a fluid-like energy [medium/substrate, known to Besant and Leadbeater as "koilon"] and which exists everywhere throughout the known universe.
- It exists at an extremely high pressure, [y]et, we move through it quite easily, since we are also made of the same "stuff."
- For all practical purposes, the energy itself is conscious, and therefore unifies all the Universe as one conscious life-form—an Ultimate Being.
- This energy can be directly harnessed to produce technologies such as limitless free energy, anti-gravity, and even teleportation.
- All moving (*propagating/dynamic*) waves in this energy medium travel in spirals of various sizes, from very tiny to very large.
- Light is simply one major type of movement of this energy—hence the aether can be thought of as "liquid light" . . .
- There are seven major "densities" or thickness levels of this fluidlike energy medium throughout the Universe, often referred to in esoteric traditions as the "seven heavens."

The Ancient Aether and Infinite Energy

While we can see, even with the mere smattering of evidence provided above, that some sort of unified field (aether) must exist, it is interesting to note that the aether was (and largely still is) thought to have been debunked. However, what we have today is what Bearden refers to as a "Lorentz-invariant, non-material virtual [a]ether,"[62] completely unlike the "lumeniferous aether" idea.

The Greeks referred to the energy that composes the universe as *"aether,"* which is their word for "shine," indicating that it has qualities similar to light—so the idea has been around for a long time. In 1904, Yogi Ramacharaka explained that the centuries-old yogi philosophy held that the "aether" had seven grades of tenuity (the "seven heavens"), the Sanskrit term *Akasha* being applied collectively to these differing grades of matter.[63]

In fact, LaViolette argues effectively in *Genesis of the Cosmos* that dynamic, subquantum entities and the transmuting aether they spontaneously arise within (spontaneous symmetry breaking) were the subjects of various well-known ancient allegorical creation myths dating back thousands of years—most likely as a legacy of an unusually technologically advanced civilization that understood the aetheric science of cosmogenesis (perhaps, we might venture, the same civilization that encoded the atomic mass numbers of certain elements in the ancient Hebrew language thousands of years ago, as Braden details in *The God Code*).

Such myths include the Egyptian Osirian creation myth, the Sumerian creation myth, the Babylonian creation myth (the *Enuma Elish*), the Greek Olympian creation myth, the Phoenician Adonis myth, and the Christian allegory of Christ's parthenogenesis (birth or "self-organization" from the safety of the "virgin womb" in the aether). Even the Tarot—which appears to have come out of Egypt—encodes this ancient creation physics.[64] The same revelations apply to the yin-yang Taoist metaphysics of the Chinese I Ching, and the Zodiac, whose seemingly arbitrary symbolism—unbeknownst to astrologers—allegorically conveys scientific knowledge of aetheric cosmogenesis (when arranged in correct order).

The evidence indicates that the designers of the Zodiac and Egyptian calendar system (to say nothing of the Mayans and other "primitive" peoples) had an intimate knowledge of the galaxy and even identified where its center (the place where its formation began) lay—something only (re)learned by modern astronomers in the last several decades.[65] Even of the description of the layout of the mythical Atlantis as told in the *Critias*, LaViolette says that a systems scientist would immediately recognize a localized dissipative-structure wave pattern.[66] Broadly speaking, LaViolette reports that general system theorists have arrived at a general theory of system genesis that is very similar to the creation physics in ancient myths and lore.

Science requires an essentially aetheric model to account for all observables today.[67] You can even rename the aether "gravity" and still retain essentially the same model. (Doubting Thomases who think the "Michelson-Morley experiment" debunked the aether idea are referred to my article *The Virtual Aether: "Empty Space" Gets an Upgrade* at www.brendandmurphy.com.)

Every exchange of every virtual particle in the aether/ZPF radiates a tiny amount of energy—half a photon's worth, McTaggart reports in *The Field*. But if you add up all the particles of all varieties in the universe constantly popping in and out of our reality, you have a vast, inexhaustible energy source—"all sitting there unobtrusively in the background of the empty space around us, like one all-pervasive, supercharged backdrop." It has been calculated that the total energy of the zero point field exceeds all energy in matter by a factor of 10^{40}, or 1 followed by 40 zeros. As the great physicist Richard Feynman once described, in attempting to give some idea of this magnitude, the energy in a single cubic meter of space is enough to boil all of the oceans of the world.[68] However, Bearden points out that if, unlike most physicists, we account for the time-energy inherent in the vacuum, we get *even more* potential energy, arriving at the order of 10^{127} joules per cubic centimeter.

We can therefore see the extraordinary importance of aether/ZPF research in terms of sustainable energy. If successfully tapped into, zero point energy would free the world from its slavery to oil and other archaic fuel sources forever (and this is actually being done by various inventors and scientists globally). No one would ever have to pay another electricity bill again (this was Tesla's goal, but he was crushed by the rapacious business tycoon J.P. Morgan who wanted to make the world pay for something that should have been free for everyone long ago).

Interestingly, in discussing earlier conceptions of the aether, Sir Oliver Lodge, in the first half of the 20th century, made a very striking estimate of the intrinsic energy of the aether: "The total output of a million-kilowatt power station for thirty million years exists permanently, and at present inaccessibly in every cubic millimetre of space."[69] The opinions of occultists Leadbeater and Besant was that this was probably a gross underestimation of the truth, and today various researchers consider the untapped aetheric/zero point energy to be essentially infinite. Leadbeater and Besant stand vindicated. We must remember that space is never empty, but that we are completely immersed in this aetheric fluid-like medium, swimming in it unawares.

Cambridge University's Dr. Harold Puthoff was one of the first to measure zero point energy using a lead-lined Faraday cage cooled to 0° Kelvin (minus 273° Celsius, a.k.a. "absolute zero"). According to Newtonian physics, at this temperature, with all electromagnetic energy shielded, all molecular and atomic movement should have ceased and no energy should be measured at all. Instead of finding no energy, Puthoff found what he called a "seething cauldron" of energy and henceforth it was given the name zero point energy (ZPE). Instead of being empty, space is actually a plenum—alive with the ceaseless "jiggling" of virtual particles flashing in and out of existence in accordance with Heisenberg's uncertainty principle, never existing long enough to be directly measured.

The term "zero point" derives from the fact that this energy is still present at "absolute zero," where there should be no form of energy remaining; and secondly, the pressures of this energy field usually cancel out to zero, a "vector zero resultant," meaning that this energy applies force (vectors) equally in all directions, and thus to us it has no typically measurable movement or force; ostensibly it cancels itself out (hence, it is referred to as the field of "scalar potential").[70]

"The message is," in the pioneering Harold Aspden's words, "[a]ccept the aether is real and has structure and you can understand how matter is created—but ignore the aether and you live in ignorance!"[71] On this basis, Aspden created a unified physics. In mainstream physics there is the Higgs Ocean, named after Scottish physicist Peter Higgs who conceived the idea of the Higgs ocean and its particulate force-carrier—the Higgs boson—in 1964 while out taking a walk. Like the aether, the Higgs ocean is described as an all-pervading fluid-like field composed of Higgs particles which creates and maintains the physical universe and accounts for the phenomenon of inertia. A scalar field (having magnitude but no direction), it possesses a non-zero energy value, accounts for the mass of particles, and is required to keep the Standard Model mathematically consistent.[72]

In mid-2012—and with much fanfare—the Higgs boson was discovered with a high degree of certainty (it was born out of the chaos of protons being smashed together in the Large Hadron Collider). In Higgs' model it is the specific subatomic particle responsible for providing matter with its mass, and its momentous discovery means that physicists do not have to scrap the standard model altogether[73] (and it also further supports the case for a fluid-like "aetheric" source of creation).

Geometry in the Aether

By collating and synthesizing the work of pioneer grid researchers Bruce Cathie, Carl Munck, Richard Hoagland, the one-time husband and wife team Drs

157

William Becker and Bethe Hagens, Ivan P. Sanderson, and others, Wilcock realized that the sum total of all their work combined was that the primary geometrical shapes of the octave must exist all nested together within the Earth's spherical field, just as they must exist in all fundamental units of existence (consciousness units) at *all* scales (as above, so below: the motto of the holofractal universe).

There is no way for me to fully encapsulate and truly do justice to the brilliant work of these people, or Wilcock's pioneering synthesis of it, but briefly, Wilcock identified what he believes to be the primary geometric forms encoded within the hyperdimensional field of Earth as being a circumscribed octahedron, a circumscribed cube (both of these being first identified by independent scientist Bruce Cathie), two interlaced tetrahedra*, a circumscribed icosahedron (identified initially by Ivan P. Sanderson), a circumscribed dodecahedron (mapped by Nikolai Goncharov, a Muscovite historian, Vyacheslav Morozov, a construction engineer, and Valery Makarov, an electronics specialist. These three scientists worked directly from Sanderson's research), and an icosahedrally derived spherical polyhedron (initially developed by Buckminster Fuller but adapted by Becker and Hagens and applied to the template the Russian researchers had developed from Sanderson's work).

For Wilcock, the Becker/Hagens grid finally "cracked the code" of the Platonic solids' positions on Earth. The grid, overlaid onto the Earth's surface, corresponds rather strikingly with the formation of the planet's landmasses, indicating a hyperdimensional energetic template *guiding the development of the 3D Earth* (and all other planetary bodies). In short, on Earth, the grid controls the positioning of the continental landmasses.[74]

Around the globe, the node points of this grid that touch the surface of the Earth produce anomalies that typically baffle conventional science: anomalies in which alternate dimensions appear to interface with one another (or to put it another way, at these points time-space appears to interface with space-time).

Sanderson tackled huge volumes of data, mostly from anomalous reports declared by hundreds of pilots and mariners, and systematically organized them, proving "beyond a shadow of a doubt that some very interesting anomalies were visible in certain areas of the Earth's oceans"—anomalies such as those being

---

* The fullest exposition of esoteric tetrahedral geometry is in the work of Drunvalo Melchizedek, who spent twenty years drawing the shapes of sacred geometry as they were revealed to him, and expounding the ancient symbol of the Flower of Life. See his two-volume publication *The Ancient Secret of the Flower of Life* (Light Technology Publishing, Flagstaff AZ, 1990–98 and 2000).

commonly reported in the Bermuda Triangle (and other lesser known places). By statistically analyzing the different places where these events occurred on the globe, Sanderson initially identified ten common points of anomalous occurrence. Five of them lined up on the same northern tropical latitude, each longitudinally separated by 72° from the next. The other five were laid out the same in the southern hemisphere, only shifted 20° to the east.[75]

In these geometrically spaced "vile vortices," as Sanderson dubbed them, disappearances (over 1,000 ships and aircraft have vanished in the Bermuda Triangle[76]) and time-warping events occurred as well. Sanderson found evidence for these time-space disturbances in the other vortices besides Bermuda, and when one astute observer pointed out to him that the North and South Poles should be included since they fit the same geometric relationships, Sanderson finally had his "twelve Devil's graveyards."[77] Once the Russian scientists had superimposed the dodecahedral grid over Sanderson's own, they discovered that over 3,300 ancient sites, complexes and monuments (often made from stone, and including the Great Pyramid) were constructed on the grid, indicating that the ancients sought to use the most "coherent" energetic locations to facilitate healing effects, the shielding of gravity, and even time travel.[78]

Further still, all of the giant, rapidly rotating fluid outer planets of our solar system (Jupiter, Saturn, Uranus, and Neptune) possess one other extremely significant attribute consistent with a hyperdimensional energetic model: they all radiate into space more energy than they receive from the sun (in Neptune's case, almost three times this amount).[79] LaViolette refers to this as genic energy, and it is the result of the aether/gravity creating matter in our reality—something conventional models cannot properly account for. (To Nikolai Kozyrev, Russian astronomer and astrophysicist (1908–83), stars were "machines" which obtained their energy from the flow of "time" as it streamed into them.)[80]

On top of this, many entities in our solar system evidence dramatic energetic activity at or close to 19.5° north and/or south of their equatorial line, indicating again that there is a hyperdimensional energy matrix in which all objects in space are immersed and, indeed, created from. The tetrahedral geometry was identified by Richard Hoagland and his colleagues at the Mission Enterprise. Hoagland proved that this geometry was not merely unique to Earth but that it occurred throughout the solar system (and in reality, throughout the universe) (see Figure 6.3).[81]

Various ancient structures on Earth have references to the inscribed tetrahedral geometry built into them, not least the Great Pyramid at Gizeh, which was constructed by a civilization in possession of far greater technical and astronomical knowledge than orthodox Egyptology will admit. The Great Pyramid, not coincidentally, "is built over the single most powerful vortex on the planet, where the lines of the tetrahedron, cube, octahedron, dodecahedron, and icosahedron all cross."[82] Whoever constructed it clearly knew something that was since lost to science for a long time: the secrets of a hyperdimensional physics—a physics of *life*. The revelation that Munck presents us with—while he does not deal with the Platonic solids—is that the ancients, just as we do today, used a 360° system for mapping the planet, which located zero longitude/ the *true* Prime Meridian not in Greenwich, England, but as *running right through the Great Pyramid*.[83]

Figure 6.3 Interlaced tetrahedral geometry identified by Hoagland et al.

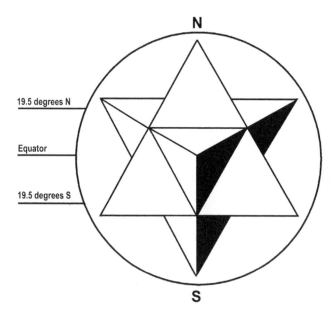

Image credit: Isis Graywood. Contact: igraywood@gmail.com; branchout.com/Isis. Graywood.

The work of Stan Tenen of the Meru Foundation has supplemented that of Hoagland and Wilcock, the latter two of whom have been collaborating for a while now in developing the aether/torsion model. Tenen's research yielded expressions of inscribed tetrahedral geometry on Earth in Ancient

Egyptian hieroglyphic manuscripts, Ancient Hebrew scrolls, Ancient Greek texts, and more, which raised the obvious question of why the ancients viewed circumscribed tetrahedra with such profundity and reverence.[84]

Hoagland's work, of course, has uncovered this tetrahedral geometry in the so-called Monuments of Mars (which include gigantic pyramid structures and a huge face staring out into space), which, according to NASA (Never A Serious Anomaly) were supposed to be merely natural landforms; however, the mathematical studies by Hoagland's team and others such as the late Tom Van Flandern have eliminated the possibility that these forms are merely natural freak occurrences, indicating there is clearly intelligence and purpose behind the mathematics at Cydonia. Certain "debunking" publications of Cydonia images (such as the infamous "cat box") have themselves been debunked and revealed essentially as hoaxes, or calculated disinformation.

The geometric properties of the aetheric medium are becoming evident in other ways too. In 2007, Cassini filmed a large, rotating hexagonal cloud formation with six almost equally straight sides over the north pole of Saturn. Kevin Baines, an atmospheric expert and member of Cassini's visual and infrared mapping spectrometer team at NASA's Jet Propulsion Laboratory, Pasadena, California, described the hexagonal formation as "very strange."[85]

Unmanned Voyager missions had initially imaged this pattern in the 1980s, as Hoagland points out in *The Monuments of Mars*,[86] but these "anomalies" have been somewhat overlooked by scientific orthodoxy, which fails to realize the hyperdimensional implications.

This is not the first case of geometrical formations showing up in weather systems (we have already noted the solar system-wide 19.5° "coincidence" above). Wilcock has also pointed out geometrical forms in storm systems right here on Earth in his Convergence series. Moreover, Stan Tenen's higher-dimensional mathematical topologies actually *predicted* such hexagonal patterns produced by the 3-space projection, in a "working fluid," of two interlocking, rotating, 4-space "hypertetrahedra."[87] In other words, the geometrical form of interlocking tetrahedra in four dimensions results in 3-dimensional forms such as the aforementioned rotating hexagonal patterns.

The Void and the Platonic Solids

In order to create worlds of relativity the Void/Infinite Consciousness had to project itself "outwards." Here is an abridged, simplified, and figurative explanation of the process in terms of sacred geometry. The Void/Spirit projected itself out in straight lines in six directions or the three spatial axes (which in two dimensions looks like a basic asterisk). The next step was to connect the ends of the lines to form a rectangle lying lengthways, so to speak. From there, we continue connecting the lines to form a pyramid/triangle above and below the rectangle/prism, and connect any remaining points to all other points (see Fig 6.4). This formation implies various 3D forms within it, including the octahedron and interlocked tetrahedra.

Spirit then rotates the three axes around the central point of this figure, so the vertices trace the outline/s of a sphere—curved lines represent the feminine principle, and straight represent male. (Hence, the Bible states that "God made man first.") Now Spirit finds itself inside a sphere, and it moves to the surface of it (where it doesn't matter).[88] Thus, the first motion out of the great Void is to move to the surface. From here—oversimplifying—the next move is to create another overlapping circle, forming the vesica piscis. Another five circles/ rotations gives the basis for the tube torus, and a rotational energy vortex has been set up. Another rotation reveals the Egg of Life, and one more yields the figure of the Flower of Life (Figure 6.4).[89]

Drunvalo Melchizedek has shown in detail in *The Ancient Secret of the Flower of Life* that the first stages of cell differentiation in a newly forming fetus follow the fundamental geometrical progression of metaphysical creation, even generating a toroidal form in the process, from which the lungs ultimately develop. The Egg of Life, the Fruit of Life, and the torus are the underlying "informational systems" that create all manifest phenomena, according to Drunvalo.[90]

Figure 6.4 The Flower of Life

From *Nothing in This Book Is True, But It's Exactly How Things Are Third Edition, Revised and Expanded* by Bob Frissell, published by Frog Ltd., distributed by North Atlantic Books, copyright © 1994, 2002 by Bob Frissell. Image use by permission of publisher.

The tube torus is, in Bob Frissell's words, "the primal shape of the universe."[91] Its uniqueness lies in the fact that as a result of its energy twisting and imploding in on itself, it is the only self-sustaining/organizing wave form that is known. Stan Tenen, over more than 20 years of research,

> tracked the spiral of a tube torus out of the middle and took out the shape. He removed the minimum amount of matter to delineate the tube torus and placed it inside a 3-dimensional tetrahedron. He found that by shining a light through it so that the shadow of that shape came out onto a 2-dimensional surface he could generate all the letters of the Hebrew alphabet, exactly as they are written and in order. He also found that by changing the shape to a different position he could project all the Greek letters. Then by changing the position again he could configure all the Arabic letters. He did this simply by moving this particular shape to different positions inside a 3-dimensional tetrahedron.[92]

So it appears that language's roots lie in hyperdimensional or "subtle" time-space geometry, as does all form, ultimately. As Atwater summarizes in *Future Memory*, the tilt of the torus, viewed from different angles as it precesses about its axis, emanates all humanly known colors, basic image designs, and ancient alphabetic characters.[93] (Thus, the torus stores information holographically.)

This is all the more fascinating when we realise that our DNA is the interdimensional interface between these torsion fields existing in time-space/implicate order, and our own space-time reality, and that in the 1990s, a team of linguists led by the pioneering Russian scientist Dr. Peter Gariaev discovered that *the genetic code in "junk" (or "potential") DNA follows uniform grammar and usage rules virtually identical to those of human language.* This research followed J. Delrow's discovery in 1990 that the four nucleotides of DNA inherently form fractal structures closely related to human speech patterns.[94]

Within non-coding DNA segments, scientists have found large numbers of "endlessly repeated sequences with no apparent meaning, and even palindromes, which are words or sentences which can be read in either direction."[95] Hence, linguist Noam Chomsky's observation that the development of human language could not have occurred as a straightforward step from animal communication; it is a true example of emergence[96]—emergence into our space-time from the twisting/spiraling energy fields in time-space—or the vacuum/implicate order, or Void, if you prefer—via our DNA interface.

Consider also that in 2007 it was reported that an international panel from the Russian Academy of Sciences, the Max Planck institute in Germany, and the University of Sydney found that galactic dust could form spontaneously into helixes and double helixes and that these inorganic creations had memory and the power to reproduce themselves.[97] The spirals of life are embedded in the informational fields of the aether (everywhere). Hence, the nucleotides A, U, G and C, have been detected in meteorites since as far back as the 1960s. For instance, adenine and guanine were found in samples of carbon-rich meteorites analyzed in a study published recently online in the Proceedings of the National Academy of Sciences.[98] But this is *far* from being all.

In *The God Code*, Braden details his discovery that the atomic mass numbers of hydrogen (1), nitrogen (5), oxygen (6) and carbon (12, simplified by gematria to 1 + 2 = 3) are, through the science of gematria, very deliberately linked to the numerical values of specific letters in the ancient Hebrew alphabet. Respectively, they are Y, H, V, and G. That the atomic masses of the very building blocks of our bodies match the numerical value for these four ancient Hebrew letters *is not an accident.* Whoever imparted this system to the Hebrews clearly knew the basic physical elements for creating life from the atomic elements emerging out of the sub-quantum aetheric chaos, which the Hebrews called *Tohu*. The ancient "Mother Letters" for *Tohu* are, as Braden details, *equivalent to the letters of God's name, YHV*! (This, in a sense, makes "God" an eternal, conscious, intelligent, hyperspatial/virtual aetheric medium—an infinite aetheric consciousness, or alternatively, a conscious, eternal holographic "implicate order.")

Since *YH*, the accepted shortened form of *YHVH*, God's ancient name, means "God/ Eternal," and the word *VG* refers to the interior of the body, then the cypher in *YHVG*—the code for our carbon-based DNA—reads: "God/ Eternal within the body." (The code produces the identical message in Arabic too.)[99] To explain the "Eternal" aspect: we know that our reality emerges from a timeless hyperspatial/virtual aetheric medium/time-space/implicate order *) in which is embedded the "signature" of "God"—the Phi spiral.

We are also about to see that *Phi governs the structure of our very own DNA*. So this means the spiraling torsion energy of the hyperspatial aether, with its Phi signature, *is* "God/Eternal" manifesting "within the body." In the light of Chapter 5's material, we can know *directly* that *we are* this timeless consciousness domain, and thus, we (and the whole universe) are self-created. We are at once both "God" itself (fundamentally) and made "in the image" of "God" physically. Wow. As our space-time is "self-created" from out of the implicate order, asymmetries such as those embedded in the Phi ratio impart an angular momentum (spin) to the flow of time/aether/gravity, bringing about polarities such as left—and right-handedness in nature. The majority of mollusk shells, for example, are spiraled to the right.[100]

Speaking of DNA and geometry in the aetheric medium, Dr. Mark White actually succeeded in mapping out the relationships between amino acids in the human genome across a 3-dimensional surface, *that of a dodecahedron*. This is truly profound. "Furthermore, the geometry of the tetrahedron is involved as well, sliding over the surface of the dodecahedron to allow the protein synthesis to take place." So, as Wilcock says, "this is the EXACT same geometry that we're seeing at work in the ENTIRE UNIVERSE . . . and it is building YOU . . . right now!"[101] Thus we see that the information to build an organism lies not in the DNA itself, but the hyperdimensional geometry of the aetheric medium/ implicate order.

---

* David Pratt reports that "a number of physicists, including Jean-Paul Vigier and several [others] at the Institut Henri Poincaré in France, explain the quantum potential in terms of fluctuations in an underlying ether." Source: Pratt, *David Bohm and the Implicate Order*. www.theosophy-nw.org/theosnw/science/prat-boh.htm. Reprinted from *Sunrise* magazine, February/March, 1993.

Now to return to sacred geometry. Within the Flower of Life is encoded the Fruit of Life, in which all of the Platonic solids are embedded—in the form of Metatron's Cube. (The Kabbalistic Tree of Life is also derived from the Flower of Life.) Metatron's Cube is an intricate geometric image derived by joining all the circle centers in the Fruit of Life with straight lines (masculine principle). If you do this, you will have drawn all five Platonic solids, with an observable self-similar repeating pattern in which each geometric figure is repeated within itself at a smaller scale. All five Platonic solids are present in that single profound "informational system," famously known to esotericists as Metatron's Cube.

As a visual aid, Figure 6.6 depicts the cube form extracted from Metatron's Cube, as seen within the Fruit of Life. Notice the nested, self-similar arrangement of cubes within cubes.

Figure 6.5 (left) The Fruit of Life, composed of the 13 smaller circles in the form of an asterisk. Figure 6.6 (right) The cube form extracted from Metatron's Cube, shown within the Fruit of Life. Note the fractal nesting of cubes within cubes, which applies to all the Platonic solids (though the others are not delineated here).

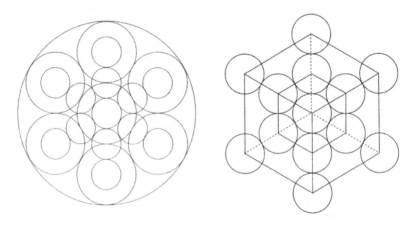

From *Nothing in This Book Is True, But It's Exactly How Things Are Third Edition, Revised and Expanded* by Bob Frissell, published by Frog Ltd, distributed by North Atlantic Books, copyright © 1994, 2002 by Bob Frissell. Image use by permission of publisher.

The Platonic solids are named after the great philosopher Plato, a student of the Mysteries who revered these forms. What makes them unique? A Platonic solid's edges are all equal, its surface features only one (repeated) shape, and it contains only one (the same) angle. All vertices fit perfectly on the surface of a circumscribing sphere, and all these points on the sphere are equidistant from one another. These geometries represent vibrational frequencies in the aether; each frequency corresponds to specific geometries, colors, and sounds in our universe.

The Platonic solids number five altogether. They are the octahedron, the tetrahedron, the cube, the dodecahedron, and the icosahedron (Figure 6.7). Because the platonic solids can be repeated inside one another infinitely, they provide the geometric basis for a "holofractal" universe where each part contains a "copy" of the whole. Yurth: "[T]he underlying information organizing fields create a fractal-based record of the way things have been 'formed.' The holographic field which operates below the 4th scale of organizational complexity is always part of the more complex physical record because it underlies it—it is, in point of fact, the 'implicate order' that Bohm speaks of."[102]

Figure 6.7 The five Platonic solids

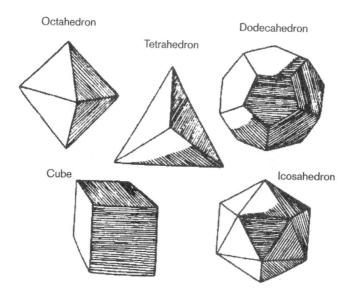

From *Nothing in This Book Is True, But It's Exactly How Things Are Third Edition, Revised and Expanded* by Bob Frissell, published by Frog Ltd., distributed by North Atlantic Books, copyright © 1994, 2002 by Bob Frissell. Image use by permission of publisher.

As Wilcock explains, particular geometric forms emerge from a given aetheric density at certain "pure frequencies." Each geometric form represents a particular energy frequency and vice versa. This makes geometry "the single most important aspect of the aether's behavior in terms of being able to construct stable structures, [because] geometry is what allows the 'field bubbles' of the aether to clump together in precise, organized patterns, forming specific molecules."[103]

In the world of mainstream physics, Michio Kaku has conceded that m-theory (string theory) may originate from an even simpler paradigm, such as geometry itself (and a geometric paradigm must be fundamentally aetheric!).[104] The subatomic psi investigations of Leadbeater and Besant certainly support this idea, but we lack space for that tangent. There is speculation, according to Lawlor, that in Hindu metaphysics the physical and subtle bodies are each linked to a particular geometry, the pranic/etheric body (the seat of the "instinctual mind") being linked to the tetrahedron.[105]

The association of the tetrahedron with the human energy body continues into the present day, as it is thought that two interlocked and counter-rotating tetrahedra envelop the physical body. (Two nested counter-rotating forms like this create a torsion field.) This tetrahedral energy (light) body has also been called the *merkaba*, in particular by Drunvalo Melchizedek, who bases his esoteric system of sacred geometry on this tetrahedral energy field.[106] It has been said that there is a star tetrahedronal field around everything, including our bodies and the Earth. The 2D representation of a star tetrahedron is the 6-pointed star that has come to be known as the Star of David.

As noted, the importance of the sphere is strongly stressed in Wilcock's work in describing the basic tendencies of energy/matter in the aether to take certain forms. As we see by looking out into space, the sphere seems to be one of the universe's favorite "neuroses," as it turns to this form time and time again in giving birth to stars and planets (and subatomic particles). Confirmation of the importance of spherical geometry continues to mount, with mainstream physics beginning to catch on. Observations of the Sagittarius dwarf galaxy being "consumed" by our Milky Way galaxy revealed "that the Milky Way's unseen dark matter is in a spherical distribution . . ." According to Princeton's Spergel, "Either our galaxy is unusual or the dark matter has richer properties than postulated by conventional models."[107] Far richer, it would appear. "Dark matter" naturally forms a spherical geometry within which it can nest the necessary geometric forms for building (and maintaining) structures in space-time.

Aether Vibrations Illustrated

Geometry is the study of spatial order through the measure and relationships of forms, and was one of the linchpins of classical education. Sacred geometry plays an important role in the snippets of aether physics that we are looking at in this book. The reason is straightforward: when the universe is shaped from only one substance (a conscious and fluid-like aetheric matrix), the only way to give the physical world the appearance of seemingly separate and distinct material things is through form. Hence the geometry of the aether is paramount in creating the phenomenal world—and the different geometries emerge within the fluid-like aether at particular vibrational frequencies.[108]

Since geometry is such a fundamental aspect of the universe and hyperdimensional aether physics, we will look at the work of Hans Jenny (1904–72) and Masaru Emoto in particular to illustrate the link between geometry and vibration.

The pointy tips or vertices of the Platonic solids represent the nodes[*] of a wave. These points are where the least amount of vibration is occurring throughout the entire sphere, caused by the surrounding pressure; they are the zones of highest strength/stability, and therefore attract any particulate matter that is present on the surface to them. Thus, the larger number of loose "colloids" would gather into these nodes in Jenny's experiments,[109] which we are about to look at. When the nodal points on a vibrating medium appear stationary and fixed, this is described as a standing wave.[110]

Though we don't normally think of color and sound as being represented by 2- or even 3-dimensional shapes, numerous researchers such as Gerald Hawkins, Buckminster Fuller, and Hans Jenny have shown that sound vibrations will form specific geometric patterns, as long as the vibrated substance is visible, unlike air. (More recently, scientists in Denmark discovered by rotating water, or the far more viscous ethylene glycol, that specific polygonal shapes emerged in the medium as certain frequencies of rotation were reached.[111] This shows again that specific vibrations in a fluid, or fluid-like medium such as the aether, "crystallise" particular geometric forms within it.)

After studying hundreds of crop circles, Hawkins discovered in the 1980s certain repeating patterns featuring circumscribed geometric forms (such as triangles, squares, etc.). When he divided the surface area of the inner shape against the area of the outer circle, the result was that the relationship precisely matched the diatonic ratios responsible for the relationships between tones in

---

[*] A node is a spatial locus along a standing wave where the wave has minimal amplitude—no vibration/motion in other words.

169

the octave.[112] This proved a geometric ratio underlying sound and how tones are related and structured in regards to one another. The same seems to apply to physical matter. Professor Amstutz of the Mineralogical Institute at the University of Heidelberg has said: "The science of musical harmony is . . . practically identical with the science of symmetry in crystals."[113] In fact, the geometric forces that create and organize matter sometimes make themselves easy to spot, as we will see.

Decades-earlier experiments by students of Buckminster Fuller were the first to prove that sound vibrations are innately 3-and not just 2-dimensional in their structure. Fuller's students dipped a spherical white balloon in a bath of dark-colored dye, vibrating it at diatonic sound frequencies. As expected, the dye collected at and stained the evenly spaced "nodes" where all of the violent motions on the surface of the balloon canceled themselves out, allowing the dye to easily accumulate. In addition, faint, straight lines of dye connected the nodes together, meaning the sounds formed simple 3-dimensional geometric shapes over the surface of the balloon.[114]

It was Ernst Chladni (1756–1827), a German jurist, physicist, and musician now known as the Father of Acoustics, who had developed the precursor to Cymatics (to *kyma*, the wave; *ta kymatika*, matters pertaining to waves, "wave matters") in the early 1800s. "Chladni repeated the pioneering experiments of Robert Hooke of Oxford University who, on July 8, 1680, had observed the nodal patterns associated with the vibrations of glass plates. Hooke ran a violin bow along the edge of a plate covered with flour, and saw the nodal patterns emerge."[115]

In a demonstration to Napoleon in 1809, Chladni placed sand in a plate fixed to a pedestal and drew a violin bow around the plate, causing the sand to shift into intricate designs, effectively making sound waves visible. In the 1900s Hans Jenny, building on Chladni's work, studied and documented the effects of sound vibrations on fluids, powders, and liquid paste. He would place these substances on a steel plate and then vibrate the plate at different frequencies, observing that a given vibrational frequency would organize the substance(s) into particular patterns. Jenny also developed the tonoscope for observing the action of the human voice on various materials in various media. It was a simple device the experimenter spoke into, thus imparting vibrations to a diaphragm on which sand, powder, or a liquid were placed. Speaking produced figures on the diaphragm corresponding to the sound of a vowel, figures specific not just to the sound, but the particular frequencies it was expressed at.[116]

When "Om," the Hindu primordial sound of creation, is intoned into a tonoscope it forms in the substance the Sri Yantra, the visual representation of the Om chant and the vibration behind the cosmos itself,[117] the "sound" of the aetheric medium. Tellingly, it displays a self-similar/fractal interlaced tetrahedra-within-concentric-circles motif. Thus we see that the Hindus knew thousands of years ago that sound possessed geometry and that underlying "physicality" there is a vibration or "tone." (Evidently, they somehow seem to have known the exact "sound" of creation and its geometry—as well as the fact that every shape has its own specific frequency.)

The Om chant itself is one for expanding consciousness by developing resonance with the cosmos. According to author David Tame, the Biblical Word and the Om are one and the same thing. "Cosmic Sound, infused with the essence of Consciousness, has been known variously as AUM, AMN, AMEN, AMEEN, OMEN, OMON, I AM, HU, YAHUVAH [Jehovah/Yahweh], the Logos, the Lost Word, and by other names besides."[118]

In Jenny's *Cymatics*, we find images of his work demonstrating the increase in geometrical complexity in patterns of matter that occurs with an increase in vibration: what starts out as a relatively simple and spare pattern will grow in detail and complexity as the pitch increases—while still retaining the same basic theme (Jenny's images have a sort of fractal self-similarity to them). This makes some sense in that the higher a frequency rises, the more informational complexity it can code for, and the more complex the data, form, or geometry becomes. Frequency determines form. As vibrational frequencies shift, they move through harmonic gradations within the aether. These gradations work, as noted, as do the harmonics of music; they are octave-based. Donald Andrews found through his research that identical shapes in the size ratio of 2:1 produced the *same fundamental tone but an octave apart.*[119]

The figures of Jenny's that crudely resemble humans are one example, a microcosm of the larger human form. Our more complex form requires a sophisticated vibrational matrix, provided by the nested subtle energy bodies and other aspects of our occult anatomy which we are yet to look at.

We are reminded that the solidity of matter is merely a convincing illusion, arising from a matrix of standing wave frequencies which arranges the "bubbles" within the aether or koilon into intelligently encoded form. A change in energetic vibration causes corresponding changes in the geometry of the matter that was being created by the energy frequency—a shape-shift, if you will. It is in fact now known and recognized increasingly that even the human genetic code can be modified or "shape-shifted" by specially targeted and modulated laser light, as well as the human voice, as in certain rare but documented instances of hypnosis, and certain shamanic healing techniques (more on this later).

In short, "sonic" vibrational frequencies create geometry in time-space/aether/implicate order, which "codes" for physical form in space-time (by determining how subatomic entities "clump" together). Contemporary sciences are increasingly verifying the ancient vision of a vibratory creation through the Creative Word or Cosmic Sound. Alain Daniélou elaborates, stating that "all substances are characterized by a particular relationship of rhythms which can be represented by a relationship of sounds."[120]

Jenny's work suggests that matter is created and maintained by standing waves: these standing wave fields can create "self-sustaining" moving/morphing objects, something that challenges the usual concepts of matter. Cymatics offers a vivid symbolic representation of the mystic's conception and understanding of creation: from the still, formless infinite consciousness that underlies all reality (the "Void"), vibrational frequencies, or as Luckman dubs them, "sonic torsion fields" (or "the Word," for Bible fans out there) and then physical form can be derived. When the vibration is removed, the physical forms (duality) disappear into the aether/implicate and all is one again; the illusion of creation, of form and multiplicity subsides "as a cloud melts away in the empyrean." In pages to come we will see that "morphic fields" that are invisible to most humans' perceptions do in fact pre-empt and guide the physical formation and maintenance of all living things.

Figure 6.8 Nested geometry in a vibrating fluid.

Source: Hans Jenny, *Cymatics: A Study of Wave Phenomena and Vibration*, 2001. Image credit: MACROmedia Publishing, Eliot, ME USA. www.cymaticsource.com.

Figure 6.8 demonstrates vividly the relationship between vibration and sacred geometry, as we see the general spherical form (imperfect due to the media being used: a water droplet on a vibrating plate), the outline of a cube, and most eye-catching of all—the interlaced tetrahedra at the center of the image. The interlaced tetrahedral form represents the harmonic of the *fourth* density in Wilcock's model and it also appears in the heart chakra symbolism in the ancient Hindu esoteric system (remembering that the heart chakra is the *fourth* chakra) as the 6-pointed star, which is the 2-dimensional representation of the 3D interlaced tetrahedra.

> The ratios of phi [0.618] and the square root of 2 are also responsible for the difference between the various tones in the octave, when measured as values of vibration in cycles per second. [Adjacent notes in an octave] *will always relate by one of these simple "spiraling" ratios.* Therefore we can now see that . . . every sound truly has a three-dimensional, geometric component. The same would be true for every color.[121]

James Clerk Maxwell's 200+ equations (known as "quaternions") have reportedly also shown that an EM wave has a hidden geometric component that determines its behavior as it moves along: a tetrahedron inside a sphere—though this has been suppressed since at least the 1800s, according to Wilcock.

Intention, Vibration and Geometry

Further illustrating the way that vibrational frequencies code for geometrical traits is the work of Masaru Emoto. What Emoto has done is to illustrate very powerfully that emotion and intention have corresponding effects on energy and matter. While researchers like Jenny have demonstrated that vibrational frequencies code for matter's many forms, Emoto has brought consciousness into the equation. How he did this (as of 2003) was by taking a water sample in a glass bottle and then exposing it to information, such as a word, picture, or music. Drops of this water are then placed on 50 petri dishes. These are then frozen in a freezer at minus 25° Celsius or lower. When they are taken out three hours later, ice grains of less than half an inch in size have been formed, with their center rolled up due to surface tension. The ice grains are then analyzed under a microscope. If things go well, a crystal starts to form as the temperature rises and the ice starts to melt. After one to two minutes, the crystal "blossoms" and is then photographed.[122]

To test his hypothesis that water is responsive to consciousness, Emoto labeled one sample with "You fool" and another with "Thank you." Following his freezing and de-freezing procedure, Emoto found that the water labeled with "Thank you" formed beautiful hexagonal crystals, while the other could manage only fragments.[123] Water even responds to the emotions associated with names of people. Mother Teresa and Adolf Hitler, for example, formed predictable images.[124] Ergo, the quality of water changes according to the information it receives. Water consistently responded to positive words by forming beautiful crystals. Water formed beautiful crystals to all the words expressing gratitude all over the world, such as "thank you" and its Chinese, French, German, Italian, and Korean equivalents.[125] This indicated that water was not merely recognizing some abstract linguistic design, but the imbued and associated meaning of the words it was being shown; a meaning that possessed a certain energetic "universality." (This subtle wave energy Emoto refers to as "hado." Depending on the researcher, it has been dubbed orgone, Qi, prana, torsion, etheric-plasma, etc.)

This does not mean that the name "Adolf Hitler" is itself "evil," or even that the man known to history as the leader of the Third Reich was inherently "evil." The geometry is related to the mental connotations (thought-waves) of the writer of the words, and perhaps even morphic fields that have built up "around" the words thanks to the collective input of humanity—the Infinite in unconsciousness of itself is capable of the most heinous acts; "evil," however, is a relative and ultimately arbitrary term.

It is worthy of note that physicist Victor Adamenko used Kirlian photography to look at printed words covered over with black paper and found that dimly glowing traces of the words were produced through the paper by the radiated light energy of the words.[126] Presumably, light emanating from the words on Emoto's labels is informationally encoding the water samples. Dankachov showed in 1984 that static torsion fields could be memorized in water. "Water proves to be a good medium for storing static torsion fields."[127]

Interestingly, Emoto found that when words possessing a "negative" hado caused water to form no crystals and perhaps even disturbing shapes, he could reverse the effect by placing the word's antonym on the water sample. The water would then form beautiful crystals as the negative hado was canceled and replaced with the positive energy. Again, the geometric structure of the water crystals was altered by the energetic connotations attached to the words—much as Jenny's configurations of sand or liquids would morph according to the vibrational frequency of the plate they rested on. It was this principle that Emoto then employed in using the hado water to help treat illness in people.[128]

All of this, of course, shows us that water can be encoded info-energetically by consciousness and not only affected by chemicals and other physical factors (which is yet another line of research validating the fundamental principles of homeopathy, much as late French scientist Jacques Benveniste's work did—a tangent we lack the required space for).[129] It has been shown that water molecules create what are known as *coherent domains*; the molecules exhibit a collective behaviour, sharing the same wavelengths.

> These single wavelengths of water molecules appear to become "informed" in the presence of other molecules—that is, they tend to polarize around any charged particle—sorting and carrying its frequency so that it can be read at a distance. This would mean that water is like a tape-recorder, imprinting and carrying information whether the original molecule is still there or not.[130]

Research in Japan has found that water molecules have a role in organizing discordant energy into coherent photons—a process called superradiance. This suggests that water acts as the essential conductor of a molecule's signature frequency in all biological processes and that water molecules organize themselves to form a pattern on which wave information can be imprinted. Water may not only store and send the signal but also amplify it.[131]

Emoto also found that prayer could affect even a large body of water—even if only one person prayed.[132] Rein and McCraty have obtained experimental results indicating that individuals who intentionally increase their cardiac coherence by maintaining a focused state of sincere love or appreciation can induce changes in the structure of water,[133] and Bernard Grad had previously shown that healer-treated water affects the growth of barley seeds. (Later we will see that intentionality can also alter the structure of metal, among other things.)

Former CIA polygraph expert Cleve Backster has proved through the use of polygraph equipment that plants are responsive to the emanating thought-waves of the humans around them. Malicious or hateful thoughts directed at his plant specimens caused measurable stress responses and inhibited growth, while loving thoughts enhanced their development. (More on Backster soon.) In *The Science of Oneness*, David Wilcock speaks of love as representing a higher level of vibration in the aether, meaning that sending loving thoughts to a plant causes the aetheric energy that the plant draws on for growth and development to increase, resulting in more vigorous plant growth.[134]

Clairvoyants can see that loving thoughts feed the plant with etheric/pranic/orgone energy (light-based aspects of torsion fields), decreasing entropy and invigorating the plant. Hateful sentiments achieve the opposite effect and hasten the onset of incoherence, chaos, and death.

Having said that, a recent experiment on the TV show "Myth Busters" resulted in plants which were exposed systematically to aggressive heavy metal far outgrew the other groups—including those spoken to lovingly. The plants faring worst were the control group which were simply ignored—a result in harmony with Emoto's research which suggests that even negative attention is, in some sense, less harmful than none at all, at least for plants and samples of rice, for instance.[135]

Sacred Geometry and the Golden Mean

By now we have clearly observed the importance of vibration and geometry in the creation and maintenance of the cosmos—and above all—we have linked it to consciousness. When we recognize the presence of geometry and maths in all of nature, we can readily understand the meaning of the saying "God is a geometer," and when we see these principles embodied in man we can then comprehend that "man is the measure of the universe."

Geometric principles and patterns scattered throughout Planet Earth and even the solar system are an obvious signal that the universe is fundamentally conscious. From my quasi-mystic perspective, this is self-evident or axiomatic. The universe is fundamentally conscious, so of course it is intelligent, of course it evidences purpose and unity—its fundamental essence is *infinite unity and awareness.*

Maybe the most important subject of sacred geometry is the Golden Mean. The Golden Mean is a special ratio expressed by the Greek letter Phi (Φ). It equals 1.618. Phi, like Pi, is an irrational number: since it is a never-ending decimal it can only be approximated. The Phi* ratio is expressed in the Golden Section. The Golden Section can be derived by taking the measurement of say, the side of a rectangle, and dividing it such that the ratio of the longer section to the whole side is exactly the same ratio as the shorter section is to the longer part (self-similarity appears once again). When the Phi ratio is applied to a

---

    *   Phi with a capital "P" is 1.618, whereas phi with lower case "p" is .618. Phi/phi = Golden Section/Mean/Ratio.

rectangle you have a Golden Rectangle, which can then be used to create the Golden Spiral.

> When [the golden rectangle is] squared, it leaves a smaller rectangle behind, which has the same golden ratio as the previous rectangle. The squaring can continue indefinitely with the same result. No other rectangle has this trait. When you connect a curve through the corners of these concentric rectangles, you have formed the golden spiral.[136]

Lawlor explains in *Sacred Geometry* that the "transcendent" Golden Proportion can be considered as "the first issue of Oneness" and "the most intimate relationship . . . that proportional existence . . . can have with Unity, the primal or first division of One." This, apparently, is why Christians have related this symbol to Jesus, the "son of God."[137]

The Golden Mean, like Fibonacci numbers, is found throughout nature, because of the fundamentally geometric nature of "hyperspace" energies that "bleed into" and create the third dimension we experience as humans. In fact, nature employs Fibonacci ratios as its way of working with infinity, the never-ending Phi decimal. Very rapidly, the Fibonacci sequence so closely approximates the transcendent Golden Ratio that it becomes virtually impossible to tell the difference.[138]

The Fibonacci sequence perfectly delineates the breeding pattern of rabbits and the ratio of males to females in honey bee hives, Lawlor tells us. Witness the nautilus shell for a well-known example of the Golden Proportion in nature. It is also present in the growth patterns of many plants. The individual florets of both the daisy and sunflower grow in two spirals extending out from the center, the first spiral consisting of 21 arms, and the other 34.[139] These are Fibonacci numbers generated by Phi.

Lawlor also points out that the distribution of leaves around a central stem is governed by the Fibonacci sequence: 3 leaves in 5 turns, 5 leaves in 8 turns, evincing an interesting 3D representation of the inherent geometric ratios within the spiraling torsion forces of the aetheric field. In terms of the human body, the Golden Mean is prominent, as da Vinci made clear with "his" well-known Vitruvian Man (which was originally conceived by Vitruvius, hence the name). According to several traditions that detail the average and ideal body proportions, the navel divides the body according to the Golden Section.[140]

The ratio of a human face from the brow to the chin is .618 of that from the chin to the crown. On a far larger scale, the average of the mean orbital distances of each successive planet in relation to the one before it approximates phi/Golden Ratio.[141] As above, so below. Gregg Braden states in *Fractal Time* that even the spiral paths traveled by quantum particles in a laboratory bubble chamber are governed by the Golden Ratio,[142] as is our very DNA: one complete turn of a DNA strand is 34 angstrom units in length and 21 wide. Each of these numbers belongs to the Fibonacci sequence, and 34 to 21 closely approximates the Golden Ratio/Phi (1.618), while 21 to 34 closely approximates phi (.618)[143]—hence "God/Eternal within the body".

Figure 6.9 The Golden Proportion in the human arm

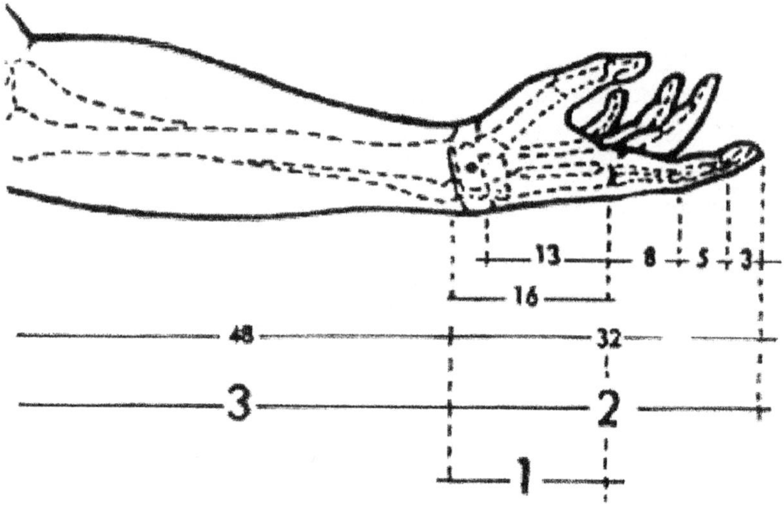

Source: *Sacred Geometry* by Robert Lawlor. Image credit: Thames & Hudson Ltd, London.

Figure 6.9 shows us the ratios of Phi in the structure of the human arm, a phenomenon repeated throughout all human bodies and other natural phenomena. Nikolai Kozyrev suggested that since life is actively drawing off this spiraling energy (which he stated was actually the energy of time) to create and maintain itself, it must therefore follow its proportions in the process.[144] Our skeletal system and DNA therefore act as "antennae" for this energy.

It was Pythagoras who discovered mathematical relationship between the harmonic notes in music. The musical ratios discovered by Pythagoras are the *same ratios as the Fibonacci sequence*, which gives us the harmonics of music.

Wicherink states that the Fibonacci sequence defines the ratios of harmonics in sound and also the electromagnetic spectrum of light: "it defines the seven colors of the rainbow!"[145] Sound frequencies supposedly continue through the octaves into light frequencies. The three main musical scales whose lowest and highest notes span an octave have, around the world and throughout time, been based on either five (pentatonic), eight (diatonic), or 13 (chromatic) notes—all of which are Fibonacci numbers.[146]

That the geometry the Phi spiral encompasses is a self-referencing/fractal is important. At the very least, it proves that the aether/physical vacuum/implicate order is innately holographic. In this aetheric medium, when these Phi spirals (comprised of sine waves) circle around the torus they meet and interfere, creating two new waves which will also have wavelengths derived from the Fibonacci sequence and harmonics. While destructive interference is the norm in wave interference, the only exception in nature, according to Wicherink, is when the waves interfere with Golden Mean ratio wavelengths. Thus, the Phi spiral can re-enter itself around the torus shape without destroying itself, meaning it is the universe's only possible way to nest and become self-organizing. "This is how stable matter can be formed from electromagnetic energy as a form of pure wave interference. Electromagnetic energy in a straight line is what we usually call light. *When this same light chases its own tail around the surface of the torus shape we call it matter.*"[147]

When we take into account the subtle energy bodies/torsion fields that precede the formation of our physical bodies, the assertion that the human form (and all other matter) is really "crystallized light," creating tangible holograms out of constructive wave interference, seems to make more sense.

Torsion and/or Scalar "Energy" and Consciousness

Torsion essentially means "twisting" or "spiralling." Thus, this is the action of torsion waves as they propagate through space. According to some, torsion waves are the missing link in the search for a final "theory of everything (TOE)," a unified field theory, or GUT (grand unified theory). Currently they cannot be fully reconciled with the established concept of a quantum wave as it stands in mainstream physical theory.

Torsion fields are generated by spin or by angular momentum. There are both left and right torsion fields (depending on the spin orientation). In any physical substance, the superposition of torsion fields generated by the atomic and nuclear spins of each molecule determines the intensity of torsion field in the space surrounding the molecule as a whole . . . The superposition of all these torsion fields determines the intensity and spatial configuration of the characteristic torsion field of that substance. Thus, each substance possesses its own characteristic torsion field.[148]

The physical property naturally open to the influence of torsion fields is spin. Therefore, every object's torsion field can be altered by the influence or application of an external torsion field.

As a result of such an influence, the new configuration of the torsion field will be fixed as a metastable state (as a polarized state) and will remain intact even after the dynamic source of the external torsion field is moved to another area of space. *Thus torsion fields of certain spatial configuration can be "recorded" on any physical object.* [149] (emphasis added)

Kozyrev discovered by experimentation that human thoughts and feelings generate torsion waves. Such a discovery opens the door for a "physical" understanding of consciousness, and a much more complete model of reality. Kozyrev was able to measure effects that were caused by sudden human emotional changes (including his own), proving that consciousness is related to vibrations in a fluid-like aether—and this non-EM force possessed a rotational aspect we refer to as torsion.[150] In his ingenious experiments he detected minute changes in systems that mimicked PK using this unknown form of hard-to-detect energy—time itself, he believed—which he pointed out united all existence within a unified field, connecting all things in real time (facilitating nonlocality or "action at a distance").

Changes in mechanical systems produced subtle alterations in the density of time/the aetheric medium, as did gravity, thunderstorms,* changes in season and matter density. Likewise, Kozyrev found that consciousness also affected time

---

* It is interesting to note that Jourdain and Moberly's strange episodes at the Petit Trianon occurred during electrical storms in Europe, which may have contributed to altering the temporal field or, as Kozyrev might have said, the density of time, thus creating the apparent time warp. Electromagnetic disturbances were also known to impede Nina Kulagina's PK abilities as well as interfering with Kozyrev's experiments.

density. Emotional thoughts produced larger effects on his equipment than did intellectual thoughts. "The measurement systems are especially strongly affected by a person in emotional excitement," Kozyrev's colleague V.V. Nasonov told an audience at Moscow University in 1985. "For instance, [Kozyrev] was able to deflect a torsion balance pointer by 40° or more when reading his favourite 'Faust.' Meanwhile, as a rule, mathematical calculations did not cause pointer deflections."[151] Thus, Kozyrev believed that our thoughts could change the density of time. He believed that in mastering the ability to make time dense at will we would be able to make telepathy occur at will. Under his conception, all psi phenomena would be stripped of their paranormal trappings.[152]

Indeed, virtually all anomalous warping effects or other "law-defying" effects caused in matter by various technologies can be replicated by the human mind. The imprint of human intention into the water samples of Masaru Emoto is yet another example that might be explained by torsion waves radiated by human thoughts and emotions. The torsion fields created by human intention are simply memorized in water, especially water containing ionized salts.[153] At a sub-microscopic level the internal structure of water has changed, causing the resultant differences in the ice crystals. At Sound Energy Research they created torsion field imprints in distilled water using scalar (torsion) wave technologies. They sent samples to Emoto who froze them and studied the crystals, which formed hexagonal structures like those created by human consciousness.[154] *The scalar/torsion technology creates the same effects as mental intent.*

According to W.E. Davis, the psionic device patented and used for years now by the De La Warr laboratories in England is a variation of the Heironymus machine that is capable of registering photographs of the L(ife) field surrounding an object. In 1958 Dr. De La Warr took a picture of a drop of ordinary tap water. The results were "normal"—there was a central point with seven bright, thin lines radiating from it. Then he asked a priest to bless the water before he took another picture. This time, the "brilliant lines of force" formed the shape of a cross![155] This phenomenon is somewhat akin to the use of kind words to metamorphose the shape of water molecules as documented in Emoto's research.

The fact that plants are able to respond to human intention in measurable ways could perhaps be related to the torsion waves created by human consciousness and broadcast to the plant, which senses them and responds accordingly—after all, if we can observe the Phi ratio (signifying the presence of this spiraling torsion energy) virtually everywhere we look in nature and realize that plants, humans, and animals are all created out of this mathematically embedded matrix, it is not so surprising that plants might be able to detect human thoughts (which generate torsion waves).

Russian scientist Dr. Victor Grebennikov is an entomologist who discovered what he called the "cavity structural effect" (CSE) created by bee nests. The particular shape of the nests caused them to harness and throw off large amounts of torsion waves that were detectable to human hands even when the nest was shielded with thick metal. These torsion waves act as a guide to trees, who detect them and guide their roots around the bees' structures rather than growing into them, as well as offering a form of nonlocal "communication" between the bees themselves.[156] The torsion harnessed by the CSE can also alter the passing of time, as Grebennikov showed, replicating Kozyrev's findings.[157]

Russian and Ukrainian research into pyramids has yielded some very interesting results regarding torsion waves. The Russians found that the pyramid shape naturally harnesses torsion waves, as if amplifying them. It has been experimentally established that objects that feature the Golden Section can be described as passive torsion generators.[158] In point of fact, objects featuring the phi ratio of 0 to 0.618 made the *best* passive torsion generators in the research carried out at the Physics Institute of the Ukraine Academy of Sciences and at Chernovitsky University by the Akimov group. The logical inference to make then, is that torsion waves *are* phi spirals. The team of Prof. A.G. Antonov from the Russian R&D Institute of Pediatrics, Obstetrics and Gynecology tested the effects of a solution of 40% glucose in distilled water after it had been stored in the pyramid. By administering only 1 ml of the glucose to 20 different prematurely born infant patients with compromised immune systems, their levels of health were seen to increase rapidly up to approximately normal levels. The researchers furthermore discovered that the glucose was not necessary, as the same effect could be produced by simply using 1 ml of ordinary water that had been stored in the pyramid.[159] Another study in Russia showed that mice drinking torsion-affected pyramid water had significantly fewer tumors develop than the mice drinking the ordinary water.[160] (Elsewhere, Russian scientists have reported that mice subjected to static torsion fields showed significantly enhanced immune function.[161])

Blunted razor blades also sharpen again as the crystalline structure is regenerated by the harnessed energy.[162] Dr. Karel Drbal, who first discovered this effect (apparently in the late 1950s), was awarded a Czech patent for his Cheops Pyramid Razor Blade Sharpener—and in 2001, Dr. V. Krasnoholovets showed with scanning-electron microscope photography that the molecular structure of the edge of the blade was indeed being altered.[163] In Russian jails, "pyramid power" reduced criminal behavior in a total population of about 5,000 prison inmates. By storing crystalline substances in one of the fibreglass pyramids built under the direction of Dr. Alexander Golod, and later distributing those objects through the jails, the incidence of criminal behaviour within the jails virtually disappeared within a few months.[164] These are just a few of the many incredible effects observed and verified by large numbers of qualified scientists.

Dr. Frank Brown, a pioneer in the study of interactions between magnetism and living organisms, found that when bean seeds were placed near one another there was an interaction between them that could not be explained in orthodox terms: it seemed to be due to the presence of a biofield or spin force.[165] That the biofield was involved is supported by Brown's observation of a connection between rotation and bean seed interaction. He found that the beans interacted more strongly when they were rotated counterclockwise than when they were rotated clockwise. (The biofield is usually observed as a clockwise force as seen from above, though it reportedly flows in one direction for men and the opposite for women.) Brown also reported on the research of R.I. Jones, who reported in 1960 that plant growth could be altered by uniform daily rotation. Clockwise rotation depressed growth, suggesting the presence of a spin force around all plants might be a factor.[166]

Some time around 1980, out-of-body explorer Robert Monroe was driving past his old home in Westchester County, New York—the site of his first out-of-body experiences. As Monroe recalled, a psychologist friend who was with him in the car took one look at the house, turned, and smiled, as he noted that the roof of the house formed a "perfect pyramid." "You were living in a pyramid. That did it!"[167] The ancient pyramids, in particular the Great Pyramid at Giza, served multiple esoteric functions such as facilitating OBEs, as in a shamanic initiation-type ritual.[168] Their placement at certain node points on the planetary grid suggests that they act to harness the planet's life-enhancing energies, and perhaps stabilize the grid itself. They are not gigantic tombs for dead pharaohs, that much is certain, and this is vividly demonstrated by the recently discovered pyramids in Bosnia.[169] Wilcock explains that any cone-shaped or cylindrical object will harness and focus the torsion fields spiraling out of the Earth; since this energy is fundamentally intelligent, harnessing it not only enhances one's physical health, but one's consciousness also.[170]

Torsion waves have the potential to initiate a fundamental paradigm shift. They are bridging the (perceived) gap between mind and matter in a way that was never thought possible, and in the process they are validating the perspectives of mystics and occultists. Various researchers consider torsion as being synonymous or identical with consciousness itself. Since torsion waves are a fundamental and ubiquitous feature of the cosmos, we can see how consciousness is also; consciousness has a real and detectable "energy" that is distinguishable from gravity and electromagnetism. Torsion fields can also act as spin fields within gravity, and they can be used to mitigate and nullify gravity, as we will see.

The first research generally credited with the discovery of this "fifth force" was that done in the late 1800s by Russian professor N.P. Myshkin.[171] Dr. Eli Cartan first termed this force "torsion" in 1913 in reference to its twisting movement through the fabric of space-time, but his important work was virtually buried by the rampant success and notoriety of Einstein's theories. In 1990, De Sabbata and C. Sivaram vindicated Cartan and demonstrated that phenomena connected with the "fifth force" can be interpreted as a manifestation of torsion.[172]

Russian scientists are reported to have written thousands of papers on torsion research in the 1990s alone, and more recently, award-winning physicist Nassim Haramein has, along with his colleague E.A. Rauscher, reworked Einstein's field equations with the inclusion of torque and coriolis effects. In the 1950s—the same decade that Watson and Crick discovered the helical structure of DNA—Russian scientist Nicolai Kozyrev conclusively proved the existence of this energy, demonstrating that, like time (and DNA), it flows in a sacred geometric spiral, as we have seen.[173]

Early in the 20th century, Nikola Tesla had theorized the existence of "scalar" waves (subsequently popularized by Tom Bearden) that transcend ordinary space-time and are capable of acting instantaneously at a distance (nonlocally). Later, Reich—not unlike Tesla before him—brought the wrath of the anti-life machinery of politics, corporate medicine, and industry down on himself for his research[*] into "orgone" (etheric) energy, which he successfully harnessed to run a 25-watt motor indefinitely, in apparent defiance (circumvention, in truth) of the Second Law of Thermodynamics.[174] For Luckman, terms like prana, Qi, and orgone are just different names for "the light-based aspect of . . . torsion energy"[175]— torsion/spin fields having mediated the creation of our universe from out of the undifferentiated information in the implicate order/aether/time-space.

Bearden reputedly discovered that the fundamental wave in the electromagnetic wave is a scalar wave. The scalar wave is the wave that

---

[*] Henry T. Moray (1892–1974), a contemporary of Reich's, also developed and successfully demonstrated his own overunity technology, earning him assassination attempts on his life. When Moray's son recently sought to retrieve his father's patent application papers from the US Patent Office, the folders were still there but their contents were gone. Moray referred to the medium providing the "anomalous" energy input as "the lumeniferous medium of the universe," its dominant trait being *time* (a fundamentally aetheric/time-space conception). (Source: Len Kasten, How Rogue Scientists Discovered Free Energy, *New Dawn* Special Issue Vol. 6, No. 4.)

remains when two opposite EM waves interfere, canceling out the electric and magnetic field components, just as Tesla did (creating a "vector zero resultant" as mentioned earlier). The result is a hitherto unrecognized component of the EM wave, a longitudinal wave vibrating in the same direction it is traveling. These scalar waves do not actually exist in our "material" world as we think of it, but only in the vacuum of space (aether/implicate order).[176]

Every electromagnetic or electrostatic field is accompanied by or contains a torsion component (following the principle of complementarity).[177] If the principle of complementarity operates at all scales (as we have good reason to believe) then, as Yurth points out, that means that wherever we find local/linear effects, we must also find non-linear/nonlocal effects.[178]

All organic and inorganic objects have their own signature torsion fields.[179] While most organic substances will not shield torsion fields, Kozyrev found that strongly right-handed molecules such as sugar can, while strongly left-handed molecules such as turpentine will strengthen them. Subsequent Russian investigations also determined that polyethylene film served as an effective shield for torsion waves.[180] Aluminum was also an effective shield: Kozyrev stated that it was an excellent reflector of *time*.[181] He discovered that torsion fields can also propagate through space as torsion waves at tremendous speeds, billions of times the speed of light, meaning they propagate in the future and past as well,[182] so tapping into them could facilitate retro- or precognition, psi experiences involving glimpses of the past or future in other words.

High technology of the future (and very likely current "black ops") will be scalar. The vacuum itself is thought of as a scalar field, meaning that the plenum that is "empty space" is loaded with scalar/torsion fields and waves. (Wilcock prefers, in his *Convergence* trilogy, to use "torsion," as it reinforces the twisting or spiraling nature of these waves and fields, and he stresses that either way, we are simply dealing with an impulse of momentum moving through the vacuum/aether/zero point field which is absent of EM properties.[183] In *The Source Field Investigations*, he opts for the more generic term "Source Field" to indicate that the torsion force is responsible for creating everything in our universe.[184])

Furthermore, researchers such as Bearden and Wilcock state that "mind," or consciousness is of a scalar wave nature, also existing in the "time domain" or vacuum/aether. In other words, this "transcendent consciousness" we have been speaking of is fundamentally composed of hyperdimensional scalar/torsion waves operating "outside" or "behind" familiar space-time. This functionality, incidentally, allows for scalar weaponry to operate nonlocally in devastating ways that bring Star Trek–type technology into the present, but this is a subject beyond our scope here.

According to A. Akimov, torsion fields coupled with the standard electric, magnetic, and gravity fields should offer a unified field theory that will extend the realm of science to include the effects of consciousness. It's interesting to note that certain effects on the spin structure of matter caused by torsion waves could only be reproduced by *psychics*. Furthermore, torsion fields transmit information *without transmitting (EM) energy*,[185] and while they can pass through physical media without interacting with it in the traditional sense, they can alter the spin state of physical matter.[186]

> From the late 80s till the late 90s . . . It was established that torsion generators allow us not only to replicate all "phenomena" [such as PK and ESP] demonstrated by so called "psychics," but they also are able to demonstrate effects that were never demonstrated by any "psychic."[187]

The Akimov group have represented the brain as a non-magnetic spin-torsion system where it is simultaneously a torsion transmitter and receiver.[188]

Iona Miller wrote in an online article that

> [s]tanding scalar waves can be coupled at exactly 180° out of phase in a resonant cavity to create zero sums through scalar resonance. There is just such a resonant cavity in the brain, between the pituitary and pineal glands. These waves of potential co-modulate each other and "lock or zip together" as a zero-vector system [scalar] wave. This allows for crosstalk or translation between dimensions . . . Hyperchannels for crosstalk between dimensions are known as "magic windows." These interdimensional nodal points have a naturally tuned frequency of a good hyperchannel between orthogonal frames where scalar wave anenergies crosstalk readily.[189]

Interestingly, the pineal gland is believed to produce DMT, an endogenous psychedelic known informally as the "spirit molecule," as well as creating 5-MeoDMT, a methoxy analogue of DMT,[190] the production of which can result from a buildup of serotonin (excess serotonin is also converted into melotonin).[191] DMT is known to facilitate intuitive functioning and mystical experiences. Could it act as an antenna for and amplifier of these hyperdimensional scalar waves? If a resonance can be set up within the cavity between the pineal and pituitary glands, does this stimulate higher levels of DMT production, allowing us to access different levels of reality? According to Bearden, "all mind operations are time-like, i.e., they are comprised as scalar EM photon functions and scalar EM wave functions. Thus the mind is a very special kind of electromagnetic system, existing in the time domain."[192]

In other words, the mind does not have its origins in the material world, but in the nonlocal "implicate" realm or torsion/scalar field. "A sizable list of attributes has been experimentally identified which demonstrates that the torsion field operates holographically, without regard to time and distance."[193] So too then does consciousness. Pertinently, it has long been a metaphysical tenet that in terms of human experience "like attracts like," and this is the case with torsion field dynamics.[194] If torsion "energy" is consciousness operating in time-space/aether/ZPF/implicate order, then this is a profound point. It appears to be the missing link that facilitates Jung's sychronistic phenomena, and our ability to draw certain people and events to us at a distance. This could prove to be the ultimate scientific support for the "law of attraction."

In terms of psi phenomena such as remote viewing and other functions of consciousness that allow us to access information from anywhere in the cosmos, the significance of torsion fields should now be obvious. Indirect support comes from the employment of gravimetric devices by various scientists who have used torsion fields to measure and record distant astrophysical events and processes *in real time* (no time delay). Their results support the premise that information at any single place in the cosmos can be instantaneously obtained at any other location.[195]

The Fourth Dimension

The notion that our 3D reality is enfolded within a 4D reality has proven useful not just to occultists and mystics, but increasingly to scientists too.[196] Picasso's cubism, in fact, was partly inspired by the fourth dimension, according to art historian Linda Dalrymple Henderson. His paintings of women with facial features oriented in "impossible" directions to each other represented a fourth-dimensional perspective, from which one could see all sides of a person's head at once.[197]

In independent researcher John Violette's schema, we do not detect this extra dimension because it is hidden and *included in our concept of time*, hence it is referred to as the *time domain*.[198] It must be extracted mentally with our occult faculties.

To lower-level beings, higher-dimensional entities who could interact with the lower planes would seem to be trans-time or time-traveling interdimensional entities outside their reality system who could enter and exit it at will, like a ghost or "alien." Hence, so-called higher-dimensional beings (channeled entities, etc.) and mystics and talented clairvoyants can dazzle us with insights into "the (probable) future": from their higher-dimensional perspective, possible and probable futures may be present in an extra spatial dimension. Their higher viewpoint allows them to see the probability that certain events will unfold. Once torsion/scalar energies and multiple dimensions beyond our familiar three are taken into account, "the paranormal" becomes very normal, and personally, I would like to see an end to the usage of that near-sighted and ambiguous term as soon as possible. I love how Violette expresses it: "There are no UFO phenomena, per se, no psychic phenomena, no near-death phenomena, and no mystical phenomena. There is just a reality phenomenon."[199]

We know other "planes" exist because many of us have experienced them. It is not constructive to discuss these things as articles of mere belief, as if they are fanciful conceptual notions without empirical evidence. If we look down upon a hypothetical 2D world with conscious, 2D inhabitants, we might find that the third dimension, depending on their level of advancement, would be an article of faith (for a relatively primitive species), or perhaps of knowledge, if enough of them have worked out how to access it (or recognize when hyperdimensional phenomena access them!). However, to us in 3-space, we can view the whole of their reality without any effort at all, and moreover, we can *know*, rather than just *believe*, that there is more to reality than they can even dream of. Not only can we *access* 3-space, *we live in it*. No belief/faith needed. No "brane theory" needed. No mathematical constructs to postulate it. Just conscious, ongoing experiential awareness. The bridge between science and religion.

An extra dimension would connect all 3D objects and every point in them. Two opposing 2D faces of a cube, for example, are "nonlocally" connected by the intervening 3D space in between. Indeed, the walls of a cube are extensions of space themselves, 3-space, while the cube itself is the 3D cross-section of the 4D hypercube (and so on).

The hyper-dimensional view directly implies that "the dead" are not really dead at all because their consciousness was *always* based in hyperspace, or extra-spatial dimensions. Reality is multidimensional and our 3D universe may only be a cross-section of a "shadow/dark" extradimensional universe which had to exist prior to ours so that ours could "unfold" along (or within) its extra spatial dimension. Even without postulating literal additional spatial dimensions, we know now, thanks to the available science, that consciousness is generated not in EM space-time, but exists in time-space/hyperspace/aether/implicate order, and even more fundamentally in the Absolute/Brahman that carries all implicate and explicate orders within it. Our torsion-plasma fields (or "subtle bodies") existed before we obtained physical bodies here on earth.

Alfred points out that objects in larger universes/planes actually "warp" the space-time in our reality and that we can actually observe the effects of gravitational fields emanating from these higher realities.[200] If we think of gravity as the multi-density aether which flows into stars and planets to fuel and maintain them, this accounts for the "curvature" or "warping" of our space.

To help understand the extra-dimensional idea, imagine a 2D flat plane. If you, a 3D observer, were to push a cone through the 2D plane from above it (outside of 2D reality), the 2D beings on that plane would experience its different expanding circular segments as flowing in one direction, forwards, in time. If you were to push the cone (point first again) through the 2D plane from *underneath*, the *complete opposite direction*, that opposite direction in your 3D world would translate to the *exact same experience* for the 2D entities—and *either way* they would perceive these events as representing the successive stages in the life of a *circle* (starting with its mysterious appearance as a point), since they cannot perceive the whole cone as it is in 3D. Two different motions in 3-space (up and down) can translate to the same motion or event in time in 2-space from this viewpoint. Perhaps we are interpreting 4D motion at the 3D level as the "flow of time." From the higher perspective, those seemingly serialized events are simultaneously present as one totality, which is what so many mystics and NDEers tell us of their experiences. This implies directly that we were never really "born" and will never really "die" in the traditional sense. Your locus of awareness can only shift from one perspective to another; it cannot be extinguished.

From the higher-dimensional perspective, variables that are invisible possibilities in future time to "Flatland" inhabitants living in 2D, are *observables*; the movement of objects such as our aforementioned cone (and the cross-sections it creates by moving through the 2D plane) can be predicted with relative ease. What would look to the 2D entity as "inexplicable knowledge of the future"/foreknowledge, would, to the higher-dimensional being, simply amount to observation of events as they unfold. A "prediction" from the higher perspective could be made with certainty insofar as causal variables remain observable.

John Randall suggests that "mind" is a "material" hyperspatial entity of which our bodies are 3D cross-sections, meaning that matter and mind are different aspects of the one multidimensional entity.[201] Randall adds that this hyperspace world is actually *more real* than this 3D world, a sentiment expressed by mystics, shamans, OBEers, and NDEers alike. Daniel Pinchbeck, for instance, described a DMT trip he had as "a seven minute rocket shot into an overwhelming other dimension that seemed more convincing than this one."[202] One NDEer has said of his experience that it was "realer than here, really. After that the world seemed like a mockery to real life—make-believe."[203]

Returning to our plane world scenario, it's interesting to consider that, if we could bend the 2D plane by making use of 3-space, we could make distant points touch, and possibly facilitate the teleportation of conscious entities or objects in 2-space from one location to another instantaneously. Higher-dimensional consciousness would be the instigating agent behind such events.

The Akashic Records and the Yogic Akasha

Akasha is a Sanskrit word referring in a general way to the nature of the universe. Literally translated, it means *space, aether, sky,* which the Hindu tradition conceives to encompass the entire make-up of existence. In yogic systems, the universal aether/medium is Akasha, which exists everywhere. Like Bohm's implicate order, the Akasha sustains all explicate form and life. Our bodies depend upon the interaction between the body's particles and the Akasha.[204]

According to theosophy, the Akashic records are the repository of history from which seers and trance mediums such as Edgar Cayce retrieve their historical information. However, Leadbeater warns that though the records are undoubtedly read from the *âkâsha*, or matter of the mental plane, it is not to it that they really belong. According to him, the Akashic records are "stored" on a plane/density/dimension far removed from normal human awareness. The closest, most accurate shimmering of them comes to those who can function competently on the mental plane (next "up" from the astral; these are terms that will be clarified in detail soon). Lower-dimensional reflections of the Akashic contents will necessarily be of an imperfect character.[205]

The Akashic field, like the Higgs field, the "quantum foam," and the aether of contemporary science, is omnipresent and all-pervading. It is more than just the birthplace of quanta. It is, according to the likes of Cayce and ancient Hindus, a record of all experience, thought, and substance over all time, which can be accessed by the few who have taken the time to develop the ability (or those who were gifted with it from birth). In the sense that the Akashic record contains all events from past, present, and future, it is congruent with time as it is increasingly conceived of by physicists—everything exists *now*. If all subatomic matter in the world is interacting constantly with the zero point field/aether, the subatomic waves of the Field are constantly imprinting a record of everything that ever happens. Thus, the Field is "a kind of shadow of the universe for all time, a mirror image and record of everything that ever was," as Lynne McTaggart puts it in *The Field*.[206] This is about as good a description of the Akashic field (in the theosophical sense) as you will find.

According to Margaret Waite, author of *The Mystic Sciences*, this field accounts for precognition and retrocognition (psychic knowledge of the past), and especially full-blown spontaneous replays of historical events—some of which have revealed factual historical information previously unknown to historians.[207]

The Akashic records may be the repository for all the information gleaned by psychometrists, who are able to consciously receive the information emanations from inanimate objects. These emanations explain how the writer Joan Grant knew information about unearthed Egyptian artifacts that was unknown to the archaeologists but verified by later research.[208] Law enforcement officials confounded by the ability of a gifted psychometrist to solve a crime when all orthodox methods have failed can find their explanation in the Akashic records—informational databanks existing at vastly higher frequencies. In altered states they are generally symbolically experienced as a vast library.

People have indeed, over the centuries, seen detailed and protracted images of scenes from the past, in most cases charged with great emotion: major and bloody battles; scenes of extreme peril and impending doom; trials and executions; murder and sudden death.

> The Duke of Argyle reported in the *London Times* something strange he had witnessed near Keinten, Northamptonshire: Two medieval armies in glistening coats of mail, battling each other to the death—another replay of the battle of Edge Hill, seen and reported by many throughout the years since it occurred. The Greek battle of Marathon has been fought over and over, down through the ages. Marie Antoinette in her Petit Trianon gardens is a re-enactment seen by many . . . The War of the Roses has been repeated. Novelist Taylor Caldwell, on a visit to Florence, looked out of her window and saw the burning of Savonarola.[209]

The events most likely to be inadvertently witnessed repeatedly by unsuspecting onlookers would be those involving the highest emotional content. If you tune in to the Akashic records *without* a definite subject in mind, you will usually find yourself viewing one of two general subject areas, according to mystic Robert Bruce:

1. Disasters, the extreme emotional energy of which makes them "stand out above everything else," and,
2. Personal material from your own life and relating to the lives of those connected to you (of which the highest energy events will tend to stand out).[210]

Peering into the future can present complex metaphorical imagery blended with apparently real-life events, which, with discernment and knowledge of how to "read" the symbolism, can yield insight into probable future outcomes.[211] In *Souls of Distortion*, Jan Wicherink relates torsion to the ancient concept of the Akashic field, stating that over time, torsion waves record the history of the universe, informationally encoding every single thought or action ever made. The resulting interference patterns form a cosmic hologram permeating the whole universe eternally.[212]

The Akashic field or records are also very much consonant with Jung's collective unconscious and meaningful coincidence (synchronicity). Perhaps his patient who saw the tube hanging from the sun causing the wind to blow was tapping into an archetypal thought-form aspect of the Akashic records: a "memory" diffused throughout the fabric of time-space; a slice of the relativistic "loaf" of all existence that is accessible to anyone, any time, anywhere. Whatever terminology we choose to employ, whether Akasha, torsion fields, aether, parallel worlds, etc., we can see that these concepts of a unified intelligent field of conscious energy have persisted for thousands of years, because the phenomena that prove it exists have continued to manifest for thousands of years (conservatively speaking).

The Ubiquitous Octave

The octave principle is central to aether theory and it has been recognized globally for centuries in different permutations. The "law of octaves" was first suggested (or rediscovered) by Pythagoras in ancient Greece, as far as "official history" goes.

> Having observed that the eight notes of the conventional Occidental musical scale were governed by definite mathematical

relationships, Pythagoras proceeded to create a whole cosmology based on 8s . . . In China, roughly contemporary with Pythagoras, the Taoists built up a cosmology based on the interplay of *yang* (positive) and *yin* (negative), which produced the eight trigrams of the *I Ching*, out of which are generated the 64 hexagrams. In India, Buddha announced . . . the Noble Eightfold Path . . . In the 1860s, English chemist John Newland showed that all the chemical elements fall into eight families . . . In the 1870s, with much more detail than Newland, the Russian chemist Mendeleyev proved once and for all that the elements do, indeed, fall into eight families . . . Nikola Tesla, in the visions from which he deduced the mechanism of alternating current, also intuited a basic Law of Octaves governing universal energy. Modern geneticists have found that the DNA–RNA "dialogue" . . . is transmitted by 64 (8 × 8) *codons*. R. Buckminster Fuller, in his Synergetic-Energetic Geometry, which he claims is the "co-ordinate system of Universe," reduces all phenomena to geometric-energetic constructs based on the tetrahedron (4-sided), the octet truss (8-sided) and the *coupler* (8-faceted with 24 phases).[213]

Kaku commented on Ramanujan's mathematical functions in *Hyperspace* that there seemed to be "some kind of deep numerology" expressing through them, the numerology being the widespread occurrence of the number eight in Ramanujan's equations, which are used to map out higher dimensions. Wilcock points out that eight fits the octave framework: "[T]he vibrations of the [aetheric] densities must conform themselves to this same octave system that is indicated by Ramanujan's function, since they are composed of a fluidlike energy source."[214]

Ramanujan's function is based on 24, or three times eight, which Kaku states can be generalized to eight (a single octave), "which is directly applicable to string theory."[215]

Thus we return to the Platonic solids, which, as Wilcock explains, "have a growth sequence that fits into the octave pattern," and which "our top thinkers are already working . . . into their mathematical models for these higher realms."[216]

Wilcock's research, synthesizing an eclectic array of scientific and metaphysical sources, presents "an eight-dimensional spacetime that is built upon a series of Platonic 'hyperframes,'" remembering that the Platonic geometries result from vibration in the fluid-like "aetheric" medium. In this eightfold dimensional model, we see that light and sound are directly correlated and both work in the octave format.[217] Wilcock explains that understanding the importance of geometry to how reality is organized renders the addition of two extra dimensions by String theorists in their attempt to preserve "symmetry" redundant. The geometry offers the "symmetry" String theorists seek, meaning a 10-dimensional framework is not necessary.[218]

The way in which the world usually treats a new truth is first to ridicule it, then to grow angry about it, and then to adopt it and pretend that it has always held that view. In the meantime the first exponent of the new truth has probably been put to death or died of a broken heart. —Charles W. Leadbeater

7

CREATING AND PERCEIVING THE SUPERHOLOGRAM: SEEING IS BELIEVING (BUT BEING IS KNOWING)

The universe wants to make itself known to those who can comprehend its language, and that language becomes more and more intelligible to us as our spiritual component unfolds. —Itzhak Bentov

Our innate superstition that the world we see is *the* world indeed is so deeply ingrained in our nature that it will rise again and again and make us believe that our world-image is the world in reality. Our primitive illusions need to be rudely shaken before a wider knowledge can be born. —J.J. van der Leeuw

A Holographic Information Processor

Some 2,500 years ago the Buddhist *Avatamsaka Sutra* described the cosmos allegorically through the imagery of Indra's net. In the heavenly abode of the deity Indra, there was cast an infinite net reaching in all directions, and at each node point in the net there was a jewel, each reflecting the light of all the others—infinitely. Should any jewel be touched, each of the infinite other jewels would instantly be affected, presaging Bell's theorem that everything is interconnected in this interdependent universe. In particular, the Buddhist vision illustrates the concepts of dependent origination and interpenetration (all phenomena arise together and are intimately connected "in a mutually interdependent web of cause and effect"[1]).

"For the Huayan school, Indra's net symbolizes a universe where infinitely repeated mutual relations exist between all members of the universe."[2] This essentially describes a holographic universe which organises its emergent phenomena fractally—*our* holographic universe. In *The Tao of Physics*, Capra explains the relevance of Indra's net to particle physics, stating that "particles are dynamically composed of one another in a self-consistent way, and in that sense can be said to 'contain' one another." This is a principle of the hologram: each part contains within it the information that codes for the whole. In other words, all information fundamentally exists nonlocally, infinitely reflected in all the facets of existence (the nested/interpenetrating geometry we saw in the previous chapter owes itself to the holographic "whole in every part" implicate order from which it arose).

So, what is a hologram? A hologram is a 3D image you can observe from different angles—produced when a single laser light is split into two separate beams. The first beam is bounced off the object to be photographed. Then the second beam is allowed to collide with the reflected light of the first on photographic emulsion (film). When this happens they create an interference pattern that is recorded on the film—an image that looks nothing at all like the object photographed, and somewhat resembling the concentric rings that form when a handful of pebbles is tossed into a pond. But as soon as another laser beam (or in some instances just a bright light source) is shined through the film, a 3-dimensional image of the original object reappears. What's more, if the film is, for example, cut down the middle, or even divided into dozens of fragments, each section will contain not a particular section of the object, but the *whole thing* (albeit at a lower resolution). The information is essentially distributed nonlocally throughout the holographic film. Sound familiar? The hologram's ability to store and process massive amounts of data is essentially due to the properties of light, which, incidentally, is crucial to the proper functioning of our DNA. The photon itself is considered to *be* localized information in its purest form.[3]

In 1997, a young physicist named Juan Maldacena used M-theory and branes (D-branes to be exact) to suggest that the entirety of the manifest world could be a holographic projection of information embodied in its boundary.[4] Using the information content from only two dimensions in space, we can create a hologram depicting *all three dimensions*. The number of pixels the hologram comprises is proportional only to the *area* of the region being described, *not the volume*.[5] This suggests that the distance from the "boundary" of our universe is ultimately unimportant in projecting our reality—it could be infinitely far away, or, more to the point, not have a true location in what we think of as space.

The assertion that the multiverse is created by holographically organized information is increasingly supported at all known levels of existence. "The latest discoveries across all scientific disciplines are revealing . . . the physical world as being imbued with and in-formed by a holographic field; thus it is innately interrelated, coherent, and harmonic at *all* scales of existence."[6] Recently, German scientists using equipment for detecting gravitational waves encountered a particular and unexpected noise, possibly the sound of the microscopic quantum convulsions of space-time, according to Craig Hogan, a physicist at Fermilab in Illinois. Hogan had actually predicted the existence of this sound and approached the Germans with his explanation, suspecting that it may be due to the universe being a "giant cosmic hologram."[7]

Physicist Raphael Bousso has written: "The world doesn't appear to us like a hologram, but in terms of the information needed to describe it, it is one. The amazing thing is that the holographic principle works for all areas in all space times."[8] Further proving this applies to all scales (quantum in this case), researchers at IBM created a holographic projection in a carefully arranged assembly of several dozen cobalt atoms 20 nm in diameter. When they inserted a magnetic cobalt atom into the ellipse and bombarded it with electrons at one focal point of the ellipse, a fully configured ghostly image of the atom appeared at the *other* focus of the ellipse.[9] Leading string theorist Leonard Susskind has pondered that "[o]ne of the strangest discoveries of modern physics is that the world is a kind of holographic image."[10]

Indeed, David Bohm and Karl Pribram discovered the holographic properties of nature concurrently for themselves, working as they were in the physical domain and the realm of the human brain, respectively. Adding to this, Laszlo and Currivan clarify that a system's information is *more fundamental* than the energy through which that system manifests and expresses itself. The probabilities describing a system are never random, but represent information, no matter the field of study—including quantum physics.[11] Everything is fundamentally informational to physicists today. Anton Zeilinger states succinctly in *Dance of the Photons* that the concepts of reality and information cannot be separated from each other.[12] A consciousness researcher would add that nor can they be separated from consciousness, from which they both emerge.

Thomas Chalko illustrated this idea in an excellent article on apparent EM randomness broadcast over the frequencies of a digital mobile phone network which college students—unaware that the frequencies they were observing belonged to actual "intelligent" conversations between living people—were instructed to investigate. The students analyzed the data using a statistical approach that allowed them to actually make predictions of many events within their frequency band. They had become quite convinced that their theory actually "described the Reality," and statistically speaking, it did to some extent. However, Chalko points out that by adopting a statistical approach the students completely missed millions of very real intelligent phone conversations, because they simply couldn't conceive that the data that "*appeared* to them as 'random' was actually the consequence of a very intelligently encoded information transfer." The thought of trying to decode their data never even occurred to them.[13]

The inference is clear: randomness is an illusion, an artifact of limited perception and knowledge. The universe deals in intelligently encoded information that is intrinsically meaningful and thereby creates an ordered and meaningful cosmos, but there are many ways to analyse and extract information and meaning from the one system (complementarity). The phone calls taking place between people manifested within the EM band as seemingly random fluctuations to the students, but in reality these fluctuations were the result of conscious choices being made each moment by the people holding the conversations that possessed and expressed meaning to them and their own particular methods of analysis.

The phone calls taking place looked random to the students because of the *way* they looked at them; they were not decoding them in a way that allowed them to extract or perceive the embedded meaning within to which only the speakers were privy. What if the vacuum's "random" quantum fluctuations are really the functions or effects of the language being spoken by the holographic cosmos as it converses nonlocally between its many component parts? What if lurking behind it all is conscious choice—on a scale we can barely begin to comprehend?

We have, in the previous chapter, looked at the role of geometry and vibration in creating the phenomenal world, so we know that in truth there is nothing randomly occurring. Bohm has stated: "The cosmos must . . . be self-referentially aware of itself as reality-in-itself. Otherwise, it would not manifest orderliness . . . which is the prior condition for all manifestations of being."[14]

Perhaps the most obvious clue to the lack of true randomness in nature is the apparent order, coherence, and meaning we perceive (and create) around us and in the cosmos at large. If subquantum processes were random in the true meaning of the word, the universe, which is a self-organizing system, could not function, let alone have spawned intelligent beings—aspects of itself—that can ponder their own existence (allowing the universe to experience itself subjectively). From a cybernetician's point of view it is possible to view the universe in terms of data (information) and data processing, and even recently (January 2010), a theoretical physicist at the University of Amsterdam has proposed that gravitational attraction could be the result of the way information about material objects is organized in space.[15]

David Foster points out that a wave is a binary system composed of two halves, its amplitude being measured from the top of one peak to the bottom of the next trough. The language of computers is, of course, binary mathematics. Thus, if we think of waves as the basic vocabulary of the universe then we can think of all of existence as being due to cybernetically programmed waves (implying the existence of a programmer, the conscious universe itself). To a cybernetician, "the complex structures of life reveal data processing on a massive scale (intelligence)," writes Colin Wilson.[16]

Naturally, as data processors, we are led to ask *who/what programmed the waves with their information?* The answer that the creationists and reductionistic materialists both miss is that the holographic universe (us) programmed itself. The mystic would point out that since lurking behind the hologram is our very own infinite cosmic consciousness (to which we are still largely oblivious), the "programmer" is actually us, though the *real* us—our nonlocal and eternal consciousness beyond the personality level and 3D space-time. Foster's own conclusion was one that would be approved by any mystic: the level of intelligence involved must be a great deal higher than our human intelligence. This was a scientific deduction rather than a metaphysical guess, Wilson explains, and it is absolutely congruent with the Perennial Wisdom. For Foster, we have established a view of the universe as a digitized information universe, which he prefers to call "the Intelligent Universe."[17]

In this vein it is interesting to note that, according to biologist Bruce Lipton, the membrane of a humble human cell is the structural and functional equivalent (homologue) of a silicon chip. To Lipton, we can better fathom the workings of the cell by comparing it to a personal computer; first, because computers and cells are programmable, and second, because the programmer lies *outside* the computer/cell. From the environment, information is downloaded into the cell, thereby regulating gene expression and biological activity. (This sphere of research is known as the field of epigenetics.) You can actually remove the DNA-containing nucleus of a cell without disrupting its normal operations or killing it. Thus, a nucleus is not the equivalent of a brain running our biological operations, the cell membrane with its environmentally responsive protein receptors is.[18] In Lipton's words, the nucleus is simply a memory disk, a hard drive containing the DNA programs that encode the production of proteins. Data is entered into the cell/computer via the membrane's receptors, which represent the cell's "keyboard." Receptors trigger the membrane's effector proteins, which act as the cell/computer's "Central Processing Unit" (CPU). The CPU effector proteins convert environmental information into the language of biology.[19]

In this epigenetic model the nucleus is relegated to the status of a gonad: it merely contains the codes for making proteins—it does not control cellular operations. Lipton's research caused him to realize that our very identity (information), which exists in the energetic environment, is being "broadcast" to and received by our cells and decoded by the brain, resulting in our sense of self. The brain effectively acts as a radio station for the mind—hence our consciousness cannot die with the body.[20]

With the foregoing in mind, the following lucid dream experience makes interesting reading; during the dream the individual asked if they could be told the meaning of the universe:

Something is emerging from the darkness. It looks like some kind of living molecular model or mathematical equation—an extremely complex, three-dimensional network of fine lines glowing like neon lights. It's unfolding itself, multiplying, constantly changing, filling up the Universe with increasingly complex structures and interrelationships. This growing movement is not erratic but consistent and purposeful, rapid but at the same time unhurried, determined.[21]

Another individual attained lucidity within a dream and asked to be taken to see "God." He found himself in a room filled with a vast array of computers. At the center console was a little old man operating the entire computer system, which the dreamer felt represented the universe.[22] How apt.

In 2006, Seth Lloyd, the designer of the world's first feasible quantum computer and researcher in the field of digital physics, stated in his book *Programming the Universe*: "The history of the universe is, in effect, a huge and ongoing quantum computation. The universe is a quantum computer."[23] He explains that "as the computation proceeds, reality unfolds."[24] Our very own

DNA quasicrystal operates computationally as well, as several studies have shown. DNA has been used to solve very specific problems requiring special forms of computation. Once DNA has absorbed light or radio frequencies, it can compute and modulate them before transmitting them for biological purposes within the body (or back into the surrounding environment).[25]

Both nature and computers run on codes. Some of nature's codes include the Golden Mean (Phi with upper case "P" is 1.618 and phi with lower case "p" is .618, both of which are forms of the Golden Mean), Fibonacci numbers, and Fourier mathematics. The Golden Mean/Ratio, says Braden, is what determines the frequency with which nature repeats the fractals that fill space, as well as being the template for what we consider to be beauty.[26] In this view, information assumes primacy over energy, and the waveform interference patterns that create the physical hologram (energy/matter) of the cosmos represent *intelligently encoded information—information coming from totally different levels of reality.* Information creates form, hence, *in-formation.* Of course, implied by this view is what Foster alludes to as an organizational intelligence that assumes primacy over information. From there the conclusion that creation is innately meaningful and purposive is unavoidable, since, as I will reiterate in TGI 2, such a profound and all-encompassing intelligence would obviously not operate without a purpose.

Frank and Iona Miller write:

> The Universe emerges from the rippling effects of immense numbers of criss-crossing interference waves. The geometry of the fields is more fundamental than the fields or emergent particles themselves . . . All existence consists of embedded holograms within holograms, and their interrelatedness somehow gives rise to our existence and sensory images . . . At the quantum level [interference patterns] create matter and energy as we perceive them—lifelike three-dimensional effects. Consciousness and matter share the same essence, differing by degrees of subtlety or density . . . The Universe is a continuously evolving, interactively dynamic hologram, [a grand Unity]. The part is not only contained within the Whole; the Whole is contained in every part, only in lower resolution.[27]

Underlying or embedded within and defining the holomovement at all levels is information, and most fundamentally, consciousness.

Wave Transformers

When a wave's peak hits another wave's trough, they cancel each other out (destructive interference); the signal is erased. When one wave's peak hits another wave's peak, you get amplification (constructive interference); the signal is strengthened. All in all, the net effect of these myriad wave frequencies propagating throughout space is that they create sophisticated interference patterns that combine to create a holographic universe. Interference patterns amount to a constant accumulation of information, and waves have a virtually infinite capacity for storage.

The 18th-century Frenchman Jean Fourier helped us further answer the question of how we humans actually receive and perceive information; in particular, visual information. Fourier developed a mathematical way of converting any pattern, no matter how complex, into a language of simple waves, and he also showed how these waveforms could be converted back into the original pattern. The equations he developed to convert images into waveforms and back again are known as "Fourier transforms." These enabled Dennis Gabor to convert a picture of an object into the blur of interference patterns on a piece of holographic film. They also enabled him to devise a way of converting those interference patterns back into an image of the original object. The "whole in every part" aspect of holograms results from the translation of an image or pattern into Fourier waveforms.[28]

Throughout the late 1960s and early 1970s various researchers contacted Karl Pribram and told him they had uncovered evidence that the visual system worked as a kind of frequency analyser, suggesting that the brain might be functioning holographically. In 1979, Berkeley neurophysiologists Russell and Karen DeValois used Fourier's equations to convert plaid and checkerboard patterns into simple waveforms, testing to see how the brain cells in the visual cortex responded to these waveform images. They found that the brain cells responded not to the original patterns, but to the Fourier translations of the patterns. The brain was using Fourier mathematics—the same mathematics that holography and MRI technology employed—to convert visual images into the Fourier language of waveforms. The DeValoises' discovery was subsequently confirmed by numerous other laboratories around the world.[29] Pribram showed that the visual information is internalized and memorized as a wave interference pattern among the brain's neurons, analogously to how holographic film stores information.[30]

The heart also operates on these principles. Individuals wired to electrocardiograms meditating in a state of "love, compassion and caring" were found to have generated more coherent ECGs (electrocardiograms)—only after Fourier transform of the electrical output. These heart rhythms were characterized by a smooth sine-wave-like pattern, the frequency peaks of which were "evenly separated by a proportionality factor identical to [the Golden Mean ratio]"![31]

Thus, we see that our human physiology is designed to receive and generate information encoded in wave frequencies. The brain takes these waves and creates a virtual reality for us (which represents of tiny fraction of what actually exists). Even though, operating through our brain-mind, we feel separate from everything in our brain-constructed virtual reality, we are not. Just as in a hologram, in our holographic universe, the whole contains each part and each part (or each part's torsion field/s) contains the (information of) whole. Time-space/implicate order, in which all information is considered as nonlocally dispersed, enfolds our whole space-time reality. As the poet William Blake once wrote:

> To see a world in a grain of sand,
> And a heaven in a wildflower,
> Hold infinity in the palm of your hand,
> And eternity in an hour.

Julian of Norwich, in her *Revelations of Divine Love*, tells us how she was shown in vision "a little thing, the quantity of a hazel nut"; and how she looked at it with the eye of her understanding and thought, "What may this be?" And it was answered generally thus: *"it is all that is made."*[32]

Individuals have, in altered states of awareness (mystical experiences, for example), experienced the wave nature of matter much more directly. Marie D. Jones, author of *PSIence*, found herself staring at where her furniture, bed, and windows should have been, and instead seeing "varying frequencies of light, similar to billions of tiny fluctuating particles, yet also waves."[33] We never see the external world precisely as it is; we see representations, approximations or *models* of it created by our brains as they use Fourier maths to reconstruct the (limited) frequency input they receive from our sense receptors. Our brains are such proficient constructors of our reality model that we don't even notice there is any constructing going on.

Additionally, we imbue our perceptual constructs with our own subjective meaning. In this light, it makes no sense for a skeptic to declare his perceptual model of the world to be better than that of a clairvoyant's, for instance. One is merely different from the other, and both are subjective, although we might note that the clairvoyant's is less stilted and much more inclusive. We need to remind ourselves that what we do perceive in terms of the visible light spectrum is less than a billionth of the rest of reality that exists. (Luckily, we have more than just a physical body for perceiving and decoding information.)

"Crucially, the mathematics of Fourier transforms is depicted in the language of complex numbers and phase space," phase space being the "plane of reality defined mathematically by complex numbers that comprise both 'real' and so-called imaginary components," the latter described in terms of the square root of −1. The inclusion of imaginary numbers indicates "that the complex plane of phase space is geometrically 90° out of phase with the materialized world."[34] From this viewpoint, the underlying informational field (aether/time-space/implicate order) that codes for physical reality is embedded and embodied in so-called *phase space*, 90° out of phase with our reality.

Karl Pribram and the Holonomic Brain

Traditionally, in line with our training in conceiving the world in particulate/corpuscular terms, the brain was thought to store memory in specific parts of the brain (locally). Karl Pribram has fundamentally challenged that view with his holonomic brain thesis that, like a hologram (and the universe at large), the brain stores information nonlocally within itself. Modern neuroscience cannot account for evidence that local lesions in the brain do not selectively impair *specific* memories. In a hologram, however, "restrictive damage does not disrupt the stored information because it has become *distributed*. The information has become blurred over the entire extent of the holographic film, but in such a precise fashion that it can be de-blurred by performing the inverse procedure."[35]

Before Pribram, Wilder Penfield had found that stimulating certain areas of the brain's surface would activate memories from this life, but that he could stimulate *different* memories through the *same* part of the brain, suggesting this holographic "blurring" or nonlocalization of memory throughout the brain (or perhaps through a holographic energetic duplicate of the brain—an "etheric double").[36]

There is, in fact, evidence that memory is stored holographically throughout the entire body. Organ transplant recipients sometimes experience thoughts, cravings, and emotions—the conditioned mental software programs/memories—that belonged to their organ donor. This suggests that the organ being transplanted is accompanied by a holographic information field that essentially contains all of the contents of the donor's psyche. One girl who received a lung and a heart from an anonymous 18-year-old boy she knew nothing of began to exhibit his tastes, habits, and thoughts. She even dreamed of a man called Tim L., who she later found fitted the name and appearance of her donor.[37]

Enveloping each physical organ there is a holographic informational field that serves memory and sensation functions which we might call the etheric field (more on this shortly). In *The Presence of the Past*, Sheldrake wrote that if the hypothesis of formative causation is correct, then memory habits of one organism should be able "to influence another organism by morphic resonance, facilitating the acquisition of the same habits."[38] This is exactly what we see in cases such as the one above, which show that our memories (and identities) are not truly stored just in the brain but in an enveloping morphic field that every part of the body is tuned into. Brain damage to specific areas would simply prevent accessing portions of that information, it wouldn't erase it (because in truth the brain neither stores memories physically, nor generates thoughts).

Holographic memory storage can explain the huge storage capacity of the brain (or brain's field): it has been estimated to be able to store some 2.8×10^{20} (280,000,000,000,000,000,000) bits of information. Holograms are also very good at explaining how the brain manages to access and remember things so rapidly from its huge repository of information. Holographic images can easily be compared and matched even when they are not 100% identical. Early in his career, Pribram had observed some of neuropsychologist Karl Lashley's research, which inspired him to go on to create his holonomic brain theory. Lashley had worked with rats, and through gruesome neurosurgical procedures and performance test drills on the unfortunate rodents, he found that their memory appeared to be dispersed holographically through their brains rather than localized.[39] Pribram showed that not only our memories but all our cognitive processes, smell, taste, hearing, and seeing may be explained by holographic principles.

Pribram found that the wave frequencies intercepted by the eye have a Fourier transformation conducted on them by the brain, which then distributes those frequencies throughout its neurons. Thus, his thesis was that the picture is stored holographically throughout the brain as a wave interference pattern among neurons. The memory of the picture can be reconstructed from the holographic interference pattern by the inverse Fourier transform, resulting in perception of a visual image seemingly in one's head.[40]

Pribram's work demonstrated that the old notion of vision being explained by a scaled-down reproduction of the external world being projected onto the retina in a one-to-one ratio was a fallacy. The process is, evidently, infinitely more subtle and complex than this. His studies on rats, monkeys, and cats also showed vision to be similarly holographic to memory. Peter Shepherd suggests that if information is stored holographically (nonlocally) throughout the brain, each localized area would process that representation differently: the limbic would represent feelings, the reticular system the amount of energy, and the cortex would process the left and right specializations of symbolic fantasies or emotional context, and so forth,[41] suggesting a sort of neurological complementarity.

In an interview with Jeffrey Mishlove in 1998, Pribram made some very interesting comments regarding the functioning of the brain. For instance, according to him, "the mathematical descriptions that we make of, let's say, single-cell processes, and the branches from the single cells, and how they interact with each other . . . [are] very similar to the description of quantum events."[42] These cells and their connections to one another

> operate on the basic principles that have been found to also operate at the quantum level . . . [T]he problems that have been faced in quantum mechanics . . . also apply at the psychophysical level and at the neuronal level . . . [I]f indeed we're right that these quantum-like phenomena . . . apply all the way through to our psychological processes, to what's going on in the nervous system—then we [have a parallel to] spiritual experiences. [T]he *descriptions you get with spiritual experiences seem to parallel the descriptions of quantum physics.*[43] (emphasis mine)

Research on brain-damaged patients reveals that while particular memories may become dimmer and less distinct, they do not suddenly vanish with the loss of small regions of brain tissue. Hydrocephalics with only a stump of brain tissue can somehow lead normal lives and exhibit perfectly normal intelligence. "The fact that different areas of the brain are linked by thousands of parallel pathways provides a basis for the neurological equivalent of the holographic laser's coherent activity." Memory may therefore be stored nonlocally in a kind of "quantum field" interpenetrating the brain, and there is evidence for such a concept, as we are about to see.[44] No evidence of physical memory traces within the brain exists.

Fortunately for us, both photographic holograms and distributed memory are very resistant to damage (courtesy of their "whole in every part" nature). "Holograms are information fields, and information (scalar [or torsion]) fields may be accessed and communicated in ways . . . that are not limited by space-time materialization." This, Shepherd suggests, "may provide an explanation for psychic phenomena, out-of-body experiences and past life recall." Thus, the brain merely serves as an interface for non-material scalar/torsion information fields (consciousness) in the aether/ZPF/time-space to interact with our space-time. Since scalar fields are holographic in nature, any individual mind can potentially tap into the infinite consciousness of the universe, "and given the appropriate coherent 'laser-beam' brain wavelengths this information can be accessed through the brain interface."[45]

The brain, therefore, acts as a filter; it prevents us from directly immersing ourselves in the implicate order/aether/time-space, as well as the Absolute underlying all implicate and explicate orders. Hence why NDEers, for instance, sometimes spontaneously find that they inexplicably possess incredible knowledge post-NDE: they directly access the implicate order/s in which all information is stored without their brain getting in the way.

"Idiot savants" are apparently accessing the universe's holographic informational field in performing their incredible feats of apparent calculation.[46] Hydrocephalics might be doing the same thing. We may only need a minimal physical anchorage point (a handful of neurons, etc.) to download information from the cosmic hologram—or upload information to it, for that matter. McTaggart speculates that many of humanity's major accomplishments and insights may have resulted from individuals spontaneously accessing "a shared accumulation of information—a collective effort in the zero point field—in what we consider a moment of inspiration," meaning our intelligence and creativity result from interactions with "The Field," rather than simply being brain-based and nothing more.[47]

Joseph Chilton Pearce considers that such savants may be "the most bona fide channellers around"[48]—but they need to be triggered into mental activity through an outside agent acting as prompter by asking a question about a particular topic. Suddenly it triggers some sort of dynamic resonance with that topic's information, and they interact, allowing the savant to download the relevant data. An identical process seems to be happening with genuine psychics. I have watched my friend Larissa rattle off specific personal details about people she has never met and knows nothing about after just mentioning their name or someone in some way related to them. A resonance with the person's information/torsion field—which is entangled with the information fields of everyone they know—is triggered and a pathway established for information transfer/download.

This is apparently the basic process behind those great scientific discoveries I mentioned in Chapter 1. A medium does a similar thing, only with the consciousness fields of the deceased, which I will cover in detail in TGI 2. The Soviet psychiatrist Vladimir L. Raikov had claimed that hypnotic phenomena could be utilized for what he referred to as "artificial reincarnations." For example, Raikov claimed that it was possible to hypnotically suggest to a boy who studied violin that he was the virtuoso violinist Fritz Kreisler. Under hypnosis, the boy's manner of playing was indeed reminiscent of that of Kriesler. By the tenth session artificially acquired talents (such as drawing) soon took hold for subjects and remained in their normal waking consciousness. One girl who initially had little artistic ability considered abandoning her studies in physics for a career in visual art after repeatedly being "reincarnated" as the great Russian painter Ilya Repin. Raikov was able to evoke this mental alteration only when the subject was in an exceedingly deep trance which was, at the time, a new form of active (as opposed to passive) trance. As opposed to normal hypnosis, the newfound talents of Raikov's subjects were retained in ordinary consciousness. Raikov explained that because the student is conscious, thinking, and acquiring their own experience during the hypnosis, the creativity and skill they tap into becomes their own.[49] We might infer that Raikov's hypnotic suggestions put the subject's mind/torsion field "en rapport" with the time-space information signatures of the masters whose abilities he wished to invoke, furnishing a profound data download.

Bentov explained that our brains create rhythmic electric currents when we think, which, with their magnetic components, emanate into space at light-speed, as do the electric waves produced by our hearts. The result is enormous EM interference patterns, radiating out from our planet.[50] When the frequencies emitted by us achieve frequency and phase alignment (whether in ratios/harmonics or directly) with other such frequencies, a resonance is established between us, forming biological channels of communication within the wave matrix of the holomovement at large. Human psyches combine with others to form an interference pattern of all consciousnesses in the cosmos, a "universal mind," or one aspect of it at least.[51] The ever-present torsion components of this interference pattern make aspects of the "past" and "future" contained in this universal mind accessible to anyone in the present moment.

Glial cells in the brain might also play an important role in our conscious experience, and our conscious perception of "psi information." They form an interactive EM field in the brain, independent from the electrochemical fields of neurons, with some ten or more glia clustered around each neuron. Joseph Chilton Pearce believes that there is a good chance that "these [EM]-

sensitive glia selectively draw from the hierarchy of [EM] fields surrounding us and translate these frequencies into electrochemical signals available to those neurons, thereby furnishing the information from which our neural system builds our world experience." Glia, surmises Pearce, "may both draw selectively on the hierarchy of torus fields we are immersed in and feed back into those fields our neural response, a reciprocal dynamic."[52] This field interactivity between living beings and ambient environmental fields is undoubtedly one facet of how evolution (in particular, adaptation) takes place.

As well as glia, microtubules—the tiny, cylindrical protein sheaths forming part of a cell's cytoskeleton—have been implicated in consciousness and psi. Based on the research by Penrose and Hameroff, Robin Kelly suggests microtubules may be the physical structures through which intention and consciousness can be broadcast nonlocally, as they are resonant structures that likely process information from quantum fields.[53]

Anthony Peake offers the theory that virtual photons emerging from the ZPF/aether are drawn into tiny networks of microfilaments in the brain called *microtrabecular lattices*. The microfibers (which include microtubules) within each of these lattices are an average of 7–9 nm in diameter, perhaps small enough to interact with virtual photons, which may then rise up into the microtubules, of which there are billions within each neuron in the brain. Research by Japanese physicists Hirano and Hirai has revealed that tiny bursts of EM energy are regularly emitted from each side of a microtubule towards the other. Peake suggests this EM energy may have been composed of virtual photons apprehended from the ZPF/aether by the microtrabecular lattice, and, upon each pulse meeting in the middle of the microtubule, wave interference patterns exactly like those used to create holograms may be generated.

This would mean trillions of nano-holograms existing simultaneously within the one brain at any given moment—but here's the kicker: in a series of experiments, Peter Marcer and Walter Schempp showed that microtubule communication operates nonlocally (instantaneously) throughout the body. Thus, each microtubule's nano-hologram in the brain is in real-time contact with the trillions of others, effectively resulting in one coherent macro-hologram "in" the brain. This seems to be an elegant way to "physically" account for mental imagery of almost any type—all of which is not being generated by the brain acting alone, but by the brain acting as a conduit for information arising from more fundamental levels/dimensions of reality.[54]

Even during an out-of-body experience, the brain could continue this activity in nonlocally reflecting the contents of the temporarily separated subtle body through which the OBE is experienced. (I will return to this notion of parallel processing in TGI 2.) Peake believes that the organ of vision for perceiving the hologram created by biophotons in the brain is the pineal gland, which, as we will see, does qualify as a kind of third eye, physiologically speaking.

The Subjectivity of Experience

To explain the visual input we receive and the resultant images we construct and perceive, we have to acknowledge that the brain is hardwired to decode waves and their frequencies/vibrations. Where the major differences in belief, perception, and, consequently, awareness come in is that the brain is not passive in decoding the wave input. It edits and rewrites information constantly.* One major force compelling the brain to edit this way or that is belief. The subconscious mind constantly intervenes and colors incoming data according to what we believe. Out of a vast sea of energy signals, "our brains notice the signals that fit what we expect to see, and we organize these signals into a model, or reality-tunnel, that marvelously matches *our ideas about what 'is really' out there*."[55]

We tend to agree on sense data that falls comfortably within the range of "normal," everyday five-sense perception, but, for data pushing the boundaries of five-sense perception, people can reach gravely different conclusions, based on what their subconscious mind is filtering out or leaving in. Modern neuroscience, as R.A. Wilson pointed out, reveals that "I see" actually means "I have made a bet."

> Constant reminding of ourselves that we do not see with our eyes but with our synergetic eye-brain system working as a whole will produce constant astonishment as we notice, more and more often, how much of *our perceptions emerge from our preconceptions.*[56]

For instance, in the case of the human energy field(s), or "auric field," our beliefs and perception vary so greatly from one person to the next that we have

---

* In fact, when it comes to visual input, our retinas—extensions of our brain matter—perform a significant amount of preprocessing inside the eye, and then send a series of 12 partial representations of a scene simultaneously to the brain for interpretation. Source: Werblin & Roska, The Movie in Our Eyes.

people who staunchly believe there is no such thing, while at the other end of the spectrum we have people who need not rely on any kind of belief because they can perceive it directly. Their subconscious programmed beliefs have not edited the incoming information to conform to their limiting preconceptions.

Hypnosis, in particular stage-show hypnosis, where people are instructed to believe that an onion is in fact a delicious apple, illustrates my point. The hypnotized person has had their fundamental beliefs so drastically changed regarding the frequency data being received, that the onion is mentally reconstructed as an apple and then tastes like an apple. If the people eating the onion while thinking it's an apple don't shed a tear ("onion eyes"), then you have proof enough that fundamental and drastic changes have occurred in the person's psyche and therefore in their physiological response mechanisms. Under normal conditions, ripping into an onion would make almost anybody's eyes run, no matter what effort they go to in trying to fight it. Such a phenomenon would be similar to the way that someone with Multiple Personality Disorder (MPD), which is a real condition, can be allergic to bee stings in one personality and non-allergic in another. The body doesn't lie—it merely does what different brain states and beliefs tell it to do. Hypnosis accesses the seemingly infinite power of the subconscious mind to effect its often spectacular psychological and physiological changes.

At present, there are some 7 billion (human) universes being perceived and contrived on this very planet—one for each of us at any given moment. By Aristotelian logic, things can only be one or the other, but not somehow both at the same time. With "quantum psychology," the way we "cohere" or "collapse" our reality into view determines what we see—or don't see. Our own individual neurology (and neuroses!) determines, perhaps not so much the state the universe is in, but our subjective *experience* of whatever state the universe is in. Thus, the somewhat shallow-sounding catch phrase that "your thoughts create your reality" is actually true in quite a fundamental way: your thoughts and accepted beliefs create your subjective experience and *interpretation* of so-called reality. This means that, ultimately, you create your own emotions. If you have created "depression" you can un-create it.[57] Tibetan Buddhists consider that we simply see what our karma allows us to see. Each perceives "truth" according to the "karmic patterns" that inform and condition his perceptions.[58]

R.A. Wilson was a proponent of E-Prime: English without "isness"; in other words, English without the words "is," "was" and any other definite existential labels. This trains one out of the Aristotelian mode of thinking that there is an "objective" experience of reality to be had, and also experiences that "are" what you might label as "terrifying," "boring," "amusing," and so on. In E-Prime, "I am skilful," becomes "within the framework of how I construct my reality, I appear to be what I would regard as skilful." You acknowledge the implicit experiential subjectivity in all scenarios with E-Prime by avoiding absolute labels that designate "isness," thus infesting the world with "spooks"; things that perhaps you see but are not necessarily an experience shared by everyone else. You acknowledge the grey area of the *maybe*; maybe I am not completely "right"; maybe I am coloring my own perceptions, maybe the model I have created is less than perfect, perhaps my mental model of reality is only a partly accurate approximation, and so on.

Snakes, for example, see heat waves (infrared), and seemingly do not see so-called objects, at least not as we do. "The world seen by a snake looks fundamentally like a spiritualist séance—fields of 'life energy' floating about in murk," explains Wilson. "The belief that the human umwelt [world field] reveals 'reality' or 'deep reality' seems, in this perspective, as naive as the notion that a yardstick reveals more 'reality' than a volt-meter, or that my religion 'is' better than your religion."[59] The unsuspecting snake lives in what we might consider to be a rather bizarre-sounding reality-tunnel or universe. It is not a "right" or "wrong" perspective, it is merely one of the trillions upon trillions of subjective experiences unfolding on this tiny planet at this moment. Charlatan? Fraud? Delusional? Crackpot? If we could describe *our* reality to a snake, it would likely think *we* were the lunatics. The world would look very different to most humans if they too could easily perceive infrared frequencies (one of Bearden's "magic windows" into hyperspace/aether/time-space/implicate order). In fact, some people (and imaging systems) do so, as well as seeing higher than "normal" frequencies (such as ultraviolet, the *other* magic window), as we shall see. Human perceptual abilities lie on a broad continuum.

In the early 1900s, in the first chapter of *Clairvoyance*, Charles Leadbeater explained that not everyone's physical perceptual faculties possess the exact same ability to apprehend information and that the few people who can see farther than ordinary at both ends of the visible light spectrum would most likely be regarded as intuitives.[60]

Subjectivity at its best is synaesthesia, "multiple sensing." Grof found during his clinical practice that LSD sessions could cause clients to experience synaesthesia: the blending or switching of sensory responses to stimuli. They could see music, hear pain, or taste colors. To me, what synaesthesia is really demonstrating is the way that frequency information can be decoded in different ways. Instead of hearing music, the frequencies are deciphered, perhaps, by faculties of the brain that are more typically associated with vision, or maybe the ears still sense the air vibrating as the music reaches them, but the brain and mind interpret this experience in terms of taste rather than audition. It gives a new meaning to listening to some "tasty tunes."

Clinical experiments identify synaesthesia as a product of the limbic (emotional) system in the brain, which, incidentally, is the part of the brain largely affected by LSD, along with the reticular system. Thus, LSD is working on parts of the brain processing sensory information and feelings about it.[61] Neurologist Richard E. Cytowic states that the phenomenon has always existed, and moreover can be developed at will.[62] As the seat of our survival urges and our "emotional centre," it (the limbic system) also seems, according to P.M.H. Atwater, to be central to the near-death experience.[63] Near-death researcher Richard J. Bonenfant did a study on the after effects of the NDE in which he found that a whopping two-thirds of participants developed synaesthesia after an NDE.[64] This signals that this phenomenon is tied to neurological "aberrations," some of which are actually induced by the NDE, heightening sense perception abilities, as we will explore further in TGI 2.

Researching for his excellent book *Supernatural*, the indefatigable Graham Hancock took a heroic dose of 13 dried grams of *P. semilanceata* (psilocybin mushrooms, which contain tryptamine, as does LSD and DMT), nearly three times the dose that landed Bill Hicks in a UFO.[65] In his altered state, Hancock listened to his daughter Shanti playing music on their old piano. He found that the notes took shape in the air, "sometimes as huge curtains of light rippling across my visual field like the aurora borealis, sometimes as fireworks and starbursts, sometimes almost as winged beings."[66] His brain-mind had been altered to convert information that would normally have been decoded as auditory data into visual data. "The arbitrary divisions which ordinarily frame our perceptions and experience are not immutable," Yurth tells us. We have internal, biologically based discriminator functions that allow us to distinguish between color, taste, sound, etc. When these discriminating biases are suspended—whether through drugs or hypnosis—we can "hallucinate" that we hear color or smell sounds, and so on.[67]

Charles Richet, who received the Nobel Prize for his discovery of anaphylaxis, told in his work *Thirty Years of Psychical Research* of the case of a person who, in a state of hypnosis, had the faculty of sight temporarily localized in the fingertips (dermo-optic vision), so that she could read a page of print with the hands instead of with the eyes.[68] Examples can be traced back to 1787 when the mesmerist Jacque Henri Petetin from Lyons reported that an entranced cataleptic woman could see, hear, and smell through her . . . *stomach*. More recent cases include that of Molly Fancher of Brooklyn. After two accidents, her lower limbs atrophied, she became blind and lost the ability to swallow, thereby apparently subsisting *without food*. In the course of her decline she developed various clairvoyant abilities. She could see what was happening in distant towns, read the contents of sealed letters, and read written text through her fingers. In double-blind experiments she was able to see the colors of objects correctly. She could see from the top of her head and from her forehead, and of that, one witness—a judge—could not "permit of a reasonable doubt."[69]

In Russia, Rosa Kuleshova was similarly talented in reading through her fingertips (and elbow), and succeeded in doing so under a variety of test conditions that proved beyond doubt that her ability was real. Nina Kulagina, a fellow Russian and PK medium, also consciously developed this ability after finding out about Kuleshova, and her abilities were subsequently verified by "scores" of scientists. Classes were even started up in Russia to teach the art of eyeless sight successfully. Many, many people were tested and instructed, with many people able to demonstrate some level of dermo-optic ability after as little as half an hour of practice.[70]

Carol Liaros of Buffalo trained the blind in the art successfully and even ended up with cases of travelling clairvoyance/remote viewing. One man even gave up using his white cane, somehow becoming aware of curbs, telephone poles, and jutting storefronts.[71] In Beijing professors have trained 10-year-olds and found that 60% of them could read with their ears. Shanghai investigators likewise trained juveniles in this art.[72] It is evident that dermo-optic vision is possible at virtually any point on the body, as French novelist Jules Romains found for himself in the early 20th century. However, it is noteworthy that Ostrander and Schroeder reported in *Psychic Discoveries* in 1970 that those with damage to the optic centres in the brain cannot demonstrate dermo-optic vision.

Now, if the subjectivity of the inner experience of consciousness of the individual can be correlated with objective information (i.e., the subject can demonstrate the ability to read accurately with their fingertips for example) as described, then clearly the internal subjective conscious experience has an innate validity. In the same way, the internal conscious experience of a clairvoyant or medium who attains accurate but hitherto obscure and unknown personal information about someone through extrasensory means clearly has its own innate validity and objectivity. We are not dealing here with the kind of subjectivity in which a schizoid personality fantasizes that their therapist is actually Satan himself or a government agent working undercover to spy on them.

Rick Strassman's DMT research provides clues that the pineal gland and the DMT it produces play an active role in mediating our perception of energy frequencies, and thus the reality we experience. Strassman actually proposes that DMT in the brain can allow our brains to perceive "dark matter" and parallel universes/hyperspace.[73] Hence the unusual DMT accounts involving UFOs, aliens, and other hyperspace entities (though there may be symbolic biological elements to some DMT encounters, as we have mentioned).

We know that the human brain is itself a frequency decoder. Research by Fritz Popp and Peter Gariaev and their colleagues reveals that all cells in the entire body are wave transmitters (and receivers), this information being transmitted to the brain but not always making it to our waking consciousness. In fact, DNA itself is an ideal frequency transmitter and receiver, making every cell in the human body a mini beacon for sending, receiving, and *storing* wave information, including light.[74] We might infer that the light and torsion waves radiated by text can be received by the cells and DNA anywhere on the body and transmitted to and decoded ("read") by the brain. Hence eyeless sight, for instance. It is interesting that the Russians found the ability to work best in bright light and that it faded, exactly like normal sight, as darkness fell.[75] It may be at least partly dependent on photon absorption.

Strassman suggests that increased levels of DMT in the brain increase the perceptual range of available frequencies. This effectively yields the experience of a different universe/reality. DeGracia proposes that hallucinogens like LSD can actually allow conscious perception of such nonphysical imagery (non-sensory perception) and even allow for perception of internal structures and workings within the brain itself ("dark noise pathways"); this may account for some of the fractal-like patterns perceived on a "trip," for example.[76]

So we see that our biology and chemistry largely mediate the type of information we receive, *how we reconstruct it in our minds*, and the general range of frequencies which we can perceive. You may live on the same planet as a snake, but you experience a completely different universe or "reality tunnel." The biological link with heightened perception, or what might be called psychic perception, is something that will be elaborated as we go. We need to dispense with any notions that "paranormal" phenomena are a "psychiatric" phenomenon; this is merely a relatively recent (in the grand scheme of things) and transient, culturally indoctrinated belief that is well and truly outdated and revealed as fallacy by vast swathes of evidence.

More constructive by far is to look at such things as a matter of genuine perception, stemming from our own particular perceptual faculties, which are not identical in functioning from one person to the next. In essence, we find that our perception of reality is basically an elaborate illusion—the perspective of mysticism from well before modern science ever realized that "solid objects" are actually 99.9% empty space (i.e., illusions), and that over 95% of the matter and energy in the cosmos is undetectable/invisible by direct technological means—it is "dark," because it radiates no light within the known and measurable spectrum.

J.J. van der Leeuw, as a theosophist, explained that it is when we take the virtual image in our minds as being the actual thing in itself, existing independently of conscious perception, that we become ensnared by illusion or *maya*.[77] Fred Alan Wolf shares his perspective as a physicist in similar terms, explaining that, though you have a sense of being present in your body, you don't actually exist anywhere in it, and therefore, it is an illusion to think that everything outside your body is "not you." "The best description we can give for this sense of presence is that you 'are everywhere' [and that] 'who we are' is an awareness or consciousness that lives in space."[78]

Physically, we are all spatial extensions of the aether/ZPF. Schrödinger said that "what we observe as material bodies and forces are nothing but shapes and variations in the structure of space." In terms of consciousness, we *are* that "space," which, at base, is really a conscious field of potential. What Wolf and other contemporary physicists, mystics, and occultists are (and for the latter two, always have been) saying is that we inhabit a subjective personal universe that *masquerades* as an objective one. But the only way we can come to realize the universe as either "real" or "unreal" is through our *subjective experience* of it, via differing states of consciousness. We cannot intimately know anything except through our experience of it.

Thus, the only "realities" that we can ever experience and talk about meaningfully are "perceived realities, experienced realities, existential realities—realities involving ourselves as editors—and they are all relative to the observer,"[79] Wilson exhorts us. The only litmus test we have of determining whether something is real is to find out if other people can see it as well, and if only *some* people (more than one but not everyone) can see it—all things being equal—then, in Bearden's model, that defines it as paranormal. But, as Talbot pointed out, the admission that two or more people can create a shared reality (as has been documented) means we no longer have a way to prove that everything else is not also created by the mind[80] (or perhaps consciousness in a broader sense), thus rendering dogmatic skepticism a position of utter impotence and futility. As self-declared ex-skeptic Steve Pavlina comments, "If our beliefs are just a self-fulfilling prophecy, then the prophecy of skepticism is a lame one to fulfill."[81] We will explore the "paranormal" effects of belief in more depth later on.

Brainwaves and the Mind as a Radio Station

It is known that energy not only forms matter, but that all matter *is* energy. According to W. Davis, writing in the 1980s, the point at which energy "became" matter was believed to be around the frequency of 9 cycles/Hertz. To Davis, this was astonishing, given that the sleeping human brain typically functions at about 6 cycles or lower (now narrowed down to 1.5 to 4 cycles/second), thus operating below the frequency of matter creation.[82]

It is also interesting to notice that in our sleep state, our brainwaves drop below the "pulse" of the planet, the Schumann frequency of about 7.8 Hz. The brain emits waves of low frequency while it is operating, with these frequencies having some correlation to the frequency range of the reality being decoded by the mind; the frequencies of theta might represent hypnagogic and hypnapompic states and dream imagery. These realities correspond, for the occultist, to the astral realm (time-space), a different level of reality composed of harmonic overtones of the physical-etheric cosmos.

There seems to be an inverse relationship between the frequency output of the brain and the frequency of the vibrational reality our consciousness decodes. The lower the brain frequency, the higher the frequency of the reality or dimension our mind experiences, and the less we identify with physical reality. (Hence, brainwaves dropping below the Schumann resonance during sleep, to me, suggests an orientation of consciousness *away* from our worldly space-time reality and towards higher octaves in time-space.)

The higher brain frequencies show thought oriented strongly towards our familiar EM reality. The case may be similar for encountering and decoding so-called *parallel worlds* that do not necessarily qualify as the occultist's astral or mental planes. Recall the words of the co-founder of string theory, Michio Kaku: "if you have a radio in your living room . . . and you have all frequencies in your living room; BBC, Radio Moscow, ABC, but your radio is tuned to one frequency—you're decohered from all the other frequencies. You're only coherent with one frequency."

Can you tune into and perceive other parallel universes in your living room? Once again, today's science not only says these realities exist, but we know they have been encountered and explored by shamans, mystics, and occultists for millennia. It has only been fairly recently that the scientific method has been applied to this exploration, and the results it has yielded are conclusive. These parallel universes in our living rooms don't just lurk silently in the background; they can sometimes be tapped into, in various ways, some more of which we will explore. Sometimes the inhabitants of these realities can tap into us.

The radio analogy as employed by Kaku (and others) is apropos. If you are tuned into Radio Moscow, the other frequencies do not stop broadcasting; they continue passing through you unnoticed, because you are not tuned into their frequency. You are "decohered" from them and cannot resonate with them. You're out of phase. It would be ignorant to say they no longer exist, and yet the average person in the normal waking beta brainwave state will not perceive these frequencies. The ill-advisedly brave might even venture to say these stations' frequencies do not exist, on the ultra-simplistic grounds that since they cannot perceive it, then it can't really be there. I wonder if such people have ever stopped to think about the kind of universe they would inhabit if they applied this form of logic to the more familiar aspects of our lives.

The irony is that while no one (to my knowledge at least) has ever *directly* perceived or intercepted something as "familiar" as radiowaves without the aid of electrical equipment, meaning our knowledge and experience of them is completely indirect (via electronic technology), we take their existence completely for granted. And yet there are people—many of them—who have directly intercepted and/or apprehended nonphysical information from what we might refer to as parallel realities, nonphysical dimensions, or hyperspace, and had the fact confirmed by rigorous, methodical scientific research (often widely replicated)—and yet still the ardent disbelievers cry foul of "the paranormal."

Our primary brainwave states are as follows:

1. Gamma: Hyper-alert and focused state, about 40–100 Hz
2. Beta: The awake and alert state, about 12–40 Hz
3. Alpha: A meditative and receptive state, about 8–12 Hz
4. Theta: A deeply intuitive state (or sleep state), about 4–8 Hz
5. Delta: The deepest sleep state, 0–4 Hz.

The gamma state has been linked with psychokinesis: manifesting intention in the physical world ("mind over matter"), though there is a higher band beyond it that most people are unaware of called lambda, extending all the way up to 200 Hz.[83]

The Institute of Heartmath in Boulder Creek, California, has developed a form of meditation where the heart rate entrains brainwaves, the heart having the more powerful rhythm, establishing a standing wave of coherence between heart, brain, and body. Rollin McCraty, research director at Heartmath, states that this synchronization of heart and brain causes brainwave patterns to dip to a very low frequency of .1 Hz, and "it is here that great power resides for healing."[84] The heart's is the most powerful field in the human body, so powerful that an ECG reading can be taken with the electrodes 3 feet away from the body.[85]

Within the context of brainwaves, it is interesting to note that children have a reputation for being strikingly intuitive for a time, before ultimately "growing out of it" (usually being conditioned out of it by ill-informed parents, peers, teachers, clergy, and so on—the "culture mind syndrome"). Between birth and two years of age, the human brain predominantly operates in the lowest band, 0.5–4 cycles per second (cps) (delta). However, according to Lipton, babies can also exhibit periodic short bursts of higher EEG activity. Between the ages of two and six, children spend more time in the theta range,[86] as their consciousness has increasingly tuned in to our level of reality.

Both the delta and theta ranges have been associated with nonlocal and/ or anomalous information processing, yet as we reach adulthood we typically spend more and more time in the beta state of the active and focused brain-mind which does not conduce to intuitive functioning. Delta and theta brainwaves are associated with the hypnagogic trance state—that pleasant state of dreamy semi-consciousness we pass through as we fall asleep, and again as we begin to wake, which we call hypnopompic—meaning that children up to the age of six are living in something akin to a hypnotic trance, operating at levels "below" normal adult waking consciousness.[87] Paradoxically, the extremely high and low (opposite) ends of the brainwave spectrum have the *same* states of consciousness associated with them, and different frequency bands can be present in different parts of the same brain and interact.[88]

Hypnotherapists drop their patients' brain activity into delta and theta because these low-frequency brainwaves put them into a more suggestible, programmable state, offering a clue explaining how children can download the voluminous information required to thrive.[89] These lower-frequency brainwave states probably facilitate the spontaneous nonlocal "acquisition" and processing of information by the child without any intent or even awareness of the fact. Thus, a child's outlook on life and fundamental belief systems are created at least partly by "osmosis" at subtle energetic levels. It is these lower brainwave states that allow that subconscious information to become conscious more readily, and we therefore end up with various "paranormal" phenomena of a more passive nature, in which, for example, the child may find itself knowing things about friends of their parents that they had no logical way of knowing or even guessing. Raikov's "artificial reincarnation" subjects must, in their altered states, have been accessing—more or less directly—the implicate order/ time-space/aether wherein all information is stored in undifferentiated form—

219

including all information about the personality traits and tics of, say, deceased musical virtuosos and other artists.

The Door to the Subconscious Observer and Editor

It is thought by many that our so-called subconscious information-processing stream is the key to intuitive functioning. You may recall the mass experiments that allegedly took place years ago that were conducted on the movie-going public in America. While the film was in progress, messages extolling the virtues of Coke and popcorn, which were for sale in the lobby, were flashed onto the screen. These images were flashed so rapidly that the conscious mind didn't notice them, but the more powerful subconscious apparently picked them up easily. The result was reportedly that both popcorn and Coke sales increased significantly.[90] This is a powerful illustration of the influence subliminal levels of consciousness can have over our conscious experience and decision-making, and more importantly in this context, how powerful a perceiver the subconscious processor really is.

The subconscious mind can detect a much more concentrated volume of stimuli than our conscious, intellect-based, serial processing minds can—about 40 nerve impulses per second for the conscious mind operating through the prefrontal cortex, versus about 40 million for the disproportionately larger brain mass devoted to subconscious processing.[91] The reason we experience our subconscious processing as being "subconscious" or "unconscious" is that it processes data so rapidly that the linear mind, which can only process relatively little information at any given moment, perceives only the *absence of activity*. It is not really unconscious, it is a different form of parallel consciousness.[92]

The subconscious mind is a very powerful tool when precisely programmed with intent. On the other hand, it can be a destructive slave driver if its imprinting is an emotionally disturbed one, or more pertinently for our discussion, if its mental programming possesses flaws like "there is no such thing as psi." Cognitive neuroscientists estimate that our conscious minds contribute roughly 5% of our cognitive activity, meaning that the vast majority of our actions, emotions, decisions, and behaviors result from the unobserved workings of the subconscious.[93] Consider the sobering fact that during the first six years of life, most of our beliefs about ourselves and the world are formed and adopted into our subconscious quite passively, according to what we experience and observe—*all before we have developed critical thinking faculties that would allow us to reject self-defeating notions before we adopt them as beliefs that then shape our thoughts and actions, and our ability to remotely attract what we want into our lives.*[94]

Remember, we do not passively perceive an external world; we decode information fields and edit the incoming data and create a model, an approximation of reality. Psychic signals are endlessly registered in the subconscious but must cross the subliminal threshold in order to be detected by conscious awareness. Swann wrote: "Since such signals are usually too weak to do this, they can be available only to those with very highly sensitized and refined senses or receptors."[95]

Dean Radin's (replicated) research has effectively proved the subliminal reception of the mysterious "psions" or some form of information by the measurable physiological responses it initiates in the body. We might say that there exists a metaphorical door between the subconscious and conscious minds, and if that door is not open but closed, information can't surface from the subconscious into our conscious awareness. We then lack overt intuition/psi abilities and our perception is limited to perceiving through the filter of our mental preconceptions and emotional biases.

Alice Bryant and Linda Seebach, a mother-daughter team of researchers into "multidimensional" humans and their supernormal abilities, wrote:

> Successful multidimensionals have simply eradicated the barriers between conscious and subconscious inputs . . . and expanded their 5 to 15 per cent conscious awareness factor by an untold amount. Human minds (conscious awareness) have been stuck or blocked into a "dislearning" mindset which has short-circuited the potential of human mind functioning. Successful multidimensionals make adjustments necessary to unlock the mindset—and, once free from that state of non-awareness—can access higher dimensions.[96]

Richard Gerber explained that if psi information reaches conscious awareness, it does so through the cerebral cortex, possibly being filtered through the right cerebral hemisphere and then transferred to the left where it is then analysed and can ultimately be expressed verbally.[97]

One can no more hope to find consciousness by digging into the brain than one can find gravity by digging into the earth. —Karl Pribram

221

8

THE OCCULTIST'S SEVEN PLANES AND THEIR CORRESPONDING VEHICLES

The intuitive mind is a sacred gift and the rational mind is a faithful servant.
We have created a society that honors the servant and has forgotten the gift.
—Albert Einstein

The separation of the two—matter and spirit—is an abstraction.
The ground is always one. —David Bohm

Seven Primary Planes

This chapter is not presented as being evidence-based, but is intended to provide a basic occult framework for understanding so-called "paranormal phenomena," for which modern science and global human experience have amassed so very much evidence. Moreover, it offers an occult framework for conceiving oneself as fundamentally immortal/eternal consciousness—something much more than just a human. The evidence for this chapter's content is found in both the preceding and subsequent chapters.

The names used in theosophical literature for the higher planes are derived from Sanskrit, but we also note the Buddhist terms. The seven planes/densities of existence (the "Seven Heavens") are said to possess seven subplanes of their own, divided still further into seven more subplanes, ad infinitum. The density of matter decreases and the frequency increases as we get deeper into the higher dimensions. Each of the seven primary planes (Figure 8.1) are designated by theosophy as follows in this—and I cannot stress this enough—*extremely simplified* schema as I present it:

1. The physical plane—"matter," subdivided into two levels: dense matter and etheric matter. The etheric body is considered part of the physical realm, just a higher frequency and lower density of opposite polarity. The physical-etheric plane/s feature three spatial dimensions.

2. The astral planes (lower, middle, and higher)—the realm of passions, anger, desire (*Kama*), fantasies, or *emotion* in general. Four dimensions of space. There is both dense and coarse astral matter, possessing slight mass—as such it is somewhat subject to gravity. The corresponding vehicle is the astral body, also somewhat subject to gravity.

3. The mental or *manasic* planes—subdivided for convenience into two levels: *Rupa* (having form), and *Arupa* (formless). The mental body has two essential aspects: the causal body is the *higher mental body*, the "true self," which survives between lifetimes and contains the best elements from each incarnation, while the lower aspect is generally regarded as the *lower mental*, where everyday cognitive functioning occurs. Five dimensions of space.

4. The buddhic plane and body—here the past, present, and future exist simultaneously, and it is said to be the plane of intuitional insight as well as utterly unselfish affection or devotion. Six dimensions of space.

5. The nirvanic plane (*atmic* in Sanskrit)—nirvanic consciousness means consciousness anywhere in the solar system—"smeared" or dispersed nonlocally, in other words. Vast and blissful experience; omnipotence; divine will; absence of anything resembling human feeling. Here resides what theosophists call the Atma.

6. The paranirvanic plane (*anupadaka* in Sanskrit), meaning literally "the plane beyond Nirvana"—where the "Monad" (higher self composed of the best of all selves from all lifetimes, including parallel reality systems) is said to reside completely beyond the constraints of our space-time system. Here lie the origins of *individual self* and the last vestiges of dualism or subject-object awareness; the final "sheath."

7. The mahaparanirvanic plane (Sanskrit: *adi*), literally "the greater plane beyond Nirvana." Completely beyond dualism; identification with Source. Each of these last three planes (5, 6, and 7) and associated states of consciousness would be generically regarded as "Father/Spirit/God"

in a Judeo-Christian framework, while the astral and mental realms would comprise the heaven worlds (with the lower astral constituting "hell," as we see in TGI 2).

Leadbeater elaborates in *Man Visible and Invisible* that the names for these last two planes simply signify either the lack of directly obtained information possessed by whoever named these planes, or that they lacked the words to express such information.[1] However, there are some surprises in store in TGI 2, where we will reserve space for delving deeper into the Monad in particular.

Figure 8.1 Representation of the planes of existence and the diffusion of consciousness through them, by Charles Leadbeater

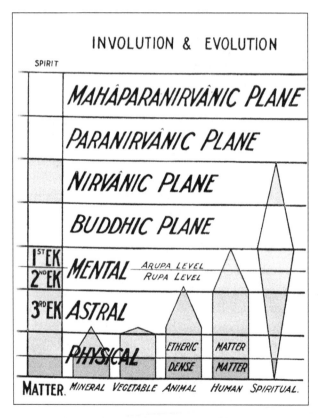

Source: *Man Visible and Invisible* by C.W. Leadbeater. © The Theosophical Publishing House, Adyar, Chennai-600 020. India. http://www.ts-adyar.org & http://www.adyarbooks.com

In the Hindu Upanishads (one of three sources of the Vedantin teachings), there is a description of five bodies, layers or "sheaths" (*Kosas*) of the human being, notwithstanding that the sheathless Spirit, or *Atman*, is identical in essence to the Universal Soul:

1. *Annamaya Kosa*: the physical body, made of *anna* (food).
2. *Pranamaya Kosa*: made of prana; the etheric body.
3. *Manomaya Kosa*: equivalent to the astral and mental bodies (which tend to work in concert and therefore are classed together here); the seat of emotion and lower mind (ordinary concrete thought).
4. *Vijnanamaya Kosa*: "discriminatory intelligence" and higher conceptual thought; Intellect with a capital "I." Equivalent to the causal body or "real man."
5. *Anandamaya Kosa*: made of spiritual bliss or joy; the buddhic body. (*Ananda* means bliss.)

Vedantin philosophy instructs us that Atman—our immortal "stream" of consciousness—passes like a thread through the five subtle bodies or kosas, and therefore is named by the Sanskrit term *Sutratman* (*sutra* meaning thread and *atman* being Self).[2]

The Physical and the Etheric

As the etheric matter is essentially a component of the physical plane, it is the most readily discernible subtle matter, even for "non-clairvoyants" whose intuitive faculties are mostly latent. Etheric matter can manifest to the untrained eye as a milky or cloudy mist close to the physical body. It is this proximity that makes it perceptible to even "non-psychics." But to the clairvoyant the etheric body proper "looks like a luminous web of fine, bright lines of force which, in a healthy person, stand out at right angles to the surface of the skin."[3] Though possessing a definite structure, the etheric body is in constant motion, as sparks of bluish-white light travel along its grid lines within and throughout the physical body. This etheric structure sets up the matrix for the body's cells to grow within.[4]

The etheric double has been given a variety of names. The Hindu name for it is *Pranamayakosha* (vehicle of prana): in German it is known as the *Doppelgänger*. After death, having separated from the physical body, it is known as the "wraith," and has also been called the "phantom," "apparition," or "churchyard ghost."[5]

According to Powell and various notable clairvoyant investigators, the etheric double is a pale violet-grey or blue-grey in appearance, slightly luminous and shimmering, like heat waves above bitumen on a hot day. It absorbs prana, or vitality (or "orgone") from food, drink, and the atmosphere, and distributes this to the whole body, as well as acting as a bridge between the physical body and the astral body, transmitting physical sensory data "through the etheric brain to the astral body, and also transmitting consciousness from the astral and higher levels down into the physical brain and nervous system."[6] (Notice the bi-directional causality here.)

Though the etheric body is generally not regarded as a center of consciousness proper, some have said that it is sometimes projected from the physical body, and can thereby appear "as an apparition of the living, of which there are many cases recorded by the societies that investigate psychical subjects."[7] Alfred observes that there are possibly two etheric doubles, one facilitating OBEs, which Bruce might regard as the real-time double. Such an idea is indicated in *Death—And After?* by Besant.

According to Powell, the etheric double/body harnesses and distributes the "vital force" (prana/orgone) emanating from the sun (and which is present floating freely in our atmosphere) and therefore is closely associated with physical health. Like the astral and mental bodies, it has its own chakras, each with its own function (though they are apparently all the same color at the etheric level). It also plays an important role in determining the kind of physical body an incarnating "soul" will receive, and, like the physical body at death, it too must ultimately be cast off and left to decay so as to release the soul for the next stage in its journey. Every particle of the physical body is surrounded with an "etheric envelope," thus making the etheric double a duplicate of the physical (which the astral body is not).[8]

The etheric body is said to extend out from the body roughly 1–6 inches for the outer portion, depending on the state of health. It is possible to glimpse (to some extent) the etheric energy in dim lighting by drawing the fingertips of the two hands close together and then slowly pulling them apart, when a plasma-like emanation may be seen flowing from one hand to the other. To seer Phoebe Payne, the outer portion of the etheric field extended 4–6 inches away from the body, depending on the health of the person,[9] hence the term "health aura." Standing in slightly dimmed lighting against a white or beige background is also a good starting point for practice at perceiving the etheric bioenergy. Squinting and turning the head so light strikes the periphery of the retina where there are more rods might assist in perceiving the infrared frequencies.[10]

Importantly, and as we will explore further in the next chapter, the etheric energy field (a.k.a. the *vital body*) precedes and even guides the formation of the physical body. This view (or some variation of it) is held increasingly by researchers and theorists such as Amit Goswami and Rupert Sheldrake, among others. Goswami has noted that "living organisms display 'program-like' behaviour giving away their secret—that they have another body that consists of the feels behind the programs that living organisms are capable of running"—the vital/etheric body (one example of a real and observable "morphic field").[11] Korotkov agrees, stating that the existence of this program makes an organism on the verge of embryogenesis "run through" all previous stages of development of the species to which the organism belongs.[12] This shows, in a microcosm, that the forces of evolution are fundamentally hyperdimensional.

Sheldrake reaches the same conclusion by noting that genes do not have the programs for morphogenesis or form-making. In Sheldrake's terminology, morphogenesis is guided by nonlocal extra-physical morphogenetic fields[13]—these are the occultist's hidden planes and subtle bodies, in point of fact. ("Morphic field" is a more versatile and inclusive variant of "morphogenetic field." The former term "includes morphogenetic, behavioural, social, cultural, and mental fields."[14]) It appears that entropy is denied and held at bay by the body's fields, in particular the etheric morphic field.

According to Tom Montalk, processes that seem mechanical and predictable on the large scale have their origins in quantum jumps that are neither predictable by physical science nor controllable by purely physical means. The etheric body is the "extra factor . . . that biases these quantum jumps at the small scale to offset the forces of entropy at the large scale." To Montalk, the etheric body is "an energy template that biases the probability of acausal biological events to produce ordered and intelligent life. It is a formative field made of coarse life-force energy."[15]

> While the physical realm and our normal waking consciousness are both highly localized . . . the etheric plane is more diffuse . . . That diffuseness is what allows the etheric body to shape quantum events, to bias probability, because it is a structure diffused across multiple possibilities instead of being localized to just one as our physical body is.[16]

Like Sheldrake's morphic fields, the etheric operates probabilistically rather than deterministically and mechanically. If the etheric realm is an inverted/reciprocal or "mirror" counterpart of ours in every sense of the term, where time does run backwards in some sense, "then it sheds further light on how it can bias probability," writes Montalk, in that, it "pulls" on the physical *from the future*, making it an influence originating in what we think of as the future and flowing *backwards* in time.[17] Likewise, Sheldrake grants the possibility of this "backwards through time" dynamic for morphic fields, even though they simultaneously become increasingly "conditioned" by the past with each moment, becoming temporally self-similar (nonlocally through time).

If you wanted to rapidly heal a wound on your body, for instance, you could visualize your desired outcome, a virtual reality existing in hyperspace/thought/time in the possible "future," which could then theoretically "flow backwards through time" via the etheric field, statistically altering quantum biological events in your body to manifest the desired future scenario: rapid healing.

Habit also has an etheric basis, as Montalk rightly observes, because repeated behaviors set up a type of momentum in the etheric that biases probability towards continuation of that behavior. Thus, a certain type of activity in a house can entrain the etheric to attract similar activity from subsequent residents.[18] In Sheldrake's model, "[m]orphic fields are shaped and stabilized by morphic resonance from previous similar morphic units, which were under the influence of fields of the same kind. They consequently contain a kind of cumulative memory and tend to become increasingly habitual."[19]

If these subtle fields are torsion/scalar fields, then this program-like habitual behavior is understandable, since torsion fields are known to be highly stable. It is interesting to note that torsion fields are conceived of as information fields lacking EM properties or locations in our space-time—the exact description of morphic fields as given by Sheldrake in *The Presence of the Past*.

According to the best occultists, although our physical bodies register sensory stimulus, we actually *feel* it via the etheric body. Steiner explained that physical pressure can cause a (clairvoyantly observable) displacement of the etheric body, resulting in the familiar "sleeping limb" sensations.[20] In fact, Dora van Gelder Kunz—an extensively tested and extremely reliable clairvoyant we will hear much more of—has observed that the effect of general anaesthetic in the body is to temporarily "squeeze" or push the etheric "fluid" up towards the head, thus causing numbness where it previously was in the body. When she observed a similar withdrawal process occurring in an animal that had *not* been anaesthetized, she correctly predicted its imminent death.[21]

The etheric body can be used to explain why, for example, a psychic medium might feel physically assaulted—say, strangled—by an entity that appears nonexistent to other people. The feeling of hands around one's throat, for instance, is being registered by a subtle body, not the physical. (See TGI 2 for evidence of such notions.) Physicist William Tiller's model places the etheric frequencies between the speed of light and 10^{10} times light speed, and astral frequencies between 10^{10} and 10^{20} times light speed;[22] fast enough to provide ostensibly nonlocal psi effects over large distances.

In sum, Jay Alfred points out in his well-researched book *Our Invisible Bodies* that physical-etheric particles constitute the first and lowest level of super particles. He believes that all such super particles or shadow/dark objects postulated by physicists can be found here. This etheric/shadow/dark matter interacts only weakly with our familiar reality, mainly through weak gravitational fields.[23]

The Astral Plane

The astral plane is the reality out-of-body experiences or astral projectors (and many NDEers) normally find themselves in. The name "astral" apparently comes from the medieval alchemist Paracelsus, and signifies "starry," so deemed due to the luminous appearance of astral matter which was associated with the more rapid rate of its vibration. The astral plane is traditionally conceived of as the world of emotion, passion, and sensation. Emotionally speaking, pleasure and pain arise from the astral, in the theosophical model. It is through the astral body— in kabbalism a "spirit body" capable of moving "up" into higher realms—that feelings exhibit themselves to one possessing clairvoyance at the astral level. Thus, the astral body continually shifts in appearance as emotions change.[24]

It is important to grasp that each plane's matter interpenetrates that of the other planes; at the Earth's surface they are all coexistent with one another, although matter from the higher planes—being of lower density—extends further away from the physical Earth than the lower. When someone "rises" from one plane or subplane to another, rather than moving through space, they are transferring their consciousness from one level to another. The individual gradually becomes unresponsive to the vibrations of one grade/density of matter, and instead begins to resonate with a higher, more refined grade. The result is that one world and its inhabitants would fade from view, while a new one of a higher kind would come into view. You may find it interesting to note that, according to Leadbeater, the "background environment" of subplanes four, five, and six of the astral (the seventh being disregarded for now) is the familiar physical world.[25]

OBE pioneer Robert Monroe, physicist Michael Talbot, and many others have also experienced and written of "zones" within the lower astral that bear close correspondence with the physical world, so we know that Leadbeater's assessment has been confirmed in essence by fellow astral travelers. This correspondence between the physical and lower astral allows for confirmatory data to be retrieved by the OBEers (and also remote viewers) and checked later against experience in the physical world to verify the reality of the astral planes and the OBE in general. The "real-time zone," Bruce tells us, is technically a part of the astral, though best considered a separate dimensional level, since it bears no direct relationship to the lower subplanes. Experience of it is akin to being "an invisible specter in the real world."[26]

Astral projectors in the real-time zone are slightly out of phase (or "decohered") with the physical and astral plane proper in Bruce's view; at a higher vibrational level than physical space-time, but lower than the astral plane proper. They occupy a "direct dimensional reflection" of the physical universe as it is in real time.[27] Bruce's real-time zone does indeed sound something like a description of the etheric level; a doppelganger of the physical world.

Worth noting, too, is that Bruce agrees with the theosophical conception that the astral plane is divided into seven major levels or planes, each harboring further subplanes, etc., though he describes it as "totally nonspatial."[28] To the theoretical physicist, this makes it an "imaginary" aspect of phase space, probably at least two "rotations" away from our reality. An astral projector's space-time location usually matches where they think they are in the world, according to Bruce, and they can be tracked if viewed by someone with real-time sight, a form of clairvoyance.[29] It is commonly acknowledged that although astral projectors exist as invisible points of consciousness, they usually perceive themselves as having a bodily form which is often seen as being connected to the physical body via a "silver cord." This is an energetic link, the severance of which results in an inability to return to reanimate the physical body ("death").

Leadbeater indicates the presence of an extra spatial dimension in the astral by explaining that, here, even physical-world objects can be seen from all sides at once (as in a Picasso work). In addition, every particle *inside* a solid body is just as clearly visible as those *external* to it, meaning that, initially, even once-familiar objects may be completely unrecognizable.[30]

This alteration of vision has been experienced and verified by others, including OBEer Preston Dennett. While the astral body has no specialized physical sensory organs—it perceives holographically and holistically—yogis have held that there is an astral counterpart to every physical sense (taste, vision, etc.).[31] Hence, the OBEer finds himself able to expand his field of vision, even to the extent that he perceives in every direction simultaneously. On top of this, Leadbeater adds that the astral sight renders visible various physical matter that the physical eyes do not see, apparently including aspects of Earth's atmospheric matter.

Recognizing that the seer is forced to interpret data coming from a higher-dimensional plane (where an object can be seen from all sides at once) in 3D terms presents us with some rudimentary sense of the difficulties involved. There is a translational or interpretive process between 3-space and 4-space that is not always 100% reliable. The astral chakras have extension in four dimensions, one more than the etheric, meaning that some part of them is always coincident with the etheric vortices, though they are not necessarily coterminous.[32] We might note that Kunz has stated that it is primarily through the solar plexus chakra that astral energies normally enter the auric field.[33]

The astral plane has been explored by many modern and contemporary OBEers, most of them initially starting out as skeptics, the late Robert Monroe and the still living Preston Dennett being two such examples. Having developed the ability to "project" almost at will, Dennett went on to have over 1,000 conscious OBEs, causing him to write that he found the astral dimensions to be an "utterly real place, richly detailed and teeming with life."[34] In point of fact, he found the astral planes to be like physical life only *more real*,[35] a not uncommon sentiment among those with firsthand personal knowledge of such realms. Modern and contemporary OBEers (and remote viewers) attest that we have strong sensory awareness on the astral planes, with the ability to discern heat, cold, different flavors, and aromas (olfactory functioning), physical impacts, pressure, speed, and so on.

Regarding the astral body as it appears around the living human, it is said to extend roughly 6–18 inches out from the body in the average man, with a clear and definite outline, and somewhat luminous quality. In a spiritually developed man it is larger and "composed of the finest particles of each grade of astral matter, the higher largely predominating."[36] The fluidic astral body features the seven colors of the rainbow in moving patches of color, though to Barbara Brennan's clairvoyance these are tinged with the "rose light of love." The chakras in the astral body also display these colors, as we will see. When people form relationships with one another, energetic cords grow out of the chakras (at more than just the astral level), connecting them. Even in everyday circumstances people exchange "blobs" of astral colors unawares as a basic (and subconscious) energetic form of communication.[37]

In occult thought, as someone develops, his/her astral body increasingly resembles their mental body, until it becomes little more than a reflection of it. The mental body is not greatly affected by a flood of emotion, though violent emotion may make it virtually impossible for activity in the mental to reach the physical brain via the astral, since the strong singular vibration of the astral will not convey vibrations that are not in sympathy with it at such moments.[38] This is why you shouldn't make decisions when you're extremely emotional: rational thought and foresight are compromised.

The three primary functions of the astral body are:

1. To make sensation possible.
2. To serve as a bridge between mind and physical matter.
3. To act as an independent vehicle of consciousness and action.[39]

The second point is interesting in light of Tiller's duplex space-time model which postulates an intermediary substance between our reality and subtle frequency domains that allows for interaction (coupling) between mind and matter and which he says occupies the emotional domain. He calls these theoretical particles "deltrons"; String theorists would speak of "super particles." We will note the strong connection between emotion and mind–matter interactions in some detail later. While mental frequencies are faster, there is something about emotion that is, as Luckman puts it, more elemental.

We might surmise that the "anomalous" or "synchronistic" coherence between the Global Consciousness Project's REG's *prior* to major emotionally charged events such as 9/11, Princess Diana's funeral, and so forth is explainable in terms of the backwards-through-time action of the astral/emotional waves in time-space as they "filter" down into our reality, with a signal strength of enough magnitude to actually influence quantum events before the highly emotional space-time event has actually occurred. Thus we see in the collective subconscious an a priori foreknowledge of the impending event/s (Radin has rigorously proven subconscious foreknowledge for *individuals*, as we will see, so it is hardly a major leap to consider *collective* subconscious "presentiment," as he calls it). In the GCP's data, it was found that the *degree of order* in the REG output seemed to match the *emotional intensity* of the events. (Another interesting fact is that despite the global coherence between the REGs, on 9/11 the strongest effects occurred in the REGs that were closest to New York.[40] Since those living closer to New York would presumably find the event more personally meaningful, on average, than those living elsewhere, the "backwards through time" emotional response would, in turn, be larger on average, thus producing stronger effects in REGs closer to New York.)

To Montalk's thinking, the astral is perpendicular to both the physical and the etheric, with its wave function consisting solely of phase and lacking any spatial or temporal component, thus explaining why life in the astral "is so *abstract, symbolic, timeless,* and *spaceless . . .*" From here, physical realms may be accessible by rotating into them, which may be how "souls" incarnate.[41] In terms of string theory, astral and mental particles are "super particles."[42]

In TGI 2, which covers survival of death, astral projection/OBE and many other important topics, I will expand on the astral and mental planes in detail and also look at some of the amazing evidence and research supporting the reality of these realms' existence.

The Mental Plane

"The mental plane is also termed in Sanskrit *Devasthan,* the land of the Gods; it is the *Svarga* of the Hindus, the *Sukhavati* of the Buddhists, the Heaven of the Zoroastrian, Christian and Mohammedan; it has been called also the 'Nirvana' of the common people."[43]

This is the plane of the intellect, of higher mind functions, noble intellectual concepts, and philosophical abstractions. It is also believed that it is only when one reaches beyond the astral plane into the mental that truly reliable work can be done with the Akashic records. Abstract thought is a function of the higher mental or causal body (consisting of matter from the uppermost three sub-planes of the mental). On the other hand, "lower," more "meat and potatoes" thought arises through the mental body/"lower mental body."[44]

The mental plane is divided into two parts, which are said to be distinguished by a difference in color and the names of *rupa* and *arupa,* meaning respectively "having form" and "formless." These names reflect certain qualities of the matter of the plane; in the lower part, human thought easily moulds matter into definite forms, while this is not the case on the higher division, where the more abstract thought of that level has been said to express itself to the eye of the clairvoyant in "flashes" or "streams."[45] The lower subplanes of the mental plane still contain form (geometry), while the higher aspects such as the causal and upper manasic do not (except perhaps as embedded potential).

The mental and astral "bodies" are primarily concerned with the production of thought-forms, which for the most part are composed of both astral and mental matter. In Sanskrit the term for mind substance at rest is *chitta,* while actively engaged mind substance is *vritta,* which literally translated means "a whirlpool or eddy [vortex] in the mind," which, as Ramacharaka put it, "is exactly what a thought really is."[46]

Thought-forms of great variety exist and even originate in the mental plane, while it is essentially absent of the emotional impulses that characterize the

233

astral (or lower emotional, depending on your framework). Ideas and thoughts originate from the mental plane and register in the mental body, filtering into our awareness from there. It should be noted that the matter of the mental plane strongly interacts with that of the astral plane, and likewise, the astral influences the etheric and physical. Thus, when people "astral-project," they can sometimes perceive thought-forms of the mental plane, due to the overlap between the astral and mental.

Arthur Powell wrote that purely intellectual and impersonal thoughts consist only of mental matter, while thoughts that feature an aspect of selfishness or desire draw astral matter together along with the mental. Deeply unselfish or spiritual thought would involve matter of the buddhic plane.[47] Because lower mental matter, *manas*, is so inextricably linked with astral matter, *kama*, thinking tends to be accompanied by some degree of feeling, and vice-versa.[48] Because our astral and mental faculties are so intertwined like this, it is often said that they act as a single body. The Vedantin classification combines them as one *kosha* or sheath: *Manomayakosha*.[49] This, incidentally, is the system Amit Goswami works from in his *Physics of the Soul*. I will, however, distinguish between the astral and mental bodies, as per the theosophical system.

The mental body, like the etheric, is a structured body, appearing mostly yellow.[50] Like the fluidic astral, it comes into contact with the forms of the mental world directly, and over its whole surface (holographically). There are thus no sensory organs in the mental body; it is more accurate to speak of an overall "mental-sense," Powell states. Here communication is essentially mind to mind, so the barrier of language no longer exists on the mental plane, as it (reportedly) does on the astral plane.[51] It is interesting that the late out-of-body veteran Robert Monroe (whose work we will look at in detail in TGI 2), noted that his communications with other beings in his disembodied state were not telepathic but "non-verbal." When he tried to "talk" or "verbalize" his thoughts to other beings he found the communication to be ineffective, whereas when he tried to radiate or impress his intent upon another non-verbally, it was highly successful.

The mental body gives meaning to both the objects of physical reality and also to our etheric/vital body feelings and sensations. It is the sorter, categorizer, and organizer, the seat of intellectual abstraction. In many people, the mental body's input and thought processes are all too easily undermined by the emotionalistic thought-feelings (often based in fear) of the astral body, and the belief programs running in the lower mind, and thus the herd mentality prevails over much of the globe, making great swathes of humanity highly manipulable by dogmas and doctrines that would otherwise swiftly crumble under a modicum of impartial scrutiny by the true intellect. For example: "The occult is the Devil," or "The occult is purely for superstitious and ignorant people and the charlatans who deceive them," or "The political left/right paradigm in its current form affords the public real and meaningful choice."

Politicians, for example, regularly prey on the tendency for the emotional "circuits" to subvert calm, rational, egalitarian thought—particularly through concepts such as patriotism, religion, "wars on terrorism," financial crisis, or any other thought matrices that can activate fear, or what R.A. Wilson referred to as "bio-survival anxiety," and the desire for Big Brother to fix the apparent problem or provide protection from a manufactured threat or bogeymen such as Osama Bin Laden (in exchange for a little thing called freedom).

To clairvoyant sight, the mental body of a living human might appear as a dense mist, of the shape of the physical body, enveloped by an ovoid of much finer mist, as a result of the attraction of the bulk of astral matter towards the center of the physical body, which in turn draws in the mental matter. The mental body grows in size as the individual develops, increasingly becoming a reflection of the causal body (which also develops).

As a result of the imperfect development of the mental body, in many people there are large numbers of "special departments" yet to become active, meaning that thought on those corresponding subjects is "clumsy and uncomprehending."[52] This is an especially intriguing notion, and I don't doubt that as the faculties of one's mental body develop, neural developments occur at the physical level virtually concurrently, though at a slightly delayed pace, given the relative solidity of the physical world as compared to the malleability of the mental matter.

According to Barbara Brennan in *Hands of Light* (1988), the mental body expands and brightens when one concentrates on mental tasks, though she admitted at the time of writing that, for her, it was the hardest of our subtle bodies to observe—perhaps because conscious and specialized use of the rational mind is only a fairly recent development, and this body is therefore fairly undeveloped.[53] For Australian psychic and medical intuitive Judith Collins, the upper mental layers—which she states can expand up to 2 feet beyond the lower mental—took years to be able to discern because of the intensely high frequency. The upper mental transfers formless information to the lower mental for interpretation.[54]

In our "sophisticated" civilization, most people think they are merely their conscious thoughts, emotions, and stored memories from this life. This is the persona/ego trap: the faithful "worship" of the isolated, linear, discriminating (lower) intellect, mired as it is in the conceptual world of finite logic and superficial appearances. Leadbeater stated that the causal body of the average man has as yet almost no consciousness of anything external to itself on its own plane;[55] it is virtually unconscious. As a result, on average we have little access to the higher intellect and true self-knowledge. Thus, rather than looking for differences in perspective in an effort to understand another's point of view, most people look for differences in order to *oppose* the other party—even violently.[56] When the faculty is better developed, however, differences will be noted calmly, for the purpose of understanding them, and nuances and subtleties that previously evaded a would-be opponent's attention will stand a chance of being noticed and grasped. For instance, it is easier for a "skeptic" to oppose some occult concept he does not and will not comprehend out of some adopted prejudice.

When this development of the intellect is more complete, organized "skepticism" will become genuine investigative discernment rather than largely being a social crusade against the unfamiliar (and it will then promptly disintegrate or become so altered as to be unrecognizable), and organized religion will recognize and respect its mystical and occult roots (and differing points of view in general). The irony for the Funda-Materialist and the Funda-Christian is that they are both essentially imprisoned by *manas*, the disconnected intellect in the *conceptual realm* of the lower mental plane and its endless abstractions and rationalizations, fueled by the individual's idiosyncratic fears and emotional prejudices.

The principle functions of the mental body are:

1. To act as a vehicle for concrete thought (thought-forms can be found in the mental body).
2. To then express such concrete thoughts through the physical body, via the intervening astral and etheric bodies.
3. To augment and aid the faculties of memory and imagination.
4. To serve as a separate vehicle of consciousness on the mental plane (especially in the "afterlife").
5. "To assimilate the results of experience gathered in each Earth-life and to pass on their essence to the [E]go, the real man living in his causal body."[57]

The highest three subplanes of the mental plane that form the causal level are not tainted by any petty human emotions or perverted intellectual designs. The causal body, home of the occultist's "Ego," is said to survive the transition from one life to the next, thus being immortal, at least as far as normal human evolution is concerned (and hence, the causal body is referred to as the "real man"). Beyond that, even the causal body must be discarded so the "soul" may continue its upward spiral towards inevitable "godhood."

The causal body derives its name from "the fact that in it reside the *causes* that manifest themselves as effects in the lower planes. It is the experience of past lives, stored in the causal body, that are the *cause* of the general attitude taken up towards life, and the actions undertaken."[58] The causal body "stores" that of a man's consciousness (as developed during earthly life) that is noble and harmonious, these being the only energies capable of operating in or affecting the matter of this plane.

To Barbara Brennan's clairvoyance, the causal body (or "ketheric template") appears as a highly structured template composed of rapidly pulsating and shimmering golden light; tiny threads of "durable" gold-silver light hold the whole auric form together. As well as a "golden grid structure" of the physical body and all chakras, it contains the current life plan, as well as information pertaining to previous lives.[59]

The causal body has two main functions:

1. To act as a vehicle for the Ego [composed of Atma-Buddhi-Manas; it is not the Freudian persona]: the causal body is the "body of Manas," the form-aspect of the individual, the true man, the Thinker [this is where abstract thought is said to occur].
2. To act as a receptacle or storehouse for the essence of the man's experiences in his various incarnations.[60]

According to occult and mystical thought, there is no legitimately "individualised" being until a causal body has been created. Possession of a causal body defines what we think of as individuality.[61] It is said to be constituted of matter from the three highest subplanes of the mental plane, though Leadbeater reported that of these most people could only use the lowest subplane, and even then only the lower matter of *that* is usually in operation. The second subplane begins to open up for the student on "the Path"[62] (of serious occult/spiritual development). As the nobler elements of character such as unselfish love and higher spirituality develop within a person, so too does the causal body evolve, growing in size, developing and altering its colors and intensity. We must note that we are necessarily skipping over much detail, the space for which we do not have here.

The power of magnification (micro-psi) belongs, according to Leadbeater, to the causal body, and is associated with the chakra between the eyebrows (third eye). Likewise, through it, pre-vision of the future may be obtained. Generally speaking, the mental and astral bodies facilitate what is experienced as telepathic or nonverbal communication between beings while in these planes, as well as communication between different planes/frequency domains/parallel worlds such as when a medium "talks to the dead." This is, of course, on top of various other well-proved psi phenomena (clairvoyance, clairsentience, etc.) which we will be looking at in the coming pages.

The Tibetan Buddhist conception of their mental body seems roughly equivalent to the astral and mental bodies, and agrees with many basics as put forth by other mystical and occult schools.[63] For instance, it can see through solid objects and travel at the speed of thought; it communicates telepathically, appears as a replica of the physical body as it was in the prime of life, possesses all the standard sensory faculties, is light, lucid, and mobile, processes and generates thoughts with great alacrity, and can "read" minds.[64] We will find all of these basic tenets powerfully validated by the consciousness research we detail in both this book and its follow-up, TGI 2.

We might briefly note that differences in various schemas of the subtle bodies need not trouble us greatly here. Whichever one we adopt, perhaps the subtle bodies can, for convenience, all be subsumed under the inverted time domain/time-space umbrella. In TGI 2 it will become even more obvious why I work with the schema used here, though my research into this area is ongoing.

Finally, the causal body is also referred to in other systems as the "spiritual subtle body" (See Luckman, *Potentiate Your DNA,* or Collins, *How to See and Read the Human Aura*). Collins adds that this is the vehicle through which we experience what some refer to as "God-consciousness"[65] a.k.a., God-realization (See Chapter 5).

The Buddhic Plane

On this plane, it is said that the Akashic records are readily accessible, as here, past, present and future are all present in the "Eternal Now."[66] Moreover, the faculty of prevision is more functional here beyond the mental plane, according to the occultist, although free will, particularly the will of the more conscious and less robotic man or woman, is a mitigating factor that introduces an amount of uncertainty, rendering reliable prevision much less attainable. Besides, this faculty is always a matter of probability rather than absolutes.

Buddhi, meaning "intuition," is known in India as *pure reason*. It is the reason of the "higher man" or Ego (not the earthbound Freudian ego), which knows right from wrong. Christ represented Buddhic consciousness. This level of awareness offers "realization of the One Consciousness" penetrating all, where one—on reaching the highest sub-plane—experiences the true infinite unity that lurks behind human perceptions.[67] It is said to be impossible in physical words to give our 3-space brain-minds more than the merest hint of what the higher buddhic consciousness is, for in the buddhic world, there are at least six dimensions, thus hugely exacerbating the difficulties involved (as compared with, say, describing astral experiences).[68] Powell's description of experience of the buddhic plane has definite shades of various mystical experiences within it:

> The sense of *union* is characteristic . . . all limitations begin to fall away, and the consciousness of man expands until he realizes . . . that the consciousness of his fellows is included within his own, and he feels and knows and experiences, with an absolute perfection of sympathy, all that is in them, because it is in reality a part of himself . . . [H]e realizes he is truly only part of a mighty whole.[69]

The predominant element of consciousness in the buddhic body is bliss and love, thus a selfish man cannot function on the buddhic plane, there being no matter or energy in which selfishness can manifest. There is no sense of separateness on the buddhic plane, though in its fullness the conscious unity with *all* belongs, according to Powell, to the atmic or nirvanic plane. The intuition of the buddhic body recognizes the inner essence of things and enables the capacity for empathic knowing, seeing things "through the eyes (being)" of another in a quite literal sense. Powell adds that in the physical body, the yellow prana that enters the heart chakra represents the principle of buddhi.[70]

By way of analogy, Leadbeater compares the higher-dimensionally based "prevision" offered by the buddhic plane to the view of a 2D Flatland as seen by someone in the third dimension (someone who can look down on the whole 2D plane).[71] We detailed this concept in Chapter 6, under the subheading "The Fourth Dimension." Our 3D cone would be able to see 2D Flatland from a bird's eye view. It could simultaneously see various Flatlanders who were far removed from one another, and obtain information not readily accessible to Flatlanders, including knowledge of probable future interdimensional events that have not yet intersected with and impacted the 2D plane. Leadbeater compares the view attained by one at the buddhic level to that of our cone overlooking Flatland. Perfect development of consciousness on this plane results in perfect prevision—at that level at least. With this faculty developed, foreknowledge will also frequently flash into one's normal waking life.[72]

The buddhic plane's link to the heart chakra is interesting at this point, and from my own observations I find it hard to conceive that there is not a link between the heart chakra's level of development/activation and one's precognitive abilities—in fact, research that we will cover in Chapter 12 on clairvoyance has shown that the heart is in fact involved in presentiment. Given our previous sentiments regarding the way in which higher-dimensional objects appear or manifest in lower dimensions in less detail than they actually possess (as cross-sections), we are perhaps given a clue as to why so many people who have near-death experiences or other types of mystical experiences in non-ordinary realities report that the reality they perceived was *more* real to them than our familiar everyday reality of the physical world. The higher dimensions possess more information, more richness of detail and feeling, and thus to the experient they *are* more real (and the experient is free of the limitations of physical sense perception). Returning to the physical after such an experience can be quite a shock to the system, as we will see more clearly in TGI 2 when we deal with the NDE and the afterlife in rare detail.

The human mind and its perceptual limitations are partly due to the number of subtle bodies information is filtered through before consciousness actually perceives it. Laboring under the maximum possible limitations, what we know as consciousness is, as Taimni puts it, "consciousness *veiled by many layers of the mind*, each of which increasingly obscures and modifies its nature as it infiltrates into . . . the human brain."[73] (emphasis added)

According to established occult ideas, the buddhic is the highest plane that we can access as humans within the context of what we understand as a "human being." "Becoming enlightened is exactly the same as opening up to the buddhic energies."[74]

The Remaining Planes

Regarding the nirvanic plane, the paranirvanic plane, and the mahaparanirvanic plane, we need not trouble ourselves too greatly here in TGI 1. These planes are relatively uncharted territory (for us), and become increasingly more abstract and increasingly confounding to our human minds, but we can still know a little about them.

The nirvanic (Buddhist)/atmic (Sanskrit) plane: on this plane, what we think of as "human" no longer makes any sense. Though there is no truly adequate way of defining the nirvanic plane, in *The Inner Life* Leadbeater offers "peace in omniscience." He adds that what we regard as the individual man has now "disappeared," but not because he is annihilated, but because he is "lost in divinity."[75] While there is still a sheath or *kosa* for the spirit at this level, it is impossible to describe with any words, according to Leadbeater.

The paranirvanic (Buddhist)/anupadaka (Sanskrit) plane: Anupadaka means literally "without vesture." It is said to be even more abstract than the atmic plane: here everything bleeds into everything else. This is where the Monad—a spark of the Absolute sheathed by the most tenuous of matter—is said to reside.

The mahaparanirvanic (Buddhist)/adi (Sanskrit) plane: Adi literally means "first." "God" or the Logos is "here," undifferentiated.

The Monad, Ego, and Personality

Essentially, a Monad is the Logos or "Creator," a spark of "God" or "Divinity," which is rendered an individual entity "by the rarest film [or "sheath] of matter, matter so rare that . . . it offers no obstacle to the free intercommunication" between one Monad and another.[76] (The Monad has no real limitations.) A Monad is thus not considered pure consciousness, pure Self, *samvit*. Rather, "a Monad is consciousness *plus* matter [on its own plane]."[77]

While the roots of the Monad are in the adi plane, it resides on the anupadaka plane, without any causal, mental, astral or etheric bodies to express itself through, as human consciousness as we know it might.[78] Put simply, your Monad is you, but not just this version of you; every life that you have lived has resulted in the addition of another personality complex to the repository that is the Monad. Thus, putting it simply, we can say that the Monadic awareness is truly outside of our ordinary space-time reference frame.

In Goswami's schema, the Monad has "quantum memory," and the "conditioned vital and mental components" obtained in a given lifetime persist in it as "a conglomerate of conditioned vital and mental possibilities." (These can be drawn on for future incarnations, and do indeed influence the development and expression of a new personality on the Earth plane, as we shall see in TGI 2.) Thus, Goswami explains a little of his physics theory of reincarnation.[79] We can say that the particulate matter of these hyperspace planes may consist of the postulated super particles of physics, and that these may be structured and organised by a sort of torsion-information field or hyperdimensional analog—a concept elaborated on in TGI 2.

The Ego is our tripartite "soul," composed of the Atma-Buddhi-Manas (spirit, intuition, and intellect) principles, thus incorporating our extension of Self down into the highest level of the mental plane, manifesting through the causal body. Let us summarize the constitution of man as Monad, (non-Freudian) Ego and (human) personality. The Monad, expressing itself simultaneously on the planes of atma, buddhi and manas, constitutes the Ego, or individuality. The Ego, in turn, expresses itself on the lower planes as a *personality*. The "top-down" link or communication line between the Ego ("higher self"), and the lower self, or personality is known as *antahkarana*, Sanskrit for "inner organ." On the other hand, the link binding the personality to the higher self is often spoken of as a silver thread.[80] Such a silver thread or "cord" is reported by many NDEers (including children with no knowledge of these concepts), OBEers, clairvoyants, occultists, and so forth, as we have noted (and will elaborate on in TGI 2).

Thus, we can simplify and divide our consciousness into Monad, Ego, and human personality, and our bodies into physical, etheric, astral, mental, causal, and buddhic, though none of these alone, nor all of them together constitute the "true self." These are merely means through which we express facets or aspects of ourselves,[81] our most fundamental "Self" being, as every mystic knows, infinite consciousness/the Absolute/Parabrahman.

"Quantum" Bodies

When we speak of these other subtle bodies we possess, we speak of what we might think of as "quantum-analogous" systems that each possess their own unique scale, density, and frequencies of energy and matter. They are not composed of scientifically known quanta but do still exhibit quantum and holographic qualities. In *Physics of the Soul*, Goswami suggests a sort of Leibnitzian "quantum-psychophysical-parallelism," meaning that rather than interact with the physical or with each other, the subtle bodies may "run parallel" to the physical body and one another, maintaining a correspondence without directly interacting. Thus, for each physical state there would be a corresponding supramental, mental, emotional, and vital/etheric state.[82]

As projections and reflections of the same extradimensional Monad/source, the subtle bodies are nonlocally correlated through space *and* time: entangled aspects of a singular "system" of consciousness. As per Bentov and also Tom Bearden, the subtle bodies are coupled to one another and the physical through their own "coupling dynamics," whatever these may be exactly. Tiller's model proposes "deltrons" as the other-dimensional particles that couple our electromagnetic space-time entities with this other "inverted" realm that, in his model, is fundamentally magnetoelectric rather than electromagnetic. Deltrons can travel sub-and superluminally and act as the coupling medium between particles and information waves, even being activated by human consciousness. Bentov offered that since the subtle bodies are only weakly coupled with the physical brain, they therefore can initially produce only a correspondingly weak signal in the brain. The brain's job is to amplify the signal into a humanly useful form.[83] Hence, when we see someone who is cognitively impaired ("disabled"), we can now recognize that the problem lies not in their subtle bodies but the physical vessel through which they must express themselves.

The Chakras

The chakras are central to Hindu, theosophical, and other esoteric philosophies, and have, for some five millennia, been acknowledged as being very real, not mere conceptual constructs. *Chakra* is Sanskrit for "wheel," because the chakras are regarded as spinning wheels of light by those who see them clearly enough to make such observations. Other people can feel the energy physically, with their hands for instance, without receiving any visual input or confirmation. In the words of the exceptional clairvoyant Dora Kunz, the chakras both transmit and transform energy from one field to another, thereby synchronizing the emotional, mental and the etheric energies. "They step the energy up or down, or slow or speed it up, from one field to another, so that the faster energy of the emotional field can affect the slower energy of the etheric, as well as the reverse."[84]

The major chakra points are generally said to be aligned vertically along the spine, up to the crown chakra on top of the head. Anatomically, each of the seven major chakras is associated with a major endocrine gland (except for the root chakra). While Kunz did not define the sacral chakra as "major," we include it here as more or less standard procedure. The following is Kunz and Karagulla's schema based on their extensive tests and observations made over the course of many years:

- Root chakra—spine/glandular system. Etherically linked to pineal gland and crown chakra, particularly in a developed individual, though partly responsible for energizing all other major centres
- Sacral chakra—ovaries or testicles
- Solar plexus chakra—adrenals and pancreas

- Heart chakra—thymus
- Throat chakra—thyroid and parathyroid
- Third eye/brow chakra—pituitary gland
- Crown chakra—pineal gland.[85]

The lower two chakras are considered by some as primarily physiological, i.e. concerned with bio-survival, reproduction, excretion and related concerns. The middle three are related more to issues of personal development and individuation. The solar plexus is linked to personal power and emotion; the heart is often linked with clairsentience (psychic empathic awareness felt bodily), and psychokinetic abilities; the throat chakra relates to the ability to express oneself, clairaudience (the ability to hear astral sounds) and more. Leadbeater explains that his micro-psi/magnification faculty arose from an etheric tube-like extension protruding from the third eye chakra[86]—symbolized millennia ago by the snake on pharaonic headdresses. He also states that development of the crown chakra endows one with the perfection of the astral psychic faculties, which actually involve all chakras in one way or another. (We will elaborate further on the psi abilities associated with certain chakras in this volume and the next as necessary.)

It is very interesting to note that according to the observations of the aforementioned Kunz, a highly accomplished and thoroughly tested and proven clairvoyant, certain energetic connections between two or more chakras indicate the presence of certain types of psi abilities—the particular abilities depended upon the connections and which chakras were involved. Having learned what chakra connections corresponded with which psi abilities, Kunz could clairvoyantly identify which talents an individual possessed by studying their energy field.[87] Overwhelmingly, those people with overt psychic abilities had more highly activated throat, brow/third eye and crown chakras, which all worked in synchrony to produce the siddhis.

It is, in Hiroshi Motoyama's view, presumably due to the correspondence between chakras and nervous plexuses that yogis are thought to undergo gradual physiological changes that result in an increased range of activities of internal organs such as the heart, stomach, urinary bladder, and sexual organs.[88] One line of his experimentation found evidence to suggest that it might be that those with "active chakras tend to have wider ranges of related autonomic activity, as revealed through functional excitement and/or instability," than those whose chakras are "not active."[89]

To clairvoyant vision, a web of light beams connects the chakras to one another and also to the physical body. The Yogis call these lines *nadis* (plural—it is said that there are 72,000 of them), and, Humphrey informs us that where the nadis plunge into the body we find the acupoints signifying the hidden meridians of Chinese acupuncture, which correspond more or less to the body's nervous pathways and are responsible for the supply and transmission of pranic/ Qi (chi) energy to nourish the body and its vital organs. Thus the acupoints are projections on the skin of a 3D holographic field structure.

There is considerable evidence that these meridians exist. Acupoints show decreased electrical resistance compared to surrounding skin, measuring an average 10,000 ohms at the center of a point, versus an average of 3,000,000 ohms for surrounding skin.[90] Their electrical parameters vary according to physiological and emotional changes in the organism, as well as disease states,[91] they propagate acoustic waves better than the surrounding skin, emit small amounts of light, and greater amounts of carbon dioxide. Analgesic acupuncture does increase the endorphins in the brain. Stimulation of an acupoint with a low-frequency current causes production of both endorphins and cortisol, while a high-frequency produces serotonin and norepinephrine. Stimulation of surrounding skin fails to elicit the same effect.[92]

Acupuncture on a meridian connected to a particular organ will "light up" the corresponding part of the brain on an fMRI scan. For instance, the meridian for the eyes surfaces alongside the outside of the foot. Stimulating these eye points will stimulate the occipital lobes in the brain at a rate far faster than neural conduction would allow.[93] On top of all this (and still more besides), there is the powerfully effective healing modality of EFT—Emotional Freedom Techniques—which utilize the method of tapping the acupoints to stimulate the meridians and simultaneously the etheric, astral, and mental fields in order to effect profound emotional, mental, and even physical healing (blood samples can be altered in just minutes).

Korean Professor Kim Bong Han in the 1960s, and Pierre De Vernejoul more recently, have shown that isotopes injected into acupoints in both rabbits and humans follow classical acupuncture meridians marked by minute tubular thread-like structures called Bonghan ducts. The meridians appear to act as spatial guides for the growth and development of the newly forming blood and lymphatic circulatory network, as well as the organs (Bonghan ducts form a web on the organ's surface). Han found that within an embryonic chick, the meridian ducts were formed within 15 hours of conception, before even the most rudimentary organs. Gerber summarized that the meridians serve as an interface between the etheric and the physical body, and are the first established physical link between the two.[94] Indicatively, terminating a meridian related to the liver causes rapid degeneration of liver tissue, as energy is cut off from the organ.[95]

It is interesting that Bonghan ducts contain a large amount of DNA: DNA granules appear to flow through these tiny ducts, adding weight to the notion that they are involved in healing and cell regeneration. Acupuncture needling generates an electrical charge in the Bonghan duct/meridian in three different ways.[96] This electrical stimulation might be what stimulates the DNA to reach the destination it is needed at for repairs.

Jay Alfred explains in terms of plasma dynamics that when meridians cross in our subtle bodies, they pinch each other, forming "knots" and collapsing as nodes, pulsating at fixed frequencies. The pulsations and intense magnetic field attract higher-dimensional ("super") particles and objects which rush into the nodes using a helical path, which excites a cone/vortex of radiation—known commonly as a chakra.[97] According to David Tansley (a radionics specialist), a major chakra is formed where meridians cross each other 21 times, while for 21 subsidiary/minor chakras the number of crossed meridians is 14.[98]

In the yogic system (on which theosophy based itself), from the root chakra upwards, each individual chakra is referred to by its Sanskrit name. Respectively, they are the *Muladhara* (root), *Svadhisthana* (sacrum), *Manipura* (solar plexus), *Anahata* (heart), *Vissudha* (throat), *Ajna* (brow/third eye), and *Sahasrara* (crown).

Colors traditionally attributed to the chakras, in ascending order are red, orange, yellow, green, blue/cyan, indigo, violet. This designation of colors seems to have been first introduced to the West by the Theosophical Society in the early 20th century. However, slight variations are found: Some designate white for the crown, while assigning violet to the third eye (or both in the crown along with silver and gold). These differences are not crucial for our exploration, but the basic recognition of these energy vortices is important. Through modern physiology we can see that these seven chakras correspond exactly to the seven main nerve ganglia that emanate from the spinal column. It is not surprising that the crown chakra, which features the most "petals" or "spokes" of the chakras (960), corresponds with the brain and its billions of neural connections! (It is also not surprising that the brain functions at least partly holographically, given that it is accompanied by a holographic etheric template.) No wonder it (the crown) is the center through which we experience enlightenment.

Furthermore, the *anahata* (heart) center is known to have a powerful toroidal EM field, the strongest in the body. This extends 5–8 feet in diameter,[99] though some state it is significantly larger: 12–15 feet.[100] As the heart beats it actually creates a powerful swirling vortex of blood within it, so a strong toroidal EM field surrounding the heart is not surprising, especially since we know that each individual cell possesses its own field.[101] Millions of cells operating in harmony creates a nonlocal field effect. There is no reason not to believe that all the body's major chakra centers feature a toroidal EM component just as is found in the heart chakra. Barbara Brennan depicts them as nested phenomena, vortices within vortices.[102]

According to Joseph Pearce in *The Biology of Transcendence*, the torus function is holographic, meaning that any point within the torus will contain the frequency spectrum information of the whole field. The same is true for Planet Earth's torus, or any other torus for that matter (and, as Pearce observes, we seem to live in a nested hierarchy of toroidal energy systems encompassing all scales). Due to these holographic field properties, Pearce thinks it likely that the frequency spectrum of any one torus may contain the sum total of the universe's torus within it.[103]

Motoyama wrote of an interesting experience his mother had pertaining to the chakras. In her twenties and thirties while practicing water asceticism, she often saw around her heart a character like an inverted sailboat, surrounded by brilliant golden light. A year or two into studying Sanskrit, Motoyama read the *Shat-chakra-nirupana* and discovered that the "inverted sailboat" described by his mother was "YAM," the *bija* mantra of the heart/*anahata* chakra. The golden light accompanying it was probably linked to the golden triangle—a 2D rendering of a *tetrahedron*—within the *bija*.[104] In his book *The Chakras*, Leadbeater also describes the *anahata* as glowing a golden color.

The chakras possess a toroidal form, and like the auric field are in constant flux, probably shifting colors (frequencies) frequently. Additionally, the chakras of each subtle body will vary in color to differing degrees. Upper planes can feature colors unknown to us at our level of experience.

The chakras, according to Leadbeater, perform various functions. The first and second chakras, having few spokes or petals (being lower frequency), are principally concerned with receiving into the body the "Serpentfire" (coarse kundalini energy) from the Earth and the other finer, higher frequency vitality/prana from the sun (they are largely physiological in their operation, in other words). The third center processes energies from the lower astral; the fourth, higher astral frequencies; center five deals with the lower mental. "All these centers seem to feed certain ganglia in the body." Centers six and seven (third eye and crown), Leadbeater stated were connected with the pituitary and pineal glands, respectively. A certain amount of spiritual development is required in order to draw these last two into action, according to him.[105]

Since these two higher centers are strongly associated with the siddhis, it is not particularly surprising that so few people are perceptive in the intuitive sense; we are, overall, a spiritually undeveloped race at this time. The crown chakra, according to Leadbeater, is mainly violet with a center that is "gleaming white flushed with gold"[106] (Kunz agrees with the gold and white configuration) and is usually the last to be awakened. In his autobiography, Yogananda states matter-of-factly that the seventh center (crown chakra) is the "throne of the Infinite Consciousness." Perhaps the human mystical experience of the Infinite cannot occur without a certain minimal level of development of the crown chakra.

According to Leadbeater, who moved to India in 1884 to undertake many years of training in mysticism (under J. Krishnamurti, no less), if an individual has certain superior traits that are related to a given center, that center is not only enlarged but also radiant, "throwing out brilliant golden rays."[107] I know an exceptionally clairvoyant woman who I will refer to as Denise. On one occasion around the age of 22, she had taken a friend and me through a guided meditation focusing on the chakras. At the end she asked us to describe what each looked like. When I got to the crown, I admitted to seeing what I referred to as "yellow" in it (I thought I was meant to see violet/purple). Denise pointed out that this was rare but, to my frustration, elaborated no further. Australian clairvoyant Judith Collins states simply that, "Gold is the color of evolved consciousness."[108]

The seven primary chakras correspond to the primary seven interpenetrating "layers" of the auric field—the subtle bodies. These layers are not rigid and fixed but interpenetrate each other in moto perpetuo, responding to external energetic factors and our own psychological and emotional processes.

A colleague and friend of Hiroshi Motoyama is Swami Satyananda Saraswati (1923–2009), a dedicated yogi from 1947. His view, like that of all yogis, is that the ultimate purpose of deliberately cultivating the chakras is the acceleration of one's evolutionary process, and this is a concept and interpretation that I advocate. Satyananda advises that before attempting to develop one's chakras and awaken the kundalini energy of the muladhara/root chakra, it is best to develop the third eye chakra.[109] (As we will see, there is another way to systematically stimulate kundalini: the Regenetics Method.)

Note that the crown chakra is sometimes described as looking like a little cyclone—a toroidal morphology, in other words. The other end of this torus is found at the root chakra, the physical basis for which lies in the perineum, between the anus and genitals. This vertical torus/vortex is the kundalini vortex. In *Beyond the Physical* DeGracia wrote of hallucinogenic experiences he had shared with friends. Pertinent here is the perception he had of his "spiral," which reads like a description of a torsion-information field:

[W]e discovered a thing called a "spiral." Your spiral is your aura, but in a different sense. Your spiral is like the magnetic force that is *you* and it animates and holds together your physical body. The sensation is of a magnetic spiral current moving through one's body, but one *controls or creates* the movement itself. Spirals . . . cause you to walk the way you do, and make the kind of faces you make. Your spiral is the way your body wobbles when you're just standing there, the way you animate your voice and move your arms when you talk . . . [E]veryone's is unique. This spiral I believe was our direct perception of what occultists call "kundalini," . . . Every motion I made flowed from this spiral sensation.[110]

Here again, we ostensibly see someone connecting kundalini to torsion. Stephen LaBerge had recommended spinning to maintain lucidity in the lucid dream state if it starts to waver. Out-of-body explorer Preston Dennett was able to verify this technique's validity and we once more have ostensible links between consciousness and torsion/spin.[111] Many, including famous clairvoyant Eileen Garret, have even reported seeing spirals of energy leaving a newly dead body.[112] In the OB state, increased spin seems to lead to increased consciousness, much as increased kundalini vortex activation supposedly raises the individual's consciousness.

The Haric Level

Identified clairvoyantly by Barbara Brennan (*Light Emerging*), this is a dimensional level deeper (and more fundamental) than the regular auric fields, and thus was discovered subsequent to her detailed observations of the latter. *Hara* is the Japanese term for the center of power within the belly, and according to Brennan's investigations this dimensional level consists of three points along a laser-like vertical line down the center of the body. It relates to one's intentions and purpose for incarnating (life task).

This line is roughly a third of an inch wide and extends from a small upward-pointing funnel-shaped vortex (representing individuation from out of the "Godhead") about 3.5 feet above the head, down through a second center in the upper chest radiating diffuse light (and relating to emotion and spiritual longing relating to life purpose) which Brennan refers to as the "soul seat," through a third spherical center (with a strong membrane around it and resembling a rubber ball) about 2.5 inches below the navel, which the Chinese refer to as the *tan tien*. This last center relates to the will to inhabit the physical body, and, according to Brennan's investigations contains the tone/note that holds the physical body together (it is even more fundamental than the chakras and auric layers).[113] This note is a harmonic of the Schumann frequency and is used by healers to connect to the earth's healing energies (the haric line continues down into the earth's core).[114]

Serious and/or long-term illness will show up in the haric system, as well as the auric and chakra system.[115]

The Core Star Level

Moving yet another dimension deeper within ourselves is the level relating to our "divine essence," our most basic nature. To Brennan's HSP, at this level everyone "looks like a beautiful star," though each person's is different. Here in this inner space is "localized the divine individuality within each one of us." I relate Brennan's observations to the Atman concept, the Atman being exactly as Brennan describes (our most basic nature), and identical in essence to Brahman, the Infinite consciousness of the universe. This star or point representing our Atman nature is located 1.5 inches above the navel on the body's vertical center line.[116]

These final two dimensional levels (haric and core star) are not part of the common occult concept of the dimensions, but I include this material because, coming as it does from such a gifted healer and clairvoyant as Brennan (with supporting evidence from others), it is helpful in offering further perspective on the nature of self and reality.

Just as the sighted painter might dismiss a congenitally blind man's artistic advice, so too must the clairvoyant dismiss the assertions of the materialist as to the perceptual limitations of man. —Author

Every rule defines the border and the boundaries of your perceptual bias. —Richard Bartlett, *The Physics of Miracles*

9

THE HUMAN AURA/BIOPLASMA/ BIO-FIELD/TORSION-PLASMA FIELD

It is the integration of logical science with intuitive experience that fosters the greatest advances in human understanding. They are the ultimate conceptual-experiential team. —Gary E. Schwartz, *The Truth About Medium*

True vision ends all speculation. True vision transcends the vacillating culture mind. —Author

Background

Regardless of scientific advances and paradigm shifts within the collective human psyche, with fashionable scientific beliefs coming and going, the human energy field or "aura" has continually been reported and the database pertaining to it expanded. In *Future Science*, John White and Stanley Krippner point out that nearly 100 different cultures refer to the human aura with nearly as many names.[1] Wilcock refers to the human energy field as the torsion-wave aspect of our physical bodies.[2] In the 1500s, Paracelsus, an alchemist born in 1493, believed that humans exude a "vital force" that surrounds the body like a luminous sphere. Anton Mesmer, in the late 1700s, also believed this and used the concept in his work, terming it "animal magnetism."

Mesmer believed it was a fluid-like energy around the human body that was highly charged in healthy people, and weak or nearly absent in ill people. He recognized that this force was somehow related to magnetism, and he thought that magnets could conduct it, finding that he could produce magnetic-like effects in his patients by stroking the space around them with magnets or his hands. His formulation was similar to what Reich (once regarded as Freud's most brilliant student in psychology) later called orgone energy.[3]

In the 1800s Baron Karl von Reichenbach, inventor of products such as paraffin and creosote, called the aforementioned luminous sphere "odic" energy or "odyle." Using hundreds of sensitives who were able to perceive extrasensory impressions, he determined that the odic force was particularly strong in sunlight, moonlight, and crystals,[4] but even more so in humans, where it can be seen as a plasma-like light streaming from the finger ends (as previously noted). Reichenbach's finding was that about a third of all people seem to be sensitive in varying degrees to the odic force; it wasn't only psychics who could perceive it.[5]

Since 1923, when Leningrad scientist Alexander Gurwitsch was able to isolate and measure it, it has been known scientifically that the body radiates energy. George W. Crile demonstrated as long ago as 1934 that brain tissue emits energy that is clearly visible in the infrared and ultraviolet ranges (Bearden's "magic windows" into hyperspace/aether). Dr. Otto Rahn of Cornell confirmed through his own research that the strongest "radiation" emanates from the fingertips of the right hand. According to Waite, writing in the early 1970s, some highly sensitive people's "odic" emanations were so strong that they could not handle undeveloped photographic film, lest they expose it.[6] Powell had written in the early 1900s, based on his extensive survey of the occult literature, that the radiation of etheric matter is strongest from the ends of the fingers and toes.[7] Scientific imaging techniques reveal that significant energetic emanations are indeed made in this way.

Konstantin Korotkov and others, such as Cambridge biologist Oscar Bagnall,[8] have shown that light streams from the fingertips, and indeed, the entire human organism (as we will see shortly). Today, contemporary researchers building on von Reichenbach's work theorize that odyle is the physical energy of consciousness. "Many important aspects of the paranormal are now explained within the odic theory as results of external odic energy interacting with internal odic systems."[9] This odic system is similar to Jay Alfred's dark plasma theory (or the traditional Western esoteric system). Alfred suggests that the auric field(s) are dark plasma, as we will see. There appear to be similarities between Qi energy and odyle as well, in particular the apparently similar speed of transmission of Qi and odyle.[10]

It appears that these various models of reality may well be attempting to comprehend the same thing in their own idiosyncratic ways. Still, despite scientific advancements in the technological arena, science in the main has yet to even decree such areas as legitimate fields of study, thus preserving its ignorance on these matters unnecessarily; we have nevertheless some very compelling information from modern out-of-the-box scientific research, which categorically proves the reality of the auric field and the chakras, the occultist's and mystic's subtle bioenergetic system.

Tim Rifat stated that 90% of the low-level light emitted by the body is filtered out of our awareness by the thalamus, part of the brain which deals with attention. The thalamus' operations are controlled by the limbic system, the emotional center.[11] In most of us, this neurological filter appears to be working overtime.

When speaking of the human aura, it is important to realize that if we take the data provided by psychics/seers/clairvoyants seriously, we are faced with a very complex phenomenon involving many subtle details. One thing that becomes obvious as one researches this topic is that the data on it provided by science is generally not nearly as rich or detailed as that provided by seers and occultists.

The Bioplasma or "Magma" Body

Viktor Schauberger (1885–1958), an Austrian independent physicist and inventor, had proposed that as molecules in nature "condensed," they cooled, and gave off energy in the form of heat, accomplished by a spiraling motion towards the center of a vortex that he called "implosion." Schauberger speculated that by deliberately compressing matter via a spiral vorticular motion, it might reach such a state that particles in atoms become "unglued" and transform into a new form of energy. What Schauberger was proposing was a form of cool plasma, brought about by vorticular motion (spin). He supplemented this idea with all manner of study of natural examples of these types of spirals which incorporate the Golden Section, and the Fibonacci sequence, thus linking plasma with torsion. Schauberger was, in his own way, talking about "cold plasmas" and cold fusion, concepts well in advance of any physics of his day, conventional or otherwise (hence the Nazis' interest in his work).[12]

According to Jay Alfred's plasma theory, the subtle bodies described in the general metaphysical literature (particularly the yoga and New Age literature) are dark plasma bodies ("dark" because normal vision doesn't detect them). They have signature features associated with plasma.[13] These include:

- Networks of filamentary currents (known as nadis and meridians in the metaphysical literature).
- Helical currents (kundalini), aligned with the spine, which resemble the helical pinches and "snakes" often found in plasma. Alfred explains in *Our Invisible Bodies* that the meridians are magnetic lines of force "frozen" into the etheric body and that the currents flowing through them are scientifically identifiable as the Birkeland currents of plasma cosmology.
- Plasma vortices (chakras) caused by the helical movement of particles entering the bioplasma body (as per Schauberger's "implosion" motion in cold plasmas). Alfred explains that charged particles in an ionized environment have a tendency to follow magnetic field lines. If the path of the particle is at an angle (neither parallel nor perpendicular to the magnetic field lines) it will spiral around the magnetic field lines using a helical path. (Recall Schauberger's decades earlier proposal that as molecules in nature "condense," they cool, releasing heat, as they spiral towards the center of a vortex.) When the particles plunge they collide with others in the ovoid, generating a light-emitting cone-shaped vortex when viewed from the side (or a spinning "wheel" if viewed front-on). Since there are many particles streaming down into the bioplasma body, taking slightly different trajectories, smaller vortices can also appear within a larger vortex.[14]
- This situation of nested vortices is exactly what clairvoyants such as Barbara Brennan describe: each chakra is actually seven nested in one, one for each field (etheric, emotional, mental, astral, etc.).
- Jets or beams of collimated light that issue out from these vortices evidence a plasma discharge (similar to what issues out of a plasma gun).
- A magnetized plasma ovoid that surrounds and shields subtle bodies from the environment (just as the Earth is protected by the magnetosphere—a sphere composed of collisionless magnetized plasma).
- A plasma (Langmuir) sheath (known as an auric sheath or auric shell in the metaphysical literature), which encloses the ovoid.
- The ability of subtle bodies to pass through each other (and physical matter), suggesting that they are composed of collisionless plasma.

- The ability of subtle bodies to emit light (not simply reflect it) that generates colorful halos.
- The ability of subtle bodies to change their degree of opacity—becoming transparent or translucent.
- The "electrical feel" of subtle bodies.[15]
- Coronal auras and discharges.
- Granulation.
- Spicules (short-lived phenomena corresponding to rising jets of plasma that move upward and last only a few minutes on the sun).[16]
- Striations in the subtle bodies (as observed by Leadbeater, Kunz, and Brennan) owing to magnetic plasma's innate tendency to separate according to densities and temperatures.[17]
- Subtle bodies change color as temperature varies (they are "thermochromic").[18]

All these features were described and documented more than 2,000 years ago, mainly in the Hindu and Chinese acupuncture literature, but also alluded to in the Buddhist and Christian scriptures and literature—long before the age of electricity and magnetism, which was only sparked off in the 18th century.[19] Alfred's Dark Plasma Theory holds that dark matter exists largely in the form of plasmas of exotic particles (the late Harold Aspden described the aether almost identically in *Physics Without Einstein*), and predicts the existence of terrestrial dark plasma life-forms (such as the plasmoidal/etheric UFOs that Trever Constable photographed in the infra-red frequencies). According to Alfred, human auras, angels, aliens, deities, ghosts, and so forth, are all composed of this magnetic plasma or "magma" for short. Magma naturally gives rise to such structures as vortices (chakras, for instance) and filaments (such as acupuncture meridians) and can be self-luminous (generating its own light).[20] Crucially, plasma can give rise to electromagnetic fields and radiation and is affected by electrical and magnetic fields. As we will further see, the human energy field creates measurable electromagnetic effects and can also be influenced by EM fields.

According to Alfred, the aura that is radiated by the human energy field and other non-physical life-forms can be seen to be composed of ordinary light when the observer uses ordinary sight and "dark light" when using "dark sight" (functional clairvoyance). Plasma is generally collisionless and has extremely low particulate density, with inter-ion distances typically a whopping 100,000 times those of liquids and solids due to the component ions possessing the same charge, thereby repelling each other.[21] (In standard physics, plasmas are held together only by external electric and magnetic fields, which, by extension, suggests for the highest known occult planes that they lack anything resembling earthly electromagnetic or gravitational fields.) However, Alfred theorizes that during certain events when particle densities increase, some dark matter particles in the aura collide with subatomic particles of *ordinary* matter. They recoil, generating ordinary plasma (and thus, light, heat, and electricity) which comprises the ordinary physical aura that some people see.[22]

The natural stable shape of dark matter—and therefore "magma"—tends to be ovoid or spherical, much as the primary natural formations of aetheric energies are spherical in the aether model. In fact, Alfred has, in *Our Invisible Bodies*, convincingly reconciled many of the most fundamental and curious aspects of metaphysics with plasma dynamics. Many of the most detailed and confounding observations of clairvoyants like Barbara Brennan and Charles Leadbeater can really only be seriously grasped in terms of the behaviour of plasma—*the last form of matter to be discovered, and paradoxically the most abundant!*[*] The irony is supreme: the light of higher-dimensional "plasma" is what mystics and clairvoyants had been talking about all along—with their own vernacular(s). The significance of this cannot be overstated. It took the development of string theory, plasma physics, and torsion physics through the 20th and 21st centuries for science to have a framework (or several) to really begin grasping many of the reports of occult phenomena by clairvoyants and occultists. Mystics and occultists were and are not "backwards"—their perceptual faculties were actually so far ahead of science's that they may as well have been from another universe.

Like Alfred, Chris Humphrey has argued that the mind is made of dark matter: dark matter is the overall structure of chakras, nadis, meridians and auric fields. The aura both emits and absorbs the probabilistic quantum de Broglie waves, he explains, which also account for the mind–brain interaction.[23] In our terminology, this roughly equates to the mind being a "torsion-plasma field" (or series of fields). "It is interesting that Psychical research provides the first evidence for both Dark Matter and for String Theory," he writes.[24] Not "interesting" so much as paradigm-shifting, perhaps.

---

[*] John B. Eichler, Nobel laureate and "father" of plasma physics, has said that over 99% of matter in our universe is in plasma form. Source: Eichler, A New Mechanism for Matter Increase within the Earth.

The Biofield Spins

Another name for the human energy field is the biofield, the most fundamental feature of which appears to be torsion/spin. In 1978, researcher Buryl Payne discovered a simple device that he calls the Biofield Meter, which can detect and measure a force around the body which he thought may be what Mesmer called animal magnetism. This shows up as a spin or rotational force on a frame that is suspended over a person's head. The frame has been made of common materials: wood, plastic, or metal, and in a variety of shapes. It is suspended by a nylon filament (fishing line leader). When a person sits under a hanging frame of any shape, it will rotate a few degrees.[25]

"In general, the more magnets the more movement, but Biofield Meters still rotate even when there are no magnets on them [showing the spin/torsion field to be more than just magnetic, more fundamental in fact] . . . Over 1,000 observations have been made," Payne explains. Devices placed in bottles or glass cases are induced to move by the presence of hands at the sides of the case. No shielding of the operator makes any difference, except for soft iron wrapped around a bottle, which apparently eliminates the effect (recall that the spin properties of certain metals, including aluminum, can shield torsion fields).

The effects have been shown not to be due to heat, air currents, or breath. Devices in bottles have been observed to move at distances up to 12 feet from the observer during times of large magnetic storms.[26] According to Payne, this energy field is over *100 million* times the size of the body's magnetic field, and is present around all types of biological matter. This force produces a circular or spiral movement at right angles to the body. Payne concludes that it does not originate from electricity, magnetism, heat, or gravity—it is simply too strong.[27]

Payne discovered that the biofield varied in fluctuation with the geomagnetic field, and also found after analyzing two years of data that 85% of the time of a new or full moon (within 36 hours), the biofield showed a reversal in direction for a few hours. This suggests that geomagnetic activity may be the largest "natural" influence on biofield activity. Payne also notes that there have been similar devices developed at earlier dates, for example, Charles Russ' invention mentioned earlier, or the even earlier invention of French scientist Hippolyte Baraduc (who was apparently born in the early to mid-1800s).[28] Also recall the experiments involving Allan Chumak from Chapter 4, revealing the human ability to direct mental energy at water, thereby "charging" it, as well as our other examples of observers affecting observed systems.

Adding to all of this, we note that in the case of humans, emotional states and vitality factors add more variability to the state of the field, as Payne observes.

In terms of the aura described by psychics over the years, a major theme of their collective discourse has been that emotional states produce significant effects within the auric field, and other aura-imaging techniques have proved that physical vitality determines to some extent the appearance of the energy field, as we will see. Further, compelling observations have been made by clairvoyants and occultists regarding whirling motions in the energy field and chakras. In 1912, the occultist Swami Panchadasi (real name William Walker Atkinson) noted that when a person manifests a strong desire, feeling, or idea filled with the dynamic force of his will, this creates a "series of strong vibrations in the body of the aura, which gradually resolve themselves into a strong whirling center of thought-force involved in a mass of strongly cohesive auric substance [dark plasma], and strongly charged with the power of the prana life-force/Qi energy of the person."[29] Thus, we see once more the link between rotational force (leading to a vortex or vortices) and the human mind (recall Ramacharaka's comments on a thought literally being a vortex in the mental body).

Variability of the Biofield

The first visual images obtained of the aura are usually credited to Dr. Walter Kilner in 1911. Kilner used various screens and dyes to capture images of the aura. Another method he used was to have the viewer stare into a bright light through a strong alcoholic mixture and then look at a subject. (This method unfortunately proved to be detrimental to the sight of the viewer.) He perfected his dye technique, the "Kilner Screen," and was able to capture images of the field surrounding the body. In addition, Kilner appears to have been the first Western scientist to call this energy field the "aura."[30] He had described seeing a glowing mist enveloping the body in three zones:

> a) a quarter-inch dark layer closest to the skin, surrounded by b) a more vaporous layer an inch wide streaming perpendicularly from the body, and c) somewhat further out, a delicate exterior luminosity with indefinite contours about 6 inches across.[31]

The aura varied considerably from person to person depending on factors such as age, gender, mental abilities, and physical health. Based on the way that diseases showed as patches and irregularities in the aura, Kilner developed a diagnostic system on the basis of the color, texture, volume, and general appearance of the field. Thus he was able to diagnose a range of disease states including tumors and different psychological disturbances.[32] The Kilner Screen had consisted of two hermetically sealed pieces of glass containing an alcohol solution of dicyanine, a coal-tar dye. Dicyanine affected the viewer's retinal rods, allowing the person to see shorter wavelengths than normal and thereby apparently perceive radiation in the ultraviolet range, a "magic window." After peering through the screen, one shifted one's gaze to the human body and could then perceive the energy field. Kilner noted what clairvoyants have attested to: *subjects could change their own aura through mental concentration*, supporting the notion that the subtle "magma" bodies are in fact centers of consciousness.

Kilner carried out a few experiments that demonstrated not only that rays could be projected by an effort of will from various parts of the body, but also that the color of a ray or a part of the aura could be varied by an effort of will. Arthur Powell offered that a careful study of Kilner's results agreed with clairvoyant observations with "considerable accuracy": Kilner's "etheric double" was that identified by clairvoyants.

> The striations of Dr. Kilner's Inner Aura are clearly the same as the Health Aura. That which Dr. Kilner describes as the Outer Aura would appear to . . . consist of etheric particles from which the Prâna has been withdrawn and other etheric matter discharged from the body.[33]

It is also noteworthy that Kilner found that two people's etheric bodies would interact with each other, flowing together, forming "rays,"[34] or what Alfred identifies as spicules (jets of plasma/charged particles). Kilner therefore pre-empted Valerie Hunt's much later quantitative (and indirect) "discovery" of what she would dub the "field transaction." Cambridge scientist Oscar Bagnall resuscitated and continued Kilner's nearly forgotten work, concluding that the aura lay mainly within the ultraviolet range of the spectrum.[35] This is an interesting finding, considering that this is the frequency range in which NASA has recorded UFOs with cameras in low Earth orbit. Meanwhile, at the opposite end of the spectrum, Trevor Constable captured many UFOs by using infra-red film.

Kirlian Photography

As far back as 1777, George Christoph Lichtenberg, a physics professor at Göttingen, had observed patterns produced in resin dust by electrical charges and was the first to observe a corona discharge from a human hand. In the late

1800s, Tesla had demonstrated luminous discharges around the body using high-voltage photography. More than 100 years ago, Russian researcher Nardkevitch-Jodko found that bringing any object to a Rumkorf induction coil or a Tesla generator caused a light-blue glow around the object. This happened with both inanimate objects and parts of the living human body, allowing images to be captured which showed that the size and brightness of this human bioenergy varied in relation to the physical and psychological state of the subject. Thanks to the advent of World War I, this discovery was virtually lost to history,[36] until it was rediscovered by fellow Russian Semyon Davidovich Kirlian in 1939 in Krasnodar in the south of Russia.

Kirlian used high-frequency electrical fields and a spark generator oscillating at 75–200K Hz (75,000–200,000 cps). The generator causes a high-frequency field to emanate between two clamps that hold the sample and photographic paper. The high-frequency electrostatic field apparently causes the etheric field's atoms to resonate and become excited, causing the electron flow from the object to trace out the etheric body's spatial pattern on the photographic film for observation.[37]

These are not direct pictures of the etheric field, but secondary effects. It is interesting that some scientists acknowledge that the Kirlian technique allows for the visual observation (of the light-based effects or aspects) of human torsion fields,[38] allowing science to see at least some of what a clairvoyant might. In general, when aetheric matter becomes "excited" it acts as a plasma. I use the term "torsion-plasma field" to acknowledge both the more fundamental torsion/spin/rotational "implicate" aspects, and the "explicate" plasmoidal light-based particulate aspects of the auric fields.

Kirlian photographs of potato plants which have had the leaves removed from the stem reveal plasma fields showing the *whole plant as if the leaves are still there*. The light retains the physical formation of the leaves, as if it knows or "remembers" the shape and structure of the plant—possibly due to the presence of a persisting static torsion field (which originally may have served as a sort of holographic growth template). This came to be known as the Phantom Leaf Effect. The phantom leaf shows a lower frequency "reflection" of the etheric body of the leaf.

Allan Detrick has performed phantom leaf experiments in which both sides of the phantom have been captured—front and back. In Romania, I. Dumitrescu cut a circular hole in a leaf and then photographed it with his electrographic equipment. *A small-scale copy of the whole leaf appeared in the hole* he cut (leaf within a leaf), demonstrating the holographic nature of the etheric body (Figure 9.1).[39]

Figure 9.1 Phantom Leaf within a leaf. This image is adapted from a photo taken by Dumitrescu.

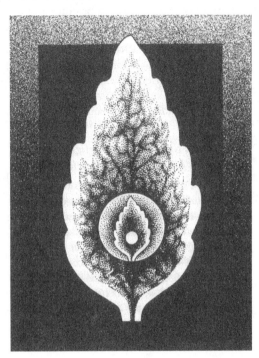

Image credit: Richard Gerber, *Vibrational Medicine*, p. 55. Bear & Company, 2001.

Typically, the true etheric body is invisible to us. Only a talented minority can perceive it unaided with any clarity, though many people can detect its physical emanations to some degree with a little effort. Russian scientists studying this field with an electron microscope hooked up to Kirlian equipment claimed it to be a unified plasma-like constellation of ionized particles (a regular plasma is a gas of ionized particles). The view in Russia as far back as the 1970s was generally that the plasmoidal biofield was responsible for physical structure and life—without it the organism dies. Furthermore, Russian scientists found that solar activity and other "cosmic occurrences" cause observable reactions in the bioplasma—in *real time*.[40]

Kirlian photography has also reconfirmed the occult tenet that the characteristics of light discharge vary with a person's physiological and mental states. Indeed, Thelma Moss' research showed that subjects in relaxed states produced by meditation, hypnosis, alcohol, and drugs generally showed a wider and brighter corona discharge on the fingertips. In states of arousal, tension, or emotional excitement, the researchers observed the appearance of red blotches on the film, and even partial coronal erasure. In the presence of a partner, close friend, or even just a member of the same sex, a brighter and wider corona results.[41]

Moss conducted many experiments with Kirlian photography, also validating the "phantom leaf effect," and demonstrating that emotion and disease states could be rendered visible around the fingers of her subjects with Kirlian photography.[42] Valerie Hunt's research utilizing Rolfing therapy, with clairvoyant Rosalyn Bruyere present to make observations, yielded a correlation between emotional releases caused by the Rolfing and observed changes in the energy field, as seen by Bruyere.[43]

It has been reported that Moss and her colleagues at the University of Rochester in New York had found a definite link between the intensity of the Kirlian image and cancer, illustrating some of this technology's potential in safe and non-invasive diagnostics.[44] Cancerous tissue is apparently easily distinguished from healthy tissue.[45] However, in terms of diagnostic potential, Harry Oldfield's technology, which we look at in a moment, may be leading the pack.

Kirlian Photography Becomes Bioelectrography/Gas Discharge Visualization

The early objections to Kirlian photography have largely been overcome because of the invention of a computerized version by Konstantin Korotkov. Korotkov studied the information aspect of the electro-photonic emissions around the human body and other objects for more than two decades and improved on the Kirlian process. The new method is known as Bioelectrography or Gas-Discharge Visualization (GDV), and it is faster and more convenient, as it requires no photography or photographic emulsion. Instead, the light from the electric discharge passes down through the glass plate to an electronic camera underneath. From here, the image goes to the computer in digital form. The resulting recordings are highly reproducible in a wide range of environmental conditions, proving yet again that the Kirlian effect is real. Most important is the fact that once the image is in digital form, it is possible to *quantify* its various parameters. The GDV software allows you to measure the area of the image, its brightness, its "fractality" (how jagged the border is) and a number of other aspects.[46] Eventually, 3,000 doctors, practitioners, and researchers worldwide came to use Korotkov's improved Kirlian technology.

The real-time sensitivity of GDV images to a person's physical, emotional and mental states suggest that we are seeing a sort of lower-dimensional electro-photonic reflection of the etheric field, which itself is reflecting the state of the emotional and mental fields. Each person's image is therefore understandably unique. In conditions of poor health, fatigue, or stress, the "beogram" (short for bio-electrogram) tends to show reduced area, with increased brightness and fractality. However, in some conditions of ill health, the area can be *too great*, and brightness and fractality too small.[47] In exploring the effects of a person's thoughts on the people surrounding him, Korotkov asked one half of a couple to send a variety of thoughts to their partners, while they were standing within close range. *Every* strong emotion (regardless of type) yielded "an extraordinary effect on the light discharge of the recipient."[48] In particular, the bioelectrography images are excellent at illustrating the difference in the energy field following acupuncture treatment, evincing greatly enhanced emissions in the "after" shots, as compared with "before" images.

Another remarkable finding (by another Russian group) was made with pairs of individuals in an emotionally close relationship. When one imagined sending love to the other (who could be miles away), a detached spot was seen on the sector of the little finger relating to the *heart*. It manifested on the left hand of the sender and the right of the receiver.[49] This data re-confirms that closely bonded couples are in fact nonlocally connected in provable ways, and that thought or feelings (as information) can potentially be "exchanged" over arbitrary distances via time-space/aether. Korotkov proved that the electro-photonic glow around human fingertips contains "astonishingly coherent and comprehensive information" about a person's physiological and psychological states. The GDV technique and equipment were approved in 1999 by Russian health authorities for unlimited general clinical use.[50]

Not surprisingly, Korotkov's images show that stimulation of the field by acupuncture dramatically enhances it. Although the GDV system is mainly used for diagnostic and therapeutic/medical purposes, the information in the electro-photonic corona seems to reflect the contents of the human mind.[51] Tests conducted by Thomas Chalko in Melbourne using the GDV system compared the electrophotonic glows around fingers on the left hands of two different people. For the first person (a cancer patient) the GDV revealed a gap in the energy indicating the presence of cancer in an area corresponding to the bowel. Sadly, in fact, the patient died from bowel cancer several weeks after the test. In the second individual—who only *feared* having cancer in the uro-genital region—a very similar "cancer spiral defect" was indeed observable in the electro-photonic glow around the fourth finger of the left hand. This defect corresponded to the uro-genital region.

Several subsequent GDV recordings after they admitted and released the fear lacked any indication of cancer, as was confirmed by medical examinations. Obviously the actual disease and the mere *fear* of disease can produce very similar patterns in the electro-photonic glow around us. This study confirms again that our psycho-emotional contents are reflected in our electro-photonic glow,[52] and by inference we can add that our thoughts and feelings are therefore instantly reflected in our legitimate subtle bodies/torsion-plasma fields.

Consider the power of our beliefs and fears within the context of the "early detection" paradigm within allopathic medicine (disease management).

Many intuitives have asserted that disease begins in the energy field and then gradually "filters" into the physical body where it may be diagnosed as a disease. True clairvoyants can often see the illness before it manifests physically or begins to produce noticeable symptoms, baffling clients who were ill and did not realize it until seeking medical diagnosis on the psychic's advice. As far back as the 1940s, Harold S. Burr, a neuroanatomist at Yale University, insisted that pathology could be detected in the energy field of the body long before physical symptoms began to emerge, and his research proved it.[53]

In the *Holographic Universe*, Talbot suggested that the field is the primary reality—more so than the physical body. The body appears to be guided into form by the field. Certainly, we now know that fields are responsible for the physical body's coalescing into being. Amit Goswami states that he believes the chakras are where "mapmaking" of the vital/etheric body "onto" the physical occurs.[54] Korotkov similarly considers the chakras to be energy and information centers that comprise part of the total holographic subtle energy system guiding morphogenesis. This is congruous with the assertions of clairvoyants such as Brennan, who state that deformity and malfunction of the chakras can lead to physical malfunction.[55]

In a separate experiment, Korotkov took GDV measurements on Allan Chumak in one room, and a young female subject unknown to Chumak in a second room. For the 10-minute period the results showed that Chumak's state influenced the female stranger's, as revealed by EEG comparisons combined with GDV comparisons.[56] This strengthens the notion that when the brainwave states of two different people separated in space are nonlocally brought into phase with one another, the synchronization is effected by our auric fields/minds. Simulating the state of death, Chumak caused the electro-photonic output to drop to zero over a period of seven minutes, during which he turned "absolutely pale." Further experiments performed with Thomas Chalko revealed that, during meditation, the bioenergy intensity gradually increased by 60% after nine minutes, and the gaps in the finger corona were also filled in. [57]

The Health Aura or Prana Aura

Kirlian and Korotkov (and Kilner even earlier) appear in their researches to have stumbled upon the "health aura" and indirectly, the etheric field. Charles W. Leadbeater wrote in *Man Visible and Invisible* (1902) that the tiny particles of physical matter (such as salt crystals) being ejected from a human body are visible to the clairvoyant as a "faint grey" or "bluish-white" mist, along with an infinitude of striations radiating perpendicularly from all over the body. The appearance of this "health aura" is greatly dependent on the physical health of the subject, hence the name.[58] This health aura has also been referred to in Eastern traditions as the prana-aura. This aspect of the biofield is actually visible to some extent to virtually anyone with slight effort. Swami Panchadasi explains that this energy field is filled with many extremely tiny "sparkling particles which are in constant motion." They give to the prana—or health aura a certain vibratory motion which anyone can see under the right conditions. This movement is comparable to that of heated air rising from, say, a bitumen road on a sweltering summer's day.[59]

As noted, the health aura is said to extend several inches beyond the physical body. Leadbeater stated that the atmospheric globules absorbed by the etheric field, and which consist of seven UPAs, give up their "charge of vitality" as they are swept along the nerves (or meridians?), some eventually being expelled through the pores, thus generating the health aura (which is partly composed of visible light).[60] The "heated air" effect Panchadasi describes can be observed of "inanimate" objects as well as "living" things. After all, all matter is fundamentally energy, it's all the same "stuff." If you want a demonstration of Panchadasi's statement in action, you can even see this "heated air-like" phenomenon occurring with your humble kitchen toaster (while it is switched off), if you place it in somewhat dim lighting and draw your eyes level with the top of it. The first time I tried this, it took a couple of goes, but sure enough, I soon perceived the heatwave-like energetic emanations. I have seen similar emanations from carpet, plants, and grass, though I have only ever observed this of healthy lawn at night (rather than daylight). The field of the grass is more lively than the carpet's.

The Etheric Field Precedes the Physical Hologram

Everything that exists in our world of matter has its own field/s, including other living organisms. By the 1900s, embryologist Hans Driesch had concluded that

265

embryonic regulation, regeneration, and reproduction indicate that something possessing an intrinsic wholeness acted on a living system without being a material part of it.[61] By the start of the 1920s, at least three biologists—including H. Spemann (1921), Alexander Gurwitsch (1922), and Paul Weiss (1923)—had proposed that morphogenesis was organized by fields, termed developmental, embryonic, and morphogenetic.[62] In the 1940s, Harold Burr had discovered that salamanders possessed an energy field shaped like a salamander and that this energetic blueprint existed even in an *unfertilized egg*. Burr discovered electrical fields around all sorts of organisms, including moulds, salamanders, frogs, and humans.[63]

We see science further confirming yet another basic tenet of the ancient eastern philosophies: the creation of physical reality is directed from and by a subtler level of reality that interacts with and influences DNA, leading to the formation of the physical hologram. Leadbeater expressed early in the 1900s that in the case of a human fetus, to clairvoyant vision this energy field initially expresses the shape and size of the baby body it has to build; some clairvoyants, spotting this small "doll-like" entity floating about (and later within) the mother's body, have mistaken this template (morphic field) for the incoming soul of the baby.[64]

Barbara Brennan, former physicist, counsellor, and present-day clairvoyant healer, has also seen this energy template, and states that *before* conception actually occurs the mother and baby's fields extend "genetic cords" of (presumably etheric) energy deep into the interior of one another's heart chakras (the mother must be receptive to this process or infertility results). This triggers a sequence in which the thymus gland is then activated, and cord connections are made through the remaining chakras. These cords keep the parent(s) "nonlocally" connected to the child for life.[65] (This certainly gives new meaning to the phrase "cut the cord.")

In the energy fields Burr discovered, changes in the electrical charges appeared to correlate with growth, sleep, regeneration, light, water, storms, the development of cancer—even the waxing and waning of the moon. For instance, in his experiment with plant seedlings, Burr discovered electrical fields that resembled what would eventually be the adult plant.[66] Interestingly, Cleve Backster found electrical cycles in a *non-fertile* chicken egg, which strongly resembled human pulse beats on a polygraph chart, occurring at a rate around 157 per minute—the established heart rate in the literature for a chicken embryo about three days into incubation.[67] Backster suspected the etheric field as the culprit.

Brennan observes that the physical vessel exists only as a result of the "vital field" that precedes it. By using "High Sense Perception," (clairvoyance) Brennan and John Pierrakos observed that a plant will project a field matrix shaped like a leaf that the leaf then grows into. The tissues follow the form of the field.[68] Frontier researcher and inventor Harry Oldfield agrees, stating that "anything physical in the body or this universe happens in energy first."[69] Oldfield's technology can be used as a powerful diagnostic tool, and threatens to supersede mainstream medical diagnostic techniques, being clearly superior in its ability to detect disease states in the body ahead of time, detecting them *energetically* before they manifest physically.[70]

What Burr, Brennan, Pierrakos, Oldfield, Kilner, Kirlian, and others have rediscovered and confirmed, in their own ways, is the reality of the occultist's etheric field: the subtle aspect of the physical body—its pre-emptive energetic template that acts as a blueprint for the physical organism's growth. This has otherwise been referred to as the "L field." Joseph Goodavage emphasized in *Magic: Science of the Future!* (1976) that the "L [Life] field" completely surrounds, envelops, and interpenetrates everything in the universe. He believed the detectable segment of the L field was "probably a reflection or component of a super-sentient force . . . a great [impersonal] conscious awareness."[71]

More than 30 years on, this sentiment is increasingly vindicated with various strains of scientific research confirming the universe's intrinsic intelligence (bearded deity not included). The body's molecules and cells may be rebuilt using material from the food we eat, but, "thanks to the L field, the new molecules and cells are rebuilt as before, and arrange themselves in the same pattern as the old one."[72]

This field, by coupling with EM matter and energy, guides processes like cell division and differentiation. Science is beginning to catch on to this and elaborate. Each cell in the human body undergoes some 100,000 chemical reactions per second—a process that repeats itself simultaneously in every cell in the body.[73] DNA simply does not contain all the information required to build an organism, let alone run it! It merely contains the information for the construction of the materials (proteins) for building the organism; it does not include the building plan itself.

In the first stage of the embryo all cells are 100% identical and differentiation takes places after the fifth cell division (32 cells). But where does the information determining what each cell is to become come from? Lynne McTaggart asks: if our genes are working together in a fashion comparable to a gigantic orchestra, then who is doing the "conducting" that keeps operations in harmony? And if these hundreds of millions of processes are attributable merely to intermolecular chemical collisions, then how can it possibly happen even remotely fast enough to account for the observably coherent behaviours exhibited by living organisms every second that they are alive?[74]

It can't. The Human Genome Project found our genome to consist of a mere 23,688 genes: almost 100,000 short of the expected number.[75] Genes and chemicals are only part of the equation; they alone can't even explain the structure or functioning of the human body (let alone account for your consciousness). It was this realization that led Rupert Sheldrake to propose that morphogenetic fields precede and guide physical life into existence.[76] The morphogenetic field is really the occultist's etheric torsion-plasma field (and its higher-dimensional *etheric template body*, which we hear more about shortly).

An article appearing in *Nature* by Pophristic and Goodman in the year 2000 revealed that the laws of quantum physics, not Newtonian laws, control a molecule's life-generating movements. In the last half-century or more, hundreds and hundreds of other studies have affirmed that all facets of biological regulation are influenced by "invisible forces" in the EM spectrum, including "microwaves, radio frequencies, the visible light spectrum, extremely low frequencies, acoustic frequencies, and even . . . scalar energy."[77]

A study done roughly half a century ago by biophysicist C.W.F. McClare revealed that energetic signaling mechanisms such as EM frequencies are 100 times more efficient at conveying environmental information within living systems than physical molecular signals.[78] A recent research report from the Institute of Electrical and Electronic Engineers reviewing 25 years of research into electromagnetism found that cells rely on a low-voltage EM circuit to transmit *information* and coordinate their activities, while using a chemical circuit to transmit *power*.[79] The speed of EM signals (light) is 186,000 miles per second, while the speed of a diffusible chemical is less than 1 cm per second.[80] Obviously chemicals are a mere part of the equation.

When molecules in the body vibrate in unison they can reach a state of coherence wherein they operate nonlocally, being in simultaneous informational contact with one another.[81] Mae Wan Ho says that the crystalline structure of tissues and organs results in harmonic resonance of the whole structure: "When the coherence builds to a certain level . . . the organism behaves as a crystal . . . A threshold is reached where all the atoms oscillate together in phase and send out a giant light track that is a million times stronger than that emitted by individual atoms." This means having a nonlocal/instantaneous feedback loop from brain to cells to tissues.[82]

Gariaev and colleagues have shown that the genetic and other regulatory wave information is both recorded and distributed nonlocally throughout the entire space of a biosystem, helping to "set a quick-response information contact among the billions of cells constituting an organism."[83] The resonant nature of the body's living info-energetic matrix suggests, as Church observes in his highly recommended *The Genie in Your Genes*, that our crystalline connective tissue system may be a quantum resonator conducting signals from the quantum field/vacuum/aether into the body and vice-versa.[84]

As noted, Sheldrake, Oldfield, Brennan, and many other credible scientific and "paranormal" sources agree that the information guiding the formation and growth of physical organisms is stored in an "external" morphic field. Dr. Valery Uvarov is the head of the department of UFO Research, Paleosciences and Paleotechnology of the National Security Academy of Russia. As well as spending nearly 20 years studying the legacy of ancient civilizations, he has also researched the human energy field. He and Carl Agar, the principal of Neilos-Etheric Products, wrote about the subtle energy system in an article published in *New Dawn* magazine in 2005. Though apparently operating from a different framework for the subtle bodies, they agreed that biological tissues grow around the etheric matrix of energy channels to form the circulatory system. They stated that any major psycho-emotional stress provokes disruptions in the second and third energy bodies, leading to a destabilization that then causes discomfort, as well as nervous and psychological disorders.[85]

Uvarov adds that the ancient Egyptians (who were far more advanced than orthodox history admits) would correct imbalances in the energy fields by synchronizing them with the Earth's own energy field. The occult etheric matter has been increasingly reconciled with and assimilated by contemporary science. Jay Alfred:

> There is mutual affinity between the bioplasma and physical-biomolecular bodies . . . [T]he bioplasma fetus wraps around the physical-biomolecular embryo while undergoing an accelerated morphogenesis (relative to the physical-biomolecular embryo). *The physical-biomolecular body therefore is cued by the [etheric] bioplasma body which acts [as] an electronic matrix and a time-resolved hologram that guides its development* . . . Complex biological evolution could not have taken place on Earth without the aid of the templates provided by subtle bioplasma bodies which interacted with biochemical fields via weak electromagnetic fields.[86] (emphasis added)

It is clear then that the pre-existing energy field that acts as a template for the growth of living organisms is the occultist's etheric field, the subtle aspect of physical matter. Meanwhile, the pioneering research by scientists such as Nordstrom, Bong Han, and de Vernejoul has not just proven the reality and supreme importance of the acupuncture meridians to the healthy functioning of an organism, but their research indicates "that *this microtubule network actually connects the physical body to the . . . etheric* and provides a blueprint for the developing organism soon after conception."[87]

The Etheric Body, Web, and Shell: Body Armor

The "etheric web," as it is known to occultists, acts to protect us from unwanted external energies and influences. Existing between the astral and etheric centers, and interpenetrating them in a way that is, according to Leadbeater, difficult to describe, the etheric web is a "sheath composed of a single layer of physical atoms much compressed and permeated by a special form of vital force."[88] (Presumably Leadbeater speaks of UPAs, not what our physicists would identify as familiar atoms.) While allowing the life-force from astral hyper-energies to penetrate to the etheric, the etheric web is a barrier to all other forces which cannot use the atomic matter of both the planes. This web is said to prevent a premature opening up of communication between the planes.

According to Jay Alfred, the sheath around the ovoid/aura that we are calling the etheric web is identified by plasma physicists as a "double layer" or a "Langmuir sheath." (The word "plasma" was unknown in the time of occultists such as Leadbeater.) As Earth's magnetosphere (which is composed of ordinary magnetic plasma) protects the planet from dangerous solar radiation, the etheric web similarly protects the etheric body proper within it.[89] According to Leadbeater, this sheath prevents full recollection of sleep and dream activity, as well as causing momentary unconsciousness at the moment of death, as the mind shifts its locus of attention to the astral density. Any damage caused to the etheric web during life—whether from major emotional trauma, shock, or violent outburst—is "a serious disaster" and has the potential to negatively impact someone's sanity.[90]

Leadbeater comments that use of alcohol and narcotics can damage the etheric web, causing a sort of "ossification" and rendering it and the person more vulnerable to negative outside influences (see TGI 2 for more).[91] Robert Bruce, a modern mystic, states that the protective sheath also serves as an energy storage area. In the waking state it is contracted, and during sleep or a trance state, it expands to absorb cosmic energy/Qi/prana from the environment. In the expanded state the "energy exchange ports" (tiny energy centers most heavily concentrated on the soles of the feet and palms of the hands) on the skin "flower" and take up and "condense" energy, feeding it into the etheric's "vitality storage areas."[92]

Thus, we can see that the etheric shield acts to receive hyper-energies and utilize them for bioenergetic purposes, as well as preventing undesirable energies from intruding into one's system. After the death of the physical body the etheric double is cast off, being destined to slow disintegration, precisely as is the astral shell at a later stage of the proceedings. This bluish-white "misty" shell remains hovering close to the physical body and is visible to anyone even moderately clairvoyant. Since the etheric disintegrates along with the physical, this ghost-like form (or "wraith") constitutes a grisly vision for the psychic. Thankfully, it is devoid of consciousness and intelligence.[93]

Powell stated that as one dies it is during the withdrawal of the etheric double, as well as afterwards, that the whole of one's life "passes swiftly in review before the Ego." In these few seconds the Ego lives its whole life once more, encountering the "Past Life Review," which we will detail in our chapters on the death experience and afterlife in TGI 2. According to theosophy, cremation of the physical body speeds the disintegration of the etheric wraith,[94] illustrating an ongoing dynamic coupling or "non-local resonance" between the physical and etheric vessels.

Filming with permission in a mortuary, independent scientist Dr. Harry Oldfield scanned the space above the corpses of a young man and an old man with his Polycontrast Interference Photography (PIP) equipment, discovering something very interesting: unexpected configurations of energy, approximately the same length and width as the physical body, reaching up to about 4 feet above it. This energy expanded and contracted, appearing as golden pulsating light, and was most vibrant above the young man. There also appeared to be faint echoes of what would once have been highly energetic meridians on this body. Above the elderly man and hovering near the ceiling was another peculiar configuration which appeared to be a "head and torso, only more ovoid in shape."[95]

It appears that Oldfield's equipment has validated yet another aspect of occult doctrine: that of the casting off (and eventual degradation) of the etheric body upon physical death (subsequently becoming known as the etheric shell or wraith). Perhaps even more interesting was the energy configuration of a figure sitting cross-legged at the end of the young man's bench. It seemed to gaze at the inanimate corpse on the bench. Was this the conscious astral body also being captured by PIP? Oldfield described the figure as "very distinctive."[96] We return shortly to Oldfield's ground-breaking work.

Field Frequencies in a Complex System

Valerie Hunt found that the human energy field (HEF) is a highly complex entity. It took the use of fractal mathematics to discover the deeply embedded order in the apparent chaos or disorder. The study of chaos is actually the study of very subtle, highly complex order in phenomena that are ostensibly random. In conversations with Michael Talbot, Hunt said that when she observed energy field data on the oscilloscope, she noticed that it changed constantly, as if the field itself were in constant flux. Hunt suspected the changes may have possessed some hidden order. Together with a mathematician she analyzed the very high frequencies of the field, and obtained a dynamic chaos pattern. It showed that the changes taking place in the energy field were actually very highly ordered and complex, though the pattern was non-repeating. Hunt dubbed it a "chaos holograph pattern."[97]

Around the early 1990s researchers found chaos patterns in EEG recordings of the brain, but they needed many minutes of data from numerous electrodes to obtain such a pattern. In contrast, Hunt obtained a chaos pattern from a mere *three to four seconds of data recorded by one electrode*, suggesting that the human energy field is far richer in information and possesses a far more complex and dynamic organization than even the electrical activity of the brain.[98] This indirectly supports the notion that the human energy fields are indeed vehicles of consciousness, and that the brain, rather than generating consciousness, actually narrows, focuses, and limits it (the "reducing valve" theory).

The HEF simply reflects the amount and type of information (including emotional states) permeating an individual's consciousness (conscious and subconscious), as well as the information pertaining to their biological systems, such as cellular photonic emissions. As the information content changes, so too does the field.

Using telemetry equipment built for her by an engineer who had developed NASA's telemetry systems, Hunt found that the field of EM energy enveloping a human facilitates energy exchange. Although at our physical level it is composed of the same electrons as inanimate matter, the living human field receives and emits energy dynamically. In contrast to the fields possessed by inert matter, the human field can interact with and influence matter, instead of simply responding passively.[99] Hunt associates this auric energy with Qi, prana and the odic force—the etheric field in other words.

Holo-Bodies

Hunt found something else that is interesting about the body, a hint of its holographic nature, if you will. As noted, a hologram contains the whole image in every part. Hunt found that every electrode recording from the body's surface featured *all* electrical activity of the body. For instance, in a reading taken of the heart, the heart frequencies would be the strongest, but all of the other muscle and organ frequencies were still present there and detectable.[100]

This shows that the body functions holistically; every part is fundamentally connected with every other part, with the harmonics of all aspects existent within each individual part, revealing a nested holographic (or "holofractal") system. All parts of the body play the "notes" of all the others. Hans Jenny had commented that "each human cell has its own frequency and the frequency of every human organ may be a harmonic of its component cells."[101] Likewise, every human body and its energy field(s) is a harmonic of its component organs and other anatomical aspects. The body is not just a machine that is the sum of its seemingly isolated parts. The mere fact that the auric field exists and envelops and interpenetrates our entire body evinces a basic level of unity. Hunt's research naturally leads us to infer that the auric fields are holographic, since they are the informational template that organizes the body into being and maintains it.

The holographic nature of the body has been recognized to varying degrees for centuries, with the body's parts and organs being mapped out in the eye (iridology), the ear, and the foot (reflexology), by advanced Eastern cultures who acknowledged the body's subtle energy system (yoga's nadis and Chinese acupuncture's meridians, for example). Natural therapists working with electropuncture diagnosis have developed a chart that shows energetic connections between specific tooth locations and specific organs or body parts on the same side of the body.[102] Steiner once said: "Wherever in the physical body separated parts exist, in the ether body everything is in living, interweaving motion."[103] The holographic etheric body is the unifying factor, and Hunt's research has shown this "interweaving motion" quite vividly in the EM domain.

Konstantin Korotkov even used his Kirlian technology to identify correlations between the chakra centers and physical region they govern and the Kirlian glow of the fingers of the right hand.[104] Earlier scientific research had already begun to reveal the holographic nature of the body. In the 1950s Dr. Paul Nogier, "the father of ear acupuncture," had observed that acupuncture points of the ear correspond to specific organs. He mapped out the shape of a fetus in the human ear, the earlobe representing the head of the fetus, with the body curled around the earlobe.[105]

> Dr. Ralph Alan Dale, the director of the Acupuncture Education Center in North Miami Beach, Florida, after spending the last two decades tracking down clinical and research data from China, Japan, and Germany, has accumulated evidence of *eighteen different microacupuncture holograms in the body*, including one in the hands, feet, arms, neck, tongue, and even the gums. *Dale feels that these microsystems are "holographic reiterations of the gross anatomy,"* and believes there are still other such systems waiting to be discovered.[106]

The occultist's etheric "torsion-plasma field" is a template for the physical body and maintains it as a living unity. Within this singular holographic field is contained the frequency information for each and every body part—a fact reflected by measurable electrical activity.

The Field Transaction

Our auric fields react with and transact with one another's, exchanging energy and information. This doesn't register consciously with most people, and most people don't physically sense or visually see auras anyway, but Hunt has confirmed in her experiments that it does happen, terming this exchange a "field transaction." Occultism has for a long time held that human energy fields interact with one another, exchanging energy/information (hence how energy healing occurs). This might happen on an etheric/physical, emotional/astral, or mental level, or some combination of them. (More developed healers can use even higher energies.)

In experiments, Hunt placed two blindfolded people back to back in chairs so that only their auric fields could touch. Each was prevented from being aware of the other person, and each was instrumented to record auric changes. The proximity of the fields alone did not guarantee a transaction. Some people did not interact well through their fields; in fact, sometimes two fields would remain absolutely separate, retaining their individual patterns. With others, one field totally dominated the other, that is, one changed while the other "master field" did not—common with successful healing. Sometimes both became identical, yet unlike either initial field's state. The new field state seemed to be more sophisticated.[107] This, not to put too fine a point on it, is a microcosm of the process of evolution at work. It is the gaining and assimilation of information in developing a more conscious, intelligent, sophisticated, robust, integrated, and resilient system/organism. The World Wide Web, for instance, facilitates this process massively in a socio-cultural sense.

As already noted, the biofield responds to stimuli regardless of our brain-level awareness. In other tests, Hunt discovered that the energy field sometimes responded to variations in light vibration, as well as to sounds outside the range of human hearing—even when the person experienced no conscious sensation. The field responded even before the brain or circulatory system, and sometimes even when the stimulus was not strong enough to engage the nervous system.[108] Thus, we see that our subtle bodies can register information that our physical senses miss, and this should be emphasised in light of Radin's proof of "subconscious precognition" (presentiment) which, by contrast, was indicated by changes not in the external field, but in electrical activity in the skin and changes in pulse rate, and blood flow, as we will see.

American inventor David Thompson, assisted by Dr. Jack Ward, had discovered at least as early as the 1970s that individual fields interact with one another, and that they instantly detect fear, aggression, panic or friendliness from another person.[109] In 1981 Friedman and Riggio found that someone in a good mood seated opposite someone in a less positive mood enhanced the latter's mood.[110]

Hunt's field transaction can legitimately be considered a form of subconscious "telepathic" interaction. Controlled experiments by James L. Hickman with Uri Geller offer visual proof of the concept. Hickman and observers randomly selected a geometric figure (a triangle) to mentally impress upon Geller's mind. In a darkened room, using Kirlian techniques, two control images were taken of the electro-photonic corona around Geller's right index finger (he did not know which shape had been selected). On the third occasion, Geller's finger was again guided onto another spot on the film, and Hickman and company now concentrated on the target image. When Geller indicated that he was ready, the high-voltage current was activated and another image was captured. The result, seen in Figure 9.2, speaks for itself.[111] (Note: other forms produced in this fashion were a circle and a straight line.)

Figure 9.2 Telepathically generated triangular electro-photonic aura

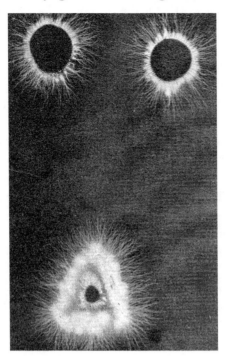

Image credit: H.S. Dakin (*High Voltage Photography* 1975) and James L. Hickman

Like neurosurgeon Wilder Penfield, Hunt's own field of research led her to conclude that the mind is not in the brain but is the auric field itself (the mind-field). In general terms, this supports the ancient mystical view that the subtle bodies that comprise the overall auric field are in fact vehicles of consciousness, used for accessing and functioning within different levels of reality. British neurologist Dr. John Lorber studied hundreds of cases of hydrocephalus ("water on the brain") and concluded that even when most of the brain's cerebral cortex, the brain's outer layer, is missing, patients can live normal lives. Witness the case of a student at Sheffield University with an IQ of 126 who gained a first-class honours degree in mathematics, is totally socially adjusted and yet "has virtually no brain," in Lorber's words. "[I]nstead of the normal 4.5 centimeters thickness of brain tissue between the ventricles and the cortical surface, there was just a thin layer of mantle measuring a millimetre or so. His cranium is filled mainly with cerebrospinal fluid."[112] The important thing is that there is *something* of a physical structure in order for his subtle bodies to interface with this reality. Three-year-old Chase Britton helped illustrate this point when doctors discovered that he is missing a cerebellum, the part of the brain that controls balance and motor skills, and is involved with emotion. His pons, part of the brain stem that controls functions such as sleeping and breathing, is also absent. "He has the MRI of a vegetable." Yet young Chase baffles doctors with an unexpectedly high level of mobility: "Things that . . . he should not be able to do, he is doing . . . walking up and down the hall, riding a bike, holding a pencil or a pen to work on projects, using scissors."[113]

Then there was the British boy named Alex. Born in 1980, his left brain hemisphere, the speech-controlling side, was "smothered in a tangle of abnormal blood vessels, leaving him mute, half-blind, half-paralyzed and epileptic until he was 8." That was when his doctors removed the entire left hemisphere in a bid to reduce the seizures. Their hopes were not high for other aspects of Alex's development, however, since he was well past the age that a mute child had ever been reported to learn to speak. Alex's right hemisphere had other plans though: just over a year later, Alex was speaking in complete sentences—and by age 16 he was speaking fluently. Dr. Eileen P.G. Vining of Johns Hopkins University reported in the August 1997 edition of *Pediatrics* on the progress of 54 epileptic children who had undergone the hemi-spherectomy for epilepsy: "We are awed by the apparent retention of memory and by the retention of the child's personality and sense of humor."[114]

The loss of half a brain did not cost these children any memory, personality, or vocabulary. It is as if the removal of the broken part of the consciousness antenna/brain frees the remaining portion not just to operate as normal, but to take on the functions that it is not normally thought to be involved in. Again, the mind/consciousness does not need every "specialized compartment" of the brain to be available to operate through it.

We have noted that healers use the field transaction process in their healings, causing the field patterns of the recipient to synchronize with their own. Hunt emphasized this transaction as "essential to hasten the healing." At the end of a healing session conducted by an experienced healer, the two fields patterns were identical. The healers were apparently terminating the session when they sensed this similitude.[115] The Kirlians had actually already photographed the energy streaming from healer to "healee" (the healing recipient) in their own work, and with Kirlian photography Russian physicist Victor Adamenko had charted an ionized electrical field between a healer's hands and a patient's body, which he considered transferred information to the patient, and which was subsequently detected by them as a feeling of heat.[116]

Hunt's auric findings have been echoed indirectly by other researchers including Fritz Popp who showed, with the use of a photomultiplier, that the

Daphnia water flea actually exchanges photons with other water fleas. Popp found the same with small fish. Even bacteria absorbed photons from their local environment.[117]

Researchers such as Hunt, Popp, Oldfield, and Kirlian have proved that all things, living or dead, possess energy fields, and that living things emit photons (as well as absorbing them, as Popp showed).[118] The cells of all living beings emit photons at a rate of up to 100 photons per second and per square centimeter of surface area (for humans, it's about 10 per second). The source of the emissions is DNA.[119] As Russian researchers Fosar and Bludorf explain, DNA is an excellent electromagnetic antenna which both absorbs and emits EM information/energy, particularly in the form of light. Our DNA acts as a harmonic oscillator, storing the absorbed EM energy which then brings the DNA molecule into oscillation; very little energy is lost by this amazing system (which is actually an organic superconductor).[120] The wavelengths at which DNA then emits biophotons range from about 900 nm at the infrared end of the spectrum (outside normal human perception), to about 200 nm at the ultraviolet end (again outside normal perception).[121] Crucially, this "DNA-treated" light is laser-like in that it is highly coherent.[122]

Even vegetables such as the humble clove of garlic emit light. In the case of garlic, strangely enough, Oldfield has found it makes slightly different emissions, radiating away what he has described as "orbs," so powerful were its photonic emissions (similar observations were made decades ago with Kirlian photography). Overcooking foods, he points out, destroys the life-force (etheric/pranic/Qi energy), hence the increasing emphasis on raw foods nowadays—as a general rule they possess more of their intrinsic light/life-force, more of their vitamin and enzyme content, and are less toxic than cooked foods. Dr. Joseph Mercola has also emphasized this point, agreeing that the body literally feeds on light.[123]

One of the most important wavelengths for our DNA is apparently 380 nm (at the lower end of the ultraviolet band, one of the "magic windows" into time-space), another reason why sunlight is so important to our health. Popp found that carcinogenic chemicals scramble light at this frequency, thus inhibiting DNA's signalling mechanisms.[124] Hands-on healers are probably directing their own 380 nm light to the DNA of their subjects in order to restore lost coherence. (Distant healers, on the other hand, may be remotely extracting this light out of the aether/ZPF directly into their targets' bodies as a result of their healing intent. Such mechanisms may also be involved in the placebo effect.)

In one experiment by Hiroshi Motoyama, a female test subject was asked to concentrate on her heart chakra, the setup being that whenever she had the subjective sensation of psi energy being emitted from that chakra, she would press a button which caused a mark to be made on a chart. It was found that when this mark appeared, a photoelectric cell signaled the presence of a weak light being generated in the light-proof room, and the electrodes of the chakra monitor detected electrical energy of high potential and frequency. This obviously implies that the energy of consciousness working through the *anahata* chakra can create EM energy in space-time (via DNA).[125] Using similar equipment, Itzhak Bentov replicated Motoyama's findings regarding electrostatic energy emission from the chakras.[126]

Aside from randomly getting occasional tactile senses of people's auric fields (excepting the infrared body heat we can all easily feel), I have done an exercise, as part of a training course spread over six weeks, that showed me in no uncertain terms the reality of the field transaction. The process runs roughly as follows. You sit facing another seated person. Having charged your primary chakras, you visualize your energy field expanding out and enveloping the person seated opposite you (while they perform the same visualization). A third person sitting to the side acts as a mediator and asks questions of one of the seated individuals.

The idea is to pay attention to the way the person being asked the questions responds through their auric field. Both myself and the person seated opposite me were asked questions. We had to explain what we felt we were picking up from the other person's aura, by paying attention to how our own felt. For instance, the mediator might ask something like "How do you feel about your love life?" The person's auric field will respond and you are to attempt first to identify how they have reacted energetically, and second to correctly interpret the *meaning* behind the sensation. You might, for example, get a sense of butterflies in your stomach.

The next step is to correctly identify why they felt that, but to do it intuitively, rather than sitting and reasoning it out. We found that our descriptions of each other's field responses consistently matched up. In that department, we demonstrated great accuracy in identifying the other individual's physical and auric sensations. Where I fell down was in assigning meaning to these feelings (left-brain interpretation). While I could correctly identify what they were feeling (because I could physically feel it within myself), I usually ascribed to it an incorrect meaning in my attempts at interpreting the sensations.

The field transaction takes many forms, sometimes assuming the form of miraculous healings at the hands of a shaman or other healer. Carol Everett is a medical intuitive, energy healer, and clairvoyant who uses her abilities for diagnosing health problems and healing, and also in assisting police investigations. One of her specialities is drawing accurate portraits of unknown criminals for the police. In 1994 in a filmed scientific experiment conducted under lab conditions by Professor Yoshio Machi of Japan, Everett correctly intuitively diagnosed a Japanese woman's medical condition, and then, in a matter of minutes, used her abilities to heal the condition with nothing more than her own focused intent. The young woman was diagnosed by Everett without any contact and without any prior information other than her name. No questions were asked. No communication between patient and diagnostician was permitted during the diagnosis.

The diagnosis given by Everett was that of an abnormal growth that had been forming in the right-hand Fallopian tube creating a blockage (Dysplasia). Thermal image information was not available to Everett, before or after intuitively diagnosing the patient or at any other stage. Researchers observed that the thermal imaging clearly showed a raised temperature in this same area, indicating a physical problem or abnormality localized here. Japanese doctors had earlier diagnosed the condition, thus confirming the accuracy of Everett's diagnosis. After three minutes, the thermal imaging clearly showed a marked decrease in the general area of the right ovary. So there could be no question of any radiated heat exchange, all healing was carried out from approximately 1.5 m distance, with no physical contact at any time. After seven minutes, the right-hand side of the abdominal cavity harboring the malfunction had cooled to match the left healthy side. Interestingly, the insides of the patient's arms actually increased in temperature while the temperature of the treated area fell. Room temperature and other factors were accounted for. Following the healing, doctors confirmed that *the condition no longer existed*.[127]

It was seen in the brain activity measurements that the right hemisphere's activity was significantly increased, as it worked "especially hard," in Machi's words, particularly the front area. According to Machi, the same effects had been observed with a Chinese psychic and spiritualists they had studied.

> [A] spiritualist's right brain works vigorously when she uses her own way of healing. In both cases, [the brain topography shows that] the healer "feels" something by using the right brain in order to make a sort of image and she looks at something with her vision in the right brain. When it comes to healing she uses her right front brain.[128]

The field transaction also helps us to explain the apparently bizarre phenomenon of healers taking on and experiencing the symptoms and illness of the people they heal. Via the field transaction, they assimilate the info-energetic state of the healing recipient, manifesting the disorder and disease, though usually only briefly. Good health = energetic coherence and harmony; ill health = incoherence and chaos, or at the other end of the spectrum, *too much order.* Tiller agrees that for healing to occur, (magnetoelectric and deltron) energy/information from the chakra/aura system of the healer is radiated to the healee (via R-space/time-space). These energies then act directly on the R-space level of the healee's body, and they also entangle regular photons with the healer's information at the same time. These newly enhanced photons then interact with the electric particles of the healee's body, sharing their information.[129] Tiller states that everyone can use focused intention to "metastably raise the local electromagnetic symmetry level of their surrounding space" in order to create a variety of different forms of healing.[130]

"The energy fields of healthy people are coherent, synchronous, but unwell people's auras are demonstrably incoherent," says Hunt. "What I have found by measuring people's auras is that disease begins in the energy field and anchors in the cells. [Therefore, the] field should be our place of primary diagnosis."[131] If you exchange or transact energy with someone who has an illness, and your body assimilates and re-creates their field information at the etheric or ordinary biophotonic level, you can "mysteriously" develop the symptoms of even a chronic illness that you've never had before in your life. It is not overly common that this type of dramatic transaction and alteration of the field takes place, but it has been experienced by healers for a long time, including chiropractor-cum-healer Eric Pearl.[132]

Eventually, most seem to develop a sort of "field immunity" and cease taking on their patient's illness for themselves, while still being able to heal. Australian medical intuitive Robyn Elizabeth Welch sometimes found that her own body would react with pain in the same area as the person she was treating energetically. "Thus I worked to increase my concentration and focus positive energy with enough power to block negative frequencies coming from their bodies and energy fields."[133]

Along with Hunt and Richards, Fritz Popp has also identified a link between photonic coherence and health with his dark room experiments during which he measured the cellular photonic output of a person in the dark room. He found that people with cancer, for instance, had lost their coherence and the innate periodicity of their photonic output; their body's rhythms were imbalanced and defective. In contrast, rather than resulting from incoherence in the field, multiple sclerosis, for example, was the result of too much order. In this case, people absorb too much light, thus inhibiting healthy cellular function.

Interestingly, stressed organisms emit larger amounts of biophotons, apparently as a compensatory effort to seek energetic equilibrium.[134] Much illness is at least partly psychosomatic, the result of unresolved mental and emotional distortions and wounds. Coupled with stress, electromagnetic pollution (such as from an electric blanket) that would be harmless to a peaceful person can combine to create a serious health malady.[135]

Barbara Brennan and her colleagues have conducted a number of experiments to measure the HEF. In one, Richard Dobrin, John Pierrakos, and Brennan measured the light level at a wavelength of around 350 nm (near-ultraviolet) in a darkroom before, during, and after people were there. Results showed a slight increase of light in the darkroom when people were in it, which supports Popp's finding that human DNA emits light in the ultraviolet spectrum. In one case, the light level actually *decreased*—an exhausted person in a state of despair was in the dark room. In another experiment, conducted at Drexel University, with Dr. William Eidson and Karen Gestla (a sensitive who worked with Dr. Rhine at Duke University for many years), Hunt and her team succeeded in affecting, by either bending or attenuating, a small 2-mw laser beam with auric energy,[136] showing again that at least some auric frequencies (and therefore conscious intention) can interact with visible light.

Hunt's experiments with people in electromagnetically shielded rooms revealed some of the short-term effects of an incoherent field: over time, her test subjects lost a sense of their spatial awareness, eventually even spontaneously and unexpectedly bursting into tears despite not feeling upset. Their mental and emotional stability was shattered with the background sea of EM energy deliberately removed, and their auras became incoherent and interacted with each other's in a haphazard, disorganized fashion, as if attempting to feed from each other since there was no longer the background EM "sea" from which to nourish themselves. Feeding on another's field in these circumstances simply weakened their own.[137]

The opposite effects were observed when the EM content of the room was increased beyond normal levels. The auric fields were restored, the subjects' thinking became clear, and they reported an expansion of their consciousness, while increased magnetism improved balance and coordination. Hunt also observed that the intuitives in the room were able to correctly locate not only the directional source of the energy but also the approximate frequencies being introduced by the physicists.[138]

Rutger Wever's research reinforces much of Hunt's own research on the effects of background EM fields on people. Becker and Selden report in *The Body Electric*:

He built two underground rooms to completely isolate people from all clues to the passage of time. One was kept free of outside changes in light, temperature, sound, and such ordinary cues, but wasn't shielded from EM fields. The other room was identical but also field-free. Observing several hundred subjects, who lived in the bunkers as long as two months, and charting such markers as body temperature, sleep-waking cycles, and urinary excretion of sodium, potassium, and calcium, Wever found that people in both rooms soon developed irregular rhythms, but those in the completely shielded room had significantly longer ones. Those still exposed to the Earth's field kept to a rhythm close to twenty-four hours. In some of these people, a few variables wandered from the circadian rate, but they always stabilized at some new rate in harmony with the basic one—two days instead of one, for example. In contrast, people kept from contact with the Earth field became thoroughly desynchronized and their metabolic systems were thrown out of synchrony.[139]

The interesting twist came when Wever began to introduce different electric and magnetic fields into the shielded room. Only one had any effect on the subjects' anomalous body cycles: that of 10 Hz (close to the Schumann resonance frequency of about 7–8 Hz). A tiny electric field of 0.025 volts per centimeter at a frequency of 10 Hz restored the normal patterns in most biological measurements. The alpha frequency of 10 Hz seemed to be the prime bio-synchronizer, with the results being later confirmed in mice and guinea pigs.[140]

Hunt, through her extensive oscilloscope observations of the auric field, found that chakras often possessed different patterns to each other at the same time, but if they had a similar amplitude and frequency, this meant they were coherent and in sync; if not, they were "anti-coherent." Hunt eventually succeeded in correlating states of anti-coherency with certain physical and emotional diseases. By creating a coherent field she and her colleagues even remedied cardiac dysrhythmia.[141]

In her earlier work, Hunt had stumbled upon the chakras when she observed high-frequency bursts of energy emanating from these energy centres, as detected by electrodes placed on the body (on top of the head for example). Since the chakras are the points of maximum energy intake, they are very important focal points of balance within the energy system. Brennan warns that imbalance in even a single chakra can result in disease. To her clairvoyance, adult chakras have a protective screen over them. In a healthy person, the chakras spin rhythmically in synchronicity with one another, pulling particular energy frequencies into them by virtue of their spin, after which the energy is conducted along the lines in the etheric field to the organs. Each chakra is "tuned" to a particular frequency required by the body for optimal functioning. Brennan agrees with Hunt when she says that the chakras do not function synchronistically in a diseased system.[142]

Field Transactions, Healing, and Energy Imprints

In the 1960s, biologist Dr. Bernard Grad of McGill University of Montreal, one of the earliest pioneers in the field, was interested in determining whether psychic healers had real energetic effects on patients. Rather than using human patients, Grad—employing elaborate double-blind procedures—had used plants (to eliminate the placebo effect) which he had planned to make "ill" by soaking their seeds in salty water in order to retard their growth. Before he soaked the seeds, however, he had a healer lay hands on one container of salt water, which was to be used for one batch of seeds. The other container of salt water, which had not been exposed to the healer, would hold the remaining seeds.

After the seeds were soaked in the two containers, the batch exposed to the water treated by the healer sprouted more often and grew taller than the other batch, while also showing higher chlorophyll content. These results Grad replicated several times himself using the same healer (Oscar Estabany) and they were also replicated by other labs in the USA using different healers.[143] (Presumably, the enhanced torsion-plasma fields of the healers interact with and improve the fields of the seeds.)

In a variation on this theme, Grad had several psychiatric patients hold glass containers of ordinary water which were to be used again to sprout seeds. One patient, a man being treated for psychotic depression, was noticeably more depressed than the others—his water sample *suppressed seed growth*. In contrast, a man with a "green thumb" accelerated growth.[144] The same held true for the woman participant who had strong depressive neurosis, while a psychiatrically normal man's sample was no different from the control sample.[145]

In later experiments, Grad chemically analyzed the water by infrared absorption spectroscopy and discovered that the water treated by the healer had minor shifts in its molecular structure and decreased hydrogen bonding[*] (slight spreading) between the hydrogen and oxygen molecules, which caused a slight decrease in its surface tension. These effects were experimentally confirmed by research chemist Dr. Robert Miller in Atlanta, who also found that magnetic fields altered the hydrogen bonds analogously, and Dr. John Zimmerman has since used a Superconducting Quantum Interference Device (SQUID) to confirm that increases in the magnetic fields of healers' hands do occur during healing (there is a minor chakra in the palm of each hand involved in healing).[146]

Based on good evidence, Benford theorises a causal chain initiated by healers in which conscious healing intention increases the EM fields in the hands, which correspondingly alters their torsion field, thus causing a distortion of the vacuum/zero point field/aether which produces a slightly higher level of background gamma radiation. This low-level ionizing radiation may then restore the subject's system to equilibrium ("radiation hormesis"), since low-dose radiation has been shown experimentally to effect similar immune enhancement to treatments by healers and static torsion fields.[147]

Grad had previously experimented on mice that had been given skin wounds in the laboratory. After controlling for a number of factors, even the effect of warm hands, he found that the skin of his test mice healed far more quickly when healers had treated them. Grad also showed that healers could reduce the growth of cancerous tumors in laboratory animals. Animals with tumors that were not healed died more quickly. Other animal studies have shown that amyloidosis, tumors, and laboratory-induced goitre could be healed in lab animals—even with no direct handling by the healer. Prophylactic effects were even observed when objects such as cotton and wool were "charged" by the healer and placed in the mice's cages for an hour in the morning and an hour in the afternoon. These mice had slower goiter formation than the control sample though they too were placed on iodine-deficient diets.

Reichenbach had said over a century before that the odic energy from a healer could charge substances and be stored in them; Barbara Brennan,

---

[*] When irradiated with mental/psychotronic energy stored in independent Czech inventor Robert Pavlita's psychotronic generators—an advancement on Baron von Reichenbach's devices for storing "odic force"—dye-filled polluted water samples in sealed bottles became purified and clear, the pollutants apparently crystallizing and falling to the bottom. Moreover, the two hydrogen atoms were reported to have spread further apart. Like Grad's and Emoto's studies, Pavlita's devices showed decades ago that the energy of consciousness could be transferred to and stored in inert matter. Source: Ostrander and Schroeder, *Psychic Discoveries*.

as a clairvoyant, has observed that this is exactly how our etheric bioplasma behaves.[148] Grad's psychic wound healing experiments were later replicated under strict double-blind conditions by Drs Cadoret and Paul at the University of Manitoba, using far larger groups of mice and the addition of a human control who claimed no healing ability. Healer-treated mice again showed faster wound healing.[149]

These experiments (like Emoto's and others we have mentioned) also have implications for psychometry and notions of "voodoo," suggesting that bio-information/torsion/scalar energy can be imparted to physical objects by physical contact. It is known experimentally that information content associated with both classical EM and non-classical (scalar/torsion) energy can be stored in a range of physical objects, including water, geometric patterns, electronic circuits, and paper, cotton wool, and more.

Glen Rein's research has demonstrated that subtle energy generated from free energy/overunity devices and the energy associated with human intention can be stored in water for several *months* if the optical properties of water are measured using a special form of ultraviolet spectroscopy.[150] This is really quite amazing because it indicates that our consciousness has a lot in common with the aetheric torsion energies of hyperspace.

What may be even more amazing is the fact that Kozyrev established experimentally, as far back as the 1970s, that it isn't simply a healer's energy that can be encoded or stored within (or transmitted from a distance to) an object, but that the time energy/information of a *process*—for instance, liquid nitrogen evaporation, or a substance dissolving in water—can be stored too.

If an object is exposed to a process and then brought near a torsion balance, it will cause the same movement of the balance as the process it was originally exposed to. Kozyrev found that the non-EM force (which he called *time* and which we are identifying more generally as aetheric torsion waves) is emitted even by ordinary events, biological processes and physical movements—and that this force could be "recorded" in an object and thereafter emanated by that object to produce very small but measurable effects on his device. The time information of a process could even be reflected from a distance by aluminum and still produce biologically enhancing effects on living systems from a distance. Onion growth, for instance, was enhanced by the reflected time/torsion waves of snow thawing outside the experiment room.[151]

Harry Oldfield's Inventions

In 2006 the genius independent inventor Harry Oldfield was awarded the Alyce and Elmer Green Award for Innovation by the International Society for the Study of Subtle Energies and Energy Medicine for his work, "which allows us to experience our multidimensional existence through his extraordinary images."[152]

On the back of his initial research into Kirlian photography, Oldfield has evolved the fields of microscopy and aura photography through his unique approach. Early on he focused on the phantom leaf effect which we have already looked at. In more than 50% of the cases, the energy outline showed the whole leaf, that is, including the portion removed. Using his Polycontrast Interference Photography, Oldfield subsequently found that this effect occurs with people, for instance, in hand, arm, finger amputees and in rare cases, some leg amputees. Many amputees report feeling pain when someone walks through their amputated leg, on the train, for example, as if the disturbance generates sensations in the energy field that are interpreted as physical pain. PIP images have also shown a phantom arm and hand associated with a spiritual healer.[153] (These would be extensions of the etheric body; healers are known to have a "looser" etheric configuration.)

Occultists and seers maintain that phantom limb sensations are felt through the etheric field. It has been stated by eminent theosophists such as Powell and Leadbeater that if a limb is lost during life, the etheric double will remain in place (hence, the phantom limb syndrome), but that gradually it will begin to withdraw back into the primary field of the body ("telescoping"), having no reason to persist as an organizing force for a limb no longer there.

Incredibly, Oldfield appears to have captured images that prove this concept. Viewing a man who lost his left arm in an accident, with his PIP technology, Oldfield asked him if he could feel his (absent) arm and hand. Upon receiving the affirmative answer, Oldfield captured the image of the man standing side-on to the camera. The image reveals the energetic template of an arm and hand that are no longer there—the etheric double in other words.[154] Moreoever, the limb is out of proportion, shorter than it should be, indicating that it had *already begun the process of withdrawing* back into the main body field.

These experiments have been succesfully repeated,* according to Oldfield, and they indicate furthermore that when the occultist suggests that we feel

---

* In fact, as early as the 1970s, an American neurologist found he could pick up traces of the electrical field pattern of the missing limb of a salamander. (Source: Ostrander & Schroeder, *Psychic Discoveries Behind the Iron Curtain*.)

physical sensation via the subtle etheric body, he is actually right, for if a man without a left arm can still perceive physical sensations such as the tickle of a feather, and an etheric version of an arm can be photographed, it is only logical to concede the possibility that we do register in consciousness our bodily sensations via the etheric double. Such perceptions must echo or reverberate simultaneously through the different "levels" of our being so quickly (or instantaneously) that we cannot perceive the "deception" taking place, and therefore erroneously consider that our physical nervous pathways are all there is to the story.

It is interesting to note that in Kunz and Karagulla's exploration, it seemed that the stronger a person's attachment to the lost limb, the stronger the phantom limb symptoms—and Kunz did indeed clairvoyantly observe such limbs. One man described his phantom foot sensations and Kunz verified the presence of an outline of an etheric foot and toes. An energetic "kink" between two etheric toes evidently caused the man to constantly feel that one was—to his irritation—folded over another.[155] In his own work, clairvoyant healer John Pierrakos treated a woman who felt that her amputated leg was doubled back (folded against itself) so that every time she sat down it felt as if she was sitting on it. After clairvoyantly observing and then straightening the folded etheric phantom limb, Pierrakos found out from the surgeon who removed the leg that he had indeed tied it in such a way for the surgery.[156]

After observing while working with Kirlian photography that sound and radio frequencies, as well as light, emanated from subjects, Oldfield decided that there must be information about the subjects in these frequencies as well as in the light frequencies.

> By lowering the voltage and increasing the frequency, he was able to introduce recognizable signals into the whole body of a human or an animal (and other objects). Measurements of the energy field taken at many locations enables the build-up of an image in three dimensions (and effectively real time) . . . ESM [Electro-Scanning Method] is able to give 3D numerical information in decibel levels about a subject's energy field, both at the surface and at a short distance.[157]

The ESM is quantitative, in other words. Focusing exclusively on light, the PIP instrumentation can distinguish between many different grades or qualities of light. The resulting image on the computer screen is shown as pulsating bands of color and light, showing variations in energy fields in three dimensions. PIP gives a real-time moving image of the energy field (including meridians and chakras) that is semi-qualitative, and so useful as a diagnostic tool that people often ask whether Oldfield is psychic, such is the detailed information he can glean about a client's present state of health, as well as their *history*.[158]

Light enters the human energy field from the environment, interacts with it subtly, and bounces off into the environment again. It is this reflected light that PIP captures. Dysfunction or injury may be depicted in the PIP imagery as a deformation or bulge in the energy field extending from a particular area of the body, and this is often the case with malignant tumors. An ESM reading will normally detect a surplus of energy in the same area as the bulge seen on the PIP scan, thus providing a quantitative confirmation of the qualitative information provided by the PIP.[159] (Recall Popp's findings that a distressed system/organism emits more light than normal.)

Oldfield has developed a non-invasive tool that visually depicts the state and movement of bioenergies, using not much more than a Tesla coil, a computer chip, and a video recorder. With the PIP system, leaks and blocks in the energy flow can be observed. In certain circumstances, this technology is able to pinpoint disturbed energy states before they become evident by standard diagnosis, allowing practitioners and healers the chance to nip problems in the bud, offering people the chance to act pre-emptively, thereby saving a lot of grief and possibly money too.[160] Oldfield believes the energy interaction with light gives us an insight into the etheric body, which he believes holds our physical body's molecules in place. PIP therefore offers a view of the energy field around someone that is similar to a clairvoyant's view. Oldfield acknowledges that PIP does not offer as much richness of detail as legitimate clairvoyance would, but hopes future developments of the technology might help level the playing field.[161]

Oldfield believes that the colors seen with PIP are the actual colors of the aura as seen by clairvoyants and mystics. In a healthy chakra, one color dominates: a healthy throat chakra appears blue, for instance. On the other hand, a defective base/root chakra will be a "muddy brown" (whereas it is red when healthy). This is highly congruent with clairvoyant observations and general occult teachings. Through PIP Oldfield can also see when the red kundalini energy has spread where it should not have, presenting dangerous potential. Serious diseases such as MS and cancer (both of which are reversible) present as "particularly dangerous distortions."[162]

More than "just" capturing the human energy field on film and confirming such elementary millennia-old wisdom, Oldfield has also recorded a number of other fascinating things, including healing energy emitted from a person, even if that individual is only *imagining* giving a healing, adding yet another researcher to the ever-increasing list of those whose research suggests that the auric field *is* the seat of our consciousness. One of Oldfield's most spectacular examples of such mental manipulations occurred when he PIP-scanned an injured Buddhist lama who had somehow survived a fall down a ravine from a height of roughly 300 feet. As the lama was positioning himself in front of the white screen for the scan, Oldfield and the lama's helper both noticed on the computer screen a "huge and vibrant aura and the most marvellous dancing lights all around the holy man"—the lights were apparently an array of symbols. Then the lama realized the camera was on and running (and filming his thought-forms); with a mysterious smile and wave of the hand the phenomena were gone, his energy field shrinking down to the usual size.[163]

Body Memory and Emotion in the Field

It has long been recognized by intuitives that emotions play a major role in our physical health, "filtering down" from the emotional body, then affecting the etheric double/template. This type of emotional imprinting is recorded in the body's EM fields and cellular memory. Hence, when a person encounters a traumatic event similar to a previous trauma that encoded itself in the body, their body will react in the same way, because the mind will subconsciously associate its present experience with its past experiences which imprinted it in the first place. Some of Hunt's research included Rolfing sessions, during which participants spontaneously relived memories as certain body parts were treated.[164] "Indeed," wrote Helena Blavatsky in the late 1800s, "every organ in our body *has its own memory*. For if it is endowed with a consciousness 'of its own kind,' every cell must of necessity have also a memory of its own kind."[165]

One case published in a distinguished medical journal tells of a woman who was regularly beaten by her husband. As her sons grew up, they prevented their father from beating her, so he attacked her with words instead. Thus, whenever he verbally assaulted her, the woman developed *psychogenic purpure*, meaning that real bruises and black-and-blue marks would appear on her skin in the very places where she had previously received bruises from her husband's beatings! "A psychiatrist watched the bruises appear on the woman's arms right before his eyes when she talked about the verbal abuse. It doesn't require much of a leap to see that the physicalized body memories of the earlier beatings were asserting themselves as the present trauma of verbal abuse recalled her past experiences," writes the accomplished medical-intuitive Mona Lisa Schultz.[166]

Modern science vindicates Blavatsky more than we have space to demonstrate. This last case just goes to show another thing about the subconscious mind: *it doesn't recognize time as passing linearly, and time alone does not heal psychological wounds.* Bradley Nelson's *The Emotion Code* illustrates brilliantly the crucial importance that emotion plays in health and disease, and how unprocessed and unreleased emotional turmoil will ultimately cause physical disorders, and I recommend it to the interested reader. In Nelson's experience, at least half of the people in pain that he treats are enduring it as a result of trapped emotion, and virtually all illnesses, he says, are attributable to trapped emotion in some way.[167] There seems to be a consensus emerging that at least 90% of illness is fundamentally psychogenic in nature. We must therefore look not to attack disease symptoms (cancer cells, for instance), but to heal psychologically, and address dietary and environmental factors that cause emotional and biochemical imbalances (such as chronic acidosis—a precursor to cancer and disease in general). I've found numerous cases of cancer healed by people operating in this way without the intervention of the medical system.

Interestingly, Stan Grof found that in general in LSD psychotherapy, all emotional distress or traumatic and incomplete psychological gestalts present specific bodily symptoms, reiterating the powerful link between emotions (mind) and physical health—hence the term "psychosomatic."[168] Grof's own research uncovered similarly spectacular cases of psychogenic physical trauma as that of the verbally abused woman cited by Schultz. One of his clients reliving a childhood case of sexual abuse at the hands of her stepfather manifested "massive circumscribed infiltration and reddening of the skin" on her forearm (the most prominent part of her body during the abuse). In a matter of minutes it became thick and hard like shoe leather and was "covered with protruding skin eruptions." This condition lingered for ten days (and was diagnosed by a dermatologist as eczema), until the *next* LSD session, when the past material was fully relived and integrated. It then disappeared over the space of several hours.[169]

This type of psychosomatic phenomenon has been seen to occur not just over several years or decades, but supposedly even *over successive lifetimes.* The case of the rival college roommates Andy and Jim provides an excellent illustration of the concept. Andy and Jim were highly antagonistic and competitive towards each other, even brawling, despite the fact that they roomed together. As fate would have it, both of them ended up receiving readings from the prolific psychic Edgar Cayce. Cayce had identified a series of incarnations spanning millennia, through which Andy and Jim had been locked in rivalry. One such case of the rivalry manifested during the Crusades where the Christian Andy fought the Moslem Jim in hand-to-hand combat. In one battle, Jim cut Andy with a sword between his thumb and index finger. Years later, Andy would recall of their college days as rivals, "when we argued, the scar would reappear there. It was weird—just a reminder."[170]

Combining Coherent Emotion with Intentionality

It has long been a matter of esoteric record that emotional disturbances can lead to illness. This fact is illustrated by various cases of modern research, not least in the instance of cell biologist Glen Rein and his colleagues at the HeartMath institute. In one experiment, one of each of 28 samples of heat-treated (and thus partially unwound/denatured) DNA inside human cells was given to a test participant. Ten were trained in HeartMath heart-based emotional coherence building techniques, while the 18 who were not trained served as controls. The DNA samples were observed so as to determine the impact emotions would have on them.

Rein discovered that anger, fear, and similar "negative" emotions have the power to increase winding of the DNA, compressing it, thus decreasing the amount of 260 nm light absorbed (by the same token, an *increased* absorption of light at 260 nm indicates increased unwinding/denaturation). One man in a state of general upset caused just such an effect completely unintentionally, merely by holding the beaker containing the DNA sample. On the other hand, emotions such as joy, gratitude, and love—when combined with intentionality—unwound or decompressed DNA exposed to them, an effect that could be created up to a half mile away.[171] Years earlier in Russia, remote influence experiments with a live human target presaged Rein's results:

- Drs Serov, Troskin, and Sverdlovsk found that positive emotion mentally directed at patients caused white blood cell counts to increase by 1,500, while negative emotion decreased white cells by 1,600.
- In 1959 Dr. Stepan Figar found that intense mental anxiety in one person caused, at a distance, a slight change in blood volume in a resting individual. His findings inspired Douglas Dean's research in America which offered subsequent validation.
- Negative emotions and nausea can be "sent" to a remote target recipient.[172]

Pertinently, in the Rein and subsequent HeartMath experiments, those subjects with coherent ECGs (signalled by highly regular heartbeat variability) could either wind or unwind the DNA at will, while those with incoherent heart energy could not—and the strongest effects correlated with the highest coherence levels. Further, in these experiments, simply *feeling* love-based emotions was not enough to affect the DNA samples—the intent to alter them had to be present. The effect was achieved up to half a mile away in an experiment using Lew Childre. Another experiment using the Russian healer Valerie Sadyrin replicated the effect with Sadyrin stationed thousands of miles away in Russia (Rein's experimental setup was in California), thus indicating that, although coherent EM heart energy does act locally within the body, it also has a non-EM (torsion/scalar) component that acts nonlocally (in time-space/aether). Ipso facto, DNA is a "torsion antenna," a biological bridge between our space-time and time-space/aether/ZPF.

Moreover, other experiments featuring talented subjects (including Childre) capable of sustained periods of heart coherence have shown that sufficiently skilled humans can affect several different DNA samples with several different intentions *simultaneously*. Conversely, the likes of talented healer Matthew Manning can *selectively* target just one sample in a group of several, leaving the others untouched.[173] It is worth noting that in these experiments of Rein's the test subjects were not working on samples of their own DNA, but samples from other humans,[174] so presumably, if they had been, these psychokinetic effects might have been stronger, being more resonant with their own DNA.

"Rein's research makes a direct connection between torsion energy and life-affirming emotions, particularly unconditional love, indicating that the latter literally propels evolution," asserts Luckman. "Only the love-based emotions stimulate DNA to decompress [partially unwind] so that messenger RNA can access codes for healing. Hatred, depression, boredom, and the like cause DNA to close down on itself, severely limiting access to genetic information necessary for healing as well as evolution."[175]

Have you ever noticed the way that stressed out people get sick more often and stay sick longer? You may have observed how chronic emotional trauma and stress can lead to something like chronic fatigue syndrome or other physical and/or chemical imbalances. Ultimately, with the exception of certain obvious physical causes, the difference between health and illness starts with consciousness, and from there impacts the DNA and the cellular and nervous systems, manifesting the emotional codes broadcast by our mind-fields. Epigenetics has recently identified "behavioral state-related" genes as one genetic pathway through which our mental states affect our bodies by altering genetic expression.[176] The DNA and cells, if altered to produce illness, will then broadcast those discordant disease frequencies back out of the body and they will be detectable as disturbances in the EM field to sophisticated technology or an advanced clairvoyant (who will see etheric, astral and/or mental abnormalities).

In indirect support of the Rein/HeartMath research, Cleve Backster, in his own experiments, established that live human cells (oral leukocytes) removed from their owner and placed in vitro still exhibit nonlocal connections to the owner, showing simultaneous reactions corresponding to the emotional changes of their owner. These experiments were replicated with Colonel John Alexander, then Chief of Advanced Human Technology at the US Army Intelligence and Security Command. They achieved replication of the effect over a distance of 12 miles.[177] The Institute of HeartMath also replicated Backster's human leukocyte work.[178] Backster continued these investigations successfully over larger distances, up to 350 miles between donor and cells.[179]

Imaging Illness in the Aura/Bioplasma

A 1972 Defense Intelligence Agency document reports that scientists at the Kazakh State University had found that "illnesses tend to show up in advance as a disordered play of flares from the 'bioplasma' long before they manifest in the physical body."[180]

There are some doctors who can see and diagnose illness using their perception of the human energy field. Due to the institutionalized ignorance of and prejudice against such "unscientific" ideas in the medical community, most such doctors don't share their abilities with their peers. One medical professional who overcame entrenched medical dogma and took the energy field seriously was the late neurologist and psychiatrist Shafica Karagulla. Starting out as a skeptic, Karagulla encountered several people who could see auras and make accurate medical diagnoses based on their clairvoyance. Then she knew for certain that something worth investigating was going on.

In the 1960s Karagulla sought to establish whether any medical professionals possessed these abilities. Unfortunately, even those who were reputedly talented in this way were loath to reveal their secrets. Karagulla booked an appointment with one such recalcitrant to see him as a patient (after being repeatedly put off for a meeting), and all but forced him to use his psi faculties to diagnose her. Cornered, he "scanned" her body and offered a quick summation of her health, including mention of an internal condition that would eventually need surgical intervention—a condition Karagulla had secretly already diagnosed. He was "correct in every detail," wrote Karagulla. This doctor admitted that he used the auric fields of patients to diagnose, though doing so without letting on, and following the standard medical procedures along the way. He could see the chakras/energy vortices associated with each endocrine gland, and identify incipient illness in the field before somatic manifestation. He also possessed natural healing ability.[181]

Karagulla's quest continued, and she met many more doctors with similar gifts. Consistently, they spoke of seeing an "energy field" or a "moving web of frequency" surrounding and interpenetrating the body. Not knowing the word "chakras," some spoke of "vortices of energy at certain points along the spine, connected with or influencing the endocrine system." Virtually every one of these closet medical-intuitives operated in secret lest they do violence to their professional status—a sad indictment of our current disease management system (or Medical Mafia, as former doctor G. Lanctot refers to it).

Karagulla was "continually surprised" at just how many medical professionals had HSP abilities. Though most were not entirely comfortable with their talents, they used them because of their practical value in their chosen line of work. "[T]hey came from many parts of the country . . . [and although] they were unknown to each other . . . they all reported similar types of experiences." She concludes: "When many reliable individuals independently report the same kind of phenomena, it is time science takes cognizance of it."[182]

One medical professional who did go public with her "paranormal" abilities is Dr. Dolores Krieger, a professor of nursing at New York University. Having participated in a study of the healing abilities of the Hungarian Oscar Estebany, Krieger developed an interest in the human energy field. Finding out that Estebany could increase hemoglobin levels in the ill just by working with their fields fired Krieger's thirst for knowledge, and she thereafter began serious research into prana, chakras, and the aura, eventually being taken on as a student of Dora Kunz. Under Kunz's tutelage, she acquired sensitivity to blockages in the field and learned the art of manipulating it with her hands in order to heal.[183]

As it happens, Karagulla worked with Kunz over several years, producing their seminal studies of the human energy fields. First, Kunz, for two or three hours (if all chakras were included), and, without speaking to them, psychically examined a patient from a distance of about 20 feet, focusing primarily on the status of the etheric body. Karagulla then obtained the subject's medical case history and made some observations of her own, and they then compared notes (ultimately for over 200 patients). Though lacking the medical jargon, Kunz was at least Karagulla's equal at medical diagnosis, with one distinct advantage: she could spot incipient illness in an auric field (astral or etheric, for instance) as much as *20 years in advance of its manifesting physical symptoms*. Such cases are detailed in their important work *The Chakras and the Human Energy Fields*.

Kunz had actually been president of the Theosophical Society for 12 years and, with Doloris Krieger, originated Therapeutic Touch, an energetic healing technique (given a suitably non-esoteric name) now employed in many hospitals. Kunz described the seven major chakras/vortices and numerous smaller ones, each having a characteristic number of subcones ("petals"), and pairing with a particular endocrine gland. The precise number of primary energy centers seems to be a matter of both perception and opinion, depending on which energy centers one ascribes "primary" status to. (Kunz, unlike Leadbeater, did not classify either the sacral *or* spleen chakras as "major," though she did agree the spleen was crucial in disseminating prana to and harmonizing the other major chakras.)

What Kunz and Karagulla found was that dysfunction in the behavior of the chakras and auric bodies could be correlated with physical disease states, as well as psycho-emotional dysfunction (schizophrenia, for instance). They classified the behavior of the etheric body and the chakras according to the following clairvoyantly observable characteristics: color, luminosity, rhythm, rate/frequency, form (size, shape and symmetry), angle (the etheric rays should extend at right angles from the body—"droopiness" indicates illness), elasticity, and texture.

Importantly, Karagulla and Kunz found that the behavior of a given endocrine gland was reflected in the behavior of the corresponding chakra. For example, *if the physiological function of the pineal gland was dysfunctional, it was also observed that the crown chakra was dysfunctional*. In all nine cases of pituitary gland disorders, Kunz observed abnormalities in the brow chakra, and in all seven of those cases in which the gland had been entirely removed, she observed an absence of etheric energy in the core of the pituitary—despite not even knowing it was possible to surgically remove it![184] Notably, partial or complete removal of a malfunctioning organ or gland could not guarantee a remedy of the corresponding etheric chakra's malfunction. Also, it could not be predetermined with certainty which body part might be affected by a corresponding chakra's abnormality.[185]

On one occasion Kunz described a woman's energy field in the abdominal region as "wilted" and "broken into fragments" and said this indicated a serious problem in the physical body. Looking into the woman's body, she saw that the colon was blocked near her spleen—a statement that shocked Karagulla since none of the symptoms (vomiting, pain, etc.) typically indicating such a serious malady were present. X-rays had been taken earlier in the day unbeknownst to Kunz and Karagulla because the woman's doctor had suspected an obstruction. When the results were in, they showed just such a blockage in the location Kunz pointed out. Three days later it was surgically removed.[186]

On a separate occasion while diagnosing patients in a New York clinic, Kunz studied a woman neither of them knew. Kunz assessed that her pituitary gland was absent, the pancreas wasn't functioning, the adrenals functioned poorly, her breasts were once affected but were no longer there, energy flow through her spine was lacking from the waist down, and she had trouble with her legs. The medical report on the woman revealed that her pituitary gland had been surgically removed, for which she was taking pituitrin and cortisone, she had had a double mastectomy due to breast cancer, and she had had an operation performed on her back to decompress her spinal cord and relieve pains in her legs.[187]

Kunz proved her ability to peer into the physical tissues and make accurate diagnoses in test after test. Not even bone brittleness escaped detection. Karagulla concluded that Kunz's clairvoyant assessments of subjects' physical status matched medical diagnoses with "amazing accuracy."[188]

Some people make careers out of being a medical intuitive. They see illness in the energy fields and sometimes, in rarer cases, can peer directly into the body to determine the client's state of health as we have seen. I have seen, in observing my psychic friend Larissa, long strings of accurate information she has received and shared, without error, where there was no possible way she could have known the information she was giving, other than by perceiving it psychically. Sure, sooner or later, if you are merely guessing, you will get something right, but think about it this way: if you are *only* guessing (or combining guessing with "cold reading") you are obviously not going to end up with 95+% accuracy for detailed personal information, spread over time, as failed skeptic demonstrations have shown.

Larissa gets the client to lie supine on a massage table, and scans their body with her hands, not making any physical contact. On one occasion, her hands would not leave one woman's chest area. She advised the woman to see a doctor to look into it. As the woman left, Larissa heard in her mind the name Ruth. She asked the woman if she knew anyone called Ruth.

"No."

"You're going to meet someone called Ruth."

OK, pretty general so far, you say. I know a Ruth and maybe you do too. Big deal. Well, the woman went to the doctor to have her chest examined. It turned out that four days before seeing Larissa, she had had a minor heart attack (hence Larissa's hands "locking" over the area) and had not checked it out, not realizing what had actually happened despite experiencing discomfort. The name of the doctor who diagnosed her? Ruth. Incidentally, she couldn't even find a Ruth in her family tree.

Sometimes a psychic will only get very limited information. Hearing the word "Ruth" isn't much to go on, so logically, they will ask something like "do you know anyone called Ruth?" If the answer is no, it can clarify what the message meant. In this instance, she was being told the name of a person the client hadn't met yet—the name of the doctor, as it turned out. "Skeptics" typically fail to appreciate that sometimes that is the extent of the information a psychic receives in a given moment. This is why a lot of psychics conduct readings in a question-based format, because otherwise they'd constantly be guessing and clutching at straws trying to work out what the words they are hearing, visions they are seeing, or sensations they are feeling actually mean.

Combining Psychics with Science

One thing that makes Valerie Hunt's aura and chakra data so interesting is that she deployed actual clairvoyants at the same time as her telemetry equipment, cross-checking the telemetry readings with observations by the psychics, who were separate from the equipment.[189] As it turned out, both data sets matched up very well. Hunt also found that multiple independent clairvoyant auric readings synched up *with each other* in undeniable ways well beyond chance occurrence. The Rolf Institute had given her a grant to study emotions, energy fields, and the neuromuscular effects of Rolfing: a deep-tissue therapy that manipulates connective tissues in order to bring the body back into alignment.[190]

> From the first session, each individual showed a unique pattern of amplitude and frequencies in chakras and in the synchrony between chakras . . . [E]ach individual kept his unique pattern, such as its strength or weakness and its variable frequency over time. For example, a physiologist, a meditator, had a more active third eye. A dancer carried hyperactivity in the legs and feet.[191]

According to Carol Dryer, a Los Angeles–based "human energy field consultant" (who by the early 1990s had seen over 5,000 clients), shallow

298

people have shallow and unremarkable auras, and more complex people have more complex and interesting fields. She compares each person's aura to a fingerprint: each is uniquely different.[192] The same applies to chakras, as, in Kunz's words, they "reveal a person's quality of consciousness and degree of personal development and abilities." In the undeveloped person, the chakras are smaller, slower, duller and more coarse texturally. Moving up the scale of development of perception, intelligence, compassion, specific talents and so on, they become increasingly bright, higher frequency, and finer texture. Hunt's findings dovetail with Kunz's own observations that particular talents are accompanied by a corresponding increase in size, luminosity, and frequency in related chakras. To Kunz's clairvoyance, meditators did indeed have increased third eye activity as a result of the increased synchrony between the crown and third eye centers of the etheric body.[193]

Further study by Hunt of clairvoyant observations during a Rolfing session, when a subject had sensors on his upper back and was lying supine, proved that the psychic was able to accurately read the state of his posterior chakras because they projected through the bed and two mattresses the subject was lying on. Sensor readings from chakra points directly matched the aura readers' descriptions of energy amount, color and dynamic quality. Additionally, it appeared that there was a "close relationship" between this data and the "emotional states, imagery, and interpersonal transactions of the subjects."[194]

For the next 20 years Hunt and her colleagues, volunteers, and assistants conducted many pilot studies of hands-on healing, various types of meditation, and energy field transactions. They established the reliability of aura readers' reports by comparing simultaneous readings from eight experienced clairvoyants. There was complete unanimity between the psychics on primary and secondary colors.[195] Hunt's research found that chakras frequently carried the colors stated in the metaphysical literature, i.e., kundalini—red; hypogastric (sacral)—orange; spleen—yellow; heart—green; throat—blue; third eye—violet; and crown—white. It was also found that activity in certain chakras seemed to trigger increased activity in another, while the heart chakra was consistently the most active,[196] dovetailing with more recent findings that the heart's magnetic field is the most powerful in the body.

According to Brennan, there are seven primary layers of the aura, associated with the seven primary (bodily) chakras. Furthermore, the aura reveals a "dualistic field pattern," with every second layer being "highly structured" and apparently consisting of standing waves of light patterns, while layers in between appear as colorful fluids in perpetual motion; each layer being of a higher frequency.[197]

Jay Alfred's comments on the plasmoidal nature of these structures make compelling reading. Regarding the dualistic layering seen by Brennan, alternately highly structured and then fluid-like, he observes that the first state appears to be crystalline magnetic plasma, and the latter liquid. Through the liquid states we express emotion, while we generate and express templates and concepts through crystalline states.[198] Our plasma-like auric fields confirm that the nature of the universal aetheric medium (in terms of its various particulate densities) is itself plasmoidal or plasma-like, for the chakras must feed off these universal fields to nourish the corresponding personal fields. The auric layers are actually "built" out of the transpersonal aetheric medium's particulate matter of varying size and densities.

Brennan says that the first layer of the aura corresponds to the first (root) chakra, the second layer to the second chakra, and so on. (Many intuitives confirm that each chakra is paired with an auric layer.) According to her, each chakra and auric layer corresponds to an aspect of the individual's overall psycho-physical makeup. Interestingly, she describes both a lower emotional body (which envelopes the etheric) *and* an astral body (with the mental body *between* the two); the astral subsumes and envelopes both. Luckman's kinesiological research similarly led him to conclude that the mental body is in fact preceded by an "emotional" vehicle, but for simplicity I will mainly reference the more common model.

Beyond the etheric, emotional, mental, and astral bodies, Brennan sees the higher-dimensional *templates* of these bodies as being: the etheric template body (a blueprint for the etheric double existing in "negative space," at which level Brennan states that *sound creates matter*); the celestial body (the level through which we experience "spiritual ecstacy" and unconditional love, which might roughly correspond to the buddhic body or bliss body described by other traditions); and the ketheric template (causal body), corresponding to the crown chakra, which contains the blueprints for all the aforementioned bodies within it, as well as the plan for the current life.[199]

For Brennan the root chakra represents physiological functions, physical sensations, pleasure, and pain; the second/sacral chakra relates to emotions and feelings; the third/solar plexus chakra relates to linear thought and the ordinary mental life. Higher chakras relate to more impersonal and transpersonal concepts such as love for others, love for mankind, "divine will," creativity, higher mind and spiritual functions and awareness. She sees the colors from root to crown as red (root), orange (sacral), yellow (solar plexus), green (heart), blue (throat), indigo (third eye), and violet-white (crown).[200]

Brennan notes that each major chakra on the front of the body is paired with its counterpart on the back of the body, and together they are considered to be the front and rear aspects of the one chakra; the frontal aspects are related to the person's feelings, the rear ones to the will, and the three on the head to the mental processes. She further adds that each chakra looks different on each density layer of the auric field. Brennan's designation of the chakra colors is more or less the standard contemporary conception as designated by clairvoyants and supported, in various cases, by scientific observations. She does not consider the spleen chakra a major center.

Brennan links the sixth chakra/third eye to the pituitary gland and designates the pineal gland to the crown chakra. Incidentally, Blavatsky assigned the third eye chakra to the pineal gland but also linked it to the crown chakra. Swami Satyananda also links it to the pineal.[201] It appears that the crown and third eye chakra are intimately linked in terms of the energy system and active siddhis (they work in concert) and our higher awareness. Ethan Vorley has written that the "crown receives higher consciousness and communication and the third eye grounds it into the dimension of which you are a part."[202]

The Voice of the Silence teaches that activation of the third-eye chakra at the etheric level stimulates the pituitary gland and thus allows the individual to hear their higher own self. The reasoning goes that the fully functional pituitary gland allows for perfect access to astral frequencies.[203] Taimni agrees that only after the pituitary is awakened do the siddhis become fully accessible to the Yogi, allowing the light of higher dimensions into brain-based awareness.[204]

In *The Mental Body*, Powell stated that the pituitary gland is the link between the physical and the astral body, and that between the physical and the mental body the link is the pineal gland.[205] Leadbeater clarified things in *The Inner Life*, stating that for many people, the astral vortices of the sixth and seventh chakras *both* converge on the pituitary body. For some other people, though, while the sixth/third eye center still attaches to the pituitary, they can bend or slant the seventh to make its vortex align with the pineal. This action vivifies it and makes it into a line of communication which passes through the astral plane in the usual way.[206]

While Eastern esoteric literature has associated each chakra with a certain number of "petals" (the root chakra having the fewest and the crown having the most), Brennan says that closer observation reveals these petals to be small rotating vortices spinning at very high speeds. According to her, each sub-vortex "metabolizes an energy vibration that resonates at its particular spin frequency," and therefore the colors in each chakra correspond to the frequency of energy being metabolized.[207]

Robert Bruce is an experienced and expert out-of-body projector and mystic who states in his book *Astral Dynamics* that the major chakras transform energies obtained by the "energy exchange ports" on the body into energies with "higher pure energetic values," depending on current energetic demands. The raw energies obtained by the "ports" can be stored in storage areas or used for bioenergetic purposes, if not channelled to the chakras.[208]

This is consonant with the standard occult view and reinforces the notion that people with inedia may indeed survive due to their subtle energy system's transformation and processing of occult energies in the place of food energy (the body actually expends vast amounts of energy in breaking down food, especially meats). Brennan states point-blank based on her remarkable clairvoyance that we bring more energy into our bodies through our auric fields than we gain by eating.[209] Aside from the spleen, the lungs and skin are the two most important points of entry for prana/etheric energy, according to Kunz.[210]

But Wait, There's a Catch . . .

With all of this talk of chakras and the obvious reality of their existence, we must introduce a confusing fact or two. Oldfield found via his imaging technology what he believes to be changes in the human chakra system since they were first charted some 5,000 years ago in the *Upanishads*. The primary colors of the major chakra centers revealed themselves to his PIP equipment in the following (ascending) order, starting with the root/*muladhara*. In this conception, yellow has switched places with green, while the remaining colors are listed as they often are by intuitives and ancient occult systems. Oldfield speculatively attributes the discrepancy to humanity's spiritual evolution, or possibly pollution, "electromagnetic invasion" and other factors.[211] (Also keep in mind that Oldfield's equipment offers *indirect* vision of the fields, as the equipment relies on the EM light spectrum.) In fact, the color of the heart chakra, according to the clairvoyance of Leadbeater, and, more recently Kunz, is indeed predominantly golden-yellow, while the navel is chiefly red-green. We thus find near-complete agreement here with Oldfield's simplified schema.

Initially, Oldfield had stumbled upon the chakras unwittingly, having not known what chakras even were. He had inadvertently found all seven of the primary centers on the physical body but didn't realize until John Hasted, a professor of physics and psi researcher, pointed it out after Oldfield had finished a presentation of his work at Birkbeck College, London, in 1982. Hasted himself had first encountered the chakras through the case of a (clearly clairvoyant) little boy who, while sitting at the family dinner table one night, declared to his mother with consternation that the "light" in his uncle Willy's heart had "gone out." His uncle died of a heart attack that night, demonstrating again for us that physical defects and catastrophes are preceded by changes in the subtle energy system of the body.[212]

The Fragmentary Body

Through extensive kinesiological testing, American author Sol Luckman and his partner Leigh discovered and mapped a total of nine primary torsion fields/ vortices in humans, only eight of which, it turns out, are really meant to be there. This disregards a tenth field (the Source or Master field) they detected which corresponds, in astrophysical terms, to Galactic Center and to *Nezah* or Eternity in the kabbalistic Tree of Life.[213] The number nine is reached due to the detection of the "fragmentation" of the second chakra (known as the Fragmentary Body), which produces an extra vortex above the head which should not be there.

According to Luckman, who does acknowledge the ancient teachings of seven primary fields, we are meant to have an octave of eight. This is confirmed independently by medical intuitive Caroline Myss, who discovered for herself the eighth chakra years after identifying the first seven. She explains that this is where our archetypal energies reside. Unlike the other seven personal chakras, the eighth is transpersonal. "Connecting to the infinite source of all archetypal energies, it also maintains a connection to every individual body and soul."

She describes this eighth chakra as a 3D infinity sign like a mobius strip that "runs between the personal unconscious and the collective unconscious, linking the literal and symbolic dimensions, your personal life and the impersonal universe . . . [it] represents a continual current of cosmic intelligence that feeds into your psyche."[214] (Note that in systems such as the theosophical one the chakra depicted *above* the head is often disregarded for practical purposes.) In Luckman's words, the torsion fields/chakras "can be thought of as an interlocking set of high-frequency 'force-fields' [Figure 9.3], each responsible for the correct functioning of a particular gland, meridian, organ system, set of emotions, etc."[215]

Figure 9.3 The Human Bioenergy Blueprint

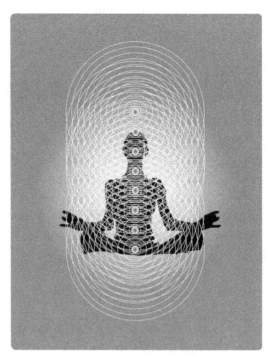

Luckman: "From the perspective of quantum biology, the human body is a hologram composed of intersecting lines of bioenergy . . . [T]he vertical, light-processing chakras interface with the horizontal, sound-generated torsion fields to create the geometric matrix necessary for physical manifestation."
Image credit: Sol Luckman, *Conscious Healing*, p. 23.

According to the esoteric literature, the Fragmentary Body poses a serious problem. This, according to Luckman, is because the second torsion field "resonates as a 'Frankenstein's monster' of energies that simply do not add up, that in many cases do not even appear to belong in the human body," and merely "siphon off the host's life energy."[216] Luckman envisions the Fragmentary Body as "an anti-enlightenment consciousness vacuum, a systemic energy drain that, until 'sealed,' limits our ability to embody the light of higher consciousness. When properly sealed through DNA activation, however, this field . . . becomes the locus for the human being's healing into a consciousness and physiology capable of expressing divine radiance."[217]

Such "divine radiance" has been observed emanating from enlightened mystics and ascetics through the ages. Did their years of meditation trigger

DNA activation? Based on personal experience and professional observation, Luckman believes that DNA activation eventually triggers the mobile "junk" or "potential" DNA into building the interlaced tetrahedral light body/merkaba,[218] a notion not without scientific support[219] (as I will elaborate on in TGI 2).

In Luckman's Regenetics model,

> the chakras (which process higher-dimensional torsion energy in the form of light) and EM fields (which process higher-dimensional torsion energy in the form of sound) establish the holographic interface that gives rise to the human body. Utilizing the genetic sound–light translation mechanism, each sonic field energizes the corresponding chakra with higher-dimensional light, which then transfers as bioenergy or kundalini to specific aspects of the subtle (energetic) anatomy.[220]

In short, without these biofields (and the more fundamental *tan tien* point in the haric dimension mentioned in Chapter 8), you would not exist for long at the physical level. With the "death" or extinguishing of the root chakra (or heart chakra for that matter), physical death is soon to follow. Chakras are primary determinants of physical health, as well as allowing for psi faculties to function; they facilitate "paranormal" perception. This point cannot be overstated. According to intuitive and author Cyndi Dale, chakras can process all frequencies of light or information energy, meaning they can convert psychic information to sensory data and back again.[221]

Luckman discovered through his research that most people appear to have two bioenergy/torsion centers floating above the head as part of their overall energetic makeup. As he used his own Regenetics (DNA activation) treatment on himself and his partner Leigh, Luckman found that the frequency of their fields noticeably increased and also caused the topmost center (9th) above the head to literally descend and "seal" the Fragmentary Body/center. From there, Luckman's health began to improve dramatically and his strength steadily increased. As he eliminated copious amounts of accumulated toxins, he found his food allergies evaporating. Likewise, Lee found that her asthma and environmental allergies completely disappeared.[222]

I have performed my own DNA activation using the 528 Hz "love" frequency and am very pleased with the results so far, the first major change being the initiation of the healing of my shoulders' rotator cuffs, decreasing pain and grinding sensations and increasing mobility. Both shoulders have improved enormously, in fact, along with my food allergies.[223] Linsteadt has reported that at this 528 Hz frequency, "the clustered water molecules that surround and support the DNA structure form a perfect six-sided hexagon,"[224] meaning you are generating your own internal "Cymatic effect."

After this energetic "sealing" through Regenetics, the previously unstable and fragmented energy structure "is recalibrated permanently to a stable and balanced 'infinity circuit' founded on the number 8."[225] All of this means a gradual shift from separation consciousness and victimhood (theoretically attributable to the fragmentary body), into sensing our oneness with the all. In light of all this, we note that Dora Kunz observed the general pattern of energy flow through the human field to be in the form of a figure eight/infinity sign crossing near the heart chakra.[226]

An increasing number of people seem to believe that there are actually *five* transpersonal chakras beyond the seven personal chakras, thus giving a twelvefold chakra system. Counting the whole as "one" gives 12 plus one—the number of semitones in an octave.[227] Dale is one author who has detailed her own conception of the twelvefold octave chakra system in *Illuminating the Afterlife*.

The Third Eye Chakra and the Pineal Gland

The pineal's name comes from the Latin *pineus,* relating to the pine, *pinus.* It is *piniform,* (shaped like a pinecone),[228] and small—roughly the size of a pea. The pineal produces melatonin and serotonin, two neurohormones that, among many other functions, directly control all of the biocycles. British anatomist J.Z. Young has shown that this organ controls the daily rhythm of skin color changes that the lamprey (which actually has a physical third eye close to the head's surface, and which responds to light) and certain lizards undergo. Pineal production of melatonin and serotonin is guided by the geomagnetic field. Application of a small magnetic field can even cause physical changes in pineal cells.[229]

In occult terms, the third eye chakra is most strongly associated with clairvoyance and the ability to perceive psychic imagery internally. It is also linked to telepathy. The interior of the pineal gland contains rods and cones just like the retina in the eye, hence the term "third eye." It also happens to become visible in a developing fetus seven weeks after conception, the same time at which appears the first indication of male or female gender.[230]

Additionally, the pineal—located approximately in the center of the skull—sits directly over the crucial emotional and sensory brain centers known as the visual and auditory *colliculi*, composed of specialized brain tissue. Electrical and chemical impulses that begin in the eyes and ears must pass through the colliculi before we experience them as sights and sounds. The pineal is separated from these colliculi only by a narrow channel of cerebrospinal fluid. Thus, pineal secretions would rapidly reach the colliculi. Additionally, the limbic system enfolds the pineal, meaning that the pineal also has direct access to our brain's emotional centers.[231]

The pineal gland has the highest relative blood flow of any body part except the kidneys. Its hollow interior is filled with a watery liquid. Unprotected by the blood-brain barrier, the pineal fluid collects mineral deposits ("brain sand") over time—it calcifies.[232] We are hastening and exacerbating the problem needlessly with fluoride in toothpaste and drinking water (in Australia and the USA, to name two countries), carbonated beverages, too much refined fats, sugars, excess refined flour, and so on, according to Wilcock in *The 2012 Enigma*.[233]

It is now known thanks to the meticulous research of Dr. Jennifer Luke, from the University of Surrey in England, that the pineal gland is the primary target of fluoride accumulation within the body. Fluoride—in particular, the sodium fluoride dumped in public drinking water—being a known and proven neurotoxin and carcinogen for over 70 years.[234] The soft tissue of the adult pineal gland contains more fluoride than any other soft tissue in the body—a level of fluoride (~300 ppm) capable of inhibiting enzymes. The hard tissue (hyroxyapatite crystals) in the pineal accumulates more fluoride (up to 21,000 ppm) than any other hard tissue in the body.[235] The buildup of fluoride depresses melatonin synthesis, producing adverse effects such as accelerating puberty onset. Pineal dysfunction and low melatonin are also correlated with multiple sclerosis.[236]

The pineal is surrounded by magnetite clusters that are carefully tuned to "perceive" and interact with magnetic fields, the same kinds of magnetic clusters that allow homing pigeons, butterflies, and bees to navigate using the earth's magnetic field. A study published in 1985 in the *British Medical Journal* found that people who were suffering from calcification or hardening of the pineal gland were significantly more likely to get lost, suggesting a pineal role in human navigational abilities.[237]

Ethan Vorley makes an interesting statement in his book *Metaphysics* that a major reason for the shrinkage of the pineal gland as we age is due to the crown chakra essentially closing after the ego structure has been formed, and that the only way to rejuvenate it is to activate the crown chakra.[238] In his classic *The Secret Teachings of All Ages*, Masonic scholar Manly P. Hall explains that the pineal gland is "the sacred pinecone in man—the eye single, which cannot be opened until CHiram (the Spirit Fire [kundalini]) is raised through the sacred seals [chakras] which are called the Seven Churches in Asia."

> The exact science of human regeneration is the Lost Key of Masonry, for when the Spirit Fire is *lifted up* through the thirty-three degrees, or segments of the spinal column, and enters into the domed chamber of the human skull, it finally passes into the pituitary body (Isis), where it invokes Ra (the pineal gland) and demands the Sacred Name. Operative Masonry, in the fullest meaning of that term, signifies the process by which the Eye of Horus is opened.[239]

Wilcock, among others, notes that the "silver cord" spoken of by OBEers and mystics over the years is anchored to the pineal gland which, whether true or not, is in itself an interesting point, especially since Descartes asserted that the pineal gland was the "seat of the soul"—something for which Hall expressed support. Dr. Bill Deagle has also emphasized this point, saying the silver cord attaches the bioplasmic spirit body to the physical body through the pineal.[240]

Wilcock explains that as ambient light is removed (and darkness sets in), the pineal generates an electromagnetic shield, protecting it from all the familiar energies that give us a reference/bearing in space-time. That then opens the door to *time-space* (in particular the astral world). Hence, during sleep people can have prophetic dreams where they access information from the time-space realm and return to make accurate "predictions" that baffle ordinary consciousness operating in linear space-time awareness.[241] The onset of tingling or pressure in the third eye chakra will be familiar to many meditators. This sensation might signal the setting up of the pineal's EM shield in order to shift awareness into the time domain. (In the case of sleep, this primarily means the astral plane.)

As already noted, the pineal is stimulated by the endogenous psychedelic DMT, and by LSD trips and other psychedelics. However, Wilcock, for one, warns that "tripping" can be dangerous, causing the pineal to possibly get stuck in the "on" mode, which results in waking hallucinations and symptoms characterizing schizophrenia,[242] which we have already touched on and will expand on in TGI 2. We can fairly speculate, then, that some of schizophrenia's symptoms may occasionally be the result of extra stimulation of the pineal, causing the overlap between this world and the next (perhaps the astral plane or even other parallel realities) that is usually reserved for sleep states. You're not "insane" as long as hallucinatory sense perceptions occur in your sleep!

According to Yogi Ramacharaka (1903), yogis have known for centuries that the pineal is the physical organ responsible for telepathic reception. Thought vibrations reaching another person's pineal gland "cause a brain action which reproduces the thought in the brain of the recipient." These thought waves may reach waking consciousness or remain in the region of the "instinctive mind," or what modern psychology less precisely regards as the "subconscious."[243] Strassman believes that the pineal is triggered into releasing a flood of DMT as the "life force" passes through on entering the body, as well as releasing more DMT at birth, in deep meditation, states of psychosis, and beginning an NDE.[244]

It is known fairly widely that certain drugs create temporary psychic abilities. Wilcock adds another dimension, however. He explains that certain aspects of our physiology are lined up with the geometric form of a tetrahedron in our head. If the back of the skull corresponds with the base of this tetrahedron, *the apex lines up exactly with the third eye/pineal* and the tilt of our ear drums align with the slope of two of the sides, which pass through them. Thus, we have a geometric relationship here with our hyperdimensional gateway (the pineal) and this basic platonic solid.[245] In Wilcock's aether model, the two interlaced tetrahedra are the primary geometry for the fourth density/dimension, and now we are faced with the realization that our DMT manufacturing gateway to hyperdimensional realities is the centerpiece of a tetrahedron. Hence Taimni's statement that, when made active by meditation, the pineal "serves as a bridge between the higher and lower consciousness and *enables the light of the higher worlds to penetrate into the brain.*"[246]

Barbara Brennan claims in *Hands of Light* that a higher-than-normal frequency of light passes through the third eye point, flows along the optic nerves, and travels through the optic chiasm, ultimately being diverted along two paths: one to the occipital lobe for normal vision, and the other into the thalamus. Through certain meditative techniques we can induce the pituitary into vibrating and radiating gold light which branches into the thalamus region and then is directed into the pineal gland, thus facilitating internal intuitive visions.[247]

A number of scientific studies going back to the 1980s have raised the possibility that the human pineal is indeed directly involved in detecting photons, and a *Science News* article by Julie Ann Miller (1985) informs us that once scientists started working together on the issue, they "discovered surprising similarities" between the pineal and the retina.[248]

After citing several studies discussing similarities between the retina and pineal in *The Source Field Investigations*, Wilcock offers the possibility that cells in the pineal may indeed be detecting photons and sending them to the brain through the process of photo-transduction. He then points out that in 2002, S.S. Baconnier et al. reported on their dissections of 20 human pineal glands, and the discovery of 100–300 microcrystals per cubic millimeter floating inside each. These tiny crystals were largely composed of calcite, a common mineral, and were very similar to crystals found in the inner ear, called otoconia. Otoconia crystals are piezoelectric, meaning they expand and contract in the presence of EM fields—and piezoelectric crystals can also tune into radio waves wirelessly.

Some piezoelectric crystals also emit light when pressure is applied to them (known as piezoluminescence)—and this, Wilcock seems to think, may be a further source of light within the pineal. Additionally, DMT has been found to be highly piezoluminescent, as well as displaying piezochromism (meaning different colored photons are emitted from the same crystalline source). While it has not been conclusively proved that the pineal synthesizes DMT, there is good reason to believe it does. Thus, pineal DMT may be yet another source of light in the pineal. Baconnier speculates that, if piezoelectricity exists in the pineal calcite microcrystals, "an electromagnetic coupling mechanism to external [EM] fields may be possible."[249]

Can this mechanism partially account for internal intuitive visions in the mind's eye?—a possible result of external EM fields triggering piezoluminescence in the pineal gland's calcite crystals? It may also be possible that torsion field dynamics within the pineal are actually generating photons quite naturally. Maybe as the pineal is impacted by torsion waves emanating from other sources (another person, for instance), this stimulates internal psychic visions by triggering internal production of photons.

It is Anthony Peake's thesis that the reason the pineal is located so deep in the skull is that it is designed to process biophotons generated by virtual photons emerging from the ZPF (aether/time-space), and that this is where images perceived in dreams, OBEs, DMT "hallucinations," and NDEs originate.[250] In essence, this is probably correct. It accounts for my own spontaneous hypnogogic visions in which various scenes, images, and locations have appeared to my inner senses unbidden while in an alpha state on the verge of sleep. In these experiences my powers of vision—both in terms of resolution and the ability to hone in on and magnify things—are *far superior* to my normal eyesight. Colors present are orders of magnitude more vivid than in "real life."

It is worth noting in the context of our discussion of light and the pineal gland that certain remote viewing experiments conducted in China and America in the 1980s employed sensitive light-detecting devices in darkened, light-shielded rooms, in which the targets were located. At the times when the RVers succeeded in viewing the targets, the number of photons in the room surged massively[251]—as if the presence of the RVer's awareness created a vortex/torsion field that "spun" detectable photons out of the aether/time-space.

Medical intuitive Robyn Elizabeth Welch has utilized the *ajna* center as a powerful healing tool, using it to heal herself of a tumor in her uterus, and then going on to use it healing others—even over the phone. Filling the third eye center with white light, she would then direct the light as a precisely focused ray towards the tumor, "zapping" it with this powerful energy. By the third day it was gone. At her next checkup at the hospital, a puzzled doctor could only send her home with instructions to see him if it ever returned.[252]

Welch's special talents as a medical intuitive were to "heal and see inside the human energy field and body" without the laying on of hands, and also to "communicate" with the body parts.[253] Indeed, Welch's abilities are utterly nonlocal if she so intends, healing people even via telephone over arbitrary distances (remember, for consciousness or torsion waves moving in aether/time-space, 3-space distance is a meaningless concept). Sarah Stacey, the Wellbeing Editor of *YOU* magazine, wrote of Welch: "In biblical times, Robyn Welch would have been hailed as a worker of miracles . . . I was skeptical of her claims, but several sessions with her convinced me that if anything she understates what she can achieve."[254]

Knowing that our pineal gland is partially a crystalline structure, Marcel Vogel, senior scientist with IBM for 27 years, has some compelling comments to add on crystals. He states that when a crystal is cut to the correct form and the human mind interacts with its structural perfection, the crystal then emits a vibration that enhances the mind's powers. The crystal radiates energy in a laser-like, coherent, highly concentrated form, which can then be directed by the will into objects or people. Vogel explains that crystal (and presumably then the pineal gland) can be used for telepathic contact or in healing—the crystal makes the energies of mind coherent.[255]

Kundalini Awakening, Evolution, and Meditation

Kundalini refers to the current of energy running up the spine to your crown, from the base or root chakra, which is to be found at the perineum, between the anus and genitals. Brennan refers to the kundalini as the "main power current." The chakras have their tips connecting/pointing into the kundalini, and their open ends extend to the edge of each layer of the field/subtle body they are located in.

Kundalini is held in high esteem because of its reputed ability to awaken higher consciousness, and it has been equated with both torsion and plasma by different researchers who have emphasized different aspects. According to Leadbeater, however, kundalini is not so much to do with psychological or emotional health as with physical health.

Unsurprisingly, kundalini, like most psychic faculties, is not very active in most people. The awakening of the kundalini is associated also with heightened creativity, perception, and intelligence. Generally speaking, the awakening of the kundalini and channeling of it through the various chakras stimulates them into higher more refined functioning, eventually resulting in functional siddhis (clairvoyance, for instance). The principal function of kundalini in occult development, according to Powell, is to pass through the etheric chakras and vivify them so that they bring astral experiences through into the physical consciousness.[256] An enhancement of the chakras at the etheric level will naturally have positive physical side-effects.

Goswami stated that the raising of the kundalini seems to unleash the dormant capacities of consciousness for making new representations of the vital (etheric) body onto the physical body. "There is evidence. People in whom kundalini has risen and been properly integrated undergo extraordinary bodily changes (for example, the development of nodules on the body that [form] the figure of a serpent)."[257]

> Bentov studied kundalini from an engineering perspective. According to [him], the 7.5 Hz oscillation of the heart muscle rhythm induces mechanical Hz frequencies in the brain, that in turn create a stimulus equivalent of a current loop. [We now know the brain's EM field can be entrained by the heart's.] The nerve endings in that loop correspond to the route through which the kundalini "rises." This current polarizes the brain part through which it flows in a homogeneous way, effectively releasing tremendous amounts of stress from the body. The body then becomes an effective antenna for the 7.5 Hz frequency, which is the primary resonant Schumann frequency of the ionosphere. In layman's terms, you then pick up information from the air.[258]

In earlier depictions of the kundalini energy it was sometimes represented by two intertwining snakes (as in the caduceus of medicine) forming a spiral. The human auric field is not only feeding on the particles of the various aetheric densities, but its toroidal structure seems to mirror Besant and Leadbeater's UPA.

What people refer to as a "kundalini awakening" means an increase in our uptake of this dense red-colored plasmoidal matter by the root chakra, possibly as a result of an increase in its spin rate. Those people who have had some kind of kundalini awakening may have had the classic mystical experience of all-encompassing transcendent consciousness, or of being immersed in incredible white light (highlighting the increased energy flow in the crown center, and probably also the pineal and even pituitary glands). Increased uptake of scalar/torsion energy leads to greater levels of insight, understanding, and perceptiveness.

In Hindu esoteric anatomy, there are two helical channels or forces running either side up the spine known as the *ida* and the *pingala*. Some people suspect these are sine waves. Richard Bartlett asks what if they are our forward wave and our time-reversed wave? He suggests that combining these channels in the central spinal channel (*shushuma*) might result in a scalar EM wave—two waves 90° out of phase with each other, yielding a vector zero resultant. It would be undetectable to current technology but would "contain the force of the vacuum."[259] Under such circumstances, levitation or other "paranormal" phenomena might be obtained.

In 1986 in fact, Harry Oldfield took an interesting Kirlian photograph of a middle-aged female patient after treatment which seemed to show the kundalini flowing in its natural twisting form. Then in 1995, Oldfield was able to capture before and after images of uncontrolled kundalini energy in a young woman who, in her distressed state, had been affecting electrical equipment—televisions turned on and off when she entered a room or other equipment would fail, and she also heard voices. Oldfield carried out a PIP scan in the usual way, by saving each picture individually in case the woman affected the equipment. Despite this precaution, when he went to view the pictures they had been wiped from the system. He started doing them again, only to have the computer suddenly crash.

One image alone had been spared: it showed a powerful and uncontrolled release of kundalini between the woman's legs. Oldfield saw what he described as "violent storms of energy swirling around her feet." The lone saved picture revealed a thick bolt of energy—large enough to block the view of her leg—coming from her right foot towards the computer just before it crashed. Fortunately, treatment with Oldfield's electro-crystal therapy yielded a return visit the next week at which the woman reported all disturbances had ceased and she was feeling much more relaxed.[260]

"Mutually entangled currents (in the form of double spirals) are frequently seen in space and laboratory plasmas . . . They are signature features within magnetic plasmas," writes Alfred. The fact that the central vertical currents in the auric field (the helical *ida* and *pingala* and the straight *shushuma*) are often depicted as a pair of mutually entangled helical currents with straight currents passing through them shows, in Alfred's view, that there is a strong connection between plasma and yoga literature.[261] He notes that kundalini is more dense than pranic energy, which is absorbed instead by the crown chakra, spleen chakra, and lungs. The two energies apparently have opposite polarities. Charged particles—including kundalini and prana—accelerate through the center helical channels' magnetic field lines, forming Birkeland currents.[262]

It is interesting that the plasmoidal kundalini is said to be drawn from the center of the earth and taken up by the downward-facing root chakra, because the universal density profile of so-called "dark matter" under the lambda cold dark matter theory (see page 000) supports a dense concentration of dark matter at the center of the earth, according to Alfred.[263] Wilcock shows in *The Science of Oneness* and *The Divine Cosmos* that the accepted "metallic dynamo" theory of earth's core is inadequate, and that a plasma core model better fits available facts and observational data. A plasma model could, for example, account for the apparent increase in the mass and size of our planet over the last several billion years.[264]

Meditation facilitates the development of hemispheric synchrony within the brain, perhaps partly by stimulating the root and crown chakras, and also by placing the brain into alpha and theta states. Sara Lazar, a neuroscientist at Massachusetts General Hospital, and colleagues, have produced research indicating that meditation can specifically alter (thicken) involved regions of the brain's cortex over time—*in proportion to the time spent practicing*. Lazar found that in a group of 20 Buddha mindfulness meditators recruited from local meditation communities, with an average of approximately nine years' experience, those portions of the brain associated with attention, awareness of sensation, sensory stimuli, and sensory processing were thicker in the meditators than in the control group of 15 non-meditators. Indicatively, *increases in cortical thickness were proportional to the overall amount of time spent meditating* and the meditator group had staved off the usual age-related cortical atrophy.[265]

Have you ever noticed how regular meditators often don't look their age? A study on Transcendental Meditation found that practitioners of at least five years were physiologically 12 years younger than their chronological age.[266] Telomeres, the "tails" of genes, are markers for aging; the older the person, the shorter their telomeres. However, this process was seen to be reversed in a pilot study by Dr. Norm Shealy, simply by placing subjects on a healthy diet and exercise routine and bathing them in an EM field featuring human DNA frequencies.[267]

The effects of meditation are not limited "merely" to the inner structure of the brain, and indeed thanks to researchers such as Candace Pert and other notables we have mentioned, there are no longer any dividing lines between the brain and the body—research in the field of neurocardiology, for example, has estimated that up to "60 to 65 percent of heart cells are neurons, all of which cluster in ganglia, small neural groupings connected through the same type of axon-dendrites forming the neural fields of our brain."[268] Pert showed that neuropeptides—the biochemical correlates of emotions—are found throughout the body.[269]

We have detailed that human thought, emotions, and intention alter the body's auric field. Regular meditation is one way to do this for the better by enhancing the field's coherence and strength, perhaps partly by increasing kundalini activity. It begins to open the door to the subconscious realm of nonlocal awareness, in other words, by expanding the locus of our awareness into higher dimensions or frequencies (time-space). This is why meditation is considered a cosmic accelerator, and the most advanced practitioners as evolutionary mutants, capable of "supernatural" feats.

The Crown Chakra

In esotericism, the crown chakra is widely held to be the seat of or opening to wisdom and higher awareness, our direct access to deeper realities and energy systems. Having an activated crown doesn't necessarily mean other chakras are also activated. It is possible to possess great wisdom and insight and not yet have functional astral vision or well-developed clairvoyant faculties in general. If someone has a very closed mind or will not listen to reason other than their own preferred form of it, it is considered that their crown is blocked or undeveloped. "Its main capacity is that of an open mind as it is indeed the opening of the mind into higher dimensions and realities. Those with closed minds prefer to be right than find the truth and so are unlikely to experience higher consciousness as it can only come in through an open mind."[270]

In this sense, it does not surprise me that I didn't have my first profound mystical experience until *after* I had my mind blown wide open by the book that catalyzed my spiritual search for truth to begin with. Thus, with a closed crown chakra/mind, becoming fundamentally "enlightened" (in the sense of recognizing you are an infinite immortal consciousness and not just a personality attached to a body) is exceedingly unlikely. So that might be the first consideration in terms of seeking "deep spiritual realities" within one's own awareness.

Atmospheric Prana/Orgone/Etheric Matter

For at least six years now a somewhat odd phenomenon has caught my attention from time to time. Mostly this phenomenon has been observed when staring at a clear sky. What I noticed was something like a matrix of very subtle wavy lines morphing in the air. These waves were so subtle that I normally didn't even notice them there. For one reason or another, that changed at some point, and I began to pay more attention to them. On one occasion I decided to spend a minute or two actually focusing in on them to see if they appeared only against the backdrop of a blue sky and I found that, instead of this enigmatic visual effect being restricted to the sky, it actually spread to encompass my whole visual field. Then I really began to think something was going on. Whatever it was I was seeing wasn't just an illusion caused by staring only at the daytime sky. It appeared to be everywhere.

As I "tuned in" more and more, I could see what appeared to be little white pinpoints of light that appeared to be causing the wave effect. They would wriggle their way around briefly and then vanish, leaving in their wake the squiggly waves. As I tried to tune into this phenomenon, I might also receive impressions of energy emanations from trees, as if they were sending out communications to one another. Once or twice, nearby trees appeared to be exchanging energy with one another via plasma-like flares (this has been noted by various clairvoyants). So, what is this dynamic matrix of squiggly energy?

According to Barbara Brennan, it is the "Universal Energy Field," or at least some part of it. The little white pinpoints she refers to as Reich's orgone energy. Reich (1897–1957) had said that if you stare at the blue sky, you see waves passing rhythmically across it. I found that these waves appear to comprise a matrix that we all are immersed in. Brennan says that if you can expand your vision you will see the whole field pulsating rhythmically. She also notes the link between sunlight and the energy levels and number of these particles. On sunny days they are greater in number and move faster. The less sun, the slower and fewer in number they are. Sunlight seems to charge them.[271]

Reading Brennan's words, I knew I wasn't suffering from some idiosyncratic optical illusion, nor was I seeing something on the cornea of my eye. Not only was a truly talented psychic seeing what I was, but she had apparently also recognized *what it was* as well. I went outside to make some more observations and found that I could focus on energy nearer or further away, something I could not do if the effect was being caused by something actually on the surface of my eye. It wasn't moisture and it sure as hell wasn't a "floater"/dust particle. I already knew that much. I too have noticed that these globules are present in greater numbers in increased sunlight, as opposed to inside a dimly lit room or outside on a cloudy day. Brennan says that if you look at the haze of energy around a tree you will not find any of the globules in it but you might see them at the periphery of the haze changing their pattern of movement and flowing into the aura of the tree, disappearing.[272]

Watching these globules more recently, it seems that two will tumble their way into each other and ostensibly mutually annihilate, vanishing from my sight (where do they go?). In *The Chakras*, Leadbeater speaks of this particle, only he refers to it as the vitality globule. Shining with a white or slightly golden light, they consist only of seven UPAs (or subquarks),[273] and would not be not large enough for the non-clairvoyant to see physically were it not for their sheer brilliance. According to Leadbeater, the globules, generated by the sun, are absorbed by the body via the spleen chakra and utilized as energy.[274] In fact, he states flatly that it is only by absorbing this vital force that our physical bodies are able to live.[275]

According to theosophy (and the ancient Hindus and Egyptians), the sun is our primary source of prana, which is the vitality force comprising the UPA. (Powell also makes a point of explaining that prana and kundalini energy are not the same thing and cannot be converted into one another.) The intensity of the presence of the globules in the air around us bears a relationship with the available sunlight: the more light, the more globules, and vice versa.[276] This matches my experience.

If it is true what eminent metaphysicists such as Leadbeater, Brennan, Powell, Bruce, and others say about the chakras essentially being energy transducers that draw energy in from the surrounding subtle energetic environment, then cases of inedia such as those of yogis and religious devotees like Therese Neumann become much more explainable. The body does not simply rely on physical food for its fuel; it can apparently survive through the actions of the chakras (particularly the spleen) as they transmute various frequencies of (non-physical) matter into fuel for the body to use, distributing it along the meridian system and nadis to the cells. It seems that Reich's orgone is indeed one and the same as the vitality globule/prana identified by occultists.

The argument that any apparent perception of orgone is definitely a hallucination does not hold water, because, as R.A. Wilson noted, "it appears to be the most common hallucination in history."[277] Atwater points out in *Future Memory* that there are over 400 different words from many cultures around the globe referring to prana/Qi/orgone.[278]

It is interesting to note the similarities between Reich's "orgone," the occultists' etheric/pranic matter, Mesmer's "animal magnetism," Reichenbach's "odyle," and Henri Bergson's *élan vital* ("vital force"). Reich believed orgone essentially created all of nature (occultists state that physical matter is created by etheric matter). Although first discovered in the human body, he learned through painstaking observation and experiment that it existed in free form in the atmosphere. Reich's finding was that the same orgone energy underlay consciousness, life, atmospheric processes, and cosmic processes. He deduced the following ten properties of orgone: [279]

- It is mass-free
- It is present everywhere.
- It is the medium for electromagnetic and gravitational phenomena.
- It is in constant motion.
- It "contradicts" the law of entropy (much as the ZPF/aether does in the increasing number of devices that exploit it).
- It forms units which are the foci of creative activity.
- Matter is created from it.
- It is responsible for life.
- Separate streams of orgone energy may be attracted to each other and superimpose.
- It can be manipulated and controlled by orgone energy devices (or the will).

Reich's experiments indicated that orgone could be measured in terms of heat or movement, and that, depending on the level of health of an organism, it is present in corresponding degree (which corresponds closely to traditional ideas about prana). Reich's major invention, the orgone accumulator, was the primary reason for his disgraceful persecution, farcical "trial" by a corrupt judicial system, subsequent incarceration, and eventual death in prison thanks to the American government and the AMA. What the orgone accumulator's anomalous temperature rise meant was that the life-force could be collected from the atmosphere. Reich and his associates could sit inside the box and "soak up a greater charge of life-force than they could by sitting outside, and improve their health."[280] For this Reich was crushed.

Inedia

The Hindu yogini Giri Bala was one of history's various notable "God-Realized" beings who did not eat or drink for extended periods of time. In her case that extended period lasted over 50 years. On meeting her, and inquiring as to her means of sustenance, Yogananda said to her that her nourishment was obtained "from the finer energies of the air and sunlight and through the cosmic power that recharges your body through the medulla oblongata," to which she agreed.[281]

Initially her vow of abstinence from physical sustenance was brought on by the ridicule and scorn poured on her by her mother-in-law as a 12-year-old for her gluttonous eating habits. One day, fed up with the jibes, Giri Bala swore to her unrelenting mother-in-law that she would never touch food again. She was not long afterwards initiated into a Kriya technique by a newfound guru. Evidently, over 56 years later, that vow had held true.

The non-eating state (inedia) is a yogic power mentioned in Patanjali's *Yoga Sutras*. Giri Bala employed a breathing exercise that affected the *vishuddha* (throat) chakra. In Yogananda's words, this chakra "controls the fifth element, akash or ether, pervasive in the intra-atomic spaces of the physical cells."[282] Of Kriya Yoga, the *Bhagavad Gita* says that the yogi/ni halts bodily decay by obtaining additional prana (life-force) as a result of quieting the lungs' and heart's activity. Similarly, mutations of growth in the body can by eliminated by control of *apana* (eliminating current).[283] A master yogini such as Giri Bala therefore has total life-force control.

She stated that she slept very little, since the two states (asleep and awake) were the same to her—this suggests the possibility of total consciousness of astral experiences in dream states. Instead of sleeping, she meditated at night. She claimed to never experience illness or disease, and to feel slight pain only when accidentally injured. She had no bodily excretions and was able to control her heart rate.[284]

Giri Bala had been placed under observation on three separate occasions for testing at the palace of the Maharaja of Burdwan. On the first occasion she stayed, free of food, for two months. Subsequent stays for observation were of 20 and 15 days each. A former neighbour of Giri Bala's said to Yogananda that he had never once seen her eat or drink during their time as neighbours.[285]

The Catholic nun Therese Neumann (born 1898) was also inedic. She had been placed under close observation by a team of doctors and nurses and had her own condition of inedia verified over two weeks of intense scrutiny. What makes Neumann an even more compelling case, in one respect, is that she never practiced any yogic techniques or any other methods to develop the ability to abstain from food; it seemed to arise as a by-product of her extreme devotion to the Christ symbolism. Neumann did not sleep at all, and had even managed to gain over 5 pounds of weight over two days without eating or drinking during the testing. She had also, on one occasion, spent some 45 minutes clinically dead, only to awaken and resume normalcy within roughly an hour, attested to by the doctors who were present.[286]

Unbelievably, despite the fact that from 1922, Neumann consumed nothing except for the daily Eucharist (insufficient to sustain normal human life), she steadily *gained* weight. In July 1927, she weighed 121 pounds, and in 1953, she had reached a robust 215 pounds.[287] This cannot be explained by orthodox theories of human chemistry and biology. The skeptic Dr. Fritz Gerlich actually went to study Neumann to "expose the Catholic fraud" but wound up reverently writing her biography.[288]

Paramahansa Yogananda had the pleasure of meeting the Catholic mystic in his wide travels. Neumann, like Giri Bala, agreed that she lived by "the ether, sun and air." Yogananda stated matter-of-factly in his *Autobiography of a Yogi* that invisible "cosmic energy" flows into the body via the medulla oblongata, then being stored in the crown chakra and brain as a reservoir of potential.[289]

Motoyama has writtten that at his institute in Tokyo experiments have been conducted which support the claim that an awakened *vishuddi* (throat) chakra, in conjunction with other centers, makes possible the conscious control of metabolism, food intake, digestion, etc.,[290] so the revered yogi's claims are not without support.

Another ascetic who survives today without eating is Hira Ratan Manek, born on September 12, 1937 in Bodhavad, India. After his retirement in 1992, he began to research and study the ancient practice of sun gazing in which he had been interested since his childhood. This method was an old but forgotten one that had been practiced in ancient times in many different parts of the world. The method adopted by Manek is to initially look at the early morning sun for a few seconds and, every week, to increase the duration by a few seconds which should ultimately reach a period of several minutes. After about three months he says the brain gets "charged" and mental strength increases, healing fears and psychosomatic diseases. According to him, at the end of six months all physical disease is eliminated and after eight to nine months there is a decline in hunger, which ultimately disappears.[291]

Manek has undergone several strict fastings, during which he relied solely on sun energy and water and was under the control and observation of various scientific and medical teams.

The first of these fastings lasted for 211 days during 1995–96 in Calicut, India directed by Dr. C.K. Ramachandran, a medical expert on allopathy and ayurvedic medicine. This was followed by a 411-day fast from 2000 to 2001 in Ahmedabad directed by an international team of twenty-one medical doctors and scientists led by Dr. Sudhir Shah and Dr. K.K. Shah, the acting President of the Indian Medical Association at that time. Maurie D. Pressman, M.D., later joined the team for the next observation on [Manek].[292]

Following the compelling results at Ahmadabad, Manek was invited to Thomas Jefferson University and the University of Pennsylvania in Philadelphia for a 130-day observation period. This scientific team wanted to observe and examine his retina, pineal gland, and brain, and was led by Dr. Andrew B. Newberg, a leading authority on the brain, and Dr. George C. Brenard, reportedly the leading authority on the pineal gland. Seven hundred photographs were taken of his brain, showing the cells to be regenerating rather than the tissue atrophying. Furthermore, the pineal gland was *unexpectedly large*: its average size is typically about 6 × 6 mm; for Manek, however, it was measured at 8 × 11 mm.[293]

Dr. Sudhir Shah, lead researcher of the team studying Manek's fast in Ahmedabad, wrote that Manek was most likely receiving energy from the sun, just as the sages and Rishis of yore.[294] Shah implicates the retina and the pineal gland since both possess photoreceptor cells "and may be considered photosensitive organs." He goes on to speculate that some process similar to photosynthesis must be taking place—the sun's energy must enter the body somehow to be used as fuel.

> The unexplored process of energy synthesis and transformation from the sun energy perhaps partly occurs [in the pineal]. While going through the details of recent scientific literature and also comparing it with ancient Indian spiritual texts, as well as Western occult and new age, [the] following things are apparent. The activation of [the] pineal gland is the key step in psychic, spiritual and energy transformation processes. Here in this gland, energy processing and re-distribution occurs.[295]

Dr. Shah suggested that Manek's enlarged pineal gland offered indirect support for the important role it plays in energy transformation.[296] (Recall Brennan's description of how light reaches the pituitary and pineal glands and the effects it produces.) Russian researchers Fosar and Bludorf, summarizing the separate research of Popp and Gariaev into DNA and its absorption and emission of light, have concluded that light "actually represents an important factor in the power supply of . . . the DNA. It provides healthy functioning of all procedures in our cells."[297]

There is something else worth noting about these renunciants of which we are speaking. Michael Grosso states that the bodies of some Christian saints behave oddly after death: "Perversely, they stay intact, moist, flexible for months, for decades, sometimes for hundreds of years. They exude mysterious oils, occasionally bleed, and often give off remarkable fragrances," as if some form of energy persists to hold entropy at bay.[298]

This defiance of decay was also the case with Yogananda; his body mysteriously remained intact, undecayed for weeks after death (evidently this is not entirely uncommon for advanced yogis). Harry T. Rowe, Los Angeles Mortuary Director at Forest Lawn Memorial-Park (in which Yogananda's body was temporarily housed), said in a notarized letter to Yogananda's Self-Realization Fellowship:

> The absence of any visual signs of decay in the dead body . . . offers the most extraordinary case in our experience . . . No physical disintegration was visible in his body even twenty days after death . . . No indication of mold was visible on the skin, and no visible dessication (drying up) took place in the bodily tissues.[299]

Serious yogic practice in meditation does not merely preserve one's youthful appearance. In the cases of some enlightened souls it mobilizes the body's subtle energetic system against entropy even after consciousness has ceased to occupy the physical vessel. Herbert Thurston in 1952, and Joan Carroll Cruz in 1977, assessed the eyewitness testimony on bodily incorruption favorably. "Contrary to nature, [the corpses] stay soft, flexible, lifelike in color, and occasionally seem to move, bleed, and exude fragrant oils."[300]

This is known also to Tibetan Buddhism. Gyalwang Karmapa, a great master and head of one of the four main schools of Tibetan Buddhism, died in hospital in the USA in 1981. Among other bizarre phenomena that baffled the medical attendants, when he finally died his body defied the usual rigor mortis pattern. After a while it was realized that the area around his heart was still warm. Dr. Ranulfo Sanchez, chief of surgery, examined the area right over his heart, around 36 hours later, and confirmed that it was somehow warmer than the surrounding area—something he could offer no medical explanation for.[301] Randall reports that Father John Baptiste Vianney's corpse remained incorruptible from his death in 1859 through to 1904, when his tomb was opened in preparation for the process of beatification.[302]

The esteemed Tibetan master Jamyang Khyentse's body demonstrated incorruptibility for weeks, even in the heat of the Indian summer.[303] It is known that some masters actually sense their death or know when it is due in advance and enter into a meditative posture and state of consciousness (*Maha Samadhi*) moments before the transition.[304] This altered state of awareness and the heightened pranic energy levels may configure the etheric body in such a way that it remains negentropic long after the animating consciousness has vacated the body. One might ask if the physical body can become purified (through deliberate spiritual practices and lifestyle—no meat, alcohol, etc.) in such a way that it allows the etheric body/template to remain attached to the body post-mortem instead of detaching and beginning the process of decomposition as per normal. (Asceticism seems to be a common feature in cases of post-mortem incorruptibility and other phenomena such as levitation.[305]) Somehow, we might speculate, the etheric fields of these individuals remains both vital and attached though their animating consciousness has de-coupled from the body.

According to researcher Tom Montalk, the etheric energies essentially exist in the time domain, in the theoretical realm of the "imaginary"—a 90° rotation into "a dimension of impossibility." To him, as noted in Chapter 8, the etheric field is responsible for the unpredictability of quantum-biological behaviour. Etheric influences also run in reverse time—at least as far as its interactions with our physical realm are concerned. I pointed out earlier that the etheric and astral planes can, for convenience, be subsumed under the time-space banner (though the etheric is really just a part of our physical reality that is harder to detect). In time-space, time is real and space is imaginary.[306]

Thus, the continued attachment of a vital etheric field would serve to hold physical molecular processes of entropy at bay; time, for the renunciant's body, would stand still—it would not decay. In this context it is interesting to know that phase-conjugated (time-reversed) waves can be produced by certain kinds of controlled *plasmas*.[307] It is also interesting to note in passing that meat treated energetically by a healer has been reported to exhibit similar incorruptibility as mentioned above, despite being unrefrigerated for a month,[308] and in the case of an Englishwoman with the same ability, for years.[309] Therefore, in our terminology, the etheric plasma field is probably responsible for corporeal incorruptibility.

In 1993 Konstantin Korotkov conducted investigations into the Kirlian glows radiated by the bodies of 10 recently deceased people between the ages 19 nineteen and 70. Analyzing the energetic output from the left-hand fingers of the cadavers, he found that there was no qualitative difference between the discharge of the living and deceased. Monitoring for between three and five days each, he found that the glow intensity of a deceased individual was lower than a living person's, but it did not drop to zero, as may have been expected, but rather to some *fixed value*.[310]

Korotkov reports that when chakras begin to operate in the opposite direction, they dump energy, causing discharge bursts—the kind observed with his cadavers.[311]

It may be worthwhile to take these GDV measurements from the body of a newly deceased master yogi over a period of weeks. A study of the energy emissions from an incorruptible body would likely prove very interesting. Emissions may be significantly lower in intensity, establishing a smooth and stable minimum baseline more rapidly than the emissions of "normal" people, with the body only decomposing extremely slowly for the first few weeks or months, or perhaps even not at all. (Recall Popp's research showing healthier systems have lower photonic output. Note also that Korotkov's finding of a small but non-zero photonic output plateau for cadavers is not surprising knowing that DNA—which both stores and emits "bio-photons" and sonic quasi-particles referred to as "phonons"—acts as a harmonic oscillator, meaning that it is extremely efficient in storing this energy and therefore "leaks" very little of it into the environment.)

If energy is equivalent to information (and, as noted, photons are considered to *be* pure, localized information) then it is as if a yogi's incorrupt body retains its informational integrity for longer. Is this the result of a mass transposon ("jumping DNA") activation—what microbiologist Colm Kelleher calls a "transposition burst"[312]—having reconfigured and "upgraded" the yogi's genome during their training, owing to the higher frequency consciousness or "torsion-plasma" energy they had harnessed?

Mobile genetic elements, known as jumping DNA, include both transposons, which can move from one area of a cell's genome to another area, and the more recently discovered retrotransposons, which, unlike transposons, use a copy-and-paste mechanism in replicating themselves in order to insinuate the copies into other regions of the genome via an RNA intermediary.[313] Transposons were originally discovered in the 1940s by Dr. Barbara McClintock (1902–92), who eventually received a Nobel prize in 1983 for her research.[314]

Jumping DNA reportedly make up as much as *half* of the total DNA nucleotides, some 97–8% of our DNA being originally dismissed by Western science as "junk," since it is not responsible for constructing the physical form (these mobile elements are non-protein-coding). These are the elements that we spoke of earlier in the chapter when discussing Luckman's DNA (and kundalini) activation technique (the Regenetics Method)—jumping DNA being "activated" in stages, starting with Potentiation. We have already covered in brief many of the effects that can result from this event. Perhaps another possible effect of large-scale DNA activation is bodily incorruptibility.

While a large portion of the non-protein-coding ("junk") regions of the genome are comprised of transposons and retrotransposons, the other portion is comprised of variable-number tandemly repeating sequences known as "satellite DNA." These may be even more significant with regard to the phenomenon of bodily incorruptibility. Microbiologist William Brown believes that through specific conformational arrangements, satellite DNA interface with the morphic field; various conformations have specific resonances with the morphic field and can therefore tune into different information programs. Since satellite DNA is very specific to each person, each of us tunes into a distinct and unique morphogenetic pattern.[315]

It seems likely that both jumping DNA *and* satellite DNA interface with the morphic field, thus responding to alterations in one's state of consciousness and morphic fields. Satellite DNA's ability to expand the number of repeating sequences means an increase in the information-carrying capacity of DNA. As a fractal antenna, DNA interacts with the vacuum/aether/zero point field, transducing the zero point energy which interacts with our consciousness. A greater interaction between our DNA and the torsion/scalar forces in the vacuum might equate to expanded consciousness, while a lesser interactivity would result in a contracted awareness. Thus, "certain modular arrangements of DNA would be more conducive to conscious awareness."[316]

Science and Occultism: the Synthesis Continues

Science seems to have reached a point where it is able to peer indirectly into the etheric and astral levels described by occultism and confirm the observations made by clairvoyants. In fact, Besant and Leadbeater wrote in *Thought Forms* that scientists had, even back in their time, begun to do exactly that—without realizing it:

> [F]orces and beings of the next higher plane of nature are beginning to show themselves on the outer edge of the physical field . . . [The physicist] finds himself compelled to speculate on invisible presences, if only to find a rational explanation for undoubted physical phenomena, and insensibly he slips over the boundary, and [contacts] the astral plane.[317]

Notable too is the comment on not just "forces," but "beings" on the next higher planes of nature beginning to show themselves, because Oldfield's technology has indeed captured beings that reside on higher harmonic frequencies in higher dimensions. These discoveries dovetail nicely with large amounts of data from the field of hypnotic regression, NDE research and other areas in occultism and consciousness research pertaining to the concept of other-dimensional beings (we deal in depth with this exciting research in TGI 2).

Early in the 20th century, Swami Panchadasi made a fitting comment in *The Human Aura* when he said, "I feel that material science should feel flattered by the backing up by occult science of the new discovery (!) of the 'human atmosphere.'"[318] Well said! With this chapter's data under our belt, we are now fundamentally aware of the validity of many basic tenets of occultism and mysticism, including (but not limited to) the following:

- We do indeed possess an occult anatomy: the auric fields, chakras, nadis, and meridians.
- These are intimately involved with "paranormal" phenomena, consciousness, and psi.
- They have a relationship with our physical selves, both creating and maintaining the physical body and acting as a key determinant in our health.
- The "torsion-plasma" or auric fields are actually vehicles of consciousness in their own right, existing on their own density levels/dimensions. They are where our locus of awareness generally shifts to after death—if it does not "reunite" with the Infinite.

Knowing now of the existence of our "other occult selves," we are aware of the basic means at our disposal for exploring other levels and planes of reality.

This includes the astral planes and the realms of the afterlife/spirit world. Furthermore, we are now also equipped to look seriously at further scientific evidence for occult phenomena and the "superpowers" innate in the human species—which we will cover in the next chapters.

> What we thought was reality is turning out to be a fairytale.
> —Steven Wolinsky

10

THOUGHT-FORMS
(A.K.A. ELEMENTALS)

A truth cannot be created, but only perceived. —Paramahansa Yogananda

Every man takes the limits of his own field of vision for the limits of the world.
—Arthur Schopenhauer

The thoughts you think represent the only power you possess.
—Harold Sherman

Perceiving and Generating Thought-Forms

Thought-forms occupy two planes or "implicate orders": the astral and the
lower mental (the rupic subplane). They are perceptible to anyone who has
developed the faculties of astral plane and/or mental plane perception, and are
therefore not articles of belief but observable fact, exhibiting correlations with
the physical, mental, and emotional realities of the beings they pertain to. It is
true to a significant extent that such assertions can be brought into the realm of
verification and therefore objectivity. Our prominent personal thought-forms
can be clairvoyantly observed hovering around us in our energy field(s).

Talbot recorded some fascinating clairvoyant observations in *The Holographic
Universe*. For example, once during a reading Carol Dryer saw a bunch of potatoes

whirling around a woman's head. She was at first dumbfounded but summoned her courage and asked the woman if potatoes had any special meaning for her. As it turned out, the woman was from the Idaho Potato Board, or something roughly equivalent. In other words, potatoes were a very significant part of her life, unlike with most people.

Such images don't always just hover around the person in their aura, but sometimes appear as extensions of the body or proximal layer of the auric field—a fact not so surprising when we consider the triangular configuration of electro-photonic energy that Uri Geller created around his fingertip, or Oldfield's recordings of the lama's thought-forms, as detailed earlier. For instance, another of Dryer's clients had a hologram-like layer of mud clinging to her hands and arms. This baffled Dryer, given the woman's immaculate presentation, so she asked if the woman could understand the image. Affirmative: she was a sculptor and the new medium she tested out that morning did indeed cling to her arms and hands just as Dryer described.[1]

Psychics of Dryer's advanced abilities (of which there appear to be comparatively few) are also able to see movie-like sequences playing in people's energy fields. The most emotionally powerful memories or precious thoughts manifest in this fashion. Likewise, illness can also be detected by psychics such as Dryer and Brennan.

Earlier we mentioned Pribram's holonomic brain theory which states that the brain's processes and functions operate holographically—including remembering: "[T]he act of 're-membering' or thinking is concurrent with the taking of the inverse of something like the Fourier transform. The action of the inverse transform (like in the laser shining on the optical hologram) allows us to re-experience to some degree a previous perception. This is what constitutes a memory."[2]

We also suggested that our memories are stored not in the brain but in the human auric field from which the brain downloads material—even Pribram himself does not believe consciousness to be located in the brain itself—though the brain shows activity correlated with holographic mental processes occurring in our mind-fields. Jay Alfred explains that our holographic dark plasma/subtle bodies generate and project holographic images in real-time in response to thoughts and feelings. The unique properties of "magnetic plasma" fields—which can be reorganized or "shape-shifted" by the will—provide these fields with all the components needed to build a "holographic machine."[3]

Gravitational lensing—the way light bends as it passes through a gravitational field—also plays a role in generating images in our mind's eye, according to Alfred. Leadbeater claimed in *The Inner Life* that an "atom" allows us to view images originating in our higher vehicles. Tackling this statement almost a century later—with gravitational lensing long since a well-established scientific phenomenon—Alfred proposes that a physical-etheric atom uses gravitational lensing to focus multi-dimensional images generated from higher vehicles to a place in front of our eyes as 3D images. (Alfred believes this "atom" to be an ensemble of two oppositely charged UPAs revolving around each other.[4]) Thus, we experience thoughts not in the brain, but in our subtle bodies *via* the brain. In point of fact, Kunz has explained that to clairvoyant sight, visualization uses the power of the brow/third eye chakra, speeding its rotation and also affecting the crown chakra.[5]

In the yogic systems thought-forms are referred to as *pratyaya*: the content of the mind functioning through a particular vehicle (or "torsion-plasma body"). For someone in the ordinary waking state working through their mental body, the *pratyaya* in their case will be the mental image in their mind. Anyone with clairvoyance operating at the appropriate level can see this mental image and gain knowledge of that mind ("mind reading").[6] Functioning in this way, the seer is able to detect form but not necessarily the *intent* or emotion that caused the form. That is why even the best clairvoyants will often conduct readings in a question-based format. Hence, Dryer asked one client, despite her reluctance, if potatoes had any special significance for her.

Powell explained in occult terms that a thought-form is a kind of living entity of high energy which is animated by the idea that spawned it. The finer the matter it is composed of, the greater the energy and power it possesses.[7]

Bruce states that astral matter reacts to thought just as physical matter responds to force. Thus, it can be molded in ways only limited by the imagination. The most convincing thought-constructs can be indistinguishable from reality.[8] The kind of higher-dimensional matter out of which thought-forms are made is referred to in theosophical doctrine as "elemental," a "strange semi-intelligent life" (to use Powell's terminology) that surrounds us. Because it is so easily molded by thought, every impulse emanating from one's mental body immediately draws around itself a temporary vehicle composed of "elemental." The same principle applies to both the astral and mental densities, though the mental matter is even faster in responding to thought because it is a higher-energy, lower-density medium in this schema.[9]

Yogi Ramacharaka explained in 1904 that a strongly charged thought—perhaps one strongly willed and motivated by positive intent—also takes with it a certain amount of prana proportional to the intensity with which the thought was propelled. "Such thoughts are often sent like a bullet to the mark," he stated.[10]

A thought, then, is a kind of living creature: the thought-force, or torsion/scalar energy, is the "soul," while the plasmoidal elemental essence (particles) comprises the "body" of the thought. Such thought-forms are sometimes referred to as artificial elementals, temporary mental constructs.[11]

There are reports of self-aware thought-forms (*tulpas*) being generated through ritual and intention. The poet W.B. Yeats reputedly managed to create one, a "white Jester," with enough independent vitality to become visible to a few of his friends.[12] Theosophist Alexandra David-Néel also achieved something similar through sustained effort and mystical rites over a period of months, though her *tulpa* gradually turned lean and sinister from its originally plump and jolly state and, with much difficulty, had to be dissolved.[13] Bearden readily accounts for such tulpoidal phenomena in a highly scientific (and somewhat technical) manner in his impressive *Excalibur Briefing*.

The variety of possible thought-forms is essentially infinite, being limited only by the imaginations of the universe's sentient inhabitants. If a thought has in it something of self or personal desire (lower frequency/vibration), its composition will include astral matter in addition to the mental. Such a "thought-emotion-form" is then capable of affecting both the mental and the astral torsion-plasma bodies of other people. This is overwhelmingly the most common type, as few thoughts of men and women at this point in history are completely devoid of desire, passion, or emotion.[14]

The generation of a purely mental thought-form results from the mental body throwing off a vibrating portion of itself which is shaped by the nature of the thought, and which then draws around itself matter of the corresponding grade of fineness from the surrounding "elemental" substance of the mental plane.[15]

From the perspective of Edgar Cayce, thoughts are literally deeds in the mental realm that have an influence on the material world. Steiner had much the same outlook, advising mindfulness of one's thoughts, as they react on one another in the "thought world"—"wrong" thoughts having a "devastating effect on others in the mental environ."[16] Thoughts are real hyperspatial aetheric energy, not merely internal neural impulses that we experience quietly in our heads; they are not generated by our brains.

Every definite thought produces two effects in the subtle vehicle/s: first, a radiating vibration; second, a floating form. The vibration set up in and radiating from the mental body tends to reproduce its own frequency in any mental body on which it impacts: that is, to produce thoughts of the same *type*. The radiating vibration carries, not the *subject* of the thought, but the *character*.[17] Thoughts of selfless devotion, for example, can create corresponding vibrations in the mental bodies they impact on, leading to similar thoughts and feelings being experienced in the other person.

The power of the vibration to produce such sympathetic effects depends mainly on the clearness and definiteness of the thought-emotion, as well as the force put into it. Its power to influence dissipates in proportion to the cube of the distance from its source, rather than the square of the distance, due to the additional spatial dimension involved. How far a thought wave radiates also depends on opposition it meets at its particular density level. Waves in lower types of astral matter have a lot of "competition" due to the high level of thought activity occurring there.[18]

The life-span of a thought-form depends on the intensity and clearness of the thought.[19] Those possessed of functional mental site will see such creations. The principles that underlie the production of all thought-emotion forms are:

1. *Color* is determined by the *quality* of the thought or emotion.
2. *Form* is determined by the *nature* of the thought or emotion.
3. *Clearness of outline* is determined by the *definiteness* of the thought or emotion.[20]

Furthermore, according to Leadbeater in *The Inner Life*, the size of a thought-form shows the strength of the emotion. Theosophy distinguishes between the thought-form and the thought-vibration by observing that a thought-form's influence has shorter reach than a thought-*vibration* (wave), though it acts with far superior precision. A thought-vibration, on the other hand, acts more imprecisely, reproducing thoughts of similar *character*, and it can affect people on a broader scale than the thought-form. A thought-form reproduces the *same* thought, but on a more limited and localized scale.[21]

Robert Monroe, founder of the Monroe Institute of Applied Sciences, told us in *Far Journeys* that he and a group of about 20 participants in his Gateway Program conducted an experiment in visualization (creating thought-forms) at night, with some spectacular results.

> [W]hen the signal came at the proper time, we looked very
> eagerly . . . Suddenly our electronics engineer yelled excitedly,
> "Look higher, look higher!" . . . Now we looked far up into
> the sky in astonishment. Against the starlit night there were
> soft, red, neonlike waves. They resembled nothing so much as
> trickling water moving across an arc of the sky directly atop

the roof of the motel. At exactly the time the exercise called for the light to be shut off, it suddenly disappeared.[22]

What is impressive about this experiment is that the strength of the mental energy generated was sufficient that all of the observers could see it. Such was their combined strength that the group managed to create a light show in the ordinary, visible section of the electromagnetic spectrum. They generated enough collective energy at the mental level to excite from the aether/ZPF *visible* physical light in the form of a plasma-like phenomenon! Thus, their thought-forms in "virtual reality"/hyperspace/aether became *objectively real,* meaning anyone could see them.

They repeated the exercise successfully at another Gateway event in California where an engineer was present with a special Polaroid camera to take photos before, during, and after the experiment. Monroe said that none of the five or six observers present saw anything during the experiment, but when they examined the photographs the "before" and "after" experiment shots were blank, while the two taken during the exercise itself showed a "round ball with a marbleized effect much like the earth seen from a distance."[23] Physicists and photographers explain that the film can "see" light frequencies that our eyes can't. The blank film before and after made the two energy photographs more significant, being in the center of the film pack—a highly unlikely place to be pre-exposed.

Here we have the reason that NASA film footage recorded from satellites and shuttles in earth orbit show many UFOs circling around and interacting with this planet. The cameras are "seeing" a different frequency range which the eyes do not. If a spacecraft's frequency can be raised to the point where it is "made of light" it could also appear invisible to the human eye and many cameras, according to physicist and ufologist David Sereda. "But NASA knows all this," writes Sereda, "and they have video cameras aboard the Space Shuttles and aboard satellites that can see into invisible spectra of light, such as the infrared and the near ultraviolet. I confirmed the wavelengths of the shuttles video cameras with NASA scientists back in 1998. *They were looking where human eyes could not see and that is where the UFOs were showing up.*"[24]

These craft or objects must be highly quantized light craft, according to Sereda. NASA now has many cameras and satellites that can peer into the invisible infrared and ultraviolet (near, far, and extreme), X-rays and gamma ray wavelengths of light. According to Sereda, "It is here that our ET encounters can be found hidden from our eyes . . . Now we know where to look and we are finding answers."[25] These UFOs are largely out of phase with our dimension, but they are close enough that the "signal strength" of their emanations are detectable in Bearden's "magic windows": the infrared and ultraviolet frequencies!

This essentially explains why we are oblivious to the abundant UFO activity right above our heads. The frequency range of photographic cameras and video cameras can also explain why certain "ghosts" and other anomalies such as orbs are sometimes caught on film while there are no human witnesses who perceive them (again, most people's psi faculties are undeveloped). American abductee Lori Briggs was told by the alien beings that they were able to turn themselves into light (by means of which they could also levitate objects), but that they were unable to hold their own physical form for very long.[26] Organized scientific remote viewing of UFOs and advanced non-human intelligences usually referred to as "aliens" has produced startling results, supporting the physical evidence and witness testimony in favor of such phenomena (albeit without the possibility of verifiable feedback).[27]

Ingo Swann recalls an (impromptu) occurrence similar to Monroe's, where thought-forms were recorded on infrared film. It was at a social event at a friend's place. He remembers: "A couple of intense psychic types had come along to try to produce energies for the film," but Swann was reluctant and professed cluelessness as to how to do this. However, goaded by his new friends, a giggling and reluctant Swann tried to make a ball of light about 3 feet above his head. "I 'pictured' a ball of light about a foot in diameter. When the film had been developed a few days later, Behold! A TINY orb of light was above my head in three separate film shots. And there were other lights outlining my body that I had not 'pictured.'"

No one else's photos had turned out. His ad hoc group of friends and acquaintances deemed Swann psychic (which he patently is, based on his remote viewing output, which we will look at), and so more photos were taken—resulting in more "successes."[28] Professional paranormal researcher Joshua P. Warren has indicated that digital cameras are naturally sensitive to some infrared and ultraviolet spectra, infrared frequencies being where ghostly orbs are often seen.[29]

It is an intriguing thought that much NASA UFO footage is derived from the infrared spectrum where lower harmonics of tulpoidal hyperspace energy can be photographed. One might speculate that perhaps many "abduction" phenomena occur at etheric or lower astral levels, in the occult frequencies/planes out of phase and normally invisible to us. Harry Oldfield's data suggests this, as his equipment is also capable of photographing a larger range of frequencies than normal cameras and human eyes can see, and guess what? He too can photograph UFOs with his PIP system, which is able to "see" phase changes in light, making things that are invisible or cloaked visible.[30]

Oldfield has been defended by Dr. Claude Swanson, one of America's top physicists, with whom he has swapped physics theories. When Oldfield's equipment and methods start spreading, the accumulation of data will accelerate again and "we the people" will be able to force an end to government secrecy on these topics. We know for a fact that UFOs are real and that governments around the world know it (see Dr. Steven Greer's "Disclosure Project"). How many thousands of radar sightings do we need? How much more deception and obfuscation before the cover-up bubble bursts?

> In August 1958, test officials at Eglin Air Force base in Florida were conducting experiments with a super-sensitive infrared camera, to see if they could photograph events *after* they had occurred. The infrared camera is sensitive to even minute heat rays emitted by objects. The camera they had devised was so refined it could detect differences in thousandths of a degree. With it they took a picture of the base parking lot, which was empty at the time. But when the film was developed, it clearly showed cars that had been parked in the lot several hours before but that were not there when the picture was taken. The report of this experiment was carried by the Associated Press in an account published in the *Miami Herald*. Because the infrared camera was classified the Air Force refused to say how far backward in time the camera was able to go, or to release any of the pictures to the press . . . [31]

This is a bizarre notion—does the past still exist right now in the infrared frequencies of the EM spectrum? Relativistic physics says the past still exists in the space we occupy, as does occult doctrine, while it is known that informational torsion fields can linger virtually indefinitely, coupling with EM energies which then leave a detectable imprint of the past in space (Poponin and Gariaev's experiments on the DNA "phantom" [see Chapter 13] speak directly to this concept). Evidently, the infrared zone is indeed a "magic window" through which we can view (to some extent at least) the Akashic record.

Improving on this, however, is (once again) Harry Oldfield's technology. Working in a cemetery with his imaging system, Oldfield captured not only discarnate presences, but the presence of a mausoleum and stone monument in the background that were *no longer standing*, which belonged to an earlier century (probably some 200 years ago, around the time of the Napoleonic wars, according to an employee at the cemetery).[32]

Thus, the past is always present as static torsion fields coupled with electromagnetically detectable light, just outside our normal perceptual range. For me, this research lays waste to the notion of time as a one-dimensional linear flow in which each present moment fades into oblivion as it becomes the "past"—and it offers strong support for the notion that the "Akashic records" of the past can be perceived consciously and "read" by sensitives with the necessary faculties. Effectively this research appears to prove Larson's theory that time is 3-dimensional—one dimension of time for each of space. Moreover, such material also supports the holofractal universe concept, since we can see now that the ever-present "past" is always nested within the present moment, meaning that time is "holographic."

Swami Panchadasi explains that what Swann and Monroe and his team of helpers achieved with mental energy can be dwarfed by the advanced and highly trained Hindu occultists:

> You have heard of the Hindu Mango Trick, in which the magician takes a mango seed, plants it in the ground, waves his hands over it, and then causes first a tiny shoot to appear from the surface of the ground, this followed by a tiny trunk, and leaves, which grow and grow, until at last appears a full sized mango tree, which first shows blossoms and then ripe fruit . . . What he really does is to produce a wonderful thought-form in the astral, from seed stage to tree and fruit stage; the astral picture reproducing perfectly the picture in his own mind. It is as if he were creating a moving picture film-roll in his mind, and then projecting this upon the screen of the air. There is no mango tree there, and never was, outside of the mind of the magician and the minds of his audience.
>
> Western visitors have sought to obtain photographs of these feats of the Hindu magicians, but their plates and films invariably show nothing whatever except the old fakir sitting quietly in the center, with a peculiar expression in his eyes. This is as might be expected, for the picture exists only in the astral, and is perceived only by the awakened astral senses of those present, which have been stimulated into activity by the power of the magician—by sympathetic vibration, to be exact . . . but still no miracle has been worked![33]

It is interesting that Swami Panchadasi notes that while people can see the conjuring of the magician, cameras would not detect them. While the non-digital photographic technology from the late 1800s to early 1900s appears to have had a more limited frequency range than that employed during Monroe's time and beyond, truly astral energies are not available for *direct* capture by anything other than our own astral faculties. For scalar thought-forms to be captured by physical technology, they must interact to some extent with our physical light, just as occultists like Leadbeater have explained.[34]

Ted Serios was a former Chicago bellhop, born November 27, 1918, who discovered the ability to project photographic images onto camera film by staring into the lens of a Polaroid camera. He sometimes used a piece of rolled cardboard (a "gizmo") to look into the camera lens at the moment the picture was taken, probably to narrow the focus of his attention. Serios also produced images using a camera *without a lens*. Parapsychologist Jule Eisenbud conducted an extensive investigation of Serios over three years, the results of which were published in *The World of Ted Serios: "Thoughtographic" Studies of an Extraordinary Mind* (1966).[35]

Among some of the extraordinary images produced by Serios with a Polaroid camera were pictures of Mariner IV and Russian Vostok rockets[36] (these could not be traced at all in the literature, according to Colin Wilson, indicating that they were not even produced by Serios' own memory,[37] but probably his subconscious mind interacting with the collective unconscious). The *Encyclopedia of Occultism and Parapsychology* records that numerous images produced by Serios were "ambiguous, in soft focus, or too vague to identify. Some contained mistakes which would have been absent from a picture of an object that had merely been reproduced via the inert 'gizmo.'"[38]

Serios had been "stripped to the skin, medically examined, X-rayed, sewn into a restraint suit that allowed him to move nothing but his head, and tested with cameras and film provided by independent and critical observers," Watson reported in *Supernature*. "In spite of all precautions . . . he still succeeds in producing his thoughtographs."[39] Between May 1964 and June 1967, Serios produced over 400 such images.[40]

His strange gift resulted from an experiment in "do-it-yourself hypnotism" involving a friend. George Johannes, a fellow bellhop at Chicago's Conrad Hilton Hotel, inducted Serios into a deep trance and implanted the suggestion that the contents of his mind could be photographed—it was as simple as that. His thought-forms had been photographed from then on, though the resulting pictures were not always things that were being visualized in his mind at all! One time Serios took a picture that no one could identify, himself included.

The only discernible clue was a sign identifying the locale as a remote Canadian town. The examiners sent the picture to the Royal Canadian Mounted Police of that village who identified it as a clear photograph of one of the town's landmarks!

Waite recorded in *The Mystic Sciences* that while Serios' thoughtographs usually depicted clearly identifiable buildings, such as the Taj Mahal, he sometimes imaged historical figures, and even prehistoric creatures.[41] In one attempted experiment in which he tried to produce an image of the Chicago Hilton, Serios accidentally produced an image (in color, by the way) of the *Denver* Hilton instead, muttering, "Missed, damn it."[42]

Erratic as it may have been, Serios' ability appears to be another demonstration of the capacity of consciousness—acting via torsion/scalar energy—to couple with (or create) and manipulate EM light in as yet unexplained ways. Our waveform thoughts can impress themselves upon physical objects (hence psychometry), decoding, for instance, on film as objects or places that can be recognized. Eisenbud treats the etheric body as a "serious hypothesis" in his book on Serios.[43]

Undoubtedly, Serios was using his subtle vehicles in order to generate or manipulate the light that was causing these images to form on film. It is noteworthy that tests under different conditions seemed to eliminate any possibility that Serios was using any known part of the electromagnetic spectrum in his thoughtography—no type of barrier, whether magnetic, electrical, or physical prevented his success,[44] ergo the energy at work was torsion/scalar.

As John Violette notes, it often requires large amounts of energy to mobilize hyperdimensional forces, and it is therefore not surprising that Serios had to work himself virtually into a state of rage during these experiments. Notably, Uri Geller has been able to achieve similar feats, taking photos of himself on high-speed black-and-white film through a solid black lens cap. Chris Humphrey explains this is due to quantum tunneling: if the (R-space/time-space) de Broglie probability wave exists on both sides of a barrier, then its particle (photons in this case) can sometimes be on one side, and sometimes on the other, without ever passing through the barrier. Geller's mind-field altered the probability that those photons could reach the other side of the lens cap to non-zero. Indeed, he pushed the probability high enough that some photons actually did "get through" or manifest on the other side—enough to show on the high-speed black-and-white film.[45] Presumably the same principles are also at work in Serios' case. In Russia, PK medium Nina Kulagina could reportedly produce the letters A or O on photographic paper, or create even the silhouette of an image she had seen.[46]

Interestingly, in a series of meticulously controlled mediumship experiments with the deceased, known as the Scole Experiments, images were produced on sealed, unopened film during the séances that were conducted. One such image (obtained in 1996) on a factory-sealed 25 mm Polaroid slide film features Sanskrit verses from the *Srimad Bhagavatam*, a Hindu spiritual text. Another picture was of the famous St Paul's Cathedral taken during the London Blitz. Upon inspection though, *it appeared that the dimensions of the Cathedral were slightly distorted compared with the original picture.* Then there were the images projected across *entire rolls of film* by the invisible guests. Intriguingly, one contained the phrase "Can you see behind the moon?"[47]—a reference to activity on the dark side of the moon? Thus, it appears that both the living and the "dead" can perform the feat of generating images on film through deliberate intent, suggesting the same non-EM aetheric hyperspace energies are being utilized by both parties to tease "virtual photons" out of the vacuum.

Dr. Richard Gerber was PIP-scanned by Harry Oldfield in England around 1993. Standing in front of the white screen and with camera rolling, Gerber asked Oldfield if he could try an experiment. He then visualized a stream of white light coming down through the top of his head and through his spine—without telling Oldfield what he was doing. As Gerber did so, Oldfield spontaneously commented that a column of white light was forming behind Gerber's spine—he was capturing Gerber's thought-form.[48] Oldfield's PIP imagery can also reveal energy manipulations by a Reiki practitioner as they create a ball of energy and disperse it towards a patient.[49] Comparisons between the observations of subjects' energy fields by clairvoyants and Oldfield's PIP technology could prove to be very instructive.

Several related findings come to us from the UCLA radiation field photography laboratory. In one experiment with Kirlian photography, a subject visualized sticking a needle into her partner—who had a fear of needles. The photograph of their fingertips revealed a sharp red line projecting from the aggressor's finger toward her partner, whose glow appeared to be retreating. In contrast, two individuals in meditation together have normally yielded a "merging and uniting of the two coronas,"[50] a "field transaction" in other words.

Physicist William Tiller conducted experiments with film in the 1970s with a man named Stan whose photos kept producing strange lights and illuminations based on the state of consciousness he was in at the time. The occasions when the optical effects were most likely to be obtained were (a) at spiritual rock concerts, (b) at religious shrines, and (c) at high-energy metaphysical lectures. Whenever he sensed a particular feeling in his seventh cervical (throat chakra zone) and fourth thoracic vertebrae (heart chakra zone) and snapped a picture, some anomaly invariably presented itself on the resultant photograph.

Over a 15-year period, out of 9,000 photographs taken, a whopping 5,000 contained easily distinguishable anomalies. In a series of studies Tiller carried out with Stan, two cameras were used, one "sensitized" by him, the other not. Both were mounted on a single tripod with a single shutter release. Standard Kodak color film and standard Kodak processing were used, and Stan was never allowed to touch the film during loading or unloading.

"Most photo pairs showed very significant differences," reports Tiller. The sensitized camera's pictures "would often show one or more people in the frame as somewhat transparent over a portion of their body so that objects behind them could clearly been seen through the transparent (translucent) portion,"* while the photos from the unsensitized camera produced no anomalies. In other experiments with a single sensitized camera, an opaque lens cap was placed over it while photos were taken, but it didn't matter: "remarkably clear photographs" were obtained through the lens cap anyway. Merely keeping the camera close to his body for several days was enough for Stan to sensitize it, and though it could be passed to someone else to take the anomalous pictures, the effect generally wore off after an hour unless continuously "pumped" (energetically) by him.

Is this another instance where "quantum tunneling" was being triggered by a human's torsion-plasma/consciousness field? Tiller seems to think that when human intention is "applied to unseen subtle domains" (implicate orders/time-space) it is the "driver of events seen in the physical domain."[51]

While in this section we have focused on the normally imperceptible becoming perceptible through the medium of film, there are opposite anecdotal cases that can be cited from the literature. For example, the great yogi Lahiri Mahasaya was once photographed despite his known aversion to having his picture taken. The picture revealed only the yogi's devotees around him with no sign of his own body to be found. A student resolved to capture an image of the yogi on film, and the next morning, as the guru sat in lotus posture on a wooden bench, the student took 12 pictures. Once again there was no sign of Mahasaya. He asked his distraught student rhetorically if his camera could "reflect the omnipresent invisible?" The next morning Mahasaya relented and allowed himself to be photographed properly by his student. That time

---

* This is an effect that Oldfield's technology has also achieved. For example, the stones at Stonehenge became see-through to the PIP system, which is sensitive to phase changes in light.

he showed up on the film, and it may have been the last time he was ever successfully photographed.[52]

This example serves to highlight the mystic's knowledge that all is ultimately One consciousness and the One cannot be photographed; the more strongly a person identifies themselves with the Infinite, the less a part of the world of the transient, illusory manifest they become. In those moments when he could not be photographed Mahasaya identified more strongly with the Infinite than he did with dualistic physicality.

By contrast, there are many examples of things appearing in pictures that should *not* have been there. Elisabeth Kübler-Ross once challenged her "spirit guide" to show itself in a photograph she was about to take to finish a role of film. Sure enough, a month or so later when the film was developed, there was the image of a serious-looking American Indian man. Evidently, he had accepted the challenge.[53] Similarly, for a long time there have been instances of apparitions inexplicably appearing in photographs—in degrees ranging from orbs, to wisps of energy, to bright lights, to partly formed bodies, to full-bodied apparitions with high levels of facial detail. There are now so many such cases that on the strength of these alone, the afterlife and existence of discarnate consciousness has to be considered utterly proved.

What Does Prayer Look Like?

Some people who have near-death experiences actually experience a vision of the prayers people pray for them, one of various siddhis (clairvoyance in this case) that can manifest during an out-of-body or near-death experience. According to P.M.H. Atwater, children are particularly outspoken about this phenomenon.

> The youngsters I interviewed often said that once they left their bodies and "could see better," they saw prayers turned into beams of radiant, golden, or rainbow light that would arc over from the one saying the prayer, no matter how many miles away, to where the children were "hovering" near death. Once the prayer beam "hit" them, they described it as being akin to feeling a "splash" of love or an incredible "warming."[54]

Of course, occultism and mysticism have ever held awareness of the nonlocal action and effectiveness of such prayer in reaching its target.

It was the use of the word "rainbow" that caught my eye in Atwater's comments, for Harry Oldfield in his Glastonbury Symposium presentation displays the image he captured using his Oldfield filter of an "adoring" grandmother and her grandchild. In it we can see waves of rainbow-like light of different hues evidently emanating from the elder to the younger. "There is something called the light of love. I truly believe that now," quips Oldfield, who notes regretfully that he's not been able to capture such an image since.[55] As noted previously, Barbara Brennan's clairvoyance confirms that both the fluidic emotional and astral bodies are comprised of all the colors of the rainbow, with the astral colors tinged by the "rose light of love." Legitimate seers such as Brennan state that our astral bodies exchange "blobs" or flashes of light energy almost constantly[56]—apparently this is what Oldfield captured.

To Think or Not to Think

Charles Leadbeater made some very pertinent comments on thought-forms in his book *The Chakras*. According to him (and any other serious occultist), thoughts on the *same subject and of the same character tend to aggregate*. Consider the implications here regarding synchronicities and also the possibilities this presents in terms of telepathy. The more like-minded two people are, the more in tune/resonant they will be, sharing the same thought-forms, and thus they will be more likely to experience what we call telepathic phenomena. Note how common it is for two good friends (or identical twins) to blurt out identical words or phrases at the exact same time as one another.

Quantum biology has extended the range of functioning of our DNA: "For practical purposes, the DNA molecule is brilliantly designed as a holographic torsion-wave-decoding biocomputer—one that magnetizes creative energy to it, and thus to our consciousness, that is aligned with our beliefs," writes Sol Luckman.[57] We therefore experience what we believe; we experience events that are resonant with our dominant beliefs, thoughts, desires, and feelings, hence the danger of inheriting beliefs and thoughts/thought-forms with little discernment. This view only makes sense if we remember that what we normally think of as physical reality is really a holographic thought-image or "dream" in the mind of the Infinite, and that everything is harmonically interlinked and informationally connected at the most fundamental levels.

For many subjects there is a thought-center—Leadbeater says it is a definite space in the atmosphere—and other thoughts about the same subject are attracted to such a center, and go to increase its size and influence. Think about what this might suggest for the many healings reported at Lourdes, for example: they are likely "man-made," certainly not the result of some contrived and anthropomorphized deity (though that is not to rule out the influence of other conscious beings, whether visible or otherwise).

Since someone can be influenced by a thought center that they also contribute to, this partially accounts for why *"people think in droves, like sheep,"* as Leadbeater put it. It's much easier for a lazy individual to accept a pre-existent thought from someone else than to weigh, consider and scrutinize, and arrive at a decision for themselves.[58] We can be influenced by subliminal energies that lead us intellectually and emotionally this way and that by affecting us at subtle levels, without us necessarily being able to rationalize why we think a certain thing or feel a certain way.

Leadbeater clarifies that while humanity's thoughts about a given subject can rapidly and easily gather or concentrate on the mental plane at a localized thought center which can be accessed by everyone *nonlocally*, astral emotion-forms tend to coalesce with others of a like nature within their local "neighbourhood." The result here is that there are large and powerful "blocks" of emotion in your general vicinity that may readily influence you through one of your chakras if contact occurs, or if your feelings resonate with them.[59] Fear-forms/energies on the astral plane, for instance, may discharge their energy through a lower chakra, such as the navel centre; hence phrases like "sick to the stomach with fear."

In the early 1900s, Steiner stated eloquently that "What man perceives as thoughts . . . is only the manifestation of the thought world as it is able to express itself through the instrumentality of the bodies."[60] DeGracia:

> Any large-scale social institution is simply the physical expression of the vast thought-form that gave rise to the physical artifacts. Take for example the social institution of the Christian religion. Here we have a behemoth thought-form that has been continuously fed and given power over centuries and centuries. Such a thought-form is actually a vast *landscape* on the astral and mental planes.[61]

If you look in the spiritualistic literature, you can find descriptions given to mediums from the "deceased" of what the "afterlife" is like. (Please note that there are other sources of information on what the afterlife realms are like, as we will see vividly in TGI 2.) In *The Golden Key*, we find descriptions of the wondrous life that allegedly awaits the more orthodoxly religious of us on the other side. We read of higher-minded continuations of earth-based religious devotional activity, such as the joyous singing of paens to "God" and so forth. Continuations of the Christian beliefs and practices in the hereafter are more enlightened and minus the fear-based hell-and-brimstone nonsense you still sometimes find on Earth. The concept of "worship" takes on a different, more transcendent meaning where reverence and gratitude for life and creation itself is at the essence, though many Christians still make the error of externalising god and paying homage to a conceptual rendering—a much more worthy conceptual rendering, but a rendering nonetheless. These are the "Belief System" or B.S. territories, as Monroe refers to them in *Ultimate Journey*, and our "travels" do not have to stop here (in fact, they *must* go further if we are to realise who and what we really are).

"These enormous thought-forms have tremendous polarizing power over an individual personality. That is to say, they can totally drown out the pattern of an individual aura (mind) and take over the aura to a very large extent."[62] Generally speaking, our minds are never entirely our own. We are surrounded by thought- and emotion-forms at the mental and astral levels, so any thoughts that arise at the level of the human mind can serve to set up a frequency resonance through which the thought-form can take hold and swell in charge and power.

R.A. Wilson observed that the mammalian reflexive thought-patterns of patriotism and (fundamentalist) religion are two cognitive systems that cannot bear two minutes of rational analysis,[63] and yet we see that the majority of individuals succumb to one or the other (or both) of these notions to some degree. Why? Wilson observes that whoever can scare people enough (produce bio-survival anxiety) can then easily sell them any verbal map that seems to give them relief from their anxiety.[64]

The polarizing power of "weapons of mass destruction," "war on drugs/terror/cancer," or "please forgive me for my sins, Lord" (and other such dubious conceptual matrices) lies partly in the fact that the human race has really only just begun to master the rational mind. We are still somewhat embedded in tribal mindsets and provincial views because of our heritage and previous travel and communication constraints, which in turn limited the amount and types of data we had access to (and thus our ability to process things intellectually).

In the grand scheme of things most of the world was illiterate until only recently. The intellect is still a relatively new and undeveloped tool in human hands. Functioning as it does so often in the absence of intuition and insight into higher-order realities, it is particularly susceptible to subversion by emotional undercurrents, particularly those of fear, survival anxiety and the need for status or approval. As DeGracia points out, the individual astral and mental bodies of many people are easily overpowered by external thought-forms given great strength by the many who have invested in them.

Understanding this, it is not surprising that most people are controlled most of the time by the ancient reptilian-mammalian "circuits" in the brain, rather than by the true intellect operating through the brain's "semantic circuit," represented by the neocortex and rational thought. Thus, when the "bio-survival circuit" signals a threat to one's life, or the emotional circuit "red-flags" a threat to one's status, the semantic circuit or "rational mind" is all too easily undermined and duped into false logics, whether they be "scientific" bigotries, supremacist ideologies, or what have you. The semantic-verbal circuit is easily manipulated by the more primitive fight/flight bio-survival circuit and the mammalian-emotional pecking-order circuit.[65]

In combination, the emotional circuit (limbic system) and the bio-survival circuit (reptilian brain) can quickly subvert the functioning of the semantic-rational circuit (neocortex).[66] We are so constantly bombarded by the "powers that be" with false imagery and concepts that are designed to induce exactly this kind of suppression and subversion of the rational mind that it is no wonder so many people never even try to uncover the truth about life on this planet. So powerful are the mass thought-forms of religion, patriotism, and science, that even in transcending or dismantling them, the individual reconfirms their power by sheer virtue of the fact that without them there would be nothing to challenge or transcend in the first place.

"The need to find legitimacy in the terms and definitions of science is a reflection of the polarizing power of the scientific thought-forms." These are by far the most powerful thought-forms existing on the astral and mental planes today, in DeGracia's view. Such large-scale thought-forms massively influence and shape the patterns of individual auras. (To oversimplify: culture minds succumb to them; civilizer minds *alter* or transcend them—at least to some extent.) These thought-forms "serve as the overriding psychosociological framework within which individual personalities develop."[67]

I would add that although every mind must operate within the various mass thought-forms to some extent, that does not mean one has to invest or believe in them totally. As DeGracia points out, the mystical experience is largely "the breaking out of this psychosocial womb or matrix, into a psychological realm of one's own unique identity."[68] This is typically done in moments of solitude, away from the crowd. Korotkov notes that history's greatest minds have had a tendency to retreat to isolation to formulate their big ideas, in order to escape the noisy mental fields of highly populated areas. With the new ideas then

345

articulated, their further development and their structuring of the collective consciousness field happen within the larger collective.[69]

By stepping back and observing your thought-forms—which physicist John Wheeler called "bubbles in a pond" or "quantum foam"—you give yourself the chance to see that you do not need to be identified *as* them:

> Each of these bubbles . . . contains feelings, thoughts, emotions, associations—but also emptiness. Usually, this is the space we do not acknowledge because we are so identified with the other material. As observation witnessing occurs, we begin to be less pulled, or identified, with these bubbles and become more aware of the space.[70]

We have a habit of unconsciously identifying with and defining ourselves through the thought-forms we inherit, about life and ourselves. When we cease mechanically identifying with these constructs and observe them instead of objectifying them, we can free ourselves from their hypnotizing power.[71] We can think more flexibly, become more conceptual, less prone to dogmatic belief and more open to change in its myriad forms. We are the creators of thought-forms, not the forms themselves. We are "merely" consciousness without beginning or end. The thought-forms are merely vorticular movements, ripples (vibrations), and bubbles of emptiness within Brahman/the holomovement—our unitive transcendent consciousness. There is no need to identify ourselves with them, and this is ultimately counterproductive because our real identity lies beyond the rupic (having form) and arupic (formless) conceptual levels of the manasic plane.

Quantum Thought

We have noted already the "quantum-holographic" processes employed by the brain (such as memory), as well as the "quantum-holographic" nature of our subtle vehicles. Subjective thought feels like a continuous stream of thought, and yet each thought initiates the formation of a corresponding individual thought-form which is ejected from the matter of the mental body. Therefore, what a clairvoyant would see is a stream of discrete or "atomized" holograms emanating from your mental torsion-plasma body and hovering nearby.[72]

The similarity of this thought process to the quantum mechanical view of a shining light bulb is "uncanny," according to DeGracia. Why? Because in both scenarios we find the source emitting a steady stream of *discrete* entities (whether photons or thoughts), and yet subjectively the discrete stream is perceived as a *continuous* stream of light waves (in the case of photons), or a continuous flow of thoughts radiating from the thinker. Thus, the psychological processes described by clairvoyant observers operate similarly to ordinary quantum mechanical processes.[73]

In *Quantum Consciousness*, psychiatrist Stephen Wolinksy made a similar comparison between the quantum wave and the thoughts we generate one after the other, where the peak of the wave represented the presence of a thought and the trough represented the absence or space between thoughts (again the description is of discrete thought-forms occurring serially). In meditation, the space between thoughts is ideally drawn longer and longer to allow expansion of awareness into higher consciousness. Tibetan Buddhists have explained that it is in the gap between each thought that the nature of mind (*Rigpa*) can be revealed.[74]

Goswami points out that there even seems to be an uncertainty principle for thought, as Bohm and August Comte before him observed. Concentration on the content of a thought means not knowing where the thought is heading. Conversely, focus on the direction of a thought means loss of the content's resolution (sharpness).[75]

Goswami asserts, along with Fred Wolf and L. Bass, that in order for intelligence to operate, the firing of one neuron must be accompanied by the firing of many correlated neurons at macroscopic distances, as much as 10 cm—the width of the cortical tissue. For this to work, we need nonlocal correlations between our synapses. Thus, even regular thought would depend on quantum nonlocality,[76] or traits of time-space/R-space, if you want to think in terms of those reciprocal models (or implicate orders).

In Salt Lake City, Utah, at the 5th Annual International Symposium of the New Energy Society (1999), David Yurth reported:

> Recent experimentation has made it clear that large-scale collective quantum phenomena occur in every brain. The human brain demonstrates both global quantum coherence and quantum entanglement, as functions of the quantum relationships between the various electrical states which operate at the level of the microtubules. This likely means that all the counterintuitive phenomena and sheer paradox of quantum reality are an integral part of consciousness itself.[77]

Penrose and Hameroff have assembled a compelling theory of quantum biocommunication and consciousness wherein delocalised *pi* electrons within microtubules in cells are so sheltered from environmental fluctuations that their quantum waves are all in a superposition, acting effectively as a Bose-Einstein condensate; they all share the same wave function. They theorise that the "collapse" of this quantum wave function could produce subneuronal information processing, and thus could be the mechanism underlying brain-based consciousness. This quantum coherence would facilitate nonlocal information processing and exchange within the body, being involved in general biological operations.

Thus, in this model it is through the quantum wave—occupying a realm between space-time and hyperspace/time-space—that every thought, feeling, and experience is transmitted to our personal consciousness, thereby allowing information exchange between the two reference frames. The same kind of delocalised electrons in microtubules are found also in DNA, "and there is a continuous connection throughout the entire body through the microtubules to the nuclear DNA from cell to cell," comments William Brown.

He theorizes that an individual sufficiently isolated from environmental perturbations (say, in meditation) who enters, say, a gamma state (wherein synchronized spatiotemporal action potentials sweep back and forth across the brain 40 times per second), thereby allows the Bose-Einstein condensate state of the electrons in the brain to coherently entangle with those in the microtubules throughout the rest of the body. As a result, the body becomes a quantum-coherent whole and the person experiences a sensation of oneness (such as those described in Chapter 5). Such a state also potentially allows access to information in the implicate order/aether.[78]

In his book *Decoding the Universe*, Charles Seife states that ideas seem to originate from a superposition state in the preconscious (time-space), and are then experienced consciously when the wave function "collapses," ending the superposition.[79] Penrose, in his theory of *objective reduction*, has suggested that the shift ("collapse") from quantum wave to particle is actually triggered by gravity (aether flow).[80] Since, for our purposes here we are not subscribing to the "wave collapse" idea, what we mean by "collapse" is that a singular experiential reality in space-time has been extracted, decoded or "cohered" out of the quantum sea of wave functions representing multiple possibilities in time-space/aether/implicate order.

Physicist F. David Peat agrees with Seife and others that thought itself has a "complex, overlaid quality which demands complementary viewpoints, including what could be loosely termed 'non-local,'" and has suggested that "our experience of space, events and processes cannot be described by any single viewpoint, rather some form of complementarity is demanded which would include some sort of non-locality as one of its aspects."[81]

It is interesting to note in reference to my own heightened states of consciousness that my perception—and this is particularly true for the first experience I talked about early on—did not shift gradually between the altered state and my regular brain-mind awareness, but *instantaneously*. There was no linear transition, it was more like an electron jumping positions around the atomic nucleus (assuming you accept the model of orbital electrons as it stands)—a metaphorical quantum jump, a discontinuous event. This highlights the fact that one does not "develop" infinite consciousness but *is* infinite consciousness to start with and merely "quantum-jumps" from unawareness of the fact to awareness—*satori*, we might say, is a metaphorical quantum leap to awareness of one's own fundamentally infinite consciousness. Just as the elusive electron does not *travel* from one orbital position to another, but rather "jumps" or seemingly teleports instantaneously from one position to the next, so too does our consciousness perform such "quantum" feats of instantaneous ingenuity—sometimes when we least expect it.

> Not only is the universe queerer than we imagine. It is queerer than
> we can imagine. —J.B.S. Haldane

11

TELEPATHY

Telepathy is normal not paranormal, natural not supernatural, and is also common between people, especially people who know each other well. —Rupert Sheldrake

Those who reject even telepathy have reached the point where they are impugning either the honesty or the sanity of *several thousand* scientific researchers on *all major continents* over a period of *decades*. Such expedient ways of disposing of data are shared only by the most ardent anti-Evolutionists among the Fundamentalist sects.
—R.A. Wilson, *Cosmic Trigger*

What is certain is: That telepathy can and ought to be henceforth considered by Science as an incontestable reality; that minds are able to act upon each other without the intervention of the senses; that psychic force exists . . .
—Camille Flammarion

Anecdotal Appetizers

The next siddhi we will look at, possessed by everyone to some extent, is telepathy. We will see that it occurs spontaneously in informal everyday circumstances as well as carefully controlled scientific settings. By this stage of our investigation we have thoroughly established the fact that, though we are mostly blissfully unaware of it, we are constantly in communication with others and our environment, transacting energy and information ceaselessly. We leave an energetic footprint wherever we go, and at the same time we are subtly affected by our surroundings. Vast amounts of anecdotal evidence indicates that the information radiating both from and to us can (potentially) be decoded and registered at the level of the conscious mind. We will look at only a tiny fraction of such evidence before proceeding.

At an alternative school based in the USA, called The Place, there was an unusually high number of psychic children attending, some of whom had been "troublemakers" or "misfits" in the mainstream education system, which could not understand them or why they were different. Gale, one of the teachers, found it a challenge to teach the telepathic children. One day she gave an oral standardized test to a particularly intuitive child. To prevent him from "hearing" the answers, she imagined a busload of campers loudly singing "I've Been Working on the Railroad." The boy seemed agitated for some reason, so Gale asked what was wrong. He explained: "I hate to complain but you have to get those children to stop singing. I can't concentrate with them here." Gale asked what they were singing. "I've Been Working on the Railroad," he said.[1]

Even during the writing of her book *Beyond the Five Senses* in the mid-1940s, L. Margery Bazette could not escape reports apparently attributable to telepathy. In 1944 a naval officer had one of his men come to him in a state of high agitation, requesting to be put on shore as soon as the first opportunity arose. He was convinced that his home had been destroyed by bombs and his eldest child killed. The impression proved true, though no information from ordinary sources had reached him. Bazette commented that a "tie of affection or a strong emotion gives impetus to the transmission."[2]

In a letter he wrote in 1915, Aldous Huxley described a mind-reading test with a friend, Gilbert Murray, who was considered one of the best telepathists of his day. Huxley had visualized "the Master of Balliol listening to an essay on *The Egoist*, a book he has not read." Murray stood holding Huxley's hand for about 30 seconds, and then began to laugh saying, "Oh of course, it's the old Master of Balliol being embarrassed."[3]

Self-styled "urban mystic" Stuart Wilde shares an example of his own telepathic activity in *Sixth Sense*. He was riding on a bus with a friend and wanted the bus to stop so they could alight. A pedestrian crossing was approaching and Wilde flashed a thought-form of an old woman walking across the road pushing a wicker basket on wheels.

> The driver saw her in his mind's eye and thinking her real, he
> put the double-decker bus into an emergency halt. Everyone

went flying off their seats, and packages and stuff went tumbling into the aisles. The driver got out of the bus and ran back toward the pedestrian crossing . . . [He] stood on the sidewalk, dumbfounded, scratching his head . . . My pal was suitably impressed as I told him what I was going to do before I did it.[4]

As the student of his guru, Sri Yukteswar, the young Yogananda found his mind wandering somewhat during meditation, though he gave no outward sign. His master reprimanded his lack of mental presence, though Yogananda protested his innocence. To prove his point, Yukteswar identified the three institutions Yogananda was tacitly creating in his mind. "One was a sylvan retreat on a plain, another on a hilltop, still another by the ocean." Exposed, Yogananda could protest his innocence no more.[5] (In fairness, Yukteswar may have simply been observing thought-forms in Yogananda's auric field. Telepathy may not have been involved here.)

Self-appointed "Beast" Aleister Crowley once sought to demonstrate an increase in his powers to a friend by venturing onto a fairly deserted stretch of pavement and falling in step with a man, walking behind him and imitating his walk. "Suddenly Crowley buckled at the knees, squatted for a split second on his haunches, then shot up again; the man in front of him also buckled and collapsed on the pavement. They helped him to his feet, and he looked around in a puzzled manner for the banana skin."[6]

It appears that Crowley sought to establish a resonance or rapport with the stranger by mimicking his mannerisms and keeping time with him so that he could increase his chances of intentionally affecting the man's subconscious processes and cause him to stumble. This mirroring incidentally, is an aspect of neuro-linguistic programming (NLP). Such techniques, based on esoteric science as they are, may be referred to as "magick." The Soviets, who also trained subjects in this exact method of attempting to cause another to stumble, called this technique "bio-rapport." Ostrander and Schroeder have reported that influence at a distance by muscle motion has a long history in Soviet psi.[7]

The power of influencing others' minds is a *vibhuti* (yogic power) mentioned in Patanjali's *Yoga Sutras*, which explains it as a result of "universal sympathy"—resonance, in other words.[8]

In the modern world, the commonest kind of human telepathy occurs in connection with telephone calls, according to Sheldrake. Over 80% of people claim to have thought of someone for no apparent reason, who then phoned them; or that they have known, in a telepathic sort of way, who was on the phone before answering it. Sheldrake reports that controlled experiments have provided highly statistically significant repeatable positive results.[9]

Some Telepathy Background

The term "telepathy" was coined in 1882 by Frederick W.H. Myers, a founding member of the London Society for Psychical Research (SPR). The word means "feeling at a distance," though this may be slightly misleading in that this is not usually how the term is deployed. Telepathy is essentially mind-to-mind contact, or the exchange of information between two different consciousnesses separated by an arbitrarily large distance. Though many of the more narrow-visioned would claim any discussion involving telepathy is "unscientific" by default, we can see that many years ago there were eminent scientists who not only recognized its existence but sought to understand the phenomenon.

The first studies of telepathy were based on collections of spontaneous experiences, with 1886 seeing the publication of the seminal classic *Phantasms of the Living*, by the British scholars Edmund Gurney, Frederick Myers, and Frank Podmore—who actually took the time and effort to analyse all reports to identify the best and most reliable cases for publication and eliminate the fraudulent.[10]

Over a decade later, Sir William Crookes spoke on telepathy before the Royal Society at Bristol, England, in 1898. This address was, in Panchadasi's words, "made before an assemblage of distinguished scientists, many of them rank materialists and quite skeptical of all occult phenomena." Crookes, facing this gathering as its president, expressed the view that it is a "fundamental law . . . that thoughts and images may be transferred from one mind to another without the agency of the recognized organs of sense—that knowledge may enter the human mind without being communicated in any hitherto known or recognized ways."[11]

If telepathy occurs, he continued, "we have two physical facts—the physical change in the brain of A, the suggestor, and the analogous physical change in the brain of B, the recipient of the suggestion." While Crookes would eventually be vindicated in these comments by the development of the EEG and other modern technology and experimental designs (as we will see), he assumed that "[b]etween these two physical events there must exist a train of physical causes,"[12] which we can accept if we modify our definition of "physical" to include subtle energies (such as torsion/scalar fields), as well as the plasmoidal particle "soups" of the various aethcric densities.

If we look back to the previous chapter on thought-forms, we will see that consciousness operates through higher grades of matter that carry thought-waves and are shaped by thought-forms used to generate telepathic contact. Swami Panchadasi has commented that Crookes' address "is in full accord with the ideas of occultism as old as the hills. And yet, the speaker had worked out the idea independently."[13]

In fact, coming at telepathy from another angle, and knowing that all information fundamentally exists everywhere, telepathy is not so much about "sending" information to a place where it was not already present (at some deeper level), but calling it forth from subconscious levels by another agent's mind acting as an external trigger through the dynamics of consciousness entanglement.

In 1888 Professor Henry Sidgwick, the first President of the Society for Psychical Research, declared his belief in "an important body of evidence—tending prima facie to establish the independence of soul or spirit—which modern science has simply left on one side with ignorant contempt; and . . . in so leaving it she has been untrue to her professed method and . . . arrived prematurely at her negative conclusions."[14]

David Conway, former Principal Director at the European Patent Office in Munich, commentated in *Secret Wisdom* that since Sidgwick's era, subsequent research has confirmed that the operations of the mind—including telepathic functions that are unaffected by distance—are not dependent on the physical senses alone.[15]

Card Tests

Telepathy was probably the first of the occult sciences to be brought from the séance room into the laboratory, and some of the credit for this goes to Dr. Joseph B. Rhine and his wife Louisa, then of Duke University. The backbone of their tests was a special set of cards called Zener Cards. There were five suits of five cards each, the suits being designated by symbols: a cross, a wavy line, a star, a square, and a circle. These symbols were selected because of their differences from one another. The basic idea was for subjects to determine what symbol was on the face of the cards without looking at them.

The tests were varied in different ways to maximize the integrity and poignancy of the results— guessing cards in runs of several at a time, or guessing cards as they were flipped at a distance—in an adjacent room, or down the hall. From chance alone, the subject might be expected to make five correct guesses out of 25. During the first three years of the testing at Duke, various subjects made a total of 3,400 runs through the deck of Zener cards, calling 85,000 separate cards. The general average for all these calls was seven hits in 25 calls, or an average of two above chance per run—especially significant because it was maintained for such a large number of runs.[16]

Many times, scores with odds against chance of over a million to one occurred.[17] One subject with a particularly strong talent called nine in a row correctly, and later scored 15 consecutive hits, the odds against this being 30 million to one.[18] A 9-year-old girl "guessed" 23 of 25 correctly when tested at school, and later got all 25 at the Duke lab when tested by an experimenter she had great affection for.[19] A graduate student in the laboratory performed the same feat.[20] This takes the odds far beyond the 30 million to one for a run of "only" 15 in a row.

One of the most frequently cited experiments by Rhine was the Pearce-Pratt distance telepathy test, conducted from August 1933 to March 1934, consisting of 74 runs of 25-card ESP decks (1,850 guesses in total). Pearce, a student at Duke University, acted as the receiver, while Rhine's colleague Gaither Pratt (located in his research room in the top floor of the Social Science Building) would select cards one by one blindly from a pack chosen from several in their supply.

The card was kept face down so Pratt couldn't identify it as he placed it on a particular book (agreed upon by Pearce and Pratt) in the middle of the table he was seated at. There it sat for one minute, while Pearce—located away in the library—tried to psychically detect each card and record his "guess," making a signed copy of his record at the end of each round of 25 guesses, and sealing both records in separate envelopes for delivery to Rhine. After each minute was up, Pratt's card was moved to the left of the table and the next card was selected and placed on the book. This procedure was repeated through a total of 1,850 trial runs. I am simplifying the procedure carried out, and omitting some details regarding the tight precautions taken to ensure the legitimacy of the results, but the bottom line here is that Pearce obtained 558 hits, 188 above chance expectation—a massive deviation representing odds of a billion billion billion to one (or 1 in 10,000,000,000,000,000,000,000,000)—with no evidence of any other plausible explanation for the feat.

Prior informal experiments by Rhine and Pratt with Pearce resulted in a 32% success rate where 20% was expected by chance—a massively significant outcome over 700 runs of 25 cards.[21] Pearce also demonstrated the ability to score significantly low (psi-missing) on demand. Low or high scores—it seemed only a matter of choice for him.[22]

Further Experiments in Physiological and Mental Entanglement

In what the authors referred to as possibly the first fMRI telepathy experiment looking at neurophysiological correlations with psi performance in a well-known mentalist/telepathist (Gerard Senehi) under controlled conditions, G. Venkatasubramanian and colleagues identified significant activation of the right parahippocampal region of the cortex during successful telepathic reception. Senehi's drawing showed striking similarity with the target image produced by one of the experimenters, while a control subject with no known psi ability whose drawing showed much less resemblance instead revealed activation of a different region—of the *left* hemisphere. The authors concluded that "the findings of this study are suggestive of a limbic basis for telepathy."[23] (A "limbic *correlation*" might be more accurate.)

Empirical laboratory evidence that two brains (or other aspects of human physiology) can become correlated with one another in measurable ways would provide further support for the telepathy hypothesis and occult perspectives. Such evidence exists. In an experiment by the Mexican neurophysiologist Jacobo Grinberg-Zylberbaum and his collaborators, two subjects were instructed to meditate together for 20 minutes until they started feeling a silent "direct communication." They then entered separate semi-silent Faraday cages 45 feet apart and were connected to EEGs while reclining with semi-closed eyes.

At random times one of the subjects was shown a flickering light signal that produces an evoked potential (an electrophysiological response to a sensory stimulus as measured by an EEG) in the light-stimulated brain. As long as the partners in the experiment maintained their sense of connection, the unstimulated brain also showed an electrophysiological activity, called a transfer potential, quite similar in shape and strength to that of the sender—though the receiver didn't sense a conscious correlation. In contrast, control subjects did not show any transfer potential.[24]

These experimental results and conclusions have been replicated in London by the neuropsychiatrist Peter Fenwick.[25] Russian physicist Victor Adamenko had earlier invented a device to measure changes in the bioplasmic energy body/aura and, not surprisingly, found in telepathy tests that as the sender's intensity of thought fluctuated, the bioplasmic energy in the receivers responded.[26]

Evidently the initial interaction between participants primes them for the experiment by creating a mental resonance or entanglement, allowing for the transfer potential to manifest itself in the receiver. However, there is more than this: the meditative intention of direct communication must be maintained for the duration of the experiment to preserve the nonlocal interaction.

Similar results have also been achieved by Charles Tart and German scientist Harald Walach. A separate 2005 study at the Bastyr University by Standish and others gathered 30 pairs of people who knew each other well, with strong psychological and emotional connections. While in rooms 10 m from each other, the "sender" was exposed to a flickering light and attempted to transmit an "image/thought" about the light to their partner. In the more successful couples, during transmission periods, the receivers showed higher activation levels of the occipital region of the brain (the visual center at the rear of the cortex)—an effect that was absent during periods of non-stimulation. Four pairs participated in a replication experiment during which one pair replicated the effect. Thus we see that the brainwave response of the sender can be mirrored in the receiver in the same place in the brain.[27] With the brain-minds acting as a nonlocally correlated system, the connection is maintained by nonlocal consciousness (in time-space/implicate order)—facilitated, Goswami believes, by the brains' "quantum nature."[28]

Such "paranormal" phenomena could be attributable to torsion waves passing between the participants' minds. The two parties have synchronized their operations in time; now spatial distance is irrelevant—they act as one system in time. It is interesting to note that torsion fields cannot be shielded by conventional means (including Faraday cages), and evidence no attenuation when propagated arbitrary distances. "As pointed out by A. Akimov, empirical exhibits of torsion fields have possibly been found previously in conventional scientific research, but not yet recognized as such." Two such examples (among others) may include the "recent discovery of the anomalous rotation of radio waves in an astrophysical context, and the quantum nonlocality phenomenon, which can be attributed to superluminal transmission of torsion potential."[29]

We should note: *any* form of meaningful contact between people can establish a nonlocal correlation, as any clairvoyant or occultist worth their salt can tell you—this is how legitimate psychics (let us ignore the plethora of phonies) can carry out "readings" over the phone or internet without ever having so much as been in the same country as the sitter or client. The subjects in the Grinberg-Zylberbaum experiment need not have been in close physical proximity to one another—a connection in time renders space moot. Even a phone call could suffice to establish the necessary mental link in time/time-space.

Ostensible nonlocal correlations between people can also be established through hypnosis. One young lady under hypnosis was told that all her feelings were drained out of her body and into a glass of water. The hypnotist dipped a pin into the water and "the girl gave a spontaneous exclamation of pain," as if she had physically been pricked. When the hypnotist removed himself to another room so that his entranced subject could not see him, in order to repeat the task under stricter controls, the girl again reacted as if in pain. Then when the hypnotist—unbeknownst to the girl—blew into the glass, she spontaneously complained of hot waves of air blowing over her![30]

Sir William Barrett achieved similar results with a variation of these experiments, where his blindfolded hypnotic subject could taste and identify foodstuffs he put into his *own* mouth. When placed in her mouth, however, "she seemed to disregard them."[31]

In the 1970s, Russell Targ and Harold Puthoff conducted some of their own telepathy experiments at SRI. The designated receiver was placed in a sealed, opaque, and electrically shielded chamber, while the scientists would situate the sender in another room where he or she was subjected to bright flashes of stroboscopic light lasting 10 seconds at regular intervals. Each of the experimental subjects was connected to an EEG machine that registered their brainwave patterns.

After a brief period, the receiver began to produce the same rhythmic pattern of brainwaves as the sender, who was exposed to the flashing light. In one out of seven runs, they spontaneously decided to tell their subject Hella Hamid that there was no one in the room acting as sender even though there was—her brainwaves remained *unaffected.* In a later run, they actually *did* remove the sender without telling her—bizarrely, *the effect on her alpha waves was some of the strongest observed.* Paradoxically, Hamid picked up on the absence of a sender, saying she didn't "feel" anyone in the other room.[32]

In 2004, psychophysiologist J. Wackermann published a conservative review of fMRI experiments such as those "transfer potential" experiments already detailed, noting that even with increasingly sophisticated experimental designs the effects do not disappear, and therefore further research is warranted.[33] Research in Russia has also proved this phenomenon. According to Radin, these experiments have been performed over a dozen times over the last four decades by independent groups—and they clearly work.

Compelling experiments in this area also known as Distant Mental Influence of Living Systems or DMILS have been carried out by psychologist William Braud at the Institute of Transpersonal Psychology in Palo Alto, California, and anthropologist Marilyn Schlitz, Research Director for the Institute of Noetic Sciences. They have repeatedly shown that if a person simply attends fully to a distant person whose physiological activity is being monitored, he or she (acting as a sender) can influence the distant person's autonomic galvanic skin responses (thus proving my previous point about a simple phone call being enough to "entangle" people).

In four separate experiments involving 78 sessions, one person staring intently at a closed-circuit TV monitor image of a distant participant, influenced the remote person's electrodermal (galvanic skin) responses. In these cases no techniques of intentional focusing or mental imaging were used by the influencer. He or she simply stared at the "staree's" image on the video screen during the 30-second trials, which were randomly interspersed with control periods.

In these studies, Braud and Schlitz discovered something even more interesting than this telepathically induced effect on our unconscious system. They found that, while they were being stared at, the most shy, anxious, and introverted people had the largest unconscious electrodermal responses, meaning they "reacted with significantly more stress to being stared at than did the sociable and extroverted people." Quiet introverts may possess, or have developed, a higher sensitivity to the consciousness or at least the attention of others.

"This experiment," write Targ and Katra, "gives scientific validation to the common human experience of feeling stared at and turning around to find that someone is, indeed, staring at you."[34] It also validates the experiments of Sheldrake and his colleagues on the sense of being stared at, which we have already mentioned (Chapter 4) in demonstrating the ability of conscious observation to act as an entangling factor between subject and object.

Interestingly, the electrochemist Douglas Dean discovered using a plethysmograph that when someone concentrates on the name of a person with whom he has an emotional tie, the distant subject registers a measurable change in blood pressure and volume in his finger (showing autonomic nervous system activation). Dean found about one in four people to have this sensitivity.[35] Thus there is a variety of physiological effects that show up during telepathic contact of various forms, whether deliberate transmission from sender to receiver, or the repetition of someone's name, or through being stared at as per Sheldrake's experiments. These could be viewed as secondary physical effects arising due to the interface of the nonlocal/hyperspatial (torsion/scalar) consciousness waves with the human physiology.

Roughly two years into my own conscious journey, I was spending a little bit of time each week with a spiritualist church in Sydney. This was mainly for the purposes of attending a weekly trance mediumship class (primarily to help my quality of meditation, and hopefully stimulate my psi faculties, which it did) and to occasionally observe mediums giving platform readings at the weekly church services. I also attended a couple of development workshops run by my gifted clairvoyant friend Denise, who was involved with the spiritualist church at the time. It was at one of these that I found myself with an opportunity to casually test Denise's clairvoyance, in particular to see if she could perceive mental energy and manipulations or projections of it. She suggested I send some love energy to some point of my own choosing on a large tree just outside the window of the hall we were in—she would clairvoyantly identify the point of contact on the tree.

Making sure there was no possibility for Denise to physically observe where my head or eyes were pointing, I silently selected a spot on the tree and mentally beamed some energy at it. Almost immediately, Denise (standing with her back to me) exclaimed "There!" and correctly identified my target, pointing without hesitation. She did this accurately and quickly each time we ran this little test. I was convinced she could see my mental energy and where I was directing it. There were no reflective surfaces or other aids that might have revealed through ordinary means where I was aiming on the tree—which was large enough and close enough that there could be no ambiguity in terms of the accuracy of her "guesses." This was my first intimate contact with the concept of consciousness energy emanating from the eyes. It showed me up close and personal that, at the very least, "mind" undeniably has a clairvoyantly visible light-based component.

Before moving on, I might note an experiment by Colin A. Ross which was reported in *Anthropology of Consciousness* in March, 2010. Ross hypothesized the extramission (emission) by the eyes of detectable EM frequencies in the extremely low 1–40 Hz range, between 1–100 microvolts. Since the skull was not there to impede EM energy leaving the eyes, he reasoned that more significant amounts may be detected there, and that perhaps this was the basis for the historical belief in the "evil eye," and also the underlying mechanism of the staring effect.

Using a high-impedance electrode in an EM-insulated environment, his results did indeed show that the EM signal coming from the eyes was stronger in amplitude in certain frequency ranges than that emanating from the skull, even if only detected at short range. While extra-low-frequency signals suffer extremely little attenuation as they propagate—and therefore may conceivably be involved in local staring effects—Ross acknowledges that the EM signals he measured cannot account for the fact that the sense of being stared at can be transmitted "through," for instance, CCTV cameras to distant people. He points out that his results obviously do not rule out other *non*-EM emissions functioning in tandem with the detectable EM frequencies, and mentions the possibility of Sheldrake's morphic fields, which we have speculatively identified as "torsion-plasma" (or scalar) fields: "The measurable component of ocular extramission in the 0–40 Hertz range could be considered to be a special limited instance of the larger theoretical category of [morphic] fields."[36]

Ergo, the EM energies in space-time may be derivative of, or local counterparts to, the "hyper-energies" of the present torsion/scalar fields. Likewise, Reich's "visual ray," identified as being composed of orgone/etheric energy (see Chapter 4), represents the light-based aspect of torsion waves at the etheric level.

In 2010, Ross actually had a patent approved for an EM eyebeam detection device (patent no. 7,806,527)[37] that, according to him, "can be used as a switch and can turn on or off any electrical device. It functions like a clapper light, but uses the electromagnetic energy emitted through the eyes instead of the sound of a hand clapping."[38] The fact that the weak ELF frequencies emitted by the human eye can be detected several feet away (Ross predicts it should work up to 30 feet away, based on the fact that ECGs can now be taken several feet from the body) takes the sense of being stared at right out of the realm of superstition, and right into the world of ordinary, testable electromagnetically based science.

Nonlocal staring effects, on the other hand, require a little more conceptual flexibility. We have provided the pieces of the puzzle needed to answer this question in Chapters 4–7. Briefly, we—and our entire universe—are all extensions or projections of an underlying holographic field of potential, Bohm's "implicate order" and the holomovement carrying both the implicate and explicate realms. It is as if the act of observing produces an instantaneous sense of "recognition" within the object we observe, because ultimately subject and object are simply different facets of the same nonlocal holographic consciousness.

Master and Apprentice

The brain-to-brain entanglement studies may provide some insight into the guru–student relationship that is cultivated over time to facilitate the transference of understanding of mind from the guru or master to the student. Studies have revealed that closely bonded pairs evince stronger nonlocal correlations, that is, they are "more strongly" entangled. The master and student then, provide a salient example of a closely bonded and strongly correlated "couple." Brainwave entrainment between one and the other is greatly facilitated, and in fact it is said by Tibetans and Hindu yogis that the master is never apart from the student, their connection to one another never severed, regardless of time or distance.

When a dying Lama Tseten was offered the chance to have his master by his side, he declined saying, "With the master, there's no such thing as distance."[39] The master and student's consciousnesses are nonlocally entangled in "time-space" in other words, as are all of ours ultimately, but the master experiences this *consciously*. (Seers such as Leadbeater and Brennan report to us that clairvoyantly visible energetic bonds literally form during life between two such meaningfully connected people. They are literally energetically linked in hyperspace, not just in the more abstract "nonlocal" standard scientific sense.)

Sogyal Rinpoche shares his second initiation experience with his master, Jamyang Khyentse, which happened around nine years of age in a cave at Lhodrak Kharchu, a cave in which the father of Tibetan Buddhism, Padmasambhava, had meditated. Seated in front of his student, Jamyang Khyentse informed him that he was going to show him the essential nature of "mind." After performing his chant with his bell and hand-drum and invoking all the masters of their lineage, Jamyang Khyentse asked his young student: "What is mind?" and stared intently into his eyes. Sogyal Rinpoche declares that his mind shattered and no thought remained. It was in that "pure shock" and absence of thought that "a gap opened," in which was exposed "a sheer, immediate awareness of the present, one that was free of any clinging. It was simple, naked and fundamental. And yet [it] was also radiant with the warmth of an immense compassion."[40]

Here we have a picture of a highly sophisticated technique for neuro-linguistic programming, programming to get the lower mind and its chatter out of the way, perhaps so that the student can become entrained/correlated with the master's own brain state, and thus open himself up to the nature of empty consciousness: *Rigpa*. Thus, we can understand why these traditions emphasize that only a master or guru can impart this knowledge and state of being to the student—it would be pointless for the seeker of Reality to become "correlated" with someone not in possession of that state of mind.

That being said, one does not need a guru to access these unitive states, as I have already detailed. Gurus are really there to open the student to that which they already are (and, as others have pointed out, the insular nature of the guru–student relationship has been known to open the way to abuse and perversions, but any so-called guru or master who abuses the privilege of that position cannot legitimately be considered as any sort of "master.") Real gurus help their followers become their own masters.

Free-response Studies

Dean Radin reports in *The Conscious Universe* that cross-cultural surveys had shown decades ago that about half of all spontaneous psi experiences occur in the dream state. Motivated by this knowledge, from 1966 to 1972, researchers led by psychiatrist Montague Ullman and psychologist Stanley Krippner at the Maimonides Medical Center in Brooklyn, New York, conducted a series of clever telepathy tests in a dream research laboratory.

Senders and receivers were separated by varying distances, ranging from dozens of feet to dozens of miles, and the receiver was situated in a sound-proof electromagnetically shielded room. Regardless, the results indicated that if someone is directed to "send" mental images to someone who is dreaming, those images will sometimes be incorporated into the dream.[41]

In 2003, psychologists Sherwood and Roe reviewed all of the dream psi studies from Maimonides up to the latest at-home dream experiments, all of which were conducted under controlled conditions to determine whether remote information could be perceived in dreams. The 47 experiments consisted of 1,270 trials with an overall hit rate of 59.1%—a 9.1% deviation from chance associated with odds of 22 billion to one.[42]

A real life case: psychotherapist Dr. Brian Weiss was woken one night, jolted from a deep sleep. He saw an image of a client's face several times larger than life size. She looked upset, as if she needed his assistance. The clock displayed the time as 3.36 a.m. Unsure of the meaning of this or what to do, he dismissed the incident and fell back to sleep. But he subsequently found out from the patient that at about 3.30 that morning she had awoken in panic from a nightmare. Attempting to meditate and relax, she visualized Weiss hypnotizing her in his office. She pictured his face, heard his voice, and gradually fell back to sleep.[43] This is a good example of telepathic sleep contact between two individuals who had forged a strong bond and created a resonance between one another; an emotional connection operating nonlocally in time.

A similar event occurred with anthropologist, author, and care-giver Joan Halifax and Matthew, a terminally ill atheistic patient—himself a physician—who had undergone controlled and guided LSD sessions with Halifax of profound benefit, leading him to peacefully accept his imminent transition into the afterlife (as opposed to what he previously believed would be his annihilation).

Halifax and Stan Grof (married and working together at the time), had visited Matthew in the hospital for what they felt may have been the last time—a sentiment he seemed to share. Before they departed he reassured them that if it was his time to leave they need not worry, "it is all right . . ." Early the next morning in their downtown Hartford hotel, Halifax awoke at 3 a.m. from a dream about Matthew, in which he appeared smiling and repeating his last words: "It is all right." She felt distinctly that Matthew had just died. The hospital confirmed the next morning when they called that Matthew had indeed died at 3 a.m. that day.[44] (As we have noted, and will expand on in TGI 2, the mental realm/time-space is where mind-to-mind contact occurs—whether one of those minds is no longer operating through a brain is irrelevant.)

These examples may remind you of Cleve Backster's plants detecting the deaths of the nearby brine shrimp, and other events we cover. We seem to be psychically sensitized to death, trauma and tragedy, perhaps partly as an evolutionary survival mechanism, and partly just because events that are intrinsically meaningful and important to us are more likely to be relayed to our conscious minds by our subconscious mental operations.

Ganzfeld telepathy experiments (developed in the 1970s) have, like the dream telepathy experiments, and spontaneous occurrences in general, provided decisive scientific evidence in favor of telepathic connections between humans—at cumulative odds of 29 quintillion to one (for experiments from 1974 to 2004).[45] The ganzfeld (German for "whole field") is a mild sensory isolation technique that aims to create an unchanging and passive sensory field, thereby increasing sensitivity to conscious psi perceptions that well up from the subconscious (typically after being "sent" by another party in a separate sound-proof room).[46] This technique offers still more evidence that with our conscious minds subdued, or taken almost entirely out of the equation (as per dream telepathy), we are often more receptive to nonlocal information and remote events and people.

Between February 1983 and September 1989 11 series of automated ganzfeld (autoganzfeld) experiments were run in which a 34.4% hit rate was obtained, as compared with the 25% expected by chance, offering still more support for psi effects. Tellingly, experienced subjects produced "exceptionally high" effect sizes. Dynamic targets produced far more successful results, and trials with friends as senders were slightly more successful than those without. "The effect size observed in the ganzfeld database is triple the much publicized effect of aspirin on heart attacks."[47]

Thoughts Through Space

In 1942 the remarkable book *Thoughts Through Space*, by Australian-born aviator-explorer Sir Hubert Wilkins (1888–1958) and American author, playwright, and "sensitive" Harold Sherman (1898–1987), was published. It detailed the first experiment (conducted from late 1937 through to early 1938) of its kind: a long-distance and long-term telepathy experiment where Wilkins, who was aiding in the aerial search for a missing Russian craft and its crew in the Arctic, would attempt to telepathically "send" information regarding his activities to Sherman, who would attempt to receive the messages and record them.

As it turned out, Wilkins never got the opportunity to take time to deliberately send any impressions to Sherman, who faithfully conducted his "psychic vigil" each night at the same time, unaware of Wilkins' situation or activities at the present moment. What Wilkins did instead was to record events and details in his log, this being the usual habit with an explorer. When Wilkins returned from the Arctic, his dated log was compared with the dated impressions of Sherman.[48]

Early in the book, Wilkins made a point of noting that, a) Sherman had already demonstrated his ability to receive impressions without the necessity of Wilkins' consciously *willing* thoughts to him at the time of their scheduled "sittings," and, b) Sherman could respond directly to Wilkins' thoughts on the occasions he *was* able to keep their "psi appointments."[49]

The role of emotion was significant in these experiments (as it is in many psi experiments), as the two participants would ultimately realize. Wilkins noted that despite his inability to regularly keep to the appointed "sending" time for the experiments, he did continue his habit of thinking the unusual incidents strongly to Sherman. When Wilkins was anxious, Sherman seemed to be particularly effective at detecting his thoughts.[50] Wilkins also agreed with the occultist's axiom that the intensity of a sender's emotional reaction to what is happening to him, or has happened, determines the degree of intensity of the "thought-waves" discharged.[51]

Also worth noting is that in some ways, this experiment—lasting as it did over five months—was something of a precursor to what would later become known as remote viewing. It also featured elements of prevision, evincing a predictable unpredictability so common to psi functioning, thus blurring the lines[*] between telepathy in real time and other forms of clairvoyance—much

---

[*] The term "general ESP," or GESP, became popular to reflect the fact that it was (and still is) difficult to distinguish cleanly among the various forms of perceptual psi. (Source: Radin, *The Conscious Universe*, 67.) How is one to know, for instance, if the image one perceives relates to past, present, or future? Sometimes it just isn't immediately clear. In time-space, past, present and future are accessible.

as this tended to occasion Sherman's uncertainty as to precisely what he was seeing at the precise moment of seeing.

Sometimes visions would turn into previsions, precipitating out of the aether days later without apparent warning. This was a complicating factor at times, as was the initial lack of feedback for Sherman, which caused him a degree of anxiety (was he "hitting" more than missing?). Nevertheless, the experiment overall can only be described as a stunning success, with some indisputably spectacular hits to be found scattered throughout.

Sherman sat three times a week to act as receiver, depositing copies of his nightly impressions to third party witnesses to ensure there could be no question of his having failed to record his impressions before receiving Wilkins' log. Let's look at some of the data. Sherman's report of Wilkins' activities for February 14 reads:

> Impression you talked three times before different interested groups since arrival at Edmonton—first time before some luncheon club—like Rotary Club—you have found a motor—you plan to take off with it tomorrow or Wednesday, if weather permits. You have dinner with three men and their wives . . . One of Edmonton's wealthiest and most prominent men has entertained you and given you some assistance relative to the expedition—word McKenzie flashes to my mind—is there a company of that name supplying you with plane? Seem to see you as guest of Church Brotherhood . . . Sunday occasion—you called on to speak—you have appointment with two men who will take you to some plant or place where you will see the packing of the equipment.[52]

Keep in mind that Sherman had been receiving little feedback on previous recordings prior to this session, and had *not* been forewarned of any of these activities, making it all the more remarkable that Wilkins was able to subsequently confirm every detail, including the fact that McKenzie Airways were furnishing the plane that would fly the new engine back to Aklavik. All of these things took place between February 10 and 14.[53]

As noted, sometimes the information being received by Sherman was a blur of present (or recent past) information and information pertaining to some point in the future. Wilkins stated that in his March 1 record Sherman had recorded almost all of his most prominent thoughts as well as describing the conditions Wilkins experienced.[54] The latter part of the entry from Sherman mentions the possibility of a company seeking Wilkins' endorsement of their liquor and whether they will offer him enough money. He also mentions that an oil or gas line to the engine seems clogged, possibly as a result of the temperature, and that Wilkins should check.[55] Wilkins was able to confirm that Hiram Walker did indeed seek his endorsement of their liquor that day by telegram (the only day of the year such an offer was made)—but did not offer sufficient remuneration[56]—and the next day the feed on the automatic control did indeed clog, just as Sherman indicated.[57]

Evidently, darkness proved to be an aid in Sherman's sittings, eliminating visual stimuli so he could become more receptive to the nonlocal stimuli filtering through from his subconscious mind.[58] Sitting in darkness to receive psi information is a good and standard way to increase the psi signal to noise ratio. An interesting fact to note is that after some time of sitting three times a week for his sessions, Sherman had trained his subconscious to feed him psi information more consistently. He commented that his mind became so sensitized that he continually received impressions and flashes unbidden. These flashes appeared sometimes to come from the mind of anyone he focused his attention on, regardless of the fact that there were unwanted insights that he did not seek.[59] There are many pieces of evidence that demonstrate that the psi faculty, like our muscular system, is responsive to training. This has been known to mystics and occultists for many centuries.

We need not go into Sherman's exact method in eliciting his results, but it is worth noting that during the sessions he could feel his mind "contact" Wilkins' mind, as he sensed "a force, a line, or stream of energy" that seemed to connect their subconscious minds. On the nights Sherman felt it the strongest, he obtained his best results.[60]

A conclusion reached by both men (and one in full accordance with occult thought) was that the degree of intensity of emotional reaction to external experience determines the intensity of the thought force projected. In their view, emotions were the batteries generating the power behind the electrical currents in the brain.[61] A recurring motif in "paranormal" research is the important role of emotion, creative force that it is. Sherman also noted that he sensed thought impressions at two places in his body: the brain (center of crown and third eye chakras) and solar plexus (the *manipura* chakra).[62] He would get a nerve reaction in the pit of his stomach (not unlike that felt when one receives a sudden shock or becomes anxious), which he came to realize always accompanied a genuine telepathic communication.[63]

On top of Sherman's amazingly accurate reports of Wilkins' far removed activities either as they happened or soon after, he sensed events yet to happen to Wilkins, as previously noted. Wilkins only had two accidents occur involving his plane during his five months away, and Sherman sensed both ahead of time, witnessing previsions of these events days before they happened.

To give further insight into the remarkably successful nature of this experiment, several friends and/or collaborators of Sherman and Wilkins signed affidavits testifying to the validity of the experimental procedure as well as Sherman's undeniable accuracy. Dr. Henry S.W. Hardwicke, a research officer for the Psychic Research Society of New York, stated in his affidavit that the authenticity of Sherman's telepathy was unquestionable.[64] Dr. A.E. Strath-Gordon was also effusive in his affidavit, stating that in all his years of research around the world into psi phenomena, never had he seen such consistent precision as Sherman's.[65]

Though we have covered more than enough evidence to convince the sane of the success of this epic psi experiment, there are further notes worth making on it. For instance, it is notorious among psychics that sensing specific numbers, dates, names, and such particulars represents one of the most difficult tasks. Sherman was exceptional at sensing names of people, companies, and more, as well as having some spectacular hits with numerical data (remembering that he was operating totally "blind").

On November 30, one of his data points was simply this: Latitude 68, Longitude 133. Wilkins recorded: Latitude 68, Longitude 135. These numbers bear no further comment. In his next sitting (December 2), Sherman recorded several spectacular hits, including a note of the intended first flight of Wilkins, which was to be a distance of 600 miles. In his own notes, Wilkins had indeed recorded that this flight was to be 600 miles.[66] Again, Wilkins did not offer foreknowledge of his intended plans or movements in these letters.

To add yet another complicating factor to all of this, Sherman found that it was difficult to distinguish between a thought in the mind of an individual and the actual materialization of that thought in action. He said he was certain that there had been occasions where he had unwittingly confused these two thought-forms.[67]

Cleve Backster found in his polygraph experiments, as we are about to see, that his plants initially encountered something of a similar situation, though they rapidly learned to distinguish between real and imagined threats. The process for a human attempting telepathy seems to present more challenges— perhaps because plants do not have an individuated mind to block or distort subconscious perceptions: they belong to a group consciousness or collective "morphogenetic field," of their own density. The human, whether particularly intelligent or not, has this discriminatory disadvantage built in. So, while it may not be much of a compliment to be told you have the intelligence of a house plant, it could, in a sense, be something of an accolade to be told you have the intuition of one!

In January 1938, Sherman made some interesting notes regarding some technicalities of the telepathic downloading process. At 11.30 on the designated nights of the appointments, wherever he was he would begin to receive strong feelings from Wilkins. He stated that unless he was somewhere he could clear his mind and complete the operation fully, he did not try to interpret those feelings, since this invited distortions by his imagination and conscious wonderings. As long as he held his impressions in his "dark room" away from the light of his conscious mind until he was ready to process them fully, he was able to retain them.[68]

The Intelligence and "Intuition" of Plants

Many people actually have anecdotal evidence of cut flowers, for instance, lasting longer when they speak nicely to them or play them music (I mentioned this earlier). The "Backster effect" demonstrates that plants are very well attuned to the energetic vibrations within their environment—including the consciousness of nearby humans.

As a polygraph expert, Cleve Backster got the idea several decades ago to delicately connect the same metallic terminals that he would normally connect to a human being for a "lie detector test" to the leaf of a plant, and graph the plant's electrochemical changes. Backster put a leaf of one plant into a cup of hot coffee (this leaf was a neighboring leaf of the electroded one) and observed no noticeable chart reaction.

Seeking to provoke a stress reaction, Backster decided to get a match and burn the plant's electroded leaf, as the ultimate plant threat. At the time, the plant was about 15 feet away and the polygraph equipment was about 5 feet away. His thought and intent was, "I'm going to burn that leaf!" The very instant that imagery entered his mind, the polygraph recording pen jumped to the top of the chart! The plant recording showed dramatic excitation. Backster decided to remove the threat and returned the matches to his secretary's desk, after which the tracing returned to the calmness displayed before the original decision to burn the electrode leaf.[69]

Further trials such as these were continued by Backster and he repeatedly noticed an interesting pattern: as his hollow threats to harm the plant were repeated, the plant apparently began to recognize this lack of real intent and ceased responding stressfully to Backster's thoughts.[70] He demonstrated this effect to his friend Ingo Swann with identical results: the plants learned the threat was empty and their stress reactions gradually diminished until they finally disappeared. Of his recognition of the plant's behavior, Swann recalls:

> "Do you mean," I asked, "that it has LEARNED that I'm not serious about really burning its leaf? So that it now knows it need not be alarmed."
> Backster smiled. "YOU said it, I didn't. Try another kind of harmful thought."
> So I thought of putting acid in the plant's pot. Bingo! But the same "learning curve" soon repeated itself. Now I already understood in my own "reality" that plants are sentient and telepathic, as all plant lovers know who talk to their plants. But that plants could LEARN to recognize between true and artificial human intent came as a thunderbolt![71]

Copper screen cages designed to block EM energies did not hamper the ability of Backster's plants to continue with this communication, showing that the energy responsible is non-EM, or torsion/scalar as we are emphasizing here.[72]

Occultism has long held that plants are quick to respond to loving care and are distinctly affected by man's feelings towards them. "They delight in and respond to admiration: they are also capable of individual attachments, as well as of anger and dislike," stated Powell in *The Astral Body,* long before Backster's pioneering research.[73] Modern scientific research is building a body of evidence in support of this occult tenet positing the rudimentary consciousness of plant life. Luther Burbank discovered that by talking to cacti, he could eventually cause them to cease growing thorns. He reassured them that they need not do so; they were safe and he would protect them. The secret to improved plant breeding was love, he believed, and he therefore talked regularly to his plants.[74]

Other tests on plants were conducted by Reverend Franklin Loehr of Princeton, who also held a degree in chemistry. Under very tight laboratory control conditions he too determined that plants responded strongly to the power of suggestion.

> His tests involved 900 unit experiments, 27,000 seeds and 80,000 measurements, with 150 people praying over one control group identical in every other respect to test groups that were

not prayed over. The "prayed-over" plants grew demonstrably faster than the others, even though all other conditions—soil, fertilizer, water, sunlight—were identical . . . [75]

Loehr's research also revealed that prayer had the ability to *negate* growth in plants, obviously indicating a power available in prayer for regressing tumors, cancers and other unwanted maladies in the human body (we will see more evidence for this in Chapter 13). Prayer is a state of focused concentration in which we can more effectively "pump" information into the nonlocal/holographic "implicate order" so that it can act to informationally re-code entities in the explicate order (space-time).

Marcel Vogel (of the Vogel Luminescence corporation) studied plant consciousness and vegetative telepathy for many years. In one experiment, he and a group of psychologists tried concentrating on sexual imagery while a plant was wired up with a polygraph. You may be unsurprised to learn now that the plant's polygraph output registered excitement. Vogel speculated that they had stirred up in the atmosphere some sort of sexual energy, such as Reich's orgone.[76]

Plants appear to develop into sensitive indicators of the emotions of other life-forms around them, particularly humans. Backster also found that his plants were particularly sensitive to the death of bacteria in the immediate environment, registering strong reactions when they were killed with boiling water, for example. Thus, Backster surmised from his research that when other life-forms were being injured, the plant would perceive its own wellbeing as being threatened also (one wonders what the intelligence of Gaia might make of humanity's perpetual stupidity and destruction of her ecology, the anthropogenic global warming scam notwithstanding). While the plants appeared to adapt to the death of non-human life after three or four repetitions, their reactions to human cell death persisted more strongly.[77]

Research using Kirlian technology has shown that the glow of plant leaves changes in the presence of ecologically harmful substances. It also lets us *see* the influence plants have on one another. Korotkov states that Kirlian images reveal how a stronger, more vital plant's aura suppresses the aura of another nearby plant. Size and color change in the electro-photonic glow of the weaker plant.[78]

The plants in Backster's lab developed a sort of territoriality whereby they did not respond to potential threats from nearby offices, but only those in their own lab space. One automated experiment of Backster's was designed to see if the termination (deaths) of brine shrimp caused reactions from the plants that were simultaneously being monitored at three separate locations within the one lab. When the brine shrimp died, the plants reacted on a statistically significant number of occasions, but it was only when humans were absent that they got their best data, as the human biological presence appears to "distract" the plants from the comparatively smaller bioenergies of the brine shrimp.[79]

The Maharishi Effect

In 1960, Maharishi Mahesh Yogi predicted that 1% of a population practicing the Transcendental Meditation (TM®) technique would produce measurable improvements in quality of life for the whole population. The collective meditations caused what the Maharishi termed "super-radiance," a physics term used to describe the coherence of laser light as well as coherent bioenergetic systems.

This phenomenon was first noticed in 1974 and reported in a paper published in 1976. Here, the finding was that when 1% of a community practiced the Transcendental Meditation program, the crime rate was reduced by 16% on average, and so the phenomenon was dubbed the Maharishi Effect. The Maharishi Effect is essentially the influence of mental and emotional coherence and positivity in the sociological and natural realms, as created specifically by the TM® and TM-Sidhi® programs.[80]

Scientists estimated on the basis of comparisons to physical systems that the coherence generated by groups engaged in the TM-Sidhi® program should be proportional to the square of the number of participants. Thus, based on the original 1% result, they predicted that a group consisting of the square root of 1% of a population would have a measurable influence on that population's quality of life. For example, a group of just 7,000 would influence 4.9 billion ($100 \times 7,000 \times 7,000$) people, the population of the world in 1960.[81]

The TM-Sidhi® program was repeatedly practiced in large groups through to the 1980s, and the first statistical analysis of the effects was published in 1987. "These showed a decrease of about 11% in violent crimes in Washington, D.C., in total crimes in Metro Manila, and in total crimes in the Union Territory of Delhi. The p values (the probabilities of the observed changes happening by chance) of these three effects were 0.01, 0.005, and 0.001, which are excellent for results in social science."[82]

Maharishi Effect research has been refined and developed to the point now where it is possible to lodge a prediction in advance with the police and mayor of a city and then create the effect—a notion that was tested in 1993 in Washington, D.C., under the careful scrutiny of "a distinguished review board." The maximum decrease in violent crimes was a startling 23.3%, though this number increased slightly when a longer baseline was used from 1988 to 1993. The statistical probability that this result could reflect chance variation in crime levels was less than two in 1 billion ($p < .000000002$).[83]

Whenever the local Super Radiance group reached the threshold number of 4,000, the rate of violent crime fell and continued to fall until the end of the experiment (this was shown not to be due to police activity or other effects). After the group disbanded, the crime rate rose once again.[84]

The Maharishi Effect is potent evidence of the existence of a unified and conscious medium or spatial "fabric" that is responsive to our conscious intent. Collectively, through coherent and laser-like intention, we appear to have the ability to create a kind of mental "super-radiance" in the world, particularly when a point of critical mass is reached. A group of like-minded people creates an inductive field that massively amplifies each individual's ability to exert influence on the world; the Maharishi Effect is a "quantum additive" effect.[85] In the following graph (Figure 11.1) from experiments done in 1990, note how the rate of violence decreases as the number of meditators increases.

Figure 11.1 Reduced violent crime in Washington, D.C.

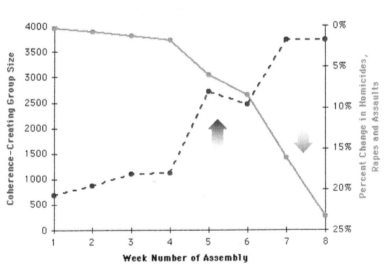

Reduced Violent Crime in Washington, DC

Note that as the size of the meditation group increases, crime rates drop.
Image credit: The Maharishi University of Management, <www.mum.edu/m_effect/ dc_md.html?

Obviously the quality of thought and state of mind we evince and radiate affects the field of consciousness we all must share. The creative power of positive thought has long been an occult tenet—"Where . . . a good and pure intelligence [works] to aid the world by diffusing through it noble and lofty thoughts, there definite service is done to man, and the lonely thinker becomes one of the lifters of the world."[86] This is merely one of many aspects of occult doctrine that has been proved by modern research methods.

Dean Radin, in fact, notes in *The Conscious Universe* something that is self-evident to the occultist when he states that the field consciousness studies conducted in parapsychology suggest the presence of something comparable to an "ecology of thought" invisibly weaving through society. He suggests—in complete congruence with established mystical wisdom—that destructive thoughts may constitute a far-reaching form of pollution of that "mental ecology" which, by infecting others at a distance, may ultimately spread like a virus right around the planet.[87]

The mental analogy to the ecology of thought that Radin is looking for comes in the form of the hyperspatial astral and mental planes of the occultist where our scalar thought-emotion forms are born. In contrast to the "mind viruses" Radin speaks of, we have the Maharishi Effect. We can extend coherence (love) or chaos (hatred, anger, etc.) into the world.

Even regular electrical brain activity generates a magnetic field detectable at small distances from the head using a magneto-encephalogram. In 1977, Itzhak Bentov suggested that due to the human body's electrical field being coupled with Earth's field, we are exchanging energy with it via a long wavelength of about 40,000 km. Bentov believed this frequency was ideal for conveying a telepathic signal, and that other people close to this frequency would have a natural tendency to lock into it and become resonant.[88] He believed that we could increase our resonance with the planet and each other through meditation, and the experiments such as those of the Transcendental Meditation Group (TMG) bear this out. What the TMG style of experiments show, however, is that others do not have to be meditating to be affected by the intent of the meditating protagonists. They can be blissfully unaware at the conscious level and the effects will still manifest.

Morphogenetic Resonance and Collective Traits

Sheldrake proposes that morphogenetic fields are not fixed forever, but evolve through time. The fields of Afghan hounds and poodles, for instance, have become different from those of their common ancestors, wolves. How are these fields inherited? Sheldrake states that they are "transmitted" from past members of the species through morphic resonance, a kind of nonlocal resonance, or, what we might think of as a correlation through time (or as a fractal unfoldment from out of the implicate order/vacuum/aether).

In Sheldrake's model, each individual member of a species draws from, as well as adds to, the species' collective memory/history. With nonlocal resonance between morphic fields, new behaviour patterns can spread faster than would otherwise be possible.[89] In time-space, all members of a species are entangled in time. New traits in space-time would therefore "self-extract" or "emerge" from the underlying holographic field.

Sheldrake's view is almost pure occultism, and his thesis of formative causation and morphic fields can be subsumed under the Perennial Philosophy (which, unlike Sheldrake's compelling model, does acknowledge ultimate causes) and enriched by the input of legitimate seers. The point is that the light-based aspects of morphic fields make them clairvoyantly observable, meaning that they are not just abstract concepts, but real entities occupying their own implicate orders.

Steiner, for example, explained that to supersensible/clairvoyant perception, the presence of a stone in the "spirit world" would be indicated by a kind of cavity: "Around this cavity, however, the [scalar] force [or 'morphic field'] is visible that gives form to the stone."[90] Apparently Steiner was tuning into what Brennan calls the etheric template level, the realm where "sound" creates matter. The "cavity" Steiner mentions is, according to Brennan, the spherical empty/negative space created by the convergence of all other planes on the same point (thus clearing an empty space), within which the perfect etheric form takes shape—a template for the lower etheric body to follow, and thus eventually the physical body. Ergo, the etheric template level of the *universal* field holds within it *all shape and form existing throughout the cosmos.*[91]

Ultimate causal origins of the universe notwithstanding, Sheldrake's theory of formative causation has, in a sense, nailed it perfectly. The universal etheric template level is the physical universe's "morphic field," and within it exists each individual morphic unit. It is a sort of "reciprocal" or inverted world which we may justifiably think of as another "time-space" dimension, where "sound" is more fundamental than light, as we suggested in Chapter 5.

The occult view regarding collective traits is that animals do indeed belong to a collective consciousness and that, as they live and experience things, these memories are stored in the creatures' collective mind-/morphic field at its own density within its own "kingdom." According to traditional occultism, when the

375

animal dies, its mind (eventually) returns to the collective group consciousness of that particular species. In this way it adds its new knowledge to the total pool of collective experience and knowledge of that species, so that future generations are more intelligent. They will know things and be able to do things that earlier incarnations of their species didn't know and couldn't do, as their physical systems download from the "quantum vacuum" the added data stored in their collective species' memory. The collective memory itself exists in this non-spatial "implicate order," and this information, while effectively present everywhere, is expressed—for the plant and animal kingdoms—primarily in the physical earth's etheric and astral fields.

The individual unit's morphic field is apparently a series of nested torsion/scalar fields (which we can think of as being our minds, or the various levels of mind), and the manifest light-based aspects are visible to developed clairvoyance. As William Brown puts it, the personal morphic field "accesses the nonphysical information field [or universal morphic field]; it can be referred to as the *higher mind*."[92] This is where thought and inspiration originate from, and ultimately where memory resides.

In this sense, we have a way of further explaining the "hundredth monkey syndrome" and similar phenomena in the animal kingdom. The process of "discarnating" (dying) is similar for humans as for animals, but because humans are individuated (individual personalities), that individual essence remains (in the causal body), while in the case of the animal, this is not so, and the individual animal's mind (lacking a causal vehicle to express through) is eventually said to be reabsorbed back into the collective mind of the species (though the essence of any given individual may be retained indefinitely within the collective morphic field).

For clarity, David Conway, author and former First Secretary at the UK Permanent Representation to the European Union in Brussels, and former Principal Director at the European Patent Office in Munich, specifies in *Secret Wisdom* that because the lower three kingdoms of occultism (mineral, plant, and animal) do not allow for an individual personality consciousness, none of us is technically entitled to claim that we were ever "a pebble, or an aspidistra, or a donkey in some previous planetary lifetime" (as we would not have been what we consider as ourselves at that point; we had no real *individuality*). Even the individual consciousness that we demonstrate now is a fairly recent acquisition.[93]

Thus, evolution takes on a grander dimension than Darwin's devotees could possibly imagine: we are leaving behind the untenable bottom-up DNA primacy model which worships blind chance as a god (as well as abandoning creationism with its "man behind the curtain"). Only the nascent Era III science of meta-genetics can explain the origin and (spontaneous) evolution of species, states Luckman: "[T]he creation and development of species are driven by consciousness interfacing with potential DNA through a process that can be called DNA activation."[94]

Adaptation—that famous Darwinian lynchpin—as Luckman rightly points out, is in fact an Era II epigenetic phenomenon. (It is driven primarily by environmental factors, not random genetic mutations!) Thus, DNA primacy is extinct. (Even Darwin himself, in his later, more mature years, began to credit the Lamarckian notion that environment drives evolution.[95])

> [M]eta-genetic theory also explains why DNA appears to contain so little information distinguishing one species from another. The life-wave in time-space, our real Brain, holds the consciousness blueprints for all species—which only manifest in DNA as, and to the extent, they are required for evolution.[96]

To return to the hundredth monkey syndrome and elaborate. The story goes that a Japanese monkey once learned to get rid of the sand in either its potatoes or wild rice by washing handfuls of it in the sea. Other members of its troop copied its behavior. Once a hundred or so of its peers had cottoned on to this technique, it suddenly started appearing in other monkey populations, far removed, even on separate islands. There is no other way to explain this than by the nonlocality of consciousness, or what Sheldrake would call morphic resonance, whereby members of the same species essentially "tune in" to the hyperspatial informational and behavioral (morphic) fields of their counterparts, regardless of distance, and "coincidentally" and spontaneously adopt/learn the same behavior.

The concept has been repeatedly demonstrated with rats, which show an accelerated rate of learning over time of knowledge of a skill (running a maze for instance)—even without *any* genetic transmissions from one generation to the next. As more and more rats learn the maze, each successive group "inexplicably" learns with less and less repetition,[97] as each rat's "morphic field" is nonlocally influenced by the morphic fields of all the rats that have previously learned the skill (again suggesting the presence of the past).

The Planaria worm continues to illustrate the point. Cleve Backster once attended a scientific presentation involving this small, centimeter-long flatworm with two knobby "eyes" at one end. While the researchers were trying to prove that knowledge acquired by one worm could be transferred to another

377

by the second worm eating the first after it had been chopped up, they had one Planaria rigged to polygraph electrodes, and the remainder of the group together and unelectroded in a separate flask. Backster asked if the researchers wanted to see how the information was *actually* being "transferred" between the worms. Thereupon, he walked over to the flask containing the whole colony of unelectroded Planaria and shook it back and forth. The single electroded Planaria isolated in the dish gave such a huge electrical reaction that the readout peaked right off the chart![98] Ipso facto, all Planaria are entangled.

Humans have, on many occasions, been seen to share similar metaphysical connections with one another, because we, like those Planaria worms, are fundamentally connected, as are all life-forms at all scales in this holofractal universe (as above, so below). One example, out of many documented and verified cases, involved a woman awakened from her slumber by what felt like a hard impact on her mouth; she learned later that it was at that moment when her husband—who was sailing out on the lake—lost control of the tiller which struck him on the mouth.[99]

In 1923 Charles Richet (1850–1935) published *On the Frequency of Monitions* in which he included over 50 pages of cases of spontaneous psi ("monitions"). Such was the specific detail and synchronicity of the cases that he concluded that if the reader could not concede that monitions existed after carefully studying the material, "then all observational and historical science must be rejected."[100] Nonlocal correlations between people have long since been established as fact by any reasonable scientific standard. It is not science that prevents acceptance of these facts, but the *outdated worldviews of certain scientists and lay people who are stuck in old models of the universe which are based on flawed assumptions.*

Early in Chapter 9 we mentioned the clairvoyantly observable "genetic cords" that link a mother with the field of the baby-to-be, as detailed by Barbara Brennan. These cords relate directly to Sheldrakian notions of morphic resonance, genetic inheritance, and the presence of the past.

Using magnifying clairvoyance, Brennan observes that there are also bioplasmic energy "cords" connecting the mother's heart chakra to her egg, and from the father's heart chakra to his sperm. Thus, when the egg and sperm merge, so do the parents' energies, and they are then both linked by these cords to the child. The parents are linked to their own parents' fields in the same way, and so on through the generations, through all bloodline connections, thus creating a "great network of light cords" which ultimately connects "all human life back to the first humans," and which "exists outside of three-dimensional space and independently of it." Therefore, it is through these "birth cords" that we carry our genetic and ancestral heritage at the auric (morphic field) level.[101]

We have already noted the Maharishi's group meditation experiments that subconsciously influence entire cities full of people in a positive way. As we have also noted, the Global Consciousness Project's research has shown that the collective psyche of a large number of people focused on a particular event can influence quantum events even in the absence of any such intent, showing that the energies of consciousness in "time-space" can couple with EM energies in space-time. RNG output is influenced regardless of intent, with a relationship shown between the intensity of emotional content and the order in the RNG data.

For all phenomena at every level of manifest existence, at all scales, everywhere in the universe, the information intrinsic to and underlying each of their operations operates holographically/nonlocally and without any attenuation (a premise required by the morphic field and formative causation concepts). It appears that "the medium by which this information . . . is simultaneously and instantaneously shared [is] a fifth primary field, referred to in the literature as the torsion field."[102]

Pet Telepathy and Precognition

Sheldrake uses his theory of morphic resonance and morphogenetic fields to explain hypercommunication such as telepathy—including that between humans and animals—and he adds that, based on the evidence, a multitude of species are telepathic and use telepathy as a normal form of communication.[103] The ability to telepathically converse with animals is referred to as anpsi, short for animal psi. Ingo Swann discovered this by accident in the 1970s with his pet chinchilla, Mercenary, who, as it turned out, could detect his thoughts.[104]

Scaling things down, even some of the most primitive familiar forms of life display clear signs of unexpected intelligence. In January 2008, a team of Japanese researchers reported that single-celled slime molds had shown the ability to memorize and anticipate repeated local environmental events. A "primitive version of brain function" was revealed in an organism completely lacking a brain.[105]

In the late 19th century, over 110 years ago, Cienkowsky observed the feeding activities of the amoeba *Colpadella pugnax* and found them so poignantly indicative of intelligence that he remarked that "one is almost inclined to see in them *consciously acting beings*!" Engelman commented similarly after studying the behaviour of the unicellular *Arcella*.[106] "The recent discovery of somatic hypermutation mechanisms reveals a process by which cells *purposefully* mutate their genes to actively engage in evolution"—a process referred to as *active/directed/beneficial mutation*[107] (emphasis added).

Scaling things up, in his fascinating 1919 study *Modern Psychical Phenomena*, Carrington detailed rigorous experiments on a group of especially talented (and highly trained) horses which were capable of carrying out complex mental arithmetic—beyond even the mental mathematical abilities of the scientific men testing them! Their intelligence and communicative abilities with humans far surpassed anything previously expected of the equine species.

The Scottish poet Hugh MacDiarmid confided to Colin Wilson that his wife always knew when he was returning from long journeys (even as far away as China) because his dog would go and sit at the end of the lane about 48 hours before he would arrive home. On one occasion, the dog did so before MacDiarmid himself knew he was returning home.[108] In fact, Sheldrake discovered in his research that some 46% of pet dogs know when their owners are coming home—even if their hours are irregular—sometimes beginning the preparation to greet them an hour before they arrive.[109]

Likewise, by charting the electrical activity of his electroded plants, Backster discovered that when he was out of his lab, running an errand, for example, his plants knew instantaneously when he had decided to return—especially if the decision was made spontaneously. Evidently, the plants become attuned to their environment and the people around them, developing active nonlocal connections with them, not dissimilar to Sheldrake's dogs.[110]

Other research of Sheldrake's focused on a male African Grey parrot who could apparently pick up the thoughts of its owner. Sheldrake and Pamela Smart also performed over 200 trial experiments on a male terrier named Jaytee and obtained statistically significant evidence that he knew when his owner (Pamela) was coming home the very instant she was randomly contacted and directed to return. Studies on another dog named Kane produced similarly significant results. In keeping with other research, Radin found that in the studies with Jaytee, higher geomagnetic flux correlated with lower anticipatory performance.[111] The benefit of modern research into pet telepathy or anpsi is that fraud, self-deception and other potential problems are practically eliminated, at least on the part of the animal participants.

Soviet research on telepathy in animals dates as far back as the 1920s and 1930s, and was devoted largely to proving that telepathy between man and animals did indeed exist. In collaboration with a well-known circus performer, Vladimir L. Durov, Bekhterev reported that Durov's trained dogs successfully solved arithmetic problems and identified or retrieved objects solely on the basis of their trainer's mental suggestion. Durov's rapport with his animals was freakish and undeniable. Interestingly, the experiments degenerated when Durov was replaced with another person acting as the controller.

It is a widely observed trend that the more familiar and "in tune" the two parties are with one another, the more telepathic they are likely to be, with the opposite usually being true also; the less familiar the parties are, the less conducive are the circumstances to telepathy. An experienced and skilled "sender" with clarity of thought and powerful visualization abilities is also essential for maximum clarity on the receiving end. While Sheldrake has effectively demonstrated statistically that spontaneous telepathy occurs between humans and animals, Bekhterev's work with Durov showed that telepathy can be used to communicate constructively with animals—it can be made operational to some extent.[112]

The legends of Padre Pio push the envelope even further for us. Pio reputedly also had the ability to direct the behavior of animals telepathically. In one account, a woman with problems getting up on time for mass was reportedly sent a bird to awaken her and a troop of dogs to escort her to the church on time. Similarly, linnets and lambs, hares and songbirds were said to obey the commands of Joseph of Copertino (1603–63), another Franciscan friar.[113]

Sleep On It

In *The Physics of Miracles*, Richard Bartlett mentions an illiterate man who would go to the library and check out books if they "looked interesting." Rather than read them conventionally, he would put them under his pillow as he slept at night and awaken in the morning to find that he would somehow know what was in the book. The greater the number of people who had previously read the book, the greater access he had to the information in it. The less people who had read it, the sketchier the details would become in scope and quality.[114]

In other words, the books possessed—like all physical items—their own thought or morphic fields which would accumulate information, and perhaps amplify this information with every subsequent read, making them easier for the man to download in his sleep. Leadbeater states that every time a manuscript is read by anyone "an addition is made to that thought aura, and if it be carefully studied the addition is naturally large and valuable."[115] I had an eccentric maths tutor once during high school who claimed to do precisely the same thing, though I never got to test him on it.

Why does this particular phenomenon—a form of psychometry—occur during sleep? Really, in the case of a developed seer, it need not. They could perform this psychometrizing action consciously with their developed astral and mental faculties. But we know that sleep opens us lesser mortals up to much "paranormal" phenomena via the subconscious levels of mind. During sleep, our locus of consciousness shifts into the astral time-space realms, and is thereby able, in principle at least, to access "quantum" information fields normally too subtle to perceive in waking consciousness, downloading the data into our own mind-fields for conscious recollection soon after.

It is worth noting briefly that Harry Oldfield, using his own technology, has filmed a meditation that involved the famous Mitchell Hedges crystal skull, where the various participants in the room were suffused with the same energy, while those present who were *not* participating were evidently not—presenting us with verification of the collective reality or morphic field concept: we can indeed tune into collective realities and energies deliberately, or choose not to participate.[116] Oldfield has also captured the collective energy fields of families, showing an energetic oneness and integration within the family unit, a collective morphic field (much as Brennan describes in *Light Emerging*).

Occult Mechanisms of Telepathy

As early as 1937 Bekhterev and other Soviet parapsychologists had concluded that no known form of EM energy was the carrier of telepathic energy.[117] Like the energetic medium that mediates precognition, the phenomenon that mediates the function of telepathy must be one that transcends the constraints of our familiar space-time, utilizing the intrinsic non-locality of our multiverse: torsion/scalar waves.

Etheric telepathy can occur through thought-forms or thought waves. In the first case, the form may be seen by a clairvoyant, and the thinker's mind read. In the latter scenario, the etheric waves generated by the thought-form radiate away and impact another's etheric brain, tending to recreate the same image. The organ responsible for both sending and receiving, Powell stated point-blank, is the pineal gland.[118] We have already noted Ramacharaka's sentiments about the involvement of the pineal (see Chapter 9).

Paramahansa Yogananda's explanation of telepathy's unseen mechanisms is also matter-of-fact: projected from between the eyebrows (third eye), the will broadcasts a thought. If feeling is focused calmly on the heart, it may act as receiver. Thoughts are transmitted through the astral medium and then through the denser earthly etheric field. As they move, they create electrical waves which transform into thought waves in the mind of the receiver.[119] Years later, it would be scientifically established in the West that the heart chakra is the most powerful EM field in the body and is indeed linked to "paranormal powers" such as precognition. This will be covered in a coming chapter.

Swami Satyananda, yogi master and guru, stated that as the brow chakra/ ajna is awakened, telepathic and psi abilities in general begin to develop.[120] The Western occult viewpoint pertaining to telepathy and its mechanisms was largely detailed in our chapter on thought-forms (Chapter 10).

The realization that every spinning "super particle" in each subtle body (that is, *all* particles) is generating torsion waves that have the potential to affect other particles in their own density range makes sense of certain intricacies within occult thought. Powell's explanation that telepathy can occur between two etheric brains, two astral bodies, or two mental bodies becomes more tractable: torsion waves emanating from, say, an astral body will affect particles in another astral body; etheric torsion waves will affect particles in the etheric density, and so forth. Etheric torsion waves or vibrations travelling from one pineal gland to another at the etheric density can potentially be transmitted to the astral and mental bodies, thus reaching consciousness.[121]

One of Kunz and Karagulla's female subjects was known to be able to perceive events at a distance, as well as having telepathic abilities. Her brow and crown chakras were of above normal size, rotational speed, luminosity, and elasticity. The pineal gland, not surprisingly, was functioning above average, since it was being stimulated by the crown chakra, which, in turn, was closely connected to the brow/third eye chakra. Synergy between these two centers seems essential for decent psi function. Her enlarged and brighter-than-normal mental body confirmed her telepathic abilities and indicated to Kunz an inflow from higher dimensions of consciousness (buddhic and beyond), which afforded her a kind of claircognizance or knowingness.[122]

The Russians have been and, for all anyone knows probably still are, decades ahead of almost everyone else in their psi research. Russian researchers have even found ways to tap into the telepathic conversations of other remote viewers. By introducing a third telepath who knew when information flowed between two other telepaths, they found that the ESP "data stream" could not only be intercepted but also skewed.[123] Just as telepathic messages can be hacked by someone they are not intended for, so too can they be sent coherently and successfully to two separate parties in different places, as the body of anecdotal testimony demonstrates.

More importantly from the physiological point of view is work done by the Russian Popov group in the 1960s. They used Karl Nikolaiev, an actor and sensitive who had trained himself to be psychic using the breathing exercises of Raja Yoga, and his friend and biophysicist Yuri Kamensky, who together had previously irrefutably proved their ability to communicate telepathically under scientific conditions.

Nikolaiev (stationed in Leningrad) would act as the receiver, and Kamensky (in Moscow, 400 miles away) the sender. Nikolaiev, wired up to a series of physiological monitors, would work himself into a "completely relaxed, but attentive" state in which his brain produced a steady alpha rhythm. He had no idea when the telepathic message was to be sent by Kamensky, and yet, just three seconds after the team in Moscow gave him the signal to send, Nikolaiev's brainwaves changed drastically as the alpha was suddenly blocked. This, evidently, was the first time in history that the moment of telepathic contact in the brain was actually captured.[124]

In later tests, EEG records showed similar dramatic changes in the brain patterns of the sender as well as the receiver. Within one to five seconds an "unusual activation" was detected. Nikolaiev's brainwaves always changed a few seconds before he realized he was receiving anything telepathically. If he was going to receive the message consciously, brain activity would switch from the front and mid-sections to the rear, afferent regions. Dr. Pavlova stated that the pattern remained present for a time after the sessions ended.[125]

When receiving an image of something such as a cigarette box, the activity in Nikolaiev's brain was localized in the occipital region, associated with sight, and when the message consisted of a series of noises being heard by the sender, activity was recorded in the temporal region, normally involved with sound.[126] The participants' brains were nonlocally synchronized.

Variations of experiments in neurological entanglement such as those we covered earlier in the chapter were performed with Kamensky and Nikolaiev, successfully. A strobe light flashing at Kamensky entrained his brain into an alpha frequency, and when the two men felt they were in contact it was found that their brainwaves were perfectly synchronized. Every time the frequency flashing at Kamensky changed, Nikolaiev's frequency altered instantly to match it, in ways he couldn't have simulated even if he tried. Flashing two different frequencies into Kamensky's and "talented" college student Alex Monin's eyes induced nausea, and guess what? Nikolaiev rapidly found himself experiencing "sea sickness." Unsurprisingly, he was not fond of those particular experiments.[127]

Later telepathy research done by V.P. Kaznacheev, A.V. Trofimov, and others in Novosibirsk from 1990–91, was based on Kozyrev's work and his ideas on the flow of time/torsion. Both sender and receiver were located in their own separate rooms (about 100 m apart), each of which featured a specially designed array of aluminum mirrors (recall Kozyrev's observation that aluminum was an excellent shielder and reflector of time). Perception of transmitted images was improved by a factor of 3–6 times using such a setup, as compared to experiments without the aluminum mirrors.

Apparently the setup served to focus torsion waves emanating from the sender, so as to be more readily apprehended by the receiver (signal strength was increased). In experiments involving groups operating over large distances, an unusual disc-like light effect appeared in the night sky above the senders' room on several occasions[128]—a case of torsion waves creating photons from out of the vacuum/aether as a result of a "quantum additive effect" produced by multiple singularly focused minds? (Recall Monroe's group's successful attempt at mentally generating visible light in the night sky.)

While telepathy seems to rely mainly on the more passive and receptive alpha state (particularly for the receiver), the more proactive forms of psi (such as PK) utilize brain states representing greater arousal, in the beta and gamma ranges. Watson believed that relaxation was essential to the telepathic process, especially since the slower respiration rate initiated a physiological reaction that ultimately led to the brain producing the kind of alpha rhythms that conduce to telepathy.[129] Sleep states, of course, induce similar internal conditions. Hence, there are many cases of psi occurring through dreams.

Emotion, Need, Novelty, and Other Factors in Psi

Watson notes in *Supernature* that the most effective telepathic messages generally are bound up in trauma and crisis—and we have seen plenty of evidence to that effect. He continues to explain that it makes sense biologically, since states of well-being and pleasure produce no sense of urgency—such information can be leisurely conveyed by the "normal" channels. However, for alarm signals to be of real use, they have to travel the fastest way possible.[130]

That "way" is superluminally/nonlocally. Much as Backster's plants could detect the death of bacteria and brine shrimp nearby, our human telepathic connections must—even if only subliminally—serve a biological imperative, helping us survive and propagate as a species by sensing and avoiding danger.

Veering momentarily away from perceptual psi and into what we might loosely refer to as "mind over matter," there are those cases of extraordinary human performance under life-or-death circumstances (with high need and urgency) that cannot be accounted for by conventional models. For instance, Angela Cavallo lifted—and held for five minutes—a 1964 Chevrolet in order to save her son trapped underneath, while neighbours arrived, reset the jack, and rescued her unconscious child.[131] If necessity is the "mother" of invention, then this mother was definitely a necessity under the circumstances. Her intense urgency apparently suspended any pre-existing beliefs she likely had about not being strong enough to lift cars—so that she could save her son by doing exactly that.

Returning to perceptual psi, in 1889 a committee of psychical researchers began a five-year project of compiling what they named a Report on the Census of Hallucinations—the first major research effort of the English SPR, featuring 410 data collectors. The committee included Henry and Eleanor Sidgwick, Alice Johnson, archskeptic Frank Podmore, and the esteemed Frederick Myers. Out of the 17,000 responses, 2,273 people reported having had "hallucinations" (psi experiences). Tellingly, most occurred in a crisis, usually a death crisis, signifying the importance of emotion, need, and above all, *meaning* in paranormal events.[132] These were some of the earliest scientific results illustrating nonlocal correlations between well-acquainted (meaningfully connected) people.

Aside from raw emotion, biological threats to loved ones (or oneself), and the like, another factor conducive to psi is simply novelty. Targ and Puthoff found that the more difficult and challenging a remote viewing task they devised for test subjects, the more likely the results were to be good. They too observed a need-serving theme in their RV research at Stanford (see Chapter 12). As a result of consistently challenging and interesting tests and protocols (with the added benefits of feedback and encouragement), they found that their subjects actually improved their psi performance over time, in contrast to Rhine and others' results with card-guessing and other repetitive and dull forms of testing, where decline effects were often observed.

Pavel Stepanek was one of the only gifted telepathists to significantly avoid the decline effect and remain potently psychic through many rounds of controlled testing by different scientists from a variety of different countries. He developed his abilities through hypnosis work with Milan Ryzl. Stepanek eventually developed a focusing effect wherein he could preferentially detect his favorite card symbols more consistently than others, despite the targets being in securely sealed envelopes.[133]

In Targ and Puthoff's RV research, it was pointed out by Dr. Arthur Hastings, a consultant, that participants seemed to focus more on certain aspects of the target than others—they developed a sort of individual perceptual signature.[134] Joe McMoneagle found in his RV that when tasked with nuclear targets his accuracy was 80–90%.[135]

Overall, the lack of emotional content in tests with Rhine's Zener cards must have made them all the more difficult to achieve above chance results. Harold Sherman expressed the view that Rhine and those who had patterned their research after Rhine's had gone about proving psi in the "hardest possible way." Others agreed, which just makes Rhine's results all the more impressive.[136]

Carl Jung wrote highly of Rhine's work, acknowledging the difficulty of verifying "synchronistic" phenomena. Since Rhine had succeeded in demonstrating the influence of mental processes on external physical processes using "unexceptional" (and often just plain boring) material, Jung therefore rated Rhine's achievement all the higher.[137] Charles Tart went further, ironically stating that card-guessing experiments are "a technique for extinguishing [psi] in the laboratory," that is, they bore the subjects into a decline effect.[138] Rhetorically, Sherman asked how he could possibly be expected to get excited over five symbols that had nothing to do with his emotional system or that of the sender (they lacked meaning/significance).[139]

In Sherman's view, the absence of a strong or even an ordinary emotional factor is the greatest handicap. Since his pioneering experiment with Wilkins, much data has accumulated indicating that there is a great deal of truth in this. The stronger the emotional charge, the greater the likelihood that psi data will penetrate from the subconscious to the conscious mind. The clairvoyant medium L. Margery Bazette found that in wartime she could literally see crews inside their planes on some occasions as they flew overhead, as well as sometimes sensing their emotional state. One night she recalled identifying a particular bomber by the "terrible feeling of hate" harbored by its crew.[140]

It is well known by occultists that emotionally charged events are more likely to impress themselves, inadvertently or otherwise, on the mind of another than are events with little emotional content. In occult terms, this interaction occurring beyond the standard space-time realm is occurring via the astral plane/octave—the home of emotion. The more strongly the astral body (or mind-field) can be made to vibrate in response to emotional content, the more likely the relevant data is to penetrate through from the subconscious to the conscious level of awareness. When sleep is involved, the conditions seem to be even more conducive to accidental telepathic contact, as it is an altered state of consciousness (theta and delta brainwave states) that opens us up to the frequencies of the astral or mental planes while simultaneously eliminating most data/noise from the physical senses.

Undoubtedly, much "paranormal phenomena" (including poltergeist phenomena, PK, and telepathy) can be linked to strong emotional content. There are indications that what we experience as presentiment or precognition may be, in some sense, the strong emotional content of a probable future event (which has been actualized somewhere in time-space) filtering back through time into our subconscious or even conscious awareness.

Hypnosis can aid our ability to peer into these future events and timelines. The young actress Irene Muza was in a hypnotic trance when she was asked if she could see what awaited her in her future. She wrote that her career would be short and her death would be "terrible," though she dared not specify how she would die. The experimenters erased what Muza had written before bringing her out of the trance so she would not see it. She therefore had no conscious knowledge of what she had written. Some months later, however, her prediction of a short career was unexpectedly fulfilled and her end was indeed terrible. Her hairdresser allowed some drops of an antiseptic lotion made of mineral essences to fall on a lighted stove, instantly enveloping Muza in flames. Her hair and clothing set alight, she was severely burned and died in hospital a few hours later.[141]

It is not surprising that Muza's mind correlated with her apparently inevitable and calamitous future and sensed her short life ending terribly—such things would have been profoundly meaningful to her subconscious mind, and it is evident that the multiverse and our minds (outgrowths of the multiverse) are *meaning-makers*. We correlate through time with things and events that are meaningful to us personally.

It is almost remarkable in this instance that Muza did *not* perceive the precise method of her death, except for one or two things: it is a notorious fact that even the best intuitives are far less successful on average when it comes to foreseeing and predicting their own futures. This may be partly due to their own emotional investments in certain outcomes clouding perception of the probabilities embedded in time-space, as well as subconsciously blocking things they may not want to see.

Events further along the spiral of time are accessible to us now, though from our perspective they appear to be merely probabilities rather than concrete facts. They are, of course, subject to the manipulations of our own will. In cases such as Muza's, however, it is difficult not to consider "fate" or "predestination" as the ultimate reason she left this world the way she did. Perhaps her soul had picked that event as an exit point for leaving this reality, and perhaps that is why she did not fully perceive the event that awaited her in advance. Perhaps she was not meant to.

The limbic system, which includes the amygdala and hippocampus, is considered today to be the emotional center in the brain, as well as the seat of our survival instinct. We might therefore suppose that life-threatening events, usually being highly emotionally charged, might ignite the temporal lobe and related structures in the brain into downloading nonlocal psi information from the vacuum/implicate order.

Dr. Melvin Morse believes humans have a sixth sensory ability located within the right temporal lobe, hippocampus, and related limbic structures. According to him, this region "interprets information obtained through communication with an interactive universe," and allows for telepathic communication with other people through their right temporal lobes. "It involves perception of other realities." According to Morse, his model allows for the storage and retrieval of memories from a location outside of the human brain—time-space and our torsion-plasma bodies. This would apply also to dream memories, OBE memories and even past life memories. He states that we perceive the operation of the right temporal lobe as "intuition."[142]

Unless there is a gigantic conspiracy involving some thirty University departments all over the world, and several hundred highly respected scientists in various fields, many of them originally hostile to the claims of psychical researchers, the only conclusion the unbiased researcher can come to must be that there does exist a small number of people who obtain knowledge existing either in other people's minds, or in the outer world, by means as yet unknown to science.
—Prof. H.J. Eysenck, Chair of the Psychology Department,
University of London

12

CLAIRVOYANCE

I regard consciousness as fundamental. I regard matter as derivative from
consciousness. We cannot get behind consciousness. Everything that we talk about,
everything that we regard as existing, postulates consciousness.
—Max Planck

Overview of Types of Clairvoyance

- Clairvoyance: meaning "clear seeing," it covers many planes of reality
  and many psi abilities, including the ability to see the human energy
  field, make accurate medical diagnoses (medical intuitive) by seeing
  into the body, see the "dead" and other discarnates, see orbs and other
  phenomena. Most such forms are strongly linked to the brow/third
  eye chakra. Mediumship is generally strongly linked with clairvoyance,
  although "channelling" in trance does not necessarily require a great
  deal of clairvoyance at all.
- Claircognizance: an "irrational" or "transrational" knowing of information
  that one could not have perceived through the ordinary five senses. For
  example, I can often sense numbers in advance with surprising accuracy,
  or anticipate answers to questions that I should not know.
- Precognition: seeing the future. This is commonly experienced in
  dreams, even by non-psychics. Presentiment is similar but a more

ambiguous (or perhaps totally non-conscious) perception, say, a gut feeling that *something*—you're not sure what—is going to happen.

- Retrocognition: seeing the past. Not as common or talked about, but usually employed by someone who has developed skill in the area (or was born with it).

- Micro-psi: perceiving tiny objects beyond the capabilities of the eyes to do so (per Leadbeater and Besant in *Occult Chemistry*). Linked to the brow chakra. Also allows for "playback" and "search forward" clairvoyance through time.

- Psychometry: seeing the past through close contact with a specific object or place by reading or decoding the energy imprint it radiates or exists within.

- Clairsentience: "clear feeling," a more tactile form of intuition that might allow the intuitive to physically sense the presence of a discarnate, for example, or the emotions of another. In this way, supernormal empathy could be considered a facet of clairsentience. This ability seems to be linked to the heart chakra.

- Remote clairvoyance (also known as travelling clairvoyance): "seeing at a distance" includes phenomena such as remote viewing, which is seeing physically distant places or events, and includes the ability to scan backwards or forwards in time at these locations. (RV can also take the form of classic out-of-body experiences/astral projection, and occultists know that the astral plane facilitates visions of the past and also the probable future.) One specialized form of clairvoyance is the ability of the trained occultist to conjure a thought-form replica of themselves at a distant place, through which they can survey the scenery while still being essentially anchored at the physical body, even being able to speak and retain conscious awareness of the fact.

- Future memory: though technically not a form of clairvoyance as we think of it, the phenomenon deserves mention, thanks to Atwater's compelling book of the same name. In essence, some scenario from the future has unfolded in the present in vivid detail; the result is that when that future event finally does come around, the experient knows exactly what they need to do and say for the best possible outcome—because they've already done it all! Think of the adventure that Moberley and Jourdain shared when they stepped haplessly back into the life and times of Marie Antoinette and witnessed and interacted with scenes and people from the past. Now reverse it and apply this concept to the future. From where I stand, the future memory phenomenon suggests the involvement or influx of buddhic energies.

I myself have fair experience with different types of clairvoyance, though my own abilities could be described as barely rudimentary. Still, I have on a couple of occasions actually seen the energy fields of several plants, spontaneously and unexpectedly. I have also, on several occasions, observed the hugely dynamic and lively energy field of the front lawn where I grew up, as well as one place I lived at in Melbourne. I only ever saw it in the evening/night time in slightly dim lighting without the sun in the sky. Bearden has written in a much more technical context that "the time channel is . . . the mental channel and the paranormal channel. The photon interaction is the destroyer or squelcher of the paranormal channel."[1] Thus, strong sunlight makes these "hyper-energies" harder to see, "drowning them out."

The field I saw always looked the same in that, while in a constant state of flux, the general appearance and transparency of it was consistent. It is hard to describe how it looked. It had a sort of shimmering transparency to it, not unlike the heat waves that radiate off bitumen on a hot day, only spikier (which indicates that I was perceiving the etheric field to some extent). The radiation I was seeing was not heat waves as it was night time, and if the grass was that hot it would have been brown and dead, not green and vital. I have also spent some (limited) time observing the energy field of—brace yourself—carpet, which, to my eyes appears to be slightly less lively, dynamic, and spikey, but definitely there. Let's face it, staring at carpet is not the most entertaining thing you can do, so the reader will probably not be subjected to any further commentary on the energy field of carpet, either now or in the future (you're welcome).

More interesting than carpet, from the ages of 21 to 23 I had begun to develop my clairvoyance by attending weekly trance mediumship development circles. I was probably the least psychic of anyone there, but I did find that over time, as I supplemented my weekly group sitting with my own irregular meditations, I began to perceive orbs, balls of light. They would appear fleetingly, not only in the periphery of my vision, but occasionally right across my primary field of vision and close to my face, clearly enough to know it was not a trick of light.

Meditation itself can yield fascinating experiences. For instance, on several occasions I have received the distinct impression that I was seeing right through my closed eyelids—a sort of etheric vision, perhaps. These trance states have also occasionally been accompanied by strange visions including a mage-like character juggling sparks of fire, and a silvery celestial fish of exquisite detail and color that swam past my face. If these were symbolic conjurings of my own subconscious, I am unaware of their meaning. With some regret, I note that after ceasing my attendance in the trance meditation circle, my nascent clairvoyance ceased to develop and actually regressed to pretty much where it was previously (almost nonexistent).

The Numbers Don't Lie

In this chapter we will look further at some anecdotal reports as well as more rigorously controlled experimental cases and data that cannot be cast aside out of prejudice. Most early research into clairvoyance used ESP cards where the subject would be asked to try and correctly identify the symbol on a card drawn by the experimenter. It was found that psi performance invariably declined with repeated testing because of boredom at the unstimulating and repetitive nature of such tests. Still, taking into account all card tests from 1882 to 1939, conducted by dozens of investigators around the world, and comprising a 4 million trial database, the results are in favor of psi at odds of *more than a billion trillion to one.*[2]

Meta-analysis was done specifically for forced-choice precognition experiments—in which the target was randomly selected after the subject's prediction—conducted between 1935 and 1987 by Honorton and Ferrari and published in 1989 in the *Journal of Parapsychology*. This included 309 studies, conducted by 62 experimenters, covering nearly 2 million individual trials and over 50,000 subjects (with the time lag between prediction and target selection varying from milliseconds to a year). It showed fairly small but extraordinarily significant positive results: the probability of obtaining them by chance was *ten million billion billion to one.*[3]

The effects experimenters had been seeing for more than 50 years were also shown to be very stable, not decreasing as study quality increased. (A popular belief of anti-psi fanatics has been that, as experimental quality increases and the margin for error is removed, the phenomenon should disappear since it can't possibly exist . . .) In fact, higher-quality studies had a slight tendency to produce stronger results. Notably, as the gap between time of feedback to the test subject and time of the actual guesses decreased, effect sizes increased, with the best results coming from the 31 studies that generated targets less than a second after the guess,[4] suggesting that time-reversed signals from the target or test results in hyperspace/time-space flowing backwards to the test subject may have a stronger signal the closer in time they occur to the actual prediction. Their close temporal proximity in time-space is equivalent to spatial proximity in space-time.

Ten years after the Honorton/Ferrari study, Steinkamp, Milton, and Morris of the University of Edinburgh published a meta-analysis of 22 forced-choice experiments (where the subject chooses from a small group of pre-selected targets) from 1935 to 1997 comparing clairvoyance with precognition and found almost no difference in the strength of the effect between the two forms of perception (at least for the somewhat psi-inhibiting forced-choice style of test). They concluded that psi works as well in the future (perception of future targets) as in real time (perception of targets in the present).[5] For consciousness operating in the nonlocal time domain, there is a certain immediacy of past, present, and future.

Premonitions and Presentiment

Until science had developed methods to systematically test for precognition, anecdotal evidence was the only thing that existed to support these members of the "paranormal family." Thus, many people found it easy to dismiss them out of hand because of the lack of hard data. Those days are long gone. Larry Dossey has said, "There are now hundreds of experiments that confirm premonitions, which have been replicated by researchers all over the world." The myth of paranormal non-replicability is another popular part of pseudo-skeptic lore, despite having been dismantled thoroughly by years of scientific research. Dossey continues: "Many people still think this stuff is mumbo-jumbo and that there's no science to back it up . . . That's wrong. We now know we can see the future, because that's what careful scientific studies show."[6]

Often it appears that premonitions or visions of the future occur in order to be of actual assistance to the seer; perhaps the seer avoids some calamity by paying attention to the details in a dream or a waking reverie. Premonitions tend to focus on disasters and mishaps, almost like a built-in psi survival mechanism. For instance, some people had a premonition or dream of the *Titanic* sinking and subsequently canceled their trip, whereupon it set sail and actually did sink. No matter which way you slice it, teleology is unavoidable if you want to study such psi phenomena honestly. Many such examples can be found in the literature. One from Louisa Rhine:

> A young mother in Washington State awakened her husband one night and related a horrible dream. She had seen the large ornamental chandelier that hung above their baby's crib crash down into the child's bed and crush the infant to death. In the

dream, as they ran to discover the terrible accident, she noticed that the hands of the clock on the baby's dresser were at 4:35.

The man laughed at his wife's story, rolled over, and went back to sleep. Although she felt foolish for doing so, the young woman slid out of bed, went into the nursery, and returned with the baby. Placing the sleeping child gently between them, the woman fell at once into a deep sleep.

A few hours later, the young couple were awakened by a loud, crashing noise. The sound had come from the nursery, and the couple found that the chandelier had fallen into the baby's crib. The clock on the baby's dresser indicated the time as 4:35.[7]

Initially the husband had dismissed the woman's premonition as silly, but he likely changed his tune when 4.35 a.m. arrived and he still had a live baby. Dreams are largely governed by the subconscious mind, with all of its attendant quirks, fears, paranoias, and desires, which works in tandem with the (slightly more) conscious level. What this example tells us is that the subconscious mind has access to what we call the future. To the subconscious mind, past, present, and future all exist as one all-encompassing "now." Recall the experimental findings in quantum physics that force us to loosen our grip on the concept of linear time and the supposed separation between past, present, and future: "The effect . . . has come before the cause. The cause (the experimenter's choice in the present moment) determines the effect (the path already taken by the photon in the past)."[8]

Of course, there are also many cases of such precognition occurring where it was, for all intents and purposes, a completely pointless premonition with no apparent purpose at all. In occult terms, some dream premonitions of the future can be attributed to the mind's encountering a reflection of the future (or the most likely future) on the astral plane.

The fact that precognition doesn't happen more often simply tells us that most people have a barrier between their conscious mind and multidimensional subconscious. In *God's Gladiators*, Stuart Wilde, the self-proclaimed urban mystic, described the collective unconscious as "a sea of pain and nastiness," so maybe our unwillingness to face ourselves and be honest about and with ourselves is part of the problem—as well as subconsciously avoiding awareness of unpleasant future events (as per Radin's analysis of online psi test scores leading up to and following 9/11). Sometimes we don't want to know (and other times I believe we are not meant to).

395

Perhaps we have dissociated from our deeper selves out of fear. Without intuitive functioning, the only thing you can use for discernment is the rational analytical mind, and many people haven't even learned how to do that very well yet. Logical deduction has its limits. It can only go as far as information from the basic five senses and/or scientific equipment allows it to.

Jung stated that we are forced to assume that in the un-or subconscious mind there is "something like an a priori knowledge, or an 'immediacy' of events," and that our usual linear conception of causality is "incapable of explaining the facts."[9] Jung had detected the nonlocality of time that the subconscious mind—operating in "time-space"—encounters. Thus, Abraham Lincoln dreamed of his own assassination ten days before it occurred. Wandering the White House searching for the source of the mysterious sobbing he was hearing in the dream, he entered the East Room:

> There I met with a sickening surprise. Before me was a catafalque, on which rested a corpse wrapped in funeral vestments. Around it were stationed soldiers who were acting as guards; and there was a throng of people, gazing mournfully upon the corpse, whose face was covered, others weeping pitifully. "Who is dead in the White House?" I demanded of one of the soldiers, "The President," was his answer; "he was killed by an assassin." Then came a loud burst of grief from the crowd, which woke me from my dream. I slept no more that night; and although it was only a dream, I have been strangely annoyed by it ever since.[10]

Sometimes clairvoyance takes the form of prevision, but in a way that is almost interactive, as if the seer has stepped into a living hologram and begun to participate in it in real time (similarly to Atwater's "future memory" concept). Bazette shared a precognitive vision she stumbled upon unintentionally when visiting a woman at her country home. As she entered the gate she psychically encountered a funeral procession coming out of the house, which passed her as she approached the front door; she seemed to walk through it. Opening the door, the lady of the house appeared healthy. When Bazette enquired after the husband, she was informed that he was resting in bed not feeling well, though it was nothing to worry about. Bazette then knew instantly that it was his death that was soon to come, and indeed, within a year he died. Evidently it was his funeral procession she witnessed that day.[11] We have noted already the prominent role played by the emotional content of a particular event in manifesting psi experiences or general paranormal phenomena.

Since the astral plane of time-space appears to be the primary dream world we inhabit during sleep, it is not surprising the frequency with which people receive veridical presentiment via dreams—if the mind moves through time here, then we could potentially peer simultaneously across a string of events that have not yet unfolded for us in space-time.

Indeed, according to Edgar Cayce, dream states open the subconscious mind up to information from past lives.[12] Anthropologist Antonia Mills suggests that nightmares and night terrors may sometimes be related to traumatic memories from a previous life. Some children seem to remember the past life in which their phobia originates.[13] While there is presently no real way to decisively test the idea that dream states open the mind to information from "past lives" in any definitive sense, there is hard scientific proof that subconscious presentiment exists and occurs with ordinary members of the population, in all probability on a daily basis; evidence for reincarnation itself is covered in detail in TGI 2. Chris Humphrey has gone so far as to state that reincarnation is the only psi phenomenon we can call scientifically established[14]—an impressive statement in favor of rebirth considering the evidence in favor of more prosaic aspects of occultism.

Dean Radin's Presentiment Proof

In a series of experiments conducted at the University of Nevada, Las Vegas, unconscious nervous system responses to future events were explored by Radin and his colleagues, using lie detectors. The unconscious responses studied took advantage of a psychological reflex known as the "orienting response," (OR) which is, put simply, an organism's response to change or novelty in its environment. It can be accompanied by physiological changes such as pupil dilation, heart rate alteration, altered brainwaves, increased blood flow to the extremities, and increased sweat gland activity.

In humans, the OR can be elicited even just viewing photographs of an emotionally evocative nature—such as those used by Radin in this presentiment study. Disturbing and/or arousing photographs, dubbed "emotional," were interspersed among "calm" photographs, and it was from this pool that a computer would randomly select a single image to show the experiment participant.

The subject is seated comfortably with electrodes measuring electrodermal activity attached to the first and second fingers of their left hand. On the third finger of the left hand is attached a device to measure heart rate and the amount of blood in the fingertip. The subject looks at the computer screen and with their free right hand uses a mouse to instruct the program that they are ready to proceed. The screen shows nothing for five seconds, then the randomly selected image for three seconds, then nothing for ten seconds, and then the cycle starts again with a different image.

The images are selected at random by the computer from a pool of 900. Five hundred and eighty-three of them are "calm" (landscapes, portraits, objects) and the remaining 317 are "emotional" (explicit sex or violence). After the subjects were shown neutral images, the skin conductivity remained largely unchanged, with decreases apparently being due to boredom. In contrast, after the emotionally evocative images were shown, there followed a large peak in skin conductivity. The subjects were emotionally aroused with increases showing in their physiological data.

However, the crux of this study is that *before* the "emotional" images were shown, *arousal levels consistently increased significantly*, as the electrodermal graph clearly revealed. Subconsciously, the subjects' minds knew that an emotionally charged image was going to be shown *before* it actually appeared on the screen; their bodies responded in anticipation.[15]

Thus Radin proved, using empirical scientific method, that a subconscious form of "bodily precognition," or, "presentiment," truly does exist and produces measurable effects within the body. (For information on successful replications, see Radin's *Entangled Minds*.) These studies suggest that the autonomic nervous system is not just responding to a future event but to the intrinsic emotional meaning of the event.

It is interesting that in the late 1980s, neuroscientist Benjamin Libet conducted research in which he found that his subjects displayed increased neural activity ("response potentials") corresponding to decisions they were yet to make, about a third of a second in advance of even becoming aware they had decided to undertake an action—perhaps something of a precursor to Radin's novel research. In fact, an earlier slow and very slight rise in the readiness potential could be seen even as early as 1.5 seconds before the action.[16]

Barbara Brennan adds another dimension (pardon the pun) to this research by pointing out that the moment we, for example, decide to make a phone call, we send a clairvoyantly observable "streamer" of "bioplasma" to the phone and *then* reach for it (the same thing happens before we travel to a new destination).

In this way we constantly subconsciously transact with the objects we think about, leaving an energetic signature behind.[17]

Returning to the main theme at present, so impressive were Radin's results that Dr. Kary Mullis, a Nobel Prize-winning chemist, volunteered to be hooked up to Radin's equipment and shown the emotionally charged images. "It's spooky," he says, "I could see about three seconds into the future." Other scientists from around the world—including Edinburgh University and Cornell in the USA—scrambled to replicate Radin's experiment and improve on it—and got similar results.[18]

Professor Dick Bierman decided to pursue this research even further, looking inside the brains of volunteers using a hospital MRI scanner while he repeated Radin's experiments. An MRI reveals which parts of the brain are active during certain tasks or with certain emotions present. As at 2007, Bierman had run these complicated and time-consuming experiments twice with more than 20 volunteers, replicating Radin's effects.

Bierman stresses that, rather than receiving specific visions of the future, people are instead receiving *feelings*. Bierman sums up that the emerging view is that "the future has implications for the past." Dr. Jessica Utts, once employed by the US military and CIA as an independent auditor of its remote viewing research, believes—based on her scholarly study of the data—that we are sampling the future "all the time" and using the knowledge to make better decisions.[19]

It is interesting to note, as McTaggart does, that if you simply reverse presentiment and call it backward influence, so that all future mental activity influences the present, you maintain the same model and results as the retrocausation studies we have mentioned.[20] All precognition might be evidence of backward-acting influence; all future decisions may always influence the past. This seems to fit the time-space/torsion picture and other theoretical propositions from various independent researchers.

Using Larson's reciprocal model, we can quite effectively account for such phenomena, and we have Kozyrev's experiments to further support the idea, since he—and others who subsequently replicated his work—were able to measure a force (the flow of time/torsion) emanating from the *future* positions of stars,[21] meaning that the "future" is in some sense really present here with us in 3D reality. Thus, time has three dimensions. Co-opting Larson's ideas, we might speculate that presentiment research has perhaps indirectly shown that the astral aspect of the psyche is responding to a stimulus that, to it, occupies the present, but which has yet to unfold linearly in our "explicate order." Its vibrational response would then be reflected at the etheric level of the brain—all in advance of the subject actually physically seeing the images with their eyes.

There is more to all of this, however. Dr. Rollin McCraty, executive vice-president and director of research for the Institute of HeartMath in Boulder, Colorado, used the original design of Radin's study while hooking up the participants to a larger array of medical equipment. In doing so, he discovered the subconscious presentiments were registered not just in the brain but in the heart (*anahata* chakra) as well. *Both* organs' EM waves would speed up or slow down just before a disturbing or tranquil picture was shown, and all four lobes of the cerebral cortex (frontal cortex, temporal, occipital, and parietal regions) appeared to be involved in this process. However, McCraty found that *the heart seemed to respond to this information moments before even the brain did.*

There were significant gender differences too. It appeared that females are more attuned to intuitive information from the heart, supporting the notion that women are indeed more intuitive on average, and more in touch with their feelings. To account for the study's results, McCraty developed a theory "based on holographic principles explaining how intuitive perception accesses a field of energy into which information about 'future' events is spectrally enfolded."[22]

Another interesting point to come up in McCraty's research was that intuitively triggered variations in skin conductance in response to emotional stimuli could not be elicited from McCraty's participants, who were experienced in meditation and emotional management techniques (they had more control over their "instinctive mind"). However, the indications for the presentiment responses were that this information appeared to be processed in the same way once in the body as regular sensory information.[23]

McCraty—already knowing that the heart's energy becomes more coherent in response to a person's entering into a "sincerely loving or caring state"—also found in other experiments that when two people touched while focusing loving thoughts on their hearts, the more coherent heart rhythms of the two *entrained the brain of the other.* Entrained signals from the "sender" detectable in the receiver's arms were even observed at a distance of 18 inches (albeit with a tenfold reduction in amplitude), offering further proof of a "field transaction." These results were achieved without the sender actively trying to do anything.[24]

On top of all this, Radin has demonstrated similar examples of nonlocal entrainment occurring in the gut (manipura/solar plexus chakra region) between remote participants—hence the term "gut instinct."[25]

Worthy of note also is Oscar Schmidt's research on precognition using RNGs in which he demonstrated that some human subjects can foretell which digits will be generated by the RNG to an extent well beyond chance—the contents of their consciousness, extending into the time-domain, was breaking through their subliminal threshold. He also showed with slightly differently wired RNGs that some people could influence the output of the machine (PK). (We have mentioned some of his research into retro-PK with Schlitz in an earlier chapter.) These data nicely supplement the positive results of card and other psi tests, leaving little room for fraud or error. Interestingly, Schmidt found that the results for PK and precognition were equally strong—it didn't matter which the machine was wired for.[26]

Thus, thanks to research such as Schmidt's and others (including Targ and Puthoff, who also successfully employed RNGs in precognition experiments[27]), we can conclude that the information from the future apparently registering subliminally in the body sometimes does translate into conscious foreknowledge.

Even just recently, while playing guitar in front of the TV, I experienced a sort of dim spontaneous pre-awareness. It suddenly occurred to me that I hadn't played Elvis' song "Love Me Tender" for quite a while (months—I rarely play it). Yet no sooner had I started to pluck away than the news reader began a segment on some kind of Elvis "festival" for an important anniversary of his (I forget what for exactly). It was the first I had heard of any such event! Apparently in my relaxed state, my a priori subconscious knowledge was able to breach my conscious awareness to a small extent: without knowing why, I spontaneously started thinking about an Elvis song, and within moments there he was (along with his many doppelgangers) all over the TV screen.

Given that science has proved the principle of precognition and presentiment to be very much real and valid, we might consider Leadbeater's lament that cases of conscious foreknowledge would be even more numerous were it not for the high density and unresponsiveness of the lower vehicles (presumably that includes the physical body) of the majority of "civilized mankind." He laid the blame primarily on the materialism of his time.[28]

Thus, prevision is entirely normal, not paranormal, and would undoubtedly happen far more regularly at a conscious level if the door between the conscious and subconscious levels of perception and experience was open in more people; if our subtle energy systems were better developed, our intuitive functioning would be heightened. Leadbeater further commented that though there may still have been some who denied the possibility of prevision, "such denial simply shows their ignorance of the evidence on the subject."[29] Consider that statement in light of the fact that it was made in 1899 and over 110 years of high-quality scientific research and personal experience have unfolded around the globe since then.

A Famous Historical Case of Prevision

We owe a celebrated historical example of amazing prevision to a Frenchman by the name of Cazotte, whose late 18th-century prediction and its fulfilment are matters of documented French history. Here is the case according to La Harpe, the French writer who was a witness to the event and whose testimony was corroborated by many others who were present at the time.

> [I]t was at the beginning of the year 1788. We were dining with one of our brethren at the Academy—a man of considerable wealth and genius. The conversation became serious; much admiration was expressed on the revolution in thought which Voltaire had effected, and it was agreed that it was his first claim to the reputation he enjoyed.
>
> We concluded that the revolution must soon be consummated; that it was indispensible that superstition and fanaticism should give way to philosophy, and we began to calculate the probability of the period when this should be, and which of the present company should live to see it. The oldest complained that they could scarcely flatter themselves with the hope; the younger rejoiced that they might entertain this very probable expectation; and they congratulated the Academy especially for having prepared this great work, and for having been the rallying point, the center, and the prime mover of the liberty of thought.
>
> One only of the guests had not taken part in all the joyousness of this conversation, and had even gently and cheerfully checked our splendid enthusiasm. This was Cazotte, an amiable and original man, but unhappily infatuated with the reveries of the illumaniti [sic, i.e. Illuminati]. He spoke, and with the most serious tone, saying: "Gentleman, be satisfied; you will all see this great and sublime revolution, which you so much desire. You know that I am a little inclined to prophesy; I repeat, you will see it."
>
> He was answered by the common rejoinder: "One need not be a conjuror to see that." He answered: "Be it so; but perhaps one must be a little more than conjuror for what remains for me to tell you. Do you know what will be the consequences of this revolution—what will be the consequence to all of you, and what will be the immediate result—the well-established

effect—the thoroughly recognized consequences to all of you who are here present?"

"Ah," said Condorcet, with his insolent and half-suppressed smile, "let us hear—a philosopher is not sorry to encounter a prophet—let us hear!" Cazotte replied: "You, Monsie[u]r de Condorcet—you will yield up your last breath on the floor of a dungeon; you will die from poison, which you will have taken in order to escape from execution—from poison which the happiness of that time will oblige you to carry about your person. You, Monsieur de Chamfort, you will open your veins with twenty-two cuts of a razor, and yet will not die till some months afterward." These personages looked at each other, and laughed again. Cazotte continued:

"You, Monsieur Vicq d'Azir, you will not open your own veins, but you will cause yourself to be bled six times in one day, during a paroxysm of the gout, in order to make more sure of your end, and you will die in the night." Cazotte went on: "You, Monsieur de Nicolai, you will die on the scaffold; you, Monsieur Bailly, on the scaffold; you, Monsieur de Malesherbes, on the scaffold."

"Ah, God be thanked," exclaimed Roucher, "and what of I?"

Cazotte replied: "You? you also will die on the scaffold."

"Yes," replied Chamfort, "but when will all this happen?" Cazotte answered: "Six years will not pass over, before all that I have said to you shall be accomplished." Here I [La Harpe] spoke, saying: "Here are some astonishing miracles, but you have not included me in your list." Cazotte answered me, saying: "But you will be there, as an equally extraordinary miracle; you will then be a Christian!" Vehement exclamations on all sides followed this startling assertion. "Ah!" said Chamfort, "I am comforted; if we shall perish only when La Harpe shall be a Christian, we are immortal."

Then observed Madame la Duchesse de Grammont: "As for that, we women, we are happy to be counted for nothing in these revolutions: when I say for nothing, it is not that we do not always mix ourselves up with them a little; but it is a received maxim that they take no notice of us, and of our sex."

"Your sex, ladies," said Cazotte, "your sex will not protect you this time; and you had far better meddle with nothing, for you will be treated entirely as men, without any difference whatever."

"But what, then, are you really telling us of[,] Monsieur Cazotte? You are preaching to us the end of the world."

"I know nothing on that subject; but what I do know is, that you Madame la Duchesse, will be conducted to the scaffold, you and many other ladies with you, in the cart of the executioner, and with your hands tied behind your backs."

"Ah! I hope that in that case, I shall at least have a carriage hung in black." "No, madame; higher ladies than yourself will go, like you, in the common car[t], with their hands tied behind them."

"Higher ladies! What! The princesses of the blood?" "Yea, and still more exalted personages!" replied Cazotte.

Here a sensible emotion pervaded the whole company, and the countenance of the host was dark and lowering—they began to feel that the joke was becoming too serious. Madame de Grammont, in order to dissipate the cloud, took no notice of the reply, and contented herself with saying in a careless tone: "You see, that he will not leave me even a confessor!"

"No, madame!" replied Cazotte, "you will not have one—neither you, nor any one besides. The last victim to whom this favor will be afforded will be—"

Here he stopped for a moment.

"Well! who then will be the happy mortal to whom this prerogative will be given?" Cazotte replied: "It is the only one which he will have then retained—and that will be the King of France!" This last startling prediction caused the company to disband in something like terror and dismay, for the mere mention of such thing was akin to treason.[30]

Swami Panchadasi offered some interesting commentary on this incredible series of predictions:

The amazing sequel to this strange story is that within the six years allotted by the prophecy, every detail thereof was verified absolutely. The facts are known to all students of the French Revolution, and may be verified by reference to any history of that terrible period . . . This celebrated instance of highly advanced future-time clairvoyance, or prevision, has never been equaled. The reason, perhaps, is that Cazotte indeed was an advanced and highly developed occultist—the account mentions this, you will notice. This class of persons very seldom prophe[s]y in this way, for reasons known to all occultists.[31]

As it turned out, amusingly enough, the atheistic de la Harpe did in fact become a Christian monk and the prophecy was found among his papers after his death in 1803. Dr. Walter Borman closely examined the matter and authenticated the reports a century later by finding plentiful evidence for it in letters and journals of the time.[32]

Remote Viewing

> When you can go out and see the universe, who wants to
> go look at a Russian submarine?
> —Former government-paid remote viewer.

Remote viewing is essentially the ability to perceive, in real time, faraway locales and events to which one does not have physical perceptual access.

Ingo Swann is a name synonymous with remote viewing, being one of the pioneers of the field, before it even became properly recognized as one. He worked with the US government and military in developing a remote viewing program and methodology, and in the process helped prove what the Russian researchers had known apparently as far back as the 1920s: that a human being can accurately perceive objects that are physically far removed from them, beyond the constraints of the human sense organs, in particular, the eyes. Trained in biology, Swann considers himself a scientist first, and does not like being referred to as a psychic.[33]

Swann worked as a consultant for the government's military RV program, rather than as an employee. This meant that the methods and techniques he developed for advancing the power and efficiency of remote viewing were his own personal property. While he has signed agreements stipulating he would not spill the beans on classified matters pertaining to the program, he could share his RV methodology with the public because he owned it.

Swann was paid to increase the accuracy of the remote viewers and sought to find a way to increase the signal to noise ratio, "noise" being input/chatter of the conscious mind ("analytical overlay") and data from the world of the five senses, and "signal" being the psi information about the selected target that was actually desired for retrieval. Of paramount importance was the need to eliminate the input of the conscious mind in terms of its usual chatter, deductions, and interpretive gestures. The subconscious mind had to surface and be allowed to speak for RV (or pretty much any other psychic endeavor) to work at or even close to the level that oversight committees wanted, which was a completely unrealistic 100% accuracy 100% of the time.

The state of awareness the remote viewers sought was a mildly trance-like one, wherein the conscious mind takes a back seat and acts as a sort of overseer but ideally does not interfere by contributing information. It is this kind of oversight provided by the conscious mind that prevents someone who has been induced into a hypnotic state from doing anything that goes against their value system or that might compromise them in a serious way.

Eventually, as the RV methods developed, viewers would lie on a bed in a small, dark room, attached to a voltmeter with electrodes. They were kept in contact with the facilitator by earphones, as the latter spoke into a microphone to guide the session. *They could see when the viewer was in the desired altered state when a head-to-toe 180° voltage polarity shift occurred.* Then the facilitator would just instruct the viewer with vague directions such as "Move to the target area" or "There is a person you need to locate." So as not to contaminate the experiment, the viewer was never given specific information about the target.[34]

This means that the subconscious levels of mind are detecting where/what the target is *automatically*—quite "paranormal" in itself, though Jung would have affirmed this as "a priori knowledge." Not only is the viewer accessing faraway destinations and defying space-time through this clairvoyance, but some part of their subconscious is psychically detecting the target area without any assistance, as if reading the intention of the facilitator or whoever had actually selected the target to be viewed. RV of this form requires a combination of a sort of subconscious "telepathy" or claircognizance to detect what the target is without assistance, and then the remote viewing faculty to actually go ahead and clairvoyantly *perceive* it.

Some Striking Early RV Results

During a second trip he made to Stanford Research Institute during the early days of RV research, Swann worked again with physicist Harold Puthoff and again yielded some striking experimental results. Some of their work was observed by two mysterious "East Coast Scientists." For one experiment, the latter were invited to put items of their own choice in boxes and tape them shut marked with their initials or some other identifier on the tape. They made sure that no one, including Puthoff (and especially Swann), knew what was in the boxes. Swann's task was to identify the contents. For two boxes Swann approximated the contents quite well, but with the other box he made a real impact.

> I indicated the box contained "something like a brown leaf"— except that it was on the underside of the lid and not at the bottom of the box. It also seemed alive, but I didn't understand how a brown leaf could be thought of as alive.[35]

In fact, the box contained a live moth that the scientists had captured outside. "It was reasonably large, was brown, and with its wings folded it resembled a brown leaf which nature had designed it to look like. When the box was opened, it was clinging to the under side of the lid." The guest scientists looked at Swann with, as he puts it, "forlorn eyes."[36]

It was results like this that gained Swann and Puthoff's research teams the funding they needed to proceed. According to Swann, the long-term involvement of the American intelligence community with remote viewing was commenced in 1973 by the CIA. The Americans were initially reluctant to get involved with it. However, when they stumbled upon the Russian research and the fact that it had a head start going back decades, coupled with the realization that it was being taken *very* seriously and progress being made in an area where America had made none, suddenly a potential "security threat" was created and the foray into the "unscientific" realm of remote viewing was necessitated.

Such striking results by Swann led to further research involving Puthoff, fellow physicist Russel Targ, the Stanford Research Institute (SRI) and the CIA. A pilot study they conducted actually included the *CIA contract monitors, participating as remote viewers themselves* in order to critique the protocols. In this role—and with no previous exposure to such concepts—three separate viewers contributed seven of the 55 viewings, "several of striking quality." As summarized in the Executive Summary of the *Final Report* of the second year of the program, the CIA personnel performed well under the controlled lab conditions; their target descriptions were of high enough quality to allow blind matching of descriptions to the targets by independent judges.[37]

It is worth reminding ourselves that these were the days when remote viewing protocol and technique were still being developed and the phenomenon was only just entering the first stages of exploration. The fact that the inexperienced visiting CIA personnel succeeded in attaining accurate information through remote viewing underscores the point we have made about intuitive faculties being built in to our species.

The SRI duo of Targ and Puthoff commented at one point in their research that they couldn't find anyone who had not succeeded in an RV task to their own satisfaction,[38] including Targ himself who once produced a stunning result during a session in which he filled in for the absent Pat Price who was to psychically detect the movements and locations of Puthoff as he travelled through Colombia in South America.[39]

To determine whether it was necessary to have a "beacon" individual at the target site, Swann suggested carrying out an experiment to remote-view Jupiter before the upcoming NASA Pioneer 10 flyby. He did so and much to his (and the rest of the researchers') chagrin he found a ring around Jupiter, and wondered if perhaps he had remote-viewed Saturn by mistake. Their colleagues in astronomy were also unimpressed, that is until the flyby revealed an unanticipated ring around Jupiter![40]

To emphasize the point: Swann remotely viewed Jupiter and perceived it had a ring around it before it was actually known to mainstream science as having a ring around it, like Saturn. The prevailing wisdom of the day declared there would be no such ring and virtually no one expected to find one, yet Swann, sitting in a room on Planet Earth, doing nothing more than relaxing and expanding his internal realm of perception, saw for himself that Jupiter had a ring.

Harold Sherman also participated simultaneously in the Jupiter probe while stationed in Arkansas to see if two viewers, separated by over 2,000 miles, would report similar data. The two independently derived data sets, matched amazingly well.[41] As well as the ring, Swann also correctly observed the hydrogen mantle, storm activity, the dominant color, magnetic and electromagnetic auroras, and more besides.* Swann also achieved a similarly impressive RV of Mercury in March of 1974, before the *Mariner 10* flyby was due to occur. Swann correctly identified Mercury's thin atmosphere, magnetic field, and the helium trail streaming out from the planet away from the sun. These (correct) observations stood in direct contradiction to the scientific thinking of the time.[42]

Subsequent to the Jupiter success, Swann proposed a series of experiments in which the target was designated by the use of geographical coordinates,

---

* For a detailed rundown of Swann's RV of Jupiter and what he saw, visit <www.biomindsuperpowers.com/Pages/1973JupiterRVProbe.html> or see Targ and Puthoff's *Mind-Reach*.

latitude and longitude in degrees, minutes, and seconds. This became known as SCANATE—scanning by coordinate. Sponsored by the CIA and beginning in 1973, Project SCANATE produced some of the best RV results until then, with Price and Swann teaming up successfully, even viewing the same targets and producing complementary results. According to author and investigator Ron McCrae, it was "the most severely monitored scientific experiment in history."[43]

The Executive Summary of the Final Report of the second year's follow-up program confirmed that under double-blind conditions (blind to the RVers as well as the experimenters) designed to simulate a real-world scenario, both Swann and Price successfully targeted a site—a "sensitive installation"—thereafter referred to as the West Virginia Site. One "drew a detailed map of the building and grounds layout," while the other "provided information about the interior including codewords," data that was subsequently verified by sponsor (CIA) sources.[44] Only the SRI personnel who had been provided with the geographical coordinates (latitude and longitude in degrees, minutes, and seconds) knew the target—Swann, Price, and the experimenters did not.

Following this, as a personal challenge, an intrigued Price scanned the other side of the world looking for a Communist Bloc equivalent: he found one located in the Urals. The report for this new site was also substantiated by CIA personnel.[45] What makes the West Virginia and Urals viewings "so remarkable," in Puthoff's words, is not that they are the best examples hand-picked from a list, but that they were the first two site-viewings performed in a simulated operational/real-world scenario. For Price, in fact, they constituted the *first two remote viewings* he had performed in the SRI research program at all. His success secured him participation in further research.[46]

Swann's inspired idea to test RV with latitude and longitude coordinates yielded striking replicability and further undeniable proof of RV's efficacy. Working with Puthoff at the SRI, this research led the way to the US military's systematic study and development of RV with Swann. The coordinates procedure was very simple. Swann would be presented with a set of randomly generated latitude and longitude coordinates that were also meaningless to the other researchers and report what he saw. His descriptions would be compared to a world atlas on the spot, and the researchers thus got immediate feedback. Some of the sites Swann was given in the form of coordinates included Madagascar, the Australian desert, Borneo, the Yukon, and the Indian Ocean.[47]

Swann said there was one particular remote viewing session that convinced him of the reality of the phenomenon. The wall map from which they were getting coordinates had a picture of Lake Victoria in Africa, so they tasked

Swann with the relevant coordinates. He reported a peninsula and described it, but was rebuffed and told that his perception was not accurate. However, Swann insisted, and suggested getting a bigger map for greater detail. One hundred and ten dollars later the group opened their new map right there in the store, and there in Lake Victoria—with the coordinates right over it—was a land peninsula sticking out with a narrow point, just as Swann described. It was something that even the experimenters testing Swann were unaware of.[48]

The SRI team went on to produce bigger and better results, with some serious new clients, namely the US government in the form of the (notorious) CIA. As usual, with coordinate RV, Swann found that his results improved over time as he fine-tuned his viewing abilities in relation to the nature of the task at hand. Practice makes perfect. Charles Leadbeater had written decades earlier in *Clairvoyance*:

> By the use of the astral body a man can move about quite freely and rapidly in any direction, and can (for example) find without difficulty any place pointed out upon a map, without either any previous knowledge of the spot or any object to establish a connection with it. [Serious occultists already knew that a "sender" at the target site was not required.] He can also . . . gain a bird's-eye view of the country which he is examining [from the air], so as to observe its extent, the contour of its coastline, or its general character . . . his power and freedom are far greater when he uses this method . . . [49]

Thus we see that the systematic study of RV in America (and Russia) "merely" proved already-known occult facts of consciousness and reality. In a way, the Psi Spies and their oversight committees had simply reinvented the (already functional) occult wheel.

Grill Flame/Stargate

In the late 1970s, the US army set up its own RV program, known only to a few dozen officials. It would become known as Project Grill Flame (the initial training program was known as Gondola Wish). In 1978, the army had been given the mission of using remote viewing as an intelligence-gathering tool. Six people, including Mel Riley and Joe McMoneagle, were recruited for Grill Flame. This unit was based in Fort Meade, Maryland, and undertook RV on a variety

410

of Soviet and Chinese installations.[50] The CIA would also be involved with the project and it would eventually be renamed Stargate in the early 1990s.

McMoneagle and other members of the Stargate group, which ranged from about eight to about 15 members, used remote viewings to search for the late Libyan leader Muammar Gaddafi, for Americans held prisoner during the Iran hostage crisis, and for plutonium in North Korea. The Grill Flame remote viewers were successful in identifying all 64 American hostages in the Iran hostage crisis, as well as an additional three held separately due to the "sensitive nature of their assignments."[51]

A specific case in 1988 that proved successful, McMoneagle said, involved the search for kidnapped US Army Brig. Gen. James L. Dozier. "According to the physicist in charge of the Stargate project, one remote viewer gave the name of the town where Dozier was being [hidden]—Padua—and another gave the name of the building. Details down to the bed where Dozier was chained were apparently accurate," writes Geoff Olsen.[52]

"The Italians ended up getting the information from a different source at the same time we did, but I'd say that's pretty important stuff," McMoneagle quipped.[53] Greg Vistica records that "[o]ne skeptical CIA officer became less dismissive after one of Stargate's psychics had predicted that an American official would be kidnapped on a certain day in 1981—and Dozier was abducted in Italy that night." The official took to calling these episodes "eight-martini nights."[54]

If programs like Grill Flame failed to yield conclusive proof of psi ability, they would have been shut down without a further thought. Instead, their funding was increased and the USA came to regard its military remote viewers very highly. On leaving Stargate in 1984, McMoneagle was "awarded a Legion of Merit for providing information on 150 targets that was unavailable from other sources."[55]

One of McMoneagle's greatest displays of remote viewing came in 1979, when he investigated a naval facility at Severodvinsk, on the White Sea near the Arctic Circle. Within a huge building in the facility, McMoneagle discovered a giant submarine, which had twenty canted tubes for ballistic missiles, a double hull and a new type of drive mechanism. During one RV session, McMoneagle saw four months into the future the Russians dynamiting a channel from the building, which was 100 yards from the water's edge. Sure enough, about four months later, satellite photos showed that the largest submarine ever observed was traveling through an artificial channel from the building to the water. Intelligence agencies had known nothing of these Russian activities. McMoneagle's spectacular abilities enabled him, as he put it, "to gain access to the insides of filing cabinets, desk drawers, rooms, buildings in restricted areas of other countries for espionage purposes."[56]

Pay the Price

In the early stages of research (mid-1970s), Puthoff was contacted by retired police officer Pat Price, who was offering his services. (While he was a police commissioner, Price had used his psi abilities—the "blue sense" as it's known to police—at times to track down suspects.[57]) Price was therefore tested by CIA liaison officer Richard Kennet, who gave him the approximate coordinates of his summer cabin in West Virginia. Price responded instead with a detailed description of a US military underground base—a secret installation. Kennet initially thought Price had failed, but when he later drove to the cabin he discovered that the base identified by Price was located nearby. Price had perfectly described the Sugar Grove—an underground National Security Agency spy satellite, communication and telephone interception center—and even identified *by name* three of the senior officers employed there.

Amusingly (but probably not so much at the time), this generated a serious probe by the DIA into Puthoff, Targ, and Price—the three were suspected of being communist spies because the Pentagon did not believe Price could have obtained such detailed information about the NSA base using RV techniques.

Price subsequently offered to remote-view the Russian counterpart to the NSA base, to mollify the perturbed CIA. To "the Company's" delight, he pinpointed the Russian underground base at Mount Narodnyna in a remote part of the northern Ural Mountains, and described its high proportion of female personnel, and radar dishes. Such was the power of Price's remote viewing that he could *read numbers and words* at a target site[58] (though these perceptions, relating more to the linear analytical left hemisphere of the brain, were not always as accurate*).

---

* To illustrate the challenge left-brain data such as words and numbers presents to psi faculties, Dr. Milan Ryzl successfully designed an experiment wherein a randomly generated 15-digit number was successfully remotely decoded. It took his star subject Pavel Stepanek 19,350 "calls" collected over a period of some *50 hours*. The results were a million billion to one against chance. Effective in the end, but not efficient (Targ & Puthoff, 42–3). In the RV research of Targ and Puthoff at SRI, a pattern emerged early and persisted: RVers detected form and patterns (right brain) far more successfully than they attributed and interpreted function (left brain).

In 1974 Price was asked by the CIA to view what he, Targ, and Puthoff would later find out was the Soviet Semipalatinsk military research facility. Armed with only longitude and latitude coordinates, he successfully viewed and described the 60-foot-diameter steel spheres and the extremely large cranes that had been constructed with the use of sophisticated welding techniques to seal these nuclear-bomb containers together. Satellite photos showed that Price's remote viewing was correct, though the steel spheres—because they were concealed in a building and not visible to the CIA satellite photos—were not confirmed for three years, after Price had died.

His sketch of a Soviet gantry crane (Figure 12.1) at the ultra-secret Palatinsk site 10,000 miles away was astonishingly accurate, even identifying the correct number of wheels on it.[59]

Figure 12.1 Gantry crane sketch by Price (left) as compared with the CIA rendering (right)

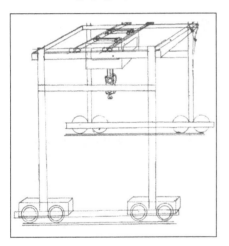

Image credit: Targ, Remote Viewing at Stanford Research Institute in the 1970s: A Memoir. *Journal of Scientific Exploration*, 10(1), 1996.

In reality, the experiment was too successful, as Targ has subsequently revealed on his website. He writes: "This trial was such a stunning success that we were forced to undergo a formal Congressional investigation to determine if there had been a breach in National Security. Of course, none was ever found, and we were supported by the government for another fifteen years."[60]

Price was perhaps too talented for his own good, as he was apparently murdered in 1975—his death suspected by some to have been caused by Russian spies who may have poisoned him, or even Russian psi-spies who may have remotely killed him. In a 1996 memoir, Targ expressed profound gratitude for being able to work so closely with the talented Price and added the view that "the remote viewing data has made a significant contribution to our knowledge of our relationship to a non-local universe in which we are interconnected and increasingly interdependent."[61]

More RV Tests and Statistics

In 2003, Jahn and Dunne reported on 25 years of RV research at PEAR. They conducted 653 formal (and 126 non-formal) trials from 1976 to 1999, involving 72 participants. Most of these trials were precognitive RV tests, meaning the target was selected *after* the percipient had recorded their impressions. The results in favor of RV were 33 million to one against chance, with the precognitive versions performing particularly strongly.

It is interesting that as the analytical techniques (not the experimental controls) became increasingly sophisticated over time and removed more and more "noise," the "signal" became somewhat compromised, suggesting that the RV "signal" might actually *require* some minimal level of "noise," as in the phenomenon of stochastic resonance, whereby an increase in noise actually aids in the detection of weak signals.[62]

Further research by British psychologist Julie Milton, from the University of Edinburgh, analyzed all free-response psi experiments conducted in an ordinary state of consciousness (including some of the early SRI studies), which encompassed 78 studies published from 1964 to 1993. She found the odds in favor of the significant effects to be *ten million to one*.[63]

In 1994 scientists at New York University published a meta-analysis of 25 ESP studies published between 1945 and 1982, contrasting the use of hypnosis with an ordinary-state condition which found that hypnotic techniques improved psi results,[64] while extroversion has been linked with slightly stronger results in free-response experiments (perhaps due to subjects' stronger self-assuredness?).[65]

In the mid-1800s a murderer had been tracked, convicted, and executed solely on evidence supplied by one of Baron Du Potet's mesmerized clairvoyant subjects—this much was admitted in open court by the Juge de Paix—and

Mesmerism was finally acknowledged as genuine (in France at least) following further investigations by the cream of French scientists.[66]

Other research conducted at SRI involving the well-known and controversial Uri Geller yielded spectacular results on occasion. In 1974, Puthoff and Targ reported on experiments conducted with Geller over 18 months. During these experiments Geller was to "blindly" reproduce 13 target drawings of which he knew absolutely nothing, over a week-long period, while physically separated from the experimenters in a shielded room. Only after Geller's isolation—in a double-walled steel room that was acoustically, visually, and electrically shielded from them—was a target picture randomly chosen and drawn.

Some of the target images included a bunch of grapes, a devil, an envelope, and the solar system. The randomly selected image was never even discussed by the experimenters after being drawn, and obviously not brought anywhere near Geller in his separate room. The rooms in which the target pictures were drawn ranged in distance from Geller from 4 to 475 m, with all but two runs situating Geller in the shielded room. In variations, the drawings were made inside the shielded room while Geller was situated in another.

Two researchers otherwise unconnected with these experiments assessed Geller's reproductions on a "blind" basis. They matched the target images to Geller's with *no errors*—odds against chance being more than one in a million per judgment. In other words, all of his psychic reproductions of the target images were clearly identifiable as such. Geller's reproduction of the bunch of grapes featured 24 closely clustered grapes, exactly matching the target image's total of 24.[67] This result alone is astonishing.

In another experiment, Geller was asked to identify the face of a die shaken in a closed steel box. One of the experimenters shook the box and put it on a table. Neither experimenter knew what side of the die was facing up, and yet Geller provided the correct answer eight out of ten times; he declined to "guess" on two of the occasions, stating his perception was not clear.[68]

In another series of 14 controlled tests, Geller successfully intuited the aluminum target can under which one of five small objects selected by Targ and Puthoff was hidden 12 times (there were 10 cans to choose from). The other two trials he passed on, preferring not to guess randomly. The odds against Geller succeeding by chance to this freakish extent are exceptionally high. Geller was not in control of these experiments at all and had no opportunity to cheat. On top of this, consulting magicians were not able to fault the experiment, some of which was also filmed.[69]

While Geller is best known for his PK abilities, for Targ and Puthoff his extraordinary clairvoyant and telepathic abilities were more reliable under test conditions, though he had little interest in the telepathy experiments, insisting (apparently quite correctly) that anyone can do it. What made him special in his view was psychokinesis.

In the last 50 years the Russians and the Americans have both poured millions into psychic research. According to Swann's estimates, the Russians were funding remote viewing and related research to the tune of $500 million a year, as far back as the late 1960s, using at least nine, and probably 14, major Soviet research centers.[70] The two countries' research yielded such undeniable results in the field of remote viewing that both nations have reportedly installed anti-psychic spying devices in their secret locations.[71]

Unfortunately we do not have space here to dismantle the CIA-related "discrediting" of the American RV program (which was actually supported by the CIA, NASA, the DIA, Army and Air Force Intelligence, and so on). Let Roger Nelson's words from his 2008 paper *Consciousness and Psi* suffice, when he states—after some 20 years of research in the field—that although RV and psi effects are subtle, "over hundreds of trials, the odds against chance explanations go to millions or hundreds of millions to one."[72]

Physiological Indicators

Experiments have been conducted in which remote viewers try to look at distant locations from shielded rooms which block out all electromagnetic radiation (presumably Faraday cages). These rooms offer no impediment, indicating again that remote viewing is not fundamentally dependent on the energies of the EM spectrum. Belief in psychic barriers or shields on the part of the remote viewers seems to be more powerful than any intrinsic disruptive facilities such devices may be supposed to possess.

A US expert in remote viewing told author and researcher Tim Rifat that when a paranormal warfare expert remote-viewed another person, there was a change in the biophysical energy field of the RVer *and* their target. Russian scientists discovered that if a remote viewer could mimic a pulsed ELF (extremely low frequency) oscillation in his or her body, and then mentally superimpose it on another person, that person would lose consciousness.[73] The mutual changes in the biophysical energy field in the viewer and viewee that were found in Russia dovetail with research conducted in the USA on the sense of being stared at. If the "watchee" grows accustomed to being observed, they can become stressed when the watcher is removed, even though they are not consciously aware that they have ceased being watched.

Ingo Swann once had the operations of his brain monitored and analyzed by Dr. Michael Persinger during a remote viewing session. Swann was tasked with identifying items in a distant room while wired to an EEG. At the moments he perceived the items, the EEG registered spikes of high-frequency activity in the high beta and gamma range, primarily occurring over the right occipital region of the cortex—to do with visual processing. MRI scans showed that the portion of the brain linked to sensory and visual input—the parieto-occipital right-hemisphere lobe—was "unusually large."[74]

In separate tests, well-documented psychic Sean Harribance showed marked increases in right parietal lobe activity during psi tasks, though alpha was the dominant state and data wasn't available as to whether or not psi was successfully demonstrated—the point was the neurophysiological correlates during the psi activity versus non-psi states. It is noteworthy that the region of the brain involved in visual search attention is found in the right parietal cortex.[75]

We have already noted that conditions of geomagnetic calm are generally more favorable to perceptual psi. Further tests by Persinger on Swann revealed that when his target images in sealed envelopes were bathed in magnetic fields his accuracy nose-dived. Different signal waveforms of varying phases were the most disruptive. In contrast, artificially generated weak horizontal magnetic fields created by a device called the Koren helmet (worn on the head) were found by Persinger to enhance the RV ability of one subject.[76]

There is a definite link between visualization/imagination and psi reception. The limbic system (which includes the pineal, amygdala, thalamus, hypothalamus, and hippocampus) mediates decision-making and emotional processing as well as providing the interface between emotional states and memories of physical stimuli. The thalamus acts as a liaison between the upper brain/neocortex and the limbic system.[77]

Since emotional content plays such a large part in psi in general, it is logical that the amygdala would be involved. We can speculate that perceptual psi such as RV is mediated by relevant layers of the auric field (mind) and their respective chakra vortices. These events trigger corresponding brain activity as the information is finally "downloaded" or "reflected" into the physical-etheric level for mental processing, ultimately arriving at conscious perception of mental images via the interpretive and constructive work of the neocortex; these are images that, because of the step-down processing involved and reflection from higher bodies to the physical level, are generally not quite as clear or precise as they could be if viewed more directly, say from the astral or mental bodies. Accuracy also depends on the individual's occult development.

The Earth's baseline Schumann resonance* lies around 7.8 Hz—where the theta zone begins. Bringing your brainwave state into alignment with the Schumann resonance should cause one's biofield to resonate with the Earth's EM frequencies, increasing your sensitivity to the psi information subtly embedded within the "noise" of the biosphere, because, as Bentov noted some 30 years ago, we are coupled to the Earth's energy field via our own body's EM field, and thus have potential access to all earthly information (as well as the rest of the cosmos' information). Being coupled to the earth's own frequencies, we are part of a "tuned resonant system."[78]

"The human condition, indeed the condition of all living things, demonstrates a coupling constant with certain frequencies and wavelengths of ELF waves," Yurth explains. "Human alpha and theta brainwaves are known to facilitate access to non-local fields of consciousness and information when synchronized with the Schumann resonances."[79]

Lian G. Sidorov has argued that

> the brain translates conscious intent into specific frequency patterns that act as modulators of the Schumann frequency in order to interact non-locally with given targets—identifying, collecting information and, if necessary, inducing specific perturbations into the target system. Intent becomes the "bandwidth," or window of EM frequency, while "focus" leads to a narrowing of this window (hence increased conversion of available energy into signal frequency).[80]

Russian researchers Fosar and Bludorf have stated that the human DNA molecule, as an organic superconductor, represents an ideal electromagnetic antenna for receiving information from the environment (and also emitting it): "On [the] one hand it is elongated and thus a blade antenna, which can take up . . . electrical pulses [very well]. On the other hand, seen from above it has [the] form of a ring and thus is a very good magnetical antenna."[81]

The Schumann resonance has also been implicated in healing, as noted. For a decade, nuclear physicist Robert Beck researched the brainwave activity of healers from all cultures and religious backgrounds (psychics, shamans, dowsers,

---

* The Schumann resonance is an ELF electromagnetic field between the surface of the Earth and the ionosphere, in the so-called Schumann cavity. These waves are said to propagate with little attenuation around the planet and have a fundamental resonance frequency in the range of 8 Hz.

Christian healers, seers, ESP readers, kahuna, Santeria, wicca practitioners, and others). He found that independent of their belief systems, they exhibited virtually identical EEG signatures during their healing moments: a 7.8 to 8 Hz brainwave activity, which lasted from one to several seconds and which was phase-and frequency-synchronized with the Schumann resonance, Earth's own electric micropulsations.[82] The healers' brainwaves were beating in time with the planet's pulse.

Supporting this was research by Dr. Andria Puharich, which identified an 8 Hz magnetic pulse emanating from the hands of healers—the more intense the signal, the greater the healing effect. Dr. John Zimmerman, founder of the Bio-Electro-Magnetics Institute of Reno, Nevada, found that once healers coupled with the Schumann frequency, the left and right brain hemispheres became balanced with each other, showing a 7.8–8 Hz alpha rhythm, just as Beck found. During hands-on healing, the brainwaves of the recipient eventually synchronize with the healer's, and the healer has thus successfully tapped the recipient into the earth's magnetic field, within which resides great healing power.[83]

The Russians found that the biophysical field of a remote viewer flared out when they were lowered into the theta state—as happens to the etheric body during sleep or deep meditation. According to Rifat, Ed Dames has confirmed that military remote viewers operate in the theta state between 4 and 7 Hz.[84] The de Broglie waves—or torsion waves, depending on the model you want to employ—of the viewer are entangled with the target's, allowing for information extraction and download to the remote viewer's brain-mind in space-time. The process of obtaining nonlocally dispersed information from the implicate/ aether/time-space is facilitated by alpha and theta states especially.

As noted, the nonphysical dimensional level closest to the physical universe is what OBEer Robert Bruce calls the *real-time zone*, a fluid-like, nonphysical environment and direct mirror-like reflection of physical space-time. This is the dimensional level the vast majority of astral projectors—and probably remote viewers—find themselves in when they first project out of body. The real-time zone's accurate reflection of the physical realm may partly be what affords the incredible accuracy often achieved in remote viewing and some astral (or etheric) expeditions. Of particular interest then, are these conclusions we can draw from the overall body of systematic scientific research into RVTGI 2:

• Some RV sessions appear to be indistinguishable from regular out-of-body experiences. It is not unreasonable to assume that these experiences are occurring on a lower astral plane, or what Robert Bruce calls the real-time zone, in which you can apparently observe the real physical world without suffering the bizarre distortions and anomalies that often manifest in the astral plane proper.

- Remote viewers can perceive each other as ghost-like translucent humanoids during group sessions—mental projections of their familiar physical form. In the movie *Matrix*, when Neo is uploaded with Morpheus into one of the Nebuchadnezzar's training programs, he finds that the plugs from his real-life body are gone and his hair and clothes have returned to the way they were in the matrix reality. Morpheus referred to the phenomenon as the "residual self image."

- Given that the Psi Spies are capable of both perceiving distant places and events (and each other) in RV states, while retaining some bodily awareness, and even being able to make sketches of these places and events while viewing them, it cannot be denied—conservatively speaking—that a form of what is ostensibly bilocation of consciousness is taking place.

Difficulties in Hyperdimensional Perception

In early RV research at the American Society for Psychical Research with Dr. Karlis Osis and Vera Feldman, Ingo Swann had, in attempting to identify a target in one session, drawn a rectangular shape which he labeled "a green thing." On it he had not with any confidence indicated the presence of letters—possibly Arabic letters. The green thing actually turned out to be a 7-UP can, not a green thing with Arabic letters.

Osis was studying Swann's drawing and the target when he turned his clipboard upside down. In his heavy Latvian accent, he then said: "Vell, Ingo, if you turn zee drawing upside down an' look at it, you haf drawn a perfect rendering of zee 7-UP can!" With the drawing turned upside down, Swann's "Arabic letters" clearly spelled out "7-UP" on the "green thing."[85] This was the experimental result that shook Swan to his core and forced him to acknowledge that the phenomenon was real. It had been noted by occultists many years before that mistakes of this sort were often to be made by the inexperienced seer, while for "a student of occultism trained by a capable Master, such a mistake would be impossible, except through great hurry or carelessness, since such a pupil has to go through a long and varied course of instruction in this art of seeing correctly."[86]

Hypothetically speaking, an additional spatial dimension would present added room for error in various psi disciplines. To illustrate the point: a 3-space being who was viewing a 2-space reality such as an Abbott-like Flatland could view objects on the surface from either *above* the 2D plane or *below* it—meaning the object would look reversed or as if it had been flipped. This would seem anomalous to Flatland researchers without the ability to extend their conscious perception into the extra (third) spatial dimension.

As a matter of fact, Leadbeater explained that even those who can extend their consciousness into the fourth/astral dimension normally perceive only three of its dimensions anyway. Until their vision develops, apparently the extra dimension is indicated only by a blurring phenomenon.[87]

It is interesting to note that our universe is primarily a left-handed universe—many interactions of particles are biased to the left, meaning they violate "parity." As Jay Alfred points out, every violation of symmetry points to a "mirror" or "shadow" universe which more scientists are coming to believe exists. Alfred states that the partners of left-handed particles in our universe are probably reflected in a super right-handed universe. "There is evidence of this in the metaphysical literature!"[88]

Robert Monroe, for instance, found that upon exiting his physical body for an OBE, everything about his "physicality" was reversed, "like a mirror image." For instance, the thick toenail normally on his left big toe was instead on the right. "There is a possibility that the Second Body is a direct reversal of the physical," he mused.[89] Alfred explains that this reversal of parity is due to the "physical-etheric" universe being righthanded—though it is also an upside-down world, revealing a double-parity reversal![90] Hence Ingo Swann's upside-down psi perception of the 7-UP can. Perhaps now we can also account for the fact that when Monroe reached for his head the top-down parity reversal meant he touched his foot instead, while the left-right reversal meant his thick toe nail had switched feet!

Alfred may be right, and therefore Constable could be correct in stating that UFOs composed of ether/orgone can't be photographed with normal photographic equipment in the usual way, because their polarity is reversed relative to our space-time energy's—they occupy a parity-reversed (or even a double-parity-reversed) parallel dimension. Based on experiments, William Tiller has confirmed that there is a "mirror" relationship between our space-time and the next, more subtle (etheric) level of reality.[91]

Most if not all of the phenomena discussed so far, and still to be discussed in the following pages, while seemingly amazing or baffling, are child's play for the advanced yogi—particularly the more extraordinary of these scientists of consciousness. RV is a siddhi well known to all yogis, arising naturally as such siddhis do following years of yogic training. The advanced yogi has full command over his innate psychic faculties.

RV Time Travel

It is interesting to observe that Price would regularly share precognitive insights informally with Targ and Puthoff and that with monotonous regularity those events would come to pass as described. It was obviously something he was predisposed to, and this was borne out in the SRI research with him, where he demonstrated the ability to perceive where the human "beacon" would be before they actually arrived.

More than precognitive RV, the Psi Spies in the USA were capable of routinely tracking *back* through time in their OB state. For instance, they could track samples of uranium isotopes from their location/s in Russia in real time, back through its production stages and finally to the mine from which the ore originated. This allowed them to distinguish between dummy warheads and real ones. Forwards or backwards in time, the remote viewers appeared to have little trouble with either—it was achieved simply by focused intent.

The Psi Spies' backtracking method may have been pioneered by McMoneagle who, according to Mel Riley, once appeared to track a wallet (the target) back in time to when it was still the hide of a cow.[92] Time travel backwards for the Psi Spies was "as easy as moving room to room," as Morehouse's monitor put it.[93] In time-space, intent that would normally produce movement through spatial dimensions instead produces movement through dimensions of time. The conscious mind constitutes the first true "time machine."

Away from the Psi Spies' arena, in an attempt to produce larger psi effects in precognitive RV, researchers developed "free-response" experiments. These allowed participants to freely describe their impressions of a future target, rather than be forced to select one target out of a few possibilities ("forced choice").

One such experiment was conducted at the PEAR Laboratory by Jahn and Dunne in 1987. A subject or "percipient" (P) wrote a description and made a sketch of a geographical location where they thought an "agent" (A) would be at some point in the near future. P also completed a predefined check sheet seeking quantitative answers to questions about the target site, such as "the degree to which water is present." Later on, A would spend 10–15 minutes at a randomly selected site (some sites were also self-selected), recording their impressions in words, sketches, and the same type of quantitative checklist used by P. A comparison between A's description and P's psi impressions was then statistically evaluated. P's impressions were cross-matched against all other possible sites in the experimental database as part of the formal assessment.

> In 334 such trials contributed by some forty people, the PEAR Lab reported odds against chance for the observed results at approximately *10 billion to one*. The time-displacement variable "x" [the time difference between P's RV session and A's actual visit to the site] in these studies ranged from –150 to +150 hours, and the observed precognitive (and retrocognitive) effect sizes were essentially the same *regardless of the value of x*. This type of experiment has been independently and successfully replicated many times.[94] (emphasis added)

Cosmic Explorers

Courtney Brown is an associate professor of political science at Emory University in Atlanta, and is the founder and director of the Farsite Institute where scientific remote viewing continues to be developed and researched. Brown was himself trained by one of America's original Psi Spies and recommends combining remote viewing with meditation to aid the process by calming the mind and shifting one's attention away from the five physical senses of the body. He points out that during RV all the senses are active, not just sight (which is exactly what occultists tell us about astral experiences).[95]

Brown and his colleagues use groups of remote viewers on single targets because there is a tendency for individuals to focus on certain aspects of a scene. By using more viewers, more information from the target site is gathered.[96]

Brown and his colleagues refer to the realm or vantage point from which RV is carried out as "subspace," which appears to include Bruce's real-time zone, the astral planes proper, and other "parallel" or intersecting realities. According to Brown, their many experiments confirm an infinite number of time lines, including past, present, and future, in the continuum that is existence. The "sub-space mind" can perceive all of these with the same ease.[97]

Brown and his fellow explorers have penetrated even further into the occult realms than perhaps the original Psi Spies managed. They not only remote-view distant places and sentient beings, but carry out what they call the "Deep Mind Probe": the viewer enters the mind of a person and obtains thoughts and personal character information. Brown states that the subspace (subconscious) mind of anyone being remote-viewed will be aware of this activity even if the person's conscious mind is not—another reason he emphasizes eliminating as much stress as possible before entering into another's mind, so as to do no harm.[98]

In his own out-of-body travels years earlier, Robert Monroe found that people would react to his interference on the subconscious or subspace level while remaining oblivious to his presence at the personality level.[99] Psi Spy Lyn Buchanan has written in *The Seventh Sense* of how merging with the minds of others during RV produced lingering physiological and psychological effects, making it a dangerous activity when tuning into the minds of the imbalanced, deranged, and depraved. The target's thought patterns can be acquired temporarily.

The scope of RV is not limited to the psyche of just one person at a time: using RV, the basic structures of social and political systems and contents can be assessed. As a social scientist by profession, Brown naturally wanted to use RV to examine politics and different societies. He therefore developed new RV protocols for that exact purpose. He dubbed these Social and Political SRV (Scientific Remote Viewing) Protocols, or SPP. Thus, he and his colleagues would use RV to examine the psychic dynamics of entire societies, regardless of their location in space *or time*.[100]

Included in these analyses are the kinds of subgroups that make up a target population, for instance the various primary ethnicities, the major religious belief systems, and so forth. Not only can individuals be targeted for mind probes, but the "flavour" of the collective consciousness of an entire nation can be gleaned as well, including dominant emotional patterns, allegiances to authority figures, and so on. Brown's methods can not only discern political workings and social structure, but they also appear to be able to distinguish the level of activity on the physical plane from intersecting "nonphysical" planes (subspace/time-space).

In his book, Brown discusses a facet of the SRV process known as "focus ratios." These are a binary division of a target population which compare the relative proportion of one form of activity to another. For example, the subspace versus physical activity ratio describes the amount of target activity in the *subspace* arena as compared to activity in the *physical* realm. One would, for instance, expect the amount of subspace activity to be higher at, say, a spiritualist meditation than at a *Playboy* photo shoot. Another primary purpose of focus ratios is even to determine the level of telepathy as communication within a population versus the usual physical language channels.[101]

Interestingly, Brown's techniques appear to allow the viewer to discern the level of interface that occurs between the physical plane and subspace/

"spiritual" planes. In phase 2 of SPP, the use of the "consciousness map" technique is employed to extract primary emotions and concepts belonging to the target population's collective consciousness, which has both subspace and non-subspace ("physical") aspects.[102]

Interestingly, Brown and his fellow subspace explorers have even been able to identify "subspace beings" (a.k.a. "spirits") waiting for an opportunity to incarnate into certain places—North Korea, for example, is evidently a desirable target site at this point in our history. Sub-space beings seem almost to compete with one another to be born into this culture—it is apparently a valued entry point into our world.[103]

So, while the official Russian and American RV research effectively proved (again) that consciousness is a nonlocal phenomenon, therefore supporting the notion of survival of death, Brown's data supports even more directly such concepts as reincarnation and the belief that we can and do indeed choose not just to be born, but *when and where.*

Experiments and Perspectives in Psychometry

By this stage we have seen ample evidence that objects can be encoded with information via "subtle" energies and that this information is then stored indefinitely. Psychometry, a term coined by Dr. J.R. Buchanan in 1842, meaning literally, "measuring the soul of things," is essentially the ability to employ the siddhis to ascertain information relating to an object or place by "reading" its information or torsion field.

Typically, the information gleaned relates to the past or simply some point in the present that is physically remote—a former owner, for instance. To illustrate the idea, say you are handed an old and worn, nondescript fragment of porcelain you have never seen before, and as you hold it in your hand, insights about its physical origin, the period it was made in, and some of the people who had come into contact with it flood your mind. Alternatively, you may provide a psychometrist with a friend's trinket and he/she may be able to relate specific personal information about that friend, including, perhaps, their physical whereabouts. That is essentially psychometry and this technique has indeed been used to successfully locate missing people. Examples of seeing into the past like this might also be referred to as retrocognition (as opposed to precognition).

The late professor J.N. Emerson (who passed away in 1978), formerly of the University of Toronto's department of anthropology, pioneered "Intuitive

Archeology" by studying the assistance of psychics in archeological fieldwork. The psychic George McMullen was a friend and a research subject of Emerson's who showed high-level abilities in psychometrizing artifacts and obtaining accurate information about their history and surrounding circumstances. Merely by walking over a site before excavation began, McMullen could identify its age, its former inhabitants, their dress, nature of their dwellings, their economy, and social behaviour. He also offered specific guidance for the excavation process. Emerson estimated McMullen's clairvoyance to be 80% accurate. According to Mishlove, Emerson obtained even better accuracy levels by using teams consisting of several psychics and then assessing their reports based on a majority-vote technique.[104]

Interesting to note in this vein is that, according to Western occultism, should the seer perceive the records of history (Akashic records) from the vantage point of the astral plane, their impressions may well be far from entirely accurate, because the astral plane is said to harbor only an imperfect reflection of these higher-dimensional records (due to emotional distortions?). The mental plane offers a full and accurate view, however, and thus does not conduce to errors in "reading." Clairvoyants examining the same record would therefore all see the same accurate Akashic "reflection."[105]

Perhaps the greatest difficulty in disseminating data gleaned from the mental plane is the sheer inadequacy of words in conveying the actual perceptions. The process requires a high degree of training and familiarity,[106] since the mental plane is said to contain not one but two extra spatial dimensions, and the filtering of perception "down" through the astral plane subjects those perceptions to an added obstacle where facts may be distorted.

Modern science confirms that all matter radiates energy, just as it "absorbs" the "fabric" of gravity/aether/time in maintaining its existence. Leadbeater had written that in his experience objects did indeed radiate energy away. I can vouch for this from my own limited observation, as can better developed intuitives the world over. Leadbeater said that it is in an object radiating energy away in all directions—though on a higher plane—that the Akashic records appear to form. He added that the phenomena of psychometry also depend on these radiations.[107]

Pre-empting visions of Talbot's holographic universe, Arthur Powell stated in the early 1920s in *The Mental Body* (which was the result of a detailed study and synthesis of Leadbeater and Besant's many works on the subject), that every particle bears forever within it the record or "impress" of every event that ever happened in its vicinity. As such, it could act as a sort of conduit between the Akashic records and anyone with the faculties to access them.[108]

This is the essence of what Leadbeater had stated in *Clairvoyance*. If every particle is itself a "knot" in space-time (as a UPA is a "knot" in the aetheric medium or koilon), as proposed by physicist Mark Hadley, and in some sense transcends all temporal boundaries, then effectively all information is present (and potentially accessible) where you stand. Up and down become meaningless concepts, and all sense of absolute spatial orientation goes out the window. (Not dissimilarly, in Dewey Larson's model, atoms are vortices in gravity, while Nassim Haramein has modelled the protons in atoms as mini black holes—in a fluid-like spatial medium.) In particular, this view of subatomic particles as knots in space-time creating "time loops" casts an interesting light on the phenomenon of psychometry (and Powell's explanation of it decades ago!).

The psychometrist might hold an historical artifact in his hand, the subatomic particles of which, acting as wormholes into time-space, vibrate detailed wave information about the object and perhaps its former (or current) owner into the body and auric field of the psychometer to consciously perceive. Some psychometers experience not mere images in their mind's eye of the past, but full-blown 3D reveries that engulf them and draw them into the scene, suggestive of the Akashic records' fundamentally holographic nature. The seer doesn't just view a past scene or event, they participate in it as it floods their senses.

To Talbot, the nonlocal nature of the ability was also holographic, since the psychometrist can access the record of a site whether they are locally present or far removed. In other words, information in the implicate order/time-space is effectively distributed nonlocally/holographically (everywhere), and can therefore be accessed from anywhere within our space-time frame.[109]

Some psychometrists might hold an object in their hand or place it against their forehead and perceive the past scenes in which the object was immersed come flooding into their mind's eye, engulfing them in historical imagery, sounds, smells. Thus, the holographic "whole in every part" motif resurfaces: the information from whole historical events and scenes are seemingly recorded in the single object itself—and every bodily sense can be engaged in the "reading."

In her work at the District Attorney's office, one of Allison DuBois' tasks as an intern was to sort crime scene photos. In so doing, she began to see flashes of what happened moments before the victim in the photo was killed. Details relating to the killer also surfaced, including names, cars, accomplices, motives, and more.[110] Her husband Joe attempts, largely in vain, to surprise her with unexpected gifts, but the minute he says "You'll never guess what I got you," her mind is set "wandering, which results in an object's popping into my head." On one occasion, Joe surprised his psychic wife with a ring, but psychics have a way of spoiling surprises intended for them. "When I touched the ring and knew exactly how much it cost, even I was amused with myself."[111] DuBois is both mediumistic and psychometric in her abilities, and has had police appear on the public record expressing their support for her assistance in investigations.[112]

It seems the hologram provides the best analogy for the way the past is stored in the Akashic records. With a "white light" hologram (whose image can be seen without the aid of a laser)—one in which multiple images of a process or event are stored in succession—a viewer moving past the holographic film will see what amounts to a virtual motion picture as one image or scene rapidly gives way to the next, thereby creating the illusion of movement; with each alteration in viewing angle, another scene emerges. Yet, the whole event—every instant in time—is always present in the hologram, even if only one image or instant is viewable at a time.[113]

KGB scientists had already begun to experiment with remotely imprinting energy fields on matter at least 25 years ago. According to Dr. Abraham Shifrin, who worked at the psi-research institute at Kazakhstan, (run by the Moscow Institute for Information Transmission), the Kazakhstan Institute had been making psychotronic generators like Robert Pavlita's in Czechoslovakia. Not only did they develop a method to store psi energy in accumulators, but by studying the ways in which various shamans, yogis, ascetics, and so forth cursed or blessed their talismans or amulets, they learned how to "negatively charge" souvenirs with depression and other mental maladies, which were then "easily" transferred to unwitting targets who acquired these tainted gifts.[114]

Provocatively, in *The Occult*, Colin Wilson argued that if the universe cannot be explained in purely mechanical terms as science had long promised, then magic's case had been built on the most solid of foundations.[115] Even then the mechanistic view of the universe had already been obliterated by quantum physics ("hard science"). Since then, evidence of the "magical" nature of reality has only continued to mount.

But what is magic? Merely the intentional direction of "subtle" energies—the torsion/scalar energies of consciousness—to create specific effects in the explicate order, or manifest scales of existence. And since we know that consciousness is immanent within the fabric of reality, the fact that consciousness can be directed to create measurable effects in the "material" world is hardly surprising. Yurth explains: "the non-local field component we refer to [as] consciousness is contemporaneous with every scale of organizational complexity. Therefore, the exercise of 'will' in the process of observation (will operates because in order to observe anything you have to be aware and thus inextricably linked with whatever is being observed) exerts an effect."[116]

Hunt agrees that thought—especially thought amplified by emotion or intent—imprints itself on matter. An old and toxic thought-form can linger in a place where it might affect people who are resonant with it and therefore susceptible. It can also be eliminated or cancelled out by strong counter-thoughts, or rendered ineffective by someone whose consciousness simply is not resonant.[117]

In *Clairvoyance and Occult Powers*, Swami Panchadasi explains that the standard "voodoo curse" is merely the result of transference of projection of thought-forms, with one catch: it only works against you if you believe you can be harmed in this way, because it sets up a resonance with the negative intent of the would-be attacker. The Hawaiians who lived in fear of the Kahunas were the only ones to be affected by their hexes or spells, while the white folk on the island did not believe, and therefore did not suffer any voodoo curses. However, the Soviet research appears to indicate that this "voodoo" may work in certain circumstances *regardless* of any belief, so long as the target is unaware of the attack and possesses some energetic susceptibility to it (yogis tell us that the instinctive or "subconscious" mind must be ready to receive and act upon a negative intention for such voodoo to be effective[118]).

A number of studies exist showing that negative intention can retard plant and fungal growth, bacterial mutation, and other processes (black magicians rejoice), just as positive intent can aid such biological processes (white magicians rejoice). Some results suggest that proximity to the target while sending positive intent may magnify the effects, while having the target removed from sight during the sending of negative intention may yield similar effects (cowards rejoice). This "negative" intent can actually be applied positively, however: some studies have shown that cancer cells can be killed through intention.[119] Medical intuitive Robyn Elizabeth Welch cured herself of a tumor by zapping it with white light from her pineal gland.[120]

Dean Radin also found through his own experimenting that voodoo dolls could be used as an instrument of positive intention: the prayers directed at them turned out to have demonstrable effects on the prayee.[121] We saw in Chapter 9 that Bernard Grad found in experiments with Hungarian healer Oscar Estebany that once the healer touched some inert object it held a phantom charge capable of producing healing effects. Likewise did Reichenbach discover with odic (etheric/orgone/pranic) energy.

Delving further into the realm that once would have been considered witchcraft, we return to the French doctor Jacques Benveniste, and a fascinating example of the human body's energy emissions in action. Benveniste was in the process of standardizing an experimental procedure in order to have it be utilized in other labs. The problem was that whenever one woman in particular was present, they didn't get any results, despite her following correct protocol. Working on a hunch, Benveniste soon discovered that she was emitting EM fields that were interfering with the communication signaling of his experiment. He then had the woman hold a tube of homeopathic granules in her hand for five minutes—long enough that she erased all molecular signalling in the sample.[122]

Thelma Moss had found in research into Kirlian photography that "brown thumbs" (people under whose care plants always seemed to get sick and die), could cause the energy corona around a leaf to disappear, while green thumbs and healers had the opposite effect.[123] (Recall from Chapter 9 the distressed man and his unintentional effect on a DNA sample held in solution in a beaker during the Rein/HeartMath experiments on heart coherence.)

Scientific research in China indicates that Qigong masters are able to affect biochemical reactions in cell cultures in vitro with their Qi (pranic/etheric/odic) field. By projecting a "peaceful Qi" they can increase the growth and respiration of the cells, while projection of a "destroying Qi" causes a reduction in the cells' biochemical reaction rates.[124]

Experiments by Rein have shown that the healer (and former OB/GYN and surgeon) Leonard Laskow could selectively increase or decrease the rate of tumor cell growth in cell cultures, and moreover, that different healing intentions produced measurably different results. The most effective was to "return the cells to their natural order,"* though underlying each intention was an underlying feeling of genuine heartfelt unconditional love which Laskow believed necessary.[125] When Laskow added visual imagery to his healing intention, the healing effect doubled.[126]

An excellent example of the way that we imprint everything we come into contact with, with our own subtle energy signature, is provided by Lawrence LeShan in *The Medium, The Mystic and The Physicist*. He had decided to conduct a double-blind study in psychometry in which the famous medium Eileen Garrett would be tested.

LeShan would package a selection of different items, including a woman's comb, an old Greek coin, and an ancient Babylonian clay tablet written in

---

* This particular mode of more generalized intent may often be preferable to, for instance, an intent to reduce a specific symptom. Case in point: Back in Russel Targ's days of SRI psi research, in one experiment a healer accidentally killed a hypertensive rat while mentally trying to lower its blood pressure. (Source: Targ, Why I Believe in ESP and Why You Should Too.)

cuneiform, among others. Each was wrapped in tissue paper, sealed in a box, put into an envelope and given a code number. These envelopes were then given to someone who did not know what was in them and who—working alone— put each envelope into a larger manila envelope with a new code number. Only this person had both code numbers, meaning that no one, including LeShan, knew which object was in which manila envelope.[127]

The last item to be packaged was the Babylonian clay tablet, but LeShan realized he was a box short. He asked the secretary in a neighboring office if she happened to have one. When she entered LeShan's room to ask what size he wanted, she noticed the clay tablet, and, picking it up, asked what it was. LeShan spoke with her for an estimated two or three minutes before she left to find him a box. (LeShan, in the meantime, found one identical to the others he was using and put the tablet in it.)

It was two weeks later before Mrs. Garrett—1,500 miles away—ultimately picked up one of the manila envelopes, read the double-coded label on it and began to speak of a woman associated with the object inside. Garrett then went on to describe the woman in such astonishing detail that, to LeShan, the description would have made it possible to single her out of a lineup of 10,000 women. Garrett spoke of the two scars on her body, her distinctive hairstyle, job history, and her special relationship with her daughter. The woman Garrett described was in fact the secretary from the office next to LeShan's.[128]

The purpose of the experiment had been for Garrett to identify the object in the box (the Babylonian tablet) but rather than do that, which you would think might have been the easier task, she rattled off a multitude of details about the woman who had chanced to have picked up the tablet for a couple of minutes while standing in LeShan's office. Cases like this illustrate why parapsychological research has in the past had trouble pinning psi down. It is often highly unpredictable when approached without the knowledge of well-practiced sensitives, yogis, or serious occultists.

We have looked at "field transactions" and recognized the reality of the human energy field, as well as the way these dynamic fields interact with other fields, exchanging information. Clairvoyant medium Judith Collins confirms what all legitimately talented empaths know to be true, that energy from one person's auric field mingles with other people's energy fields, particularly those closest to them (particularly at the astral level).

"When we share our lives with other people, whether at home or at work, a part of the company we keep is absorbed by the vital auric body. Hence, when you visit a clairvoyant for a reading you can expect to hear something about how those with whom you share your life are affecting your life force."[129]

Decades before any of the modern scientific pioneers whose work we have
touched on, Leadbeater had made his own informal tests on psychometers
and written in some depth on the subject. He once obtained a tiny sample of
stone—no bigger than a pin's head—from Stonehenge, put it in an envelope,
and handed it to a psychometer for analysis. Despite having no clue as to what
she was holding, the psychometer described Stonehenge and the surrounding
country. Not stopping there, she then seemed to see scenes from its early
history, showing that the tiny sample she held was enough to connect her with
the hyperspace records of the area.

To Leadbeater, the particles of stone held by the psychometer established a
connection with the cells of her brain, thereby putting her mind *en rapport* with
the relevant portion of the records. Thus the psychometer "remembered" the
scenes from the records, possibly in much the same way that we might recall
an ordinary memory.[130]

Following closely on the heels of the pioneering work of Dr. J.R. Buchanan,
was William Denton, a Boston geology professor in the mid-1800s. Denton had
concluded that psychometry was the only really practical way of learning about
the physical history of the Earth, and stated that Nature recorded every moment
of the planet's history. He believed that our physico-psychic radiations imprint
themselves forever on all they have touched, waiting to be accessed at some
future stage by a suitable vessel. We cannot so much as leave a room without
leaving behind an energetic "portrait" of ourselves as well—a portrait that will
be preserved and perhaps "submitted" to some future clairvoyant visitor who
may then "view" it and gain some insight into our minds.[131]

"I am sometimes inclined to think that the universe is contained in every
pebble, and it only needs the all-compelling soul to call it forth," he said.
Denton had good reason for holding this holofractal view of reality. During
the 19th century he documented some of the earliest recorded psychometry and
became involved in the study of viewing far-off locations by means of holding
some object connected to the particular place.

He found excellent psychometric subjects in both his wife, Elizabeth,
and his sister, Annie Denton Cridge, among others. Cridge was not only able
to sense some of the contents of a concealed letter when she held it to her
forehead, but sometimes she could describe the appearance of the author as
well, including their hair and eye color—despite knowing nothing whatsoever
of who the letter originated from. Mrs. Denton's impressively successful record
of "seeing" by touching objects was well documented. She was even able to
discern different periods of history from a specimen, and Denton was able to
cross-correlate virtually identical and accurate psychic impressions of the same

object from other subjects. Mrs. Denton sometimes seemed to experience in the first person the "lives" of geological specimens as they passed through the ages.[132]

Perhaps the last word on psychometry should, however, be reserved in tribute to the ground-breaking work of J.R. Buchanan, who set the stage for Denton and subsequent researchers. At the 150th anniversary celebration of Yale University, Buchanan's (re)discovery of the ability which he termed psychometry, was hailed as the dawn of a new civilization.

In front of between 1,200 and 1,500 Yale alumni, Reverend John Pierpont, poet and philanthropist, delivered a highly regarded oration in which he alluded to the many discoveries and achievements since 1777, and *referred to Buchanan's work as transcending them all.* Unlike Reichenbach, Reich, and so many other civilizer-mind pioneers, Buchanan's research was well received by his colleagues and many intellectuals of the day.[133]

> That which is looked upon by one generation as the apex of human knowledge
> is often considered an absurdity by the next, and that which is regarded as a
> superstition in one century, may form the basis of science for the following one.—
> Paracelsus (1493–1541)

13

Psychokinesis and the Belief Effect

A scientist would have to be either massively ignorant or a confirmed bigot to
deny the evidence that the human mind can make connection with space, time
and matter in ways which have nothing to do with the ordinary senses. Further, he
cannot deny that these connections are compatible with current thinking in physics,
and may in the future become accepted as a part of an extended science in which the
description "paranormal" no longer applies, and can be replaced by "normal."
—Dr. Kit Pedler, Head of the Electron Microscopy department,
University of London[1]

Micro-Scale Psychokinesis

The term *psychokinesis* (PK) has often been used interchangeably with *telekinesis*.
Telekinesis is from the Greek *tele*, at a distance, and *kinesis*, motion. The word
refers to the ability to influence an object mentally. There is a PK myth that
is popular among even some researchers into and observers of psi. That myth
states that PK effects are evinced only on atomic and subatomic scales small
enough for us to influence Heisenberg's uncertainty principle by playing on
particles' "tendencies to exist."

Certainly we have seen via Leadbeater and Besant's micro-psi experiments
that PK can be used at subquantum/aetheric levels (Chapter 6). In fact, in order

to make some of their clairvoyant observations, Besant and Leadbeater actually had to use their will to literally "press back" and "wall off" the matter of space (the aetheric medium), and create an opening in this tiny bubble so that the surrounding aetheric force could flow in for observation. They had literally to manipulate the "spatial fabric."

We also saw some of Schmidt's retro-PK effects through time in Chapter 4. The existence of this micro-PK has received further experimental support. For example, in an account published in 1967, Professor Remy Chauvin of Strasbourg University described how he and his laboratory technicians experimented with an atom of uranium, to see if they could influence the rate of disintegration with intention alone. When they again checked the rate of decay the professor and his men were astounded to discover that they had actually succeeded. The rate of atomic disintegration had been slowed. They repeated the experiment for 15 days with different personnel with identical results, *regardless of who was doing the intending.* The tests were then reportedly done all over again, by other physicists, using more modern and intricate equipment and a more complicated strontium atom. The results were the same.[2]

This sort of result has been achieved by others. In France, two schoolboys succeeded in either accelerating or slowing the emission of radioactive particles from unstable chemical elements at will, with odds against chance of a billion to one.[3]

Much more recently Dean Radin performed a subtle experiment on remote intentionality in which the task of the intenders was simply to *imagine* that they could intuitively perceive the photons in a low-intensity laser beam in a distant Michelson interferometer, or withdraw their attention and let the beam flow freely. Theoretically, if such observation were possible, it would perturb the photons' de Broglie waves and produce a lower level of illumination, whereas withdrawal of attention would allow a free flow.

The optical apparatus was located inside a light-tight, EM-shielded chamber with double steel walls, outside which the subjects sat with eyes closed. As predicted, the nine sessions using highly experienced and dedicated meditators produced significant perturbations during the "observation" sessions versus non-observation periods, while the session with the less experienced and/or less consistent meditators ("non-meditators") did not—overall the latter group could not significantly influence the laser.[4] The results show once more that consciousness can occupy and operate in the same domain as the quantum de Broglie waves, and indicates once more the importance of meditation, visualization and imagination in psi.

435

But as Watson points out in *Supernature*, simply moving your limbs is a demonstration of psychokinesis. Every voluntary and involuntary movement of the body is a feat of "mind over matter." When we look at it this way the only question then is not whether or not PK can operate at the macro level (such as on the human body), but if it can be *exteriorized*—and we have already seen that mental intention *can* generate quantifiable effects on external systems, even nonlocally through time.

Sometimes PK or its effects can be spectacular and observable (one way or another) with the naked eye, and not just a statistical phenomenon. We have already seen some examples of mental intention influencing living systems, both directly and indirectly. Sometimes, as in Grad's seedling experiments, the effects brought about by the participants' mental condition was both indirect and *unintentional*. The Global Consciousness Project has shown that the collective unconscious has an ordering effect on the quantum realm, not only unintentionally (through intensity of emotion and collective focusing of attention) but in a transtemporal "precognitive" sort of way. Schmidt's experiments, in contrast, operated retroactively.

There is nothing abnormal, mysterious, or spooky about psychokinesis. We are connected to and part of everything that exists, all part of the same system. Hence, in quantum physics we see nonlocality occurring over arbitrarily large distances. From the perspectives of higher dimensions, the fact that "all is One" is a banal truism (I can hear occultists dozing off as I type this). For what it is worth, we might note that Leadbeater stated in *The Inner Life* that PK may utilize an extra spatial dimension, or it may be effected without such. The two approaches need not be mutually exclusive.

Since the matter in the physical universe possesses very low levels of consciousness, it tends to not be overly responsive to the human will. This becomes decreasingly the case in higher dimensions as the plasmoidal matter/energy becomes less dense, more conscious, and more energetic, and increases in frequency and information-carrying capacity. It becomes highly sensitive to the contents of one's mind, almost instantaneously being shaped in response to, say, an astral being's thought stream.

PK and Random Number Generators (RNGs)

Also known as a Random Event Generator (REG), an RNG is an electronic circuit that creates sequences of "heads" and "tails" by repeatedly flipping an electronic "coin" and recording the results. A participant in such an experiment is asked to mentally influence the RNG's output so that in a sequence of predefined length, it produces, say, more "heads" than "tails." In reality, most RNGs produce sequences of bits (the numbers 1 and 0); so the subject's task usually involves intending for an RNG to produce more 1s or 0s, depending on the instructions. Statistically, if truly randomized, the string of bits generated over an extended period should produce a split of almost exactly 50% 1s and 50% 0s. If a collection of all similar RNG studies were to produce an average effect that is greater than 50% to statistically significant levels with odds greater than chance, then it would constitute evidence of PK.

Seven years of PEAR RNG results from 1989 to 1996 showed that the mind–matter interactions were a widespread ability distributed throughout the population (which is not surprising given the results of the GCP). Some experiments in the PEAR database involved cooperating pairs using the same mental intention on the same RNG. Interestingly, on average the effects were larger for pairs, and moreover, when the pair was a "bonded" couple, such as spouses or close family members, the effect size was *more than four times that of individuals*.[5] It seems that resonance between the subjects' mind-fields amplifies their "signal" strength through a "quantum additive effect." Also noteworthy is the fact that the results between local and remote studies (where the RNG was located anywhere from an adjacent room away to thousands of miles from the subject) were the same, with no decline in effects showing as a function of distance. (Dunne and Jahn suggest that a "more radical proposition" than already widely known physical forces being responsible for these effects "seems unavoidable.") A smaller subset of the PEAR studies was also conducted with time delays, where the participant made their effort to affect the outcome *before* the RNG data was generated. The different temporal sequence did not negate the results,[6] suggesting again the involvement of a hyperspatial consciousness or torsion energy operating in time-space/aether, or, if you prefer to phrase it this way, nonlocal correlations arising from the underlying holographic implicate order. A review of 12 years' worth of mind–matter experiments from PEAR yielded an estimate of approximately one in every 10,000 bits being influenced away from chance behavior, giving a cumulative effect of odds of 35 trillion to one for the whole database.[7]

All of this of course gives weight to the traditional assertion of occultists that the siddhis are, at the very least, dormant within all people, and that these abilities can be amplified by training (the techniques of which are beyond the scope of this book, although some form of meditation is of course one important facet of virtually any occultist's training regime). Jahn and his colleague Brenda Dunne decisively demonstrated over the course of more than 2.5 million trials that human intention can influence the RNGs in the desired direction. Moreover, even animals can influence electronic devices in such ways, as Dr. Peoc'h's experiments with baby chicks showed: The chicks, caged at one end of the room, were able to influence the robotic "mother hen" (a mobile RNG) to come closer to them 2.5 times more often than it should have according to chance. In over 80 similar studies in which a lighted candle was placed on a moveable RNG, 15 baby chicks kept in the dark managed to influence the robot to spend far more time than normal in the vicinity of their cages, demonstrating vividly that it is not just the intention of humans that can influence the external environment.[8]

In his own experiments on intention, William Tiller established that ordinary volunteers were capable of influencing the rate of electron discharge from a specially constructed gas discharge device. In the majority of roughly a thousand experiments, Tiller found that during the five-minute period of intended influence the number of recorded electron pulses could be increased by up to 50,000 from the normal rate by the subject holding their hands about 6 inches from the device with intent to increase the output. A mind-electron effect was maintained over "appreciable distances" with increases in the range of 10–20,000 with hands not near the device. If a subject's attention was directed away from the task no increase was observed.[9]

On a larger biological scale, Nigel Richmond found through 3,000 trials that he could mentally influence the tiny protozoan *Paramecium caudatum* to swim in certain directions with odds against chance of 10 million to one. The *Paramecium* made an ideal subject due to its innately random trial-and-error movements in water, making it something of a biological REG.[10]

Torsion Waves and PK

Torsion/scalar waves are the most viable scientifically proposed candidate as the mechanism behind PK. David Wilcock explains in *The Divine Cosmos*:

> By rotating either magnetic or non-magnetic materials in certain specific patterns and speeds, torsion fields can be generated. In Russia, this method has been used by A.I. Veinik, K.N. Perebeinos, V.M. Yuritovsky, V.V. Bobyr and many others . . . [W]e should note here that the spin polarization of an atom is not necessarily fixed in either a right-handed or left-handed direction. The Institute of Material Research in Kiev, Ukraine

performed a series of experiments where an object was exposed to torsion radiation . . . They found that if the torsion radiation was strong enough, then the spin state of the atoms themselves could be changed . . . Even more interestingly, the Institute of Material Research also determined that people with strong psychic abilities were also capable of creating identical changes in the spin polarization of various substances by the sheer focus of their consciousness. No other known technologies could create such changes in a physical object. This again suggests that consciousness and torsion-waves are actually one and the same . . . [11]

Since we alternate between referring to de Broglie/quantum waves and torsion waves, we may as well acknowledge that, at present, mainstream physics cannot fully account for all available data from the field of torsion/scalar research, let alone properly assimilate it into quantum physics and reconcile it with the quantum wave concept. I defer to David Yurth, perhaps the world's foremost expert on this problem:

Reconciliation between quantum effects and scalar wave fields is not possible in the current context because while the phenomenon of scalar waves is both measurable and quantifiable, quantum field effects are improperly and incorrectly described by the formulations in current use by the scientific community.

The simple fact of the matter is that complementarity holds the answer to the conundrum—at the finest scales both scalar (non-local, non-linear) and quantum (local-linear) field effects are contemporaneous [occurring at the same time]. *They are in point of fact indistinguishable from one another in any meaningful sense, at any scale.* And that is why the problem exists.[12] (emphasis added)

Soviet PK Research

In the 1975 DIA Report on Soviet and Czech parapsychology, it was noted that Dr. Viktor G. Adamenko of the Moscow Institute of Radiophysics, Dr. Viktor Inyushin of the Kazakh University, and Dr. Sergeyev were the leading Soviet theoreticians studying PK at the time. Both Sergeyev and Inyushin had developed theories based on the bioplasma, or human auric field, to account for PK. They felt that movement in PK resulted from the interaction of the object's electrostatic charge and EM field with the human operator's field, the energy of which appeared to be under conscious direction of the subject, who could make an object start or stop motion, change direction or rotate.[13]

Dr. Genady Sergeyev of the A.A. Uktomskii Military Institute in Leningrad was a prominent mathematician for the Soviet military and worked closely with an electrophysiologist from the University of Leningrad, Dr. L. Pavlova. Sergeyev had apparently devised important mathematical and statistical methods for analyzing the EEG which allowed parapsychologists to follow and depict the actions of telepathy in the brain.[14]

Sergeyev had conducted several years of intensive lab research on Nina Kulagina, the outstanding PK psychic in Leningrad. The *Encyclopedia of Occultism and Parapsychology* records that Kulagina (1926–90) had been tested by several accomplished and respected Czech and Russian scientists, including Sergeyev and Vasiliev.

> Tested by Vasiliev in the 1960s, Kulagina caused a compass needle to spin by holding her hand a few inches above it and also moved matchboxes at a distance. She was filmed demonstrating her ability to move small objects such as a pen or cigarettes without contact. In 1968 this film was presented by Sergeiev before an international meeting of parapsychologists in Moscow. American parapsychologists who tested her, including Montague Ullman and J.G. Pratt, considered her a most successful subject with respect to producing PK regularly on demand.[15]

Sergeyev found increased biological luminescence radiating from Kulagina's eyes when she moved objects by PK. Unusual occurrences were also reported in the USA regarding the eyes during psychic photography. Sergeyev postulated that the "bioplasma" of the human body must interact with the environment to produce PK. He emphasized that when target objects were placed in a vacuum, Kulagina was unable to move them. This would seem to lend some credence to the notion that PK, at least in Kulagina's case, was being effected at least partly through electromagnetic mechanisms operating at the target site.

Kulagina was versatile in her PK experiments, managing to move bowls, clock pendulums, bread, matches, and more. She once stopped the beating of a frog's heart in solution and also reactivated it, recalling for us the experiments of

Jacques Benveniste, where the heart of a guinea pig had its blood vessels dilated and also constricted by the wave signatures of histamine and antihistamine, as projected by specialized electronic equipment.[16] Evidently, human consciousness can cause similar effects with its own focused energetic emanations, although Kulagina's reanimation of the frog's heart after it stopped wins this round, so to speak, in the battle of mind versus machine. Religions have been started over lesser "miracles."

With the frog heart located in a jar 2.5 feet from her, an electrocardiogram showed that its rate of contraction increased or decreased at her command. Five minutes after the experiment began, Kulagina stopped its beat entirely, when typically the heart is expected to continue beating in the solution for *several hours*.[17] When a second preparation was placed in the jar, its beat was stopped in 23 minutes.

In other experiments, Kulagina imprinted images on unexposed film sealed in black envelopes. During these experiments Sergeyev measured the energy around the psychic's body and found it to be half that of a non-psychic individual. This led Sergeyev to believe that she absorbed or drew energy from around her and then discharged it on the target object.[18]

Sergeyev reported in the British newspaper *Sunday People* (March 14, 1976) that Kulagina somehow drew energy from around her. "On several occasions the force rushing into her body left burn-marks up to 4 inches long on her arms and hands . . . I was with her once when her clothing caught fire from this energy-flow—it literally flamed."[19]

Not dissimilarly, shamans have also been known to emit flames from their bodies—even their mouths—during some rituals. Two members of the Finnish SPR actually developed burn marks after being touched by Kulagina, marks that remained for several hours.[20]

This would appear to give some basic level of credence to the many reported cases of spontaneous combustion that have been recorded over time. This and Kulagina's fiery effects can perhaps be accounted for by activity in the "magnetic plasma"/subtle bodies: when different regions of the magma body are moving relative to each other and pulsating at different rates, powerful electrical effects can be generated—too intense for the physical body to handle.[21] Manipulation of the subtle bodies also accounts for the ability of monks and mystics to generate extraordinary heat in their bodies at will—even in subzero outdoor conditions that would send "normal" people into a hypothermic state and eventual death. Likewise for the ability to cool themselves at will.

In contrast to spontaneous combustion, humans have demonstrated throughout history anomalous instances of imperviousness to heat. In the anecdotal literature, there are many accounts of numerous individuals (and entire groups of people) who have demonstrated both planned and spontaneous cases of imperviousness to heat, ranging from being able to run across lava hot enough to burn shoes right off their feet, to fire immunity of both flesh and clothing, to the young Gabrielle Moler, whose exploits in the 1700s were even more amazing.

A Convulsionaire for several years from the age of 12, Moler could resist physical damage of *any kind*. In addition to being impervious to the powerful thrusts of pointed rods and swords, heavy mallets, and fierce blows delivered by a sharp-edged shovel, she could stick her head into a fire and hold it there without consequence, never singeing so much as a hair.[22] Spectators even joined in the attack to verify her imperviousness to physical harm, and no less than 21 individuals, some being people of distinction, signed statements testifying to the phenomenon's reality.[23]

The requests of the Convulsionaires for the vicious yet futile attacks were actually to seek *relief* from their religiously inspired convulsions and ecstacies of faith which occurred at the burial site of the Diacre Paris in the small churchyard of St. Medard in Paris. Marie Sonnett was another who demonstrated fire immunity during her convulsions, being closely watched and timed by serious observers who signed sworn statements attesting to what they had seen.[24]

Joseph Pearce details in *The Crack in the Cosmic Egg* how he demonstrated to his dorm mates at the time that lit cigarettes could be pressed against his skin without harm. A couple of physics majors in the group were inspired to measure the heat generated by the diminutive "fire sticks" and found them to be 1380° F (749° C). Hot enough that it "should" have burned his eyelids as he held it against them. Hot enough that it "should" have scarred his face. Having accepted death as part of the moment, Pearce explains that he therefore felt he had nothing to lose.[25] It is interesting to note that of those who participate in organized fire walking, the people who expect the coals to burn them get burned, while those who do not, don't.[26]

Powell explains in *The Etheric Double* that through an act of will or imagination, a layer of etheric matter can be gathered around the body— or particular limbs—which will shield heat. Our torsion-plasma bodies are certainly versatile. The *production of fire* (a plasma itself) is supposedly within the resources of the astral plane, as well as the ability to counteract its effect.[27] Colin Wilson commented in *The Occult* that, rather than being the "science" of the past, magic is the science of the future.[28] Soon, it seems, the two will be indistinguishable.

If, as was indeed the case in various experiments with Kulagina, there can be no EM fields detected in between the subject and the target during PK, then the energy transmission is presumably occurring in a realm (time-space/implicate order) or form of energy (torsion) to which the detecting instruments in the room do not have access. Interestingly, Kulagina did not cause any distortion of shape when moving soft objects.[29] The "force" she seemed to control did not show any localized effects on the particular target objects; rather, it seemed more to envelop the entire object as a field would.

Bearden's theory is that Kulagina's bio-field, "which is connected through hyperspace to the object being moved, is orthorotated [rotated through right angles] into ordinary fields at the interface of the object. Thus an electric field is created, and also a momentum field that causes the object to move by ordinary physics."[30]

Kulagina was subjected to a number of physiological electronic measuring devices and tested for important body functions during her PK demonstrations. The Soviets found that at the moment an object began to move, all of Kulagina's body processes sped up dramatically. Her heartbeat, breathing, brain activity, and the EM fields around her body all began to pulse in rhythm as well.[31]

At the onset of her "activated" state, she experienced thirst and tasted iron or copper in her mouth, and even experienced states of dizziness or nausea. Following the session a weight loss of 1.5–2 pounds could be measured. The taste of iron or copper is an intriguing phenomenon. Russian scientist Dr. Victor Grebennikov, who discovered the "cavity structural effect" created by bees' nests throwing off torsion waves, experienced an inexplicable metallic taste in his mouth when he was standing over the nests. Was the taste of iron or copper due to Kulagina's chakras activating at higher levels of intensity, thus harnessing higher levels of the aetheric torsion energy? Interestingly, Kulagina could move a vertical cyclinder more easily than a horizontal one. Was this also due to the tendency of vertical cylindrical shapes to better harness and amplify the spiralling aetheric torsion energy?

Other aspects of Kulagina's phenomena were listed in the Defense Intelligence Agency report as follows:

- She can exert no effect on an object situated in a vacuum [which seems to support Bearden's contention that, once the hyperspace energies of consciousness are orthorotated into ordinary EM fields at the interface of an object, the object is then moved by ordinary space-time forces—in a vacuum, there is "only" the virtual energy of the "zero-point field"].
- Electrostatic screening has no effect on her powers, which seem to be better with the object under a dielectric cover, but she is unsuccessful

during storms or other atmospheric conditions when there is a greater than normal amount of electricity in the air. She cannot, at any time, exert an influence on an electroscope.

- She can cause luminescence of crystal lumiphores and produce changes in the spectrum of visible light absorbed by liquid crystals.[32]

Adamenko found that Alla Vinogradova could produce effects similar to those of Kulagina, but with far less physiological stress. In some of his experiments with her in Moscow, during which she moved a variety of objects about on a dielectric surface, a great deal of electrostatic energy was measured around the objects (supposedly enough to light a small neon glow tube), increasing with proximity.

The measurements detected *field pulsations which were synchronous with Vinogradova's respiration rate, heartbeat, and brain alpha rhythm pattern*; but the region *between* Vinogradova and the object contained no detectable energy fields or frequencies.[33] Again, the intentional induction of hyperspatial (torsion/scalar) energy is indicated—Bearden looks to be correct in saying that it is orthororated into ordinary EM fields when it interfaces with an object in space-time.

Evidently, PK, or certain forms of it at least, requires heightened states of arousal, which certainly accords with anecdotal reports of spontaneous PK occurring through highly intense emotions. Research on eight of the Dalai Lama's most seasoned practitioners of *Nyingmapa* and *Kagyupa* meditation by neuroscientist and psychologist Richard Davidson supports this notion.

In an experiment, Davidson attached 256 EEG sensors to each monk's scalp and the monks then carried out a meditation which focused on "utter readiness to help others and a desire for all living things to be free of suffering." The EEG readings soon showed a level of brain activation that no scientist had ever seen. The EEG monitors showed sustained bursts of high beta—and gamma-band activity—rapid cycles of 25–70 Hz.

Gamma waves (40–100 Hz) represent the brain working at a high level of intensity. Davidson found that when the brain operates at these extremely high frequencies, the phases of brainwaves (when they peak and trough) all over the brain start operating in synchrony.[34] Such heightened synchronization is thought crucial for achieving elevated awareness and creativity, and studies of yogis have also evinced high-frequency brainwave activity in the beta and gamma ranges.

An interesting point about this experiment was that even during their non-meditative hours, the monks' brains featured enduring gamma waves—the more hours in meditation, the stronger and more enduring the gamma signal.[35]

(One study has identified bursts of 40 Hz gamma oscillations appearing in the brain just moments before insight occurs. "This oscillation is conducive to *creating links across many parts of the brain*,"[36] facilitating a whole-brain state.)

Heightened states of arousal were certainly evident decades ago in Soviet research into Nina Kulagina, who was tested by over 40 top scientists, including two Nobel laureates. During successful PK tests, Sergeyev found her to have 50 times more voltage being generated at the back of her head than at the front. Among other impressive feats performed under controlled conditions, Kulagina succeeded in mentally separating an egg yolk from the white as it floated in a saline solution 6 feet from her, as cameras recorded every second.

Her EEG showed "intense emotional excitement," with great activity in the deeper levels of the reticular formation, which coordinates and filters information in the brain. The cardiogram showed an irregular action of the heart, consistent with a state of "great alarm," her pulse increased to an amazing 240 bpm, and high percentages of blood sugar were recorded together with other endocrinal disturbances typical of a stress reaction. During this 30-minute test, Kulagina lost 2 pounds in weight, was weakened and temporarily blinded by the end, and suffered other adverse physical effects.[37]

Of interest is the fact that as she struggled to bring her influence to bear, the measured electrostatic field around her began to pulse until it assumed a rhythm of 4 cps. This was linked to a heavy theta brainwave action at the same frequency, normally a state linked to sleep or deep meditation. It was as if her body rhythms produced a beat that was then amplified by her bioplasmic field and concentrated on the spot where she gazed.[38] In fact, Sergeyev found that the electrostatic, heart, and brain fields were all synchronized at 4 beats per second in theta during PK actions, with other readings showing Kulagina to be in what Watson refers to as a state of "controlled rage."[39]

There is No Spoon

It was 1983, and Major General Albert Stubblebine, III, was the Commanding General of INSCOM, the US Army Intelligence and Security Command. At an intelligence school in Fort Huachuca, Arizona, Stubblebine gave what would be remembered by those who were there as a highly unorthodox pep talk. It started out in an un-extraordinary manner, but after Stubblebine had finished summarizing the tremendous advances that had been made in intelligence-gathering techniques and technology in the preceding years, he took a turn that few, if any, had seen coming.

Paul Smith, a retired Major in the US Army and former remote viewer, recalls the speech:

> "As impressive and amazing as are all the advances we are making through technology," he (Stubblebine) continued, reaching into the pockets of his dress green uniform, "they cannot compare to the power that lies within our own minds. We only have to learn to tap it." He began tossing small, glinting objects into the audience. "Now I want these back when you're through looking at them," he added nonchalantly.[40]

What those in attendance were holding were pieces of silverware that had been mutilated into unnatural shapes.

Since the age of 11 Smith had spent his summers as hired help on farms and ranches in the West. He'd worked with tools and heavy machinery, and seen metal of all descriptions bent deliberately or by accident, both mechanically and with heat—but none of it resembled the forms taken by Stubblebine's warped silverware. The latter featured spoons buckled and twisted into tight spirals, and forks the tines and stems of which had also been twisted and curled—some looking like pigs' tails. Stubblebine's cutlery showed none of the normal evidence of having been heated to high temperatures to produce the effects.

Then he dropped a bomb on his befuddled audience: Stubblebine announced that his unfortunate silverware had been bent by him and his staff—*using nothing but the power of the mind*. He then insisted that anyone could learn how to do it, even "old farts" like him and his colonels. Since Stubblebine's talk that day, Smith recalls having read and seen attempts by "skeptics" to debunk this form of PK, but states that the results bear little resemblance to Stubblebine's.[41] This is typical of many debunker demonstrations: they fail to achieve the authenticity of even low-level phenomena, and absolutely fail to convincingly simulate higher-level phenomena.

As a matter of fact, highly controlled research into PK outside Russia goes back at least as far as the 1970s. An obscure translation of a French research report translated and edited by the Eyring Research Institute appeared over a decade ago, detailing some of the significant PK effects documented (and filmed) under rigorously controlled conditions. They included deformations of target samples (some metallic), transformations and remotely inflicted effects.[42]

It is interesting to note that certain psychokinetic phenomena are comparable to the types of anomalous effects that renegade independent scientist John

Hutchison has apparently managed to elicit with his own technology. The "Hutchison Effect" is actually a range of phenomena discovered accidentally by John Hutchison when he was researching Tesla's longitudinal waves back in 1979. "The Hutchison Effect occurs as the result of radio wave interferences in a zone of spatial volume encompassed by high-voltage sources, usually a Van de Graff generator, and two or more Tesla coils," Mark Solis informs us.[43]

Hutchison effects include (but are not limited to) the levitation of heavy objects, the fusion of different materials (say, metal and wood), and temporary as well as permanent alterations to the crystalline structure and physical properties of metals. Dissimilar materials fusing together indicates a powerful effect on Van der Waals forces, the attractive and repulsive forces within or between molecules.[44]

Extremely intriguing is that dissimilar substances can simply merge together, yet the individual substances do not dissociate. For example, a block of wood can "sink into" a bar of metal, and yet neither individual component breaks apart. There is also *no evidence of displacement*,[45] suggesting that the volume of the bar that should have been displaced by the wood has effectively being "displaced" into the aether/time-space/implicate order—some of its atomic content is literally leaving our space-time reference frame, reducing its solidity.

It has been asserted that "the same dynamics which drive torsion field devices are the ones which have produced Hutchison's effects as well."[46] While Hutchison's work has apparently not been rigorously scrutinized or verified, these displacement effects have been documented as occurring in natural phenomena for some time—tornadoes are a major culprit, for example. Their rotating vortices have been known to hurl, for instance, tree branches or planks of wood straight into (and part-way through) objects made of metal—without damage to the wood, *or any visible displacement of mass*. There are numerous examples.[47]

As with the Hutchison effect, dissimilar substances simply merge together, owing to the partial dematerialization of the substances' atomic content; some of the substance's atoms have apparently been unwound and "dematerialized" or accelerated into time-space. In the process, these substances therefore become soft and almost sponge-like—how else could a bean be absorbed half way into a chicken egg without so much as a crack in the egg?[48]

Of most interest to us here is that the human mind can achieve the same effects—as we noted earlier in speaking of the anomalous effects created by torsion fields. Leonard E. Buchanan, better known as Lyn Buchanan—of Psi Spy fame—was born in 1939 in Waco, Texas. As a youngster, Buchanan would play and experiment innocently as any child might, except that he found that he could put a rock on a metal plate and use his mind to push the rock *through* the plate. He even managed to perform the feat with a childhood friend present as a witness.[49]

Apparently Buchanan, using only focused intent, succeeded in partially disaggregating the underlying field effects that organized information into the atomic energy/matter that formed the metal plate. With some of the metal's atomic content "unwound," it was softened just enough for the rock to pass right through it.

As science advances, we can see that its "impossible" achievements that defy the "laws" of physics have actually always been mimicked and pre-empted by the human mind. Saints and mystics were levitating long before Hutchison got his bowling ball to hover weightlessly in the air, and in Moscow, Dr. Venyamin Pushkin confirmed in tests the ability of one Boris Ermolaev to suspend small objects (such as matchboxes or several pencils) in the air for a number of seconds using intense mental intention. Pushkin eliminated electrostatic and electromagnetic explanations and concluded that Ermolaev could generate a gravitational field for suspending the objects. Pushkin's report was checked and signed off on by five members of the Soviet Academy of Sciences, including world-famous brain researcher A.A. Luria.[50]

Regarding spoon-bending, Solis comments intriguingly on some of John Hutchison's own cutlery abuse, stating that some temporary changes in the metal's crystalline structure and physical properties are reminiscent of Uri Geller's spoon-bending. In one of Hutchison's videos a spoon flaps up and down like a rag in the wind.[51]

Geller is the best known cutlery abuser. He has been extensively tested, with his talents widely verified by competent researchers, as well as magicians. Bearden has offered an explanation of Geller's metal-bending effect in analyzing Kirlian images taken of a ring and Geller's finger during a PK experiment conducted by James L. Hickman. In the experiment, Geller's intent was to bend the ring without physical contact. The resulting image reveals a striking "kindling" of his bioenergy in a line intersecting and seemingly cutting through the ring, as if to break it.

Bearden explains that in such an intense kindling as this, the nuclear currents moving between protons and neutrons inside the nuclei of the silver atoms are also being strongly kindled. "Reductions in the positive charges steadily reduce the charged exchanging particles to quarklike particles, severely affecting the structural integrity and crystalline lattice directions of the base metal. By this means metal bending—or even breaking—is accomplished."[52]

Figure 13.1 reveals an image taken from a similar experiment with Geller, this time using a Seiko wristwatch. Note the "torsion-plasma" bioenergy extending away from Geller's finger and reaching towards the watch, as if to break it. Scientist and author Henry S. Dakin was one of the observers present for the experiment, and described the line of bioenergy as a "streak of light."[53]

Figure 13.1 Kirlian photograph of Uri Geller's bioenergy directed at wristwatch

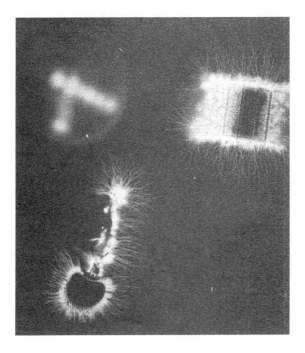

Image credit: H.S. Dakin (*High-Voltage Photography*, p. 30).

Bearden adds that in other experiments where actual breakages have occurred, the metal in and around the fracture has shown the effects of severe localized EM fields, e.g., as if it had been treated with intense heat.[54]

Geller has been found to mysteriously and irreversibly alter the crystalline structure of nitinol, an alloy of nickel and titanium, warping its shape in ways the researchers could neither explain nor replicate. In 1977, John Randall and Peter Davis replicated this effect using a 13-year-old boy as a subject. Similar effects were apparently achieved by Frenchman John-Pierre Girard, who in the mid-1970s seemingly managed to alter the atomic configuration of stainless steel, converting it from austenite to the form known as martensite.[55]

John Hasted (1921–2002), former head of experimental physics at Birkbeck College in London, conducted his own PK experiments with children. He suspended metal objects—usually latchkeys—from the ceiling and placed the children 3–10 feet away so they could have no physical contact. Embedded in each key was a resistive strain gauge, which was wired up to an amplifier and a pen recorder, and would register on the strip chart recording any deformation in the key—even if too small to be visually detected. The subjects were to bend the keys with intent alone.

Not only did the keys sway and sometimes fracture, but abrupt and enormous spikes of voltage pulses up to 10 volts—the limits of the chart recorder—were registered. Moreover, when the children were asked to influence several keys hung separately, the individual strain recorders noted *simultaneous* signals.[56] This field effect is a signature of hyperdimensional consciousness (scalar/torsion forces) in action, and a staple of poltergeist phenomena.

All of the above, while it shows us macro-PK, pales in comparison to biologist Lyall Watson's encounter in Indonesia with a girl named Tia. Unaware that Watson was observing her from a distance, Tia actually demonstrated the ability to cause an entire grove of kenari trees to vanish in broad daylight—a small child with her was the witness for whom this feat was apparently performed. After Tia caused the trees to "blink" back into existence, the delighted child ran around touching them as if to confirm they were really there. Tia then proceeded to repeat the procedure several times. At the end of this incredible display, a shattered Watson simply left in shock.[57]

As Thomas Henry Huxley said: "Sit down before fact as a little child, be prepared to give up every preconceived notion, follow humbly wherever and to whatever abysses nature leads, or you shall learn nothing." Amen.

China's Super Psychics

One of China's top psi subjects is Zhang Baosheng (born in 1958), and if the stories are to be believed, his talents may surpass even those of Geller. It is reported that Baosheng has been recorded moving small objects and even live insects in and out of sealed containers, passing the objects right *through* the container (sound familiar?).

"Films and freeze photos show objects such as a pill in the process of exiting a sealed bottle," John Violette informs us. At a film speed of 400 frames per second, the pill can be seen exiting the mouth of a sealed bottle during a PK demonstration for China's Ministry of Space Industries. The accelerated speed may be, Violette suggests, due to motion in hyperspace translating to higher speeds in space-time. Even more intricate and tamper-proof experiments have seen Baosheng successfully demonstrate his PK teleportational abilities to dramatic effect, and there is much anecdotal evidence of his ability to make objects (such as traffic tickets) disappear, or burn holes in clothing without touching it.[58]

But Baosheng isn't the only PK star in China. Professors Tianming, Xing, and Mingling found several children who, like Uri Geller, could make watch hands move rapidly without touching them, despite the watch face being separated from the mechanism. More impressive, however, is a young girl named Yang Li. Li could mentally remove cigarettes from inside a cardboard box one by one until there were none left, using only mental intention. Where the cigarettes ended up no one knows.

There were also children who could apport flowers and flower buds into teacups with lids on them. The Chinese studies suggest that children around 10–12 years of age are more likely to exhibit spontaneous psi, more trainable, and improve with practice.[59] Remember, these are not magicians operating in conditions that they control—quite the opposite. (We might also note that there is, according to author Paul Dong, an altogether higher "top secret class" of psychics in China whose abilities surpass even the likes of Baosheng, and who are kept tightly under wraps by the Chinese government. They are not publicly known.)

We can reasonably extrapolate from this data that *some* "poltergeist" activity is probably the unconscious hyperdimensional "reach" of a particular (incarnate) human.

Levitation

Richard Bartlett states flatly in *The Physics of Miracles* that all humans possess the "spiritual technology" to levitate, heal, and perform other miracles. This "technology" is, he believes, centered within the heart's torsion field.[60] Phenomena such as levitation have often been associated with states of transcendent joy or ecstasy, and where do we feel those most strongly? In the heart chakra, also the location of the body's strongest EM field.

Bartlett writes that torsion fields create a hyperdimensional geometry which has access to extradimensional realities. In Chapters 4 and 6 we have linked torsion fields to the nonlocality of two entangled photons, tetrahedral geometry, aether/time-space/implicate order, the Golden Mean, Phi, and geometry in general. Bartlett thinks that the saints and mystics who levitated were accessing extradimensional states through the force of love located in the heart's torus field,[61] the gateway to buddhic hyper-energies.

Reports of human levitation continue to be generated today. Bodily levitation was reported in 7% of poltergeist cases studied by Gauld and Cornell. Mircea Eliade states that the ability to fly is claimed by Siberian, Eskimo, and North American shamans, and sorcerers and medicine men globally (most of this "flight" is probably occurring in the astral planes, however).[62]

Someone with advanced esoteric knowledge of harmonics obviously left it to the protection of the high priests of Tibet a long time ago, as the technique of utilizing sound (including vocal intonations) to levitate huge boulders roughly 250 meters high into the air—and over a similar horizontal distance—for construction purposes was still being used until as recently as the first half of the 1900s.[63, 64] The Tibetan technique of *lung-gom*, which involves specific breathing exercises and vocal intonations (mantras), appears to be the method employed by some Tibetan monks to accelerate nearly half of their atomic content into time-space in order to mitigate the downwards push of gravity, and utilize the forces of levity emanating from the core of our planet.[65]

If it is correct that the body of a God-conscious or a maximally DNA-activated person is enveloped by a merkaba,[66] a geometric field comprised of two nested counter-rotating tetrahedra (one pointing up and the other pointing down), then by using correct breathing techniques and focused intent, we may be able to accelerate the rotation of these geometric fields enough to "dematerialize" just enough of our bodily atoms to capitalize on the force of levity. (Too much and we might disappear from space-time altogether.)

Antigravity appears to be a matter of utilizing what are apparently basic principles—putting them into practice successfully is a different matter of course. However, our reality, it must be remembered, is a virtual reality, a giant conglomerate of consciousness software programs interacting. If you are running a mental software program called Levitation is Impossible, how likely do you think you are to ever experience (or even witness) a levitation?

As Bartlett suggests, ask yourself "what if there are no rules?" That is a much more psi-conducive form of mental software to run because it opens your own reality program up to the massive variability and potential of the endless software programs of the Infinite. Watch *The Matrix* film—it is a brilliant metaphor for our own reality, particularly (in this context) the scenes wherein Morpheus is training Neo in the combat training programs/virtual realities.

Bartlett is not alone in emphasizing the role of the heart in manipulating reality. Gregg Braden (along with myriad others) also emphasizes the crucial role played by the heart in manifesting and co-creating our experiences at this level of reality. He emphasizes that in making our intention known, we must "drop" into the field of the heart and actually feel gratitude—it is this emotion that is so powerful in drawing to us what we desire.[67] Interestingly, it has been said in occult and mystic circles that awakening the heart chakra brings on psychokinetic powers, as well as healing abilities—and this is a notion taken seriously by some scientists also.[68]

Perhaps both spontaneous and meditative states of ecstasy and joy accelerate the spin field/s around the human body (which we looked at in Chapter 9), counteracting the downward push of gravity. *Laghima* (Sanskrit)—the power to become extremely light (and levitate)—is detailed in Book III (Vibhuti Pada) of Patanjali's *Yoga Sutras*. The *vishudda* (throat chakra) is associated with the space/ aether "element." By mastering this chakra and the "space element" through the practice of *samyama* meditation on *vishudda*, it is said that the thrust of gravity may be overcome.[69] (This is not a party trick, and would likely take a lifetime of work to do deliberately.)

According to the *Markandeya Purana*, *Laghima* means "to have an extreme speed"—an extreme rotational speed in one's biofield/torsion field? Several websites that refer to this ancient doctrine state that in obtaining *laghima*, one is developing in each "cell" (or perhaps more precisely, the *atoms* of each cell) the "opposite (centrifugal/spin) tendency." Perhaps in order to exercise *laghima*, the extreme spin speed of one's accelerated biofield must simultaneously affect the spin speed and even direction/s of the body's atomic content, essentially accelerating some of it into the aether/time-space. Thus, the influx of gravity could no longer act on that atomic content, and the body's mass would be lessened, potentially allowing for levitation within one's own gravitational field (not unlike a UFO).

The yogi would point out that mastery of breath control through Pranayama is also essential to this process, as the energy harnessed by the etheric/pranic body (*pranamaya kosa*) is channelled into five different primary "winds" or *pancha vayus*. The *vayu* (wind/breath) associated with levitation is the *udana vayu* (udana meaning "up-breath"). The *udana vayu* "governs upward moving energy and is involved with the soul leaving the body at death."[70]

Perhaps states of ecstacy and joy accelerate the spin field/s around the human body. There are some ground-breaking experiments that speak to the issue of human levitation in surprising ways. For example, "rogue researcher" the late Dr. Bruce DePalma showed experimentally in the 1970s that when two ball bearings, each of 1 inch diameter, are catapulted at the same speed and angle through a vacuum—one of them spinning at 18,000 rpm and the other not spinning—the one that is spinning will travel higher, *fall faster*, and move farther overall than its non-spinning counterpart.[71]

It is as if the ball's spin lessens its mass and thereby the effect of gravity—but not only that, the fact that the rotating ball also *falls* faster suggests, as Wilcock observes, that it is moving faster in *time*. DePalma had said that "the inertia of objects relates to the time energy flowing through them."[72] Similarly, Kozyrev had shown that by shaking, spinning, vibrating, or impacting physical objects, their weight can be decreased by small but measurable amounts. Even shaking a weight up and down by hand caused a measurable drop in mass.[73]

Also working independently, Harold Aspden had demonstrated experimentally that an object that has been rapidly rotated and returned to a stationary position can then be accelerated up to the same speed again using *less* energy than on the first go, suggesting once more that an "anomalous" decrease in mass has occurred as a result of rotational movement.[74]

Next we need to factor in Vladimir Ginzberg's paradigm-shattering discovery that by simply reversing a classic Einstein equation, an increase in velocity now means that atoms and molecules *lose* mass, rather than gaining it, as Einstein's original equation predicted. Now when an object or particle starts to move, part of its matter is converted into a field, and if the particle reaches the speed of light, its mass and charge become zero, rather than infinitely large, as Einstein thought.[75] This is a complete reversal of traditional thinking, but it seems to make sense in light of UFO behaviour, UFOs (some of them at least) being composed of light of an orgone/etheric nature, which is *massless*.

Wilcock points out that if you can push the whirling motion within an atom past the speed of light, then the atom "pops" over into time-space. A key point to note is that apparently the motion inside an atom is *already* moving at light-speed, or close to it, so it doesn't require much of a "push" to breach the threshold.[76]

So, if Kozyrev's, Aspden's, and DePalma's methods actually caused the transition of some atoms from space-time into time-space through a rotational motion (as well as shaking, impacting, etc.), thus decreasing the weight of various substances and objects, can we induce human levitation by accelerating the rotational speed of the spin force around the human body? According to this model, this would convert some of our atomic content into its counterpart time-space state where it is no longer pushed on by gravity in space-time, but is "lifted" by what Wilcock dubs "levity" in time-space (the planet's aetheric outflow).[77]

Wilcock has done a brilliant job of collating and synthesizing high quality frontier science with reliable "real world" observation to enunciate and support his cutting-edge take on Larson's Reciprocal System model. It is also interesting to note that the physicist and inventor Thomas Townsend Brown demonstrated back in the late 1950s that powerful electrostatic fields could induce an antigravity effect (levitation) in a disk-shaped apparatus, fatally wounding the relativistic notion that matter can only produce an *attractive* force.[78]

Does diet factor in to considerations for would-be levitators? Like fellow levitator Joseph of Copertino, the famous 19th-century physical medium Daniel Dunglas Home fasted in order to purify himself. He stated that without heeding this provision, the "spirits" would not be able to lift him off the ground. Sir William Crookes had subjected Home's various phenomena to high scientific scrutiny, and wrote of Home's levitation:

> There are at least a hundred recorded instances of Mr. Home's rising from the ground, in the presence of as many separate persons . . . To reject the recorded evidence on this subject is to reject all human testimony whatever; for no fact in sacred or profane history is supported by a stronger array of proofs. The accumulated testimony establishing Mr. Home's levitations is overwhelming.[79]

The issue of purification of one's body arises in many esoteric streams. In yoga, it is essential before embarking on a hardcore path of one-pointed training. Theosophists like Leadbeater have advised against consuming white flour as it lowers one's vibration, and virtually all mediums (and spiritualists) appear to subscribe to a view that one should eat as little animal flesh as possible (preferably none, both on ethical *and* nutritional grounds*).

Depriving the body of food in general seems to make consciousness more receptive to deeper levels of reality (which includes facilitating mystical experiences as well as facilitating psi powers like clairvoyance). Aldous Huxley believed that the enforced undereating during the Middle Ages affected collective brain chemistry, explaining the high incidence of visionary experience in those times. Native American shamans went for days without eating or

---

* Both white flour and animal flesh are acidifying to the blood, which is highly undesirable and contributes to chronic acidosis—a necessary condition for most cancer and countless other diseases. Protein, calcium, iron, and other vital nutrients can be found in higher quantities per gram in plant-based foods.

455

drinking, tiring themselves in order to become more receptive to sacred visions and hallucinations. The Eleusinian rites included a nine-day fast capped by a potent entheogen. Joseph of Copertino fasted "relentlessly," and an aging Padre Pio was known to have eaten almost nothing.[80] Therese Neumann, as we have seen, spent the last 35 years of her life not eating *or* drinking, and is known to have spent many hours entranced in visionary states. (She also did not sleep, and yet, possessed robust health.)

The Power of Intent in Healing

We have covered the undeniable evidence that mental intention can influence "non-living" systems such as dice, RNGs, metal and various other media, and reviewed some of the evidence for the ability of entangled minds to influence one another and even cause physiological changes in experiment participants such as increased electrodermal activity, alterations in blood pressure, brainwave synchronization, and so on, as a result of nonlocal correlations in time-space/implicate order. This is to say nothing of the Rein/HeartMath research into the mind's ability to selectively increase and/or decrease DNA winding.

"There are literally hundreds of studies, spanning many decades and several continents, which consistently show that focused intent can accelerate the growth rate of cell cultures, yeasts, bacteria, and plants, and which correlate with more recent histo-molecular studies demonstrating statistically significant increases in DNA, RNA, and protein synthesis."[81] We might therefore expect that focused intent can be used in remote (or local) healing on people—and this is what many experiments demonstrate.

Following months of preparation and refinement of an earlier study, the late Elisabeth Targ and psychologist Fred Sicher studied AIDS patients and whether or not energy healing could slow AIDS' progress. The AIDS patients had been divided into two groups, one receiving remote healing and the other not. They both received the same orthodox medical treatment. Crucially, neither group had any idea as to whether or not they were being remotely healed, and neither did their doctors know (the experiment was double-blind). The patients had been as closely matched as possible for T-Cell count, the amount they smoked, whether they exercised, their age, religious beliefs, their degree of illness, and any recreational drug-taking.

The healers were an eclectic mix, with only a minority describing themselves as conventionally religious. Their particular healing methods were equally varied and highly idiosyncratic. The patients and healers had no contact whatsoever.

The only thing the healers had to work with was a photo, a name and a T-Cell count, while the patients themselves did not know if they were being prayed for or not.

After six months, the treatment group receiving healing was healthier on every parameter—significantly fewer doctor visits, fewer hospitalizations, fewer days in hospital, fewer new AIDS-defining illnesses, and significantly lower severity of disease. Only two of those in the treatment group had developed any new AIDS-defining illnesses, while 12 of the control group had, and only three of the treated group had been hospitalized, compared with 12 of those in the control group. The treated group also registered significantly improved moods on psychological tests. On six of the 11 medical outcome measures, the group treated with healing had significantly better outcomes.

Potential placebo effects and any other variables in the patients that might have contributed to the results were controlled for and/or eliminated through detailed analysis, and irrespective of the type of healing employed, or their view of a "higher being," the healers were "dramatically contributing to the physical and psychological wellbeing of their patients."[82] Significantly, most healers agreed on the need for them to "get out of the way" and let the universe act upon their intention, usually consisting of a request for the patient to be healed. None of the successful healers believed they possessed the power in and of themselves.[83]

In another large study of distant healing, not only did the recipients show improvements in all major preselected parameters, but the healers themselves did too—sometimes even more than the targets.[84] Leadbeater wrote in the first decade of the 20th century: "Every outpouring of affection or devotion produces a double result—one upon the being to whom it is sent, and another upon ourselves, who sent it forth."[85]

A study by pharmacist Constance Grauds of 2,700 men over time found that those who engaged in regular volunteer activities had death rates half of those who did not. HeartMath Institute research has shown that feelings of care and compassion increase the production of immune factors. Another study showed that even just watching someone else act altruistically can trigger the same effect![86]

Note also that evidence of characteristic EM signatures reflecting varying mental intents has already been reported by Rein and Laskow, who found that four different intentions by the same healer produced *distinct* magnetic signatures and corresponding biological effects on tumor cell cultures.[87] Dr. Justa Smith, in experiments inspired by Bernard Grad's work, found that the well-tested Hungarian healer Oscar Estebany could accelerate the enzyme trypsin's reaction rates in test tubes, which in the body would enhance health.

Smith's work with healers in this direction always showed the energy operating was intelligent and "goal-directed," always effecting change in a direction most beneficial to life, even if this meant simultaneously increasing the activity of one substance, leaving another unaltered, and decreasing still another's activity.[88] (The effect of our hyperspatial consciousness/torsion energy is always in the direction of enhanced/increased order—unless actively intended otherwise.)

A similar study from 1999 by Toni Bunnell studied the effect of healing touch on the enzyme called pepsin and found that a healer sped up its conversion rate through the series of 20 trials. A 1984 study showed that a group of 52 people were highly significantly able to selectively increase and decrease the rates of mutation of E-coli samples through intent. Likewise, Qigong practitioners in a joint 2004 study found that they could accelerate the rate of growth of human-cultured brain cells held a minimum of 10 cm from their bodies, in 20-minute sessions of directed healing intention.[89]

Conversely, careful experiments at the Institute of Agronomy in France showed with odds against chance of many millions to one, that the growth of two parasitic types of fungi were retarded in 33 out of 39 cultures as compared with control samples simply by the experimenters sitting by the dishes and willing to inhibit their growth for 15 minutes a day.[90]

Joseph Pearce writes that prayer might be efficacious by establishing resonance between discrete intelligences.[91] In a holographic universe composed of torsion/information fields, the healer's field may be tuning into and becoming resonant with the healee's field, which might "download" the healer's "healthier" information, leading to an informational recoding, and therefore resolution of physical symptoms.

In 1988 Dr. Randolph Byrd published in the *Southern Medical Journal* a successful double-blind and randomized demonstration of distant healing. The study involved 393 of his cardiac patients at San Francisco General Hospital. Areas of statistical significance in favor of healing for those who did receive prayers included less need for cardiopulmonary resuscitation, less need for potent medications, and a lower incidence of pulmonary edema and pneumonia.[92] And in 1999, cardiologist William Harris of the University of Missouri in Kansas City published a similar successful study with 990 heart patients. His paper appeared in the *Archives of Internal Medicine.*[93]

Jeanne Achterberg and colleagues performed a study (published in 2005) at a Hawaiian hospital using 11 highly experienced healers who would work on a patient they knew and with whom they felt an "empathic, compassionate, bonded connection." The experiment was a success with odds against chance of 10,000 to one. During times that healing energy was being sent (which were randomized and which the recipients were oblivious to), Achterberg found that particular areas in the recipients' brains became activated. These included the anterior and middle cingulate areas, precuneus, and frontal areas.[94]

In a large and novel randomized and blinded experiment reported in 2001, evidence for a retroactive healing effect in former sepsis patients was observed—*ten years after they had been hospitalized*. In another study reported in 2007, a healer was able to heal mice injected with cancer cells, "followed by an apparent immunity to mammary cancer, as re-injection of cancer cells failed to 'take.'"[95]

Masaru Emoto has found that prayer can also positively affect bodies of water, even as big as Fujiwara Dam. Before the prayers, Emoto could obtain no crystal from the water sample, and yet after the prayers the water sample gave a crystal of "heavenly beauty."[96] The effects of increased consciousness in a system include increased order, coherence and *beauty* (both in an objective and subjective sense).

Interestingly, water held by healers has been shown to expose photographic film sensitive only to the *high ultraviolet range*. It has also been shown experimentally that "Qi" (pranic/etheric) energy can accelerate chemical reactions by up to 400% from a distance of 2–10 m—an effect consistently replicated by different Qigong masters over 500 times (while control samples showed no such changes).[97] Even blood pressure can be lowered by intention at a distance, and the bursting of hypertonic (salty) blood cells can be slowed by distant intent.[98]

William Tiller has actually shown that human intention can be recorded electronically and used to increase the *in vivo* ATP to ADP ratio in fruit fly larvae and thus hasten the development of the fruit flies. Over some eight months and experiments on approximately 10,000 larvae and 7,000 adult flies, those exposed to the electronic memory of the recorded intention were seen to have developed 15% faster and been healthier than those not so exposed to the recorded intention.

Further, such experiments aimed at both increasing and decreasing the pH of water by one whole pH unit (by decreasing the hydrogen ion thermodynamic activity by a factor of 10) through recorded intent were successful, as were attempts at raising the *in vitro* level of a liver enzyme called alkaline phosphatise (ALP). More than this, however, Tiller found that these broadcast emanations of recorded intention actually had a conditioning effect on the rooms in which they took place; after three months, progressively better results in the

459

experiments began to develop. Tiller had used recorded intention to entrain the ambient energies of his research rooms, or what he referred to as the indwelling consciousness of the experimental space. This effect occurred over four separate laboratories. The electromagnetic gauge symmetry in the rooms was being increased.[99]

Consistent intention seems to be able to set up an energetic pattern or trend that might influence other thought processes (and biochemical processes for that matter), whether conscious or not, to move in the same direction. The effect in Tiller's labs was so pronounced that even when the devices were altogether removed, the targets, whether water pH, ALP, or fruit flies, *continued to be affected*. The removal of equipment from the experiment would initially diminish the effects, but it was found that after several weeks they would resume once more, seemingly recovering the energetic equilibrium that had been established in the aetheric or zero point medium (implicate order). Somehow Tiller and his colleagues had done the "impossible" and created an SU(2)-gauge space where electric and magnetic monopoles coexisted (only magnetic dipoles, not single poles, are thought to exist in nature in regular space-time).

Perhaps just as interesting is the fact that Tiller also discovered that an intention-imprinted electronic device (IIED) would "leak" information to an unimprinted electronic device (UED) 100 m apart—*even though they were both switched off!* After four to five days the UED became "converted" to an effective IIED—through a *non-electromagnetic* form of information transfer.[100] In the non-spatial "implicate order," the devices would have been entangled—meaningfully connected—and therefore no EM transmission of information would be required to convert a UED to an IIED(!)

Other scientists have also witnessed the conditioning of experimental space by intention, where their results progressively improved as the room became "energetically entrained." These effects are clearly replicable. Radin, Taft, and Yount utilized four Johrei healers in a three-day healing experiment and found that, along with increased growth in healer-treated brain cell cultures versus controls, they too had created a conditioned space, as shown by output from RNGs in the vicinity which had become synchronized with one another.[101]

Dossey states in *Prayer is Good* that there are over 1,200 scientific studies demonstrating the link between prayer and intention, and health and longevity. Meta-analyses in *The Annals of Internal Medicine* and the *Journal of Alternative and Complementary Medicine* compiling the results of many studies have shown that prayer, distant healing, and intentionality do have significant effects on healing.[102]

Taking Intent One Step Further

In terms of co-creating or manifesting our reality to suit our purposes, there is something about the nature of the cosmos that we must realize. It is responsive to our beliefs and emotions because it is fundamentally conscious and intelligent. This means that we don't "get what we wish for," so much as we "receive what we believe." Belief is creative. E-motion is energy in motion, or so the cliché goes. Emotion is creative because it is a function of consciousness, the source of everything, the ultimate creative agency.

Walsch stated in *Conversations with God* that the biggest key to creation "is to be grateful *before*, and for, the creation. Such taking for granted is not only condoned, but encouraged. It is the sure sign of mastery. All Masters know in advance that the deed has been done."[103] Does such a notion work in practice?

In *The Divine Matrix*, Gregg Braden details the story of a middle-aged woman who had been diagnosed with a malignant bladder tumor believed (there's that "b" word again!) by Western doctors to be inoperable. In a Chinese health clinic with three practitioners behind her and an ultrasound technician seated in front of her, the woman was filmed during a treatment that would last less than four minutes. The practitioners selected and agreed on a word that would reinforce for them a sense of the woman already being healed. The mantra translated loosely as "already done, already done." You can find the footage of this on youtube.com in a clip from one of Braden's live presentations. At first, not much seems to happen, but soon the tumor starts to quiver or blink in and out of view, as if alternating between realities. In seconds it fades and then totally disappears from the screen.[104] No more tumor.

Paramahansa Yogananda has said: "Any word spoken with clear realization and deep concentration has a materializing value."[105]

How long does the healing effect last? The studies have shown a 95% success rate after five years (far superior to mainstream cancer treatments) for clients who continue with the life-affirming changes in nutrition, breath, and movement learned in the clinic.[106] Here we have an extremely potent example of the ability of consciousness to intervene in "material reality" and select a new reality, to alter the programming of the "Matrix." Emotion, intention, and belief can access the "hidden codes" for reality and rewrite them in our favor.

In this case, the combined consciousness fields of the practitioners apparently disaggregated the underlying field effects that organized the energy and matter of the tumor into form. Thus, the tumour was "unwound" or "disorganized" from an observable state in the explicate order, perhaps to a state of informational potential in the implicate/time-space.

It is time to stop looking for the reality of PK in decimal places. Own the abilities immanent within you. Shamans and mystics have long known of our species' innate PK abilities. There is good evidence that human consciousness can even manipulate weather (hence "rain dances"), whether through a rare and highly talented individual (such as Black Elk or Ted Owens, to name two), or groups gathered for the purpose.[107]

As previously noted, it appears that high levels of geomagnetic activity often aid in producing PK. Research into the Brazilian sensitive Amyr Amiden showed that his PK effects actually *anticipated* increased geomagnetic flux. On one occasion, as an example, a religious medallion suddenly materialized (a phenomenon known as an *apport*) in the room, appearing to drop from the ceiling. It was followed by another a few minutes later. These events preceded a sudden rise in the area's geomagnetic field.[108]

I had a friend in Sydney who told me of one of his good friends who had a spectacular talent for moving objects at a distance. Aside from seemingly influencing a candle flame to jump and flare up from a distance on one occasion, I have not spent any real time on my own PK capacities, whatever they may be. Incidentally, my friend Larissa, in a state of rage, once apparently caused a television set to "blow," just by her mere presence near it. The repairman said he'd never seen a TV blow in such a way in 25 years of experience. Evidently, *her* proverbial "fuse" blowing caused the same effect in the TV.

This is an interesting trait of some PK phenomena: it often manifests in ways that are highly symbolic. If you "blow a fuse" emotionally, you might just blow an electrical fuse nearby! Braden (who shares a similarly symbolic story involving a couple in *The Divine Matrix*) explains that since we are "tuned" to our world, the world around us represents on a physical level the energy of our emotional experience.[109] Given that all electromagnetism is accompanied by torsion/scalar forces, and that human consciousness seems to be indistinguishable from these forces, is it really so surprising that such synchronistic phenomena as the above TV incident occur? I do not believe so, not in this fundamentally entangled and integrated cosmos ("ordered whole").

Experiments in psychokinesis show that emotion is a key factor in eliciting stronger psi results. Of course, not all experiments or attempts at manifestation go to plan. An occultist by the name of A.O. Spare attempted to manifest freshly cut roses from thin air, waving symbolic drawings around, vigorously repeating the word "roses" with a contorted face. However, instead of roses appearing, the plumbing overhead exploded, inundating Spare and his friend with sewage.[110]

Paracelsus, the great occultist who lived at the tail end of the Middle Ages and early stages of the Renaissance, offered some advice to aspiring occultists: "*Faith* must confirm the imagination, for faith establishes the *will* . . . Determined will is the beginning of all magical operations . . . It is because men do not perfectly imagine and believe the result, that the arts (of magic) are uncertain . . ."[111] Boredom, as noted, has a stultifying effect. Rhine's eight-year research into the ability of gamblers to influence the roll of the dice showed that people's first tests yielded affirmative results at well above chance. On subsequent runs, however, the scores dropped at an increasing rate—the repetitive task was temporarily extinguishing the participants' psi faculties.[112]

Examples such as those of Larissa's kind illustrate that PK can operate subconsciously, and not just through conscious intent. Ergo, the "Pauli Effect" was named in dubious homage to physicist Wolfgang Pauli, who became infamous for apparently causing laboratory apparatus to fall, break, shatter, or burn merely by walking into a lab—or even just passing by in a train at the precise moment of a mishap! Interestingly, no matter how much chaos Pauli seemed to "create" around him, he always escaped unscathed.[113] Drunvalo Melchizedek has said in his *Flower of Life* books that the merkaba, the conscious, interlaced tetrahedral field interpenetrating the body, can be responsible for such phenomena in people who have "activated" it, or in whom it is malfunctioning. Such mishaps can be prevented simply by instructing one's merkaba not to create such effects any more, he says.

The Belief Effect: Sheep, Goat or Jackass?

> Repeated ignorant or stubborn denial of the existence of certain powers does not keep them from existing—except for *us!* —Harold M. Sherman

Have you ever noticed how closed-minded skeptics rarely if ever have any experiences with the siddhis or "the paranormal"? Soviet research into psychokinesis involving Nina Kulagina demonstrated qualitatively that a skeptic's mere presence does have an effect on a psychic's ability to function properly. Hence, with a skeptic (or several) in the room or otherwise involved in the experiment, the psychic is more likely to "fail," thus "proving" the CMS right (at least in his own narrow reality tunnel). It is merely a case of self-fulfilling prophecy.

Wilcock has written that if consciousness creates all known energy, can manipulate matter, and is ultimately a vibrational movement of aetheric energy, then the level of consciousness, intelligence, or love present is directly proportional to the vibrational speed of aether/torsion in that locality. Higher speeds invite higher degrees of intelligence and/or love because there is then more energy available, meaning will has more fuel for exerting effects on "external" systems.[114]

Hunt's research in *Infinite Mind* showed a correlation between auric frequencies and the "level" of consciousness occupied by the individual. Healers, mediums and mystics showed higher frequencies than others not of those categories, illustrating that those possessed of "higher" consciousness are, in some sense, literally "on a higher frequency." Those fixated on or believing solely in "material reality" exhibited lower dominant frequencies and were bereft of the higher.

For Wilcock, all the above explains why Nina Kulagina's PK abilities "worked better in an atmosphere of friendly mutual trust and belief"—PK, as we know, generally requires *higher* brain frequencies and large amounts of bioenergy. It is a higher brain function. Kulagina experienced less stress when working alone and it was said that her PK ability was mood-dependent (both her own mood and that of the observers) and expended more energy in a hostile or skeptical atmosphere[115] (where the collective vibration would have been lowered). Hostile skeptics have something of an innate psi-or consciousness-damping effect; they literally operate at a lower frequency.

Some time before 1919, Emma Hardinge Britten said, "experience has shown that the conditions under which spiritual phenomena are produced through mediums are not only helped or hindered by their mental states, but also by the will, magnetism, and mental states of those who surround them."[116] The situation hasn't changed a great deal since then and similar observations have been made by researchers such as Amit Goswami and Russel Targ.[117]

The difference between open-minded skepticism and closed-minded skepticism can be the difference, for example, between genuine and obvious mediumship as compared to a less successful demonstration (or a complete non-event). Allison DuBois comments amusingly that when she brought through her first deceased professional psychic-medium, communicating with and understanding him was very easy; communicating with deceased former skeptics, on the other hand, she likens to pulling mud through a colander. For her, the more open-minded people are more pleasant in death than those who lived with closed minds.[118]

Negativity causes chaos or entropy in the field, whereas positivity, gratitude, or love cause coherence, beauty and order—just look at the instances of saints and yogis whose dead bodies have remained impervious to decay for weeks, months, and years. Hence, the mere presence of a skeptic (especially a dogmatic and belligerent one) during psychical research may cause disorder and potentially negate psi effects; they create incoherence or "psi-damping" effects. They act as human frequency scramblers and—somewhat ironically—manifest their own beliefs, albeit *unconsciously*. (Fear of failure, which might be likely to increase around hostile observers, also plays a role in some psi experiments, creating inner conflict in the subject that can negate results.)

Practically speaking, the minds of the experimenter/s and the subject are entangled in time-space/implicate order, and therefore psi-negative beliefs belonging to the mind/torsion field of the former can deleteriously affect the psi operations of the latter's.

Need, novelty, and emotion also play a part, as we detailed earlier. Jung noted with interest that the English medium Eileen Garrett fared poorly in the Rhine experiments because she was unable to conjure any feelings for Rhine's "soulless" test-cards.[119] Much experimentation has shown that psi effects have a tendency to start out higher in the initial stages of testing and then drop off as the participants lose interest.

In 1942 psychologist and parapsychologist Gertrude Schmeidler initiated her infamous "sheep-goat" experiments, designed to test whether belief and open-mindedness would enhance psi function in contrast to skepticism. Two groups, "sheep" who believed in or were open to psi, and "goats" who did not believe, were put through identical standard controlled ESP tests. The outcome indicated that believers in the possibility of ESP scored better than those who did not: the disbelievers scored lower, ergo belief is a legitimate variable mediating psi functions.[120]

Some disbelievers have actually produced results significantly *below* chance,[121] manifesting their negative belief in psi—to statistically significant levels. The irony is delicious. Dr. Mario Varvoglis, was President of the Parapsychological Association from 2001–02, and has been involved in psi research since the mid-1970s. Of Schmeidler's research he has said that the sheep-goat discrepancy "has been confirmed by many other researchers. A meta-analysis by [psychologist Tony Lawrence], covering seventy-three experiments by thirty-seven different researchers, clearly confirms that subjects who believe in psi obtain, on the average, higher results than those who do not believe in it."[122]

Lawrence's meta-analysis involved all sheep-goat forced-choice* experiments conducted between 1947 and 1993 and consisted of more than 685,000 guesses by 4,500 participants. The overall results were strongly in favor of the sheep-goat effect—to such an extent, in fact, that to reduce the results statistically to chance would have required an additional 1,726 unpublished and/or non-significant studies. No plausible explanations for this result other than psi have been put forth.[123]

As David Hamilton puts it regarding his own psychic explorations: "Faith, I discovered, meant the difference between broadband and dial-up."[124] Harold Sherman had noted in the early 1940s that while it is possible to receive thought impressions from a skeptic, it is extremely difficult for someone of that mindset to act as receiver.[125] Even for professionals, trying to "receive" from a skeptic can be a big ask (as per DuBois' previous comments). Varvoglis confirms that the more open we are to psi experiences, the better the chances that the world will "respond" by creating them.[126]

Ingo Swann weighs in on Schmeidler's sheep-goat tests, stating that the results initially came as a bombshell because "[s]keptics and disbelievers, of course, very much desired not to be seen as dysfunctional regarding something they were trying to debunk." Ergo, after these experiments were replicated variously by other researchers with similar results, "skeptics and disbelievers decided NOT to take part in ESP tests. In any event, here was something to be swept under mainstream carpets . . ."[127]

It is important to realize, as Mishlove points out, that the sheep-goat studies do not necessarily distinguish those who believe in ESP from those who do not. In most studies, the "sheep" merely accepted the *possibility* that ESP could occur in the test situation, while many of the "goats" were willing to accept that ESP could occur between people who loved each other, or in certain times of crisis; but they did not accept that ESP might operate for them *in their test situation*.[128] On that basis, imagine how psi-negative the beliefs of the fanatical "skeptic" must be. Far better to be open to possibility than closed to it for fear of one's beliefs being wrong.

Harold Sherman, who was ahead of his time, articulated the role of belief and the subconscious mind in the attempt to function as a successful receiver

---

* Forced-choice studies tend to engage the analytical left brain more because of front-loading the subject with data from the start, whereas in free-response studies the subject is unaware of what the target may be and leaves the right hemisphere to operate with less interference. Targ and Puthoff found in their early research that the latter method was more effective. Hence you often hear psychics in informal situations say to their sitter before the reading, "Don't tell me anything!"

in a psi endeavour, explaining that telling yourself with certitude that there is no such thing as psi is tantamount to instructing your subconscious mind to shut down the psi faculties so they do not operate for you.[129]

Edgar Cayce found that there were various factors that could prevent him from giving a reading for someone by hindering or blocking his subconscious mind, for instance the thoughts of those in the room who were "not in accord with the type, class or character of information sought at that particular time." Because of the sensitivity of the process, as well as the difficulty of interpreting the Akashic records themselves, "anyone present for a reading had to be unified in his or her desire to be of help to the questioner." The absence of this synergistic factor could and in some cases *did* blunt Cayce's ability "to reach that position, that plane, that sphere, from which the [data] was being sought."[130]

The openness of individuals present during a psychic reading—in particular the individual being read—is widely acknowledged by intuitives as being of major significance in determining whether or not a given reading is going to be successful. "Openness" does not mean plying the intuitive with information and "helping them along" if they get "stuck," but being open to the possibility that the psychic just might be genuine and might come up with information otherwise unknown to them, demonstrating psi ability. It also means not being openly obstructive.

I am reminded of ex-skeptic Steve Pavlina's comment that all skepticism achieves is the manifestation of more reasons to continue disbelieving: "It would be hard to manifest a more boring reality than that."[131] Boring, limiting, and *disempowering*. In a dream-like reality, it pays to be open-minded.

Assuming our reality to be a mechanistic and observer-independent universe devoid of consciousness merely creates that appearance in that individual's subjective perception and experience of it. When you open your mind, strange things can start to happen that otherwise would not be permitted by your subconscious filters and your limiting conscious beliefs.

The power of belief was demonstrated profoundly to various members of the American Psi Spies in their "nonphysical" excursions. They discovered that when a target site had some form of protection against them, they could circumvent that protection and resume viewing if the session monitor simply asked the viewer what he would find without the protection there.[132] The mere belief in the reality of the psychic blockers on the part of the remote viewer meant that those blockers or scrambler frequencies appeared to succeed in doing their job. However, their effectiveness could be undermined by not believing in them or disregarding them altogether.

Out-of-body explorer Robert Monroe's experience with the Faraday cage where he found he could not penetrate it may have been caused by his own internal expectations and beliefs. Perhaps he believed the mind-field in the OB state was fundamentally electromagnetic, meaning that he would be unable to penetrate the cage, since he knew that Faraday cages blocked EM energy. (The "out-of-body" state is, in reality, a step deeper into mind.)

R.A. Wilson shares an interesting anecdote in *Cosmic Trigger* regarding his youngest daughter, Luna. She had been meditating with two of her siblings when a sudden thud jolted them out of their trances. Luna, who had been on the right of her siblings, was suddenly on the left. Her brother and sister believed she had either levitated or teleported, though Luna herself could not remember moving. When Wilson discussed it with her, she made a stunningly insightful comment by any child's standards: "You believe in ESP, so it happens around you. You don't believe in levitation, so it doesn't happen around you."[133]

Belief is a creative act. In the laboratory of life we can observe this by the fact that disbelievers, on average, experience very little of "the paranormal," while the more open-minded people (not necessarily "believers") tend on average to have much more such experience. The Funda-Materialist responds that they are all mistaken or delusional, which of course the Funda-Materialist could never be, since they inhabit an immutable reality and experience "objective" perceptions of it.

Yet, observe one of the few cases where skeptics actually attempted to provide empirical evidence for one of their "it must be other than psi" rationalizations for positive results. In 1939, psychologists Kennedy and Uphoff asked 28 observers to record 11,125 mock ESP trials to see if "motivated recording errors" could explain positive ESP results. They found that 1.13% of the data were misrecorded (as expected), but of the errors made by believers, 71.5% increased the ESP scores, while for skeptics, *100% of their errors decreased the ESP scores.*[134] Such is the power of fanatical disbelief. With such ardency, anything resembling objectivity is impossible.

Conditioning and Belief as Perceptive Filters

In light of the evidence, dogmatic materialism can justifiably be looked upon as an unconscious ego defence mechanism, designed to preserve the individual's conception of self at the expense of a vast array of fascinating and factual information. Denial is a nice place to visit but I wouldn't want to live there.

In *The Holographic Universe*, Michael Talbot relays an amazing personal experience particularly relevant to the theme of belief and perception. We can see once more here how powerful subconscious conditioning is, given that hypnosis is all about altering the subconscious programs running our brain-minds: Talbot's father had hired a hypnotist to entertain some friends in their home. The most significant part of the show followed the hypnotist's instruction to the entranced man, Tom, that when he exited the trance state his daughter would be invisible to him. Not only could Tom not see his daughter—standing right in front of his face—but he was able to identify a concealed object held in the hypnotist's hand pressed against her back. Not only that, but Tom—staring *through* his daughter—successfully identified the hidden object as a watch and then read the inscription on it, reciting both the name of the watch's owner and the message. The hypnotist then revealed that the object was indeed a watch and passed it around the room so that everyone could see that Tom had read its inscription correctly. Tom confided afterwards to Talbot that all he had seen was the hypnotist holding the watch in his hand.[135] (This underscores that consciousness is fundamentally nonlocal, if you think about it.)

Tom's mind-field had been instructed to remove his daughter from his awareness, and so he automatically decoded the matrix of wave information he was immersed in, in a way that created the appearance of his daughter's absence. The mind in a relaxed hypnotic state is extraordinarily pliable, and this incident serves to show just how powerful a role our subconscious faculties actually play in the way in which we subjectively perceive. It has been reported by Ostrander and Schroeder that in Russia, blanking out someone's ability to see a person or object right in front of them was a routine hypnotic experiment.[136]

Other experiments in which a subject's vision was inverted and turned upside down have shown that the mind quickly reorganizes its perception to allow the subject to view things as per normal. This is not a physical transformation, it is a perceptual one. Without the inverting lenses, the individual's vision becomes upside down again, but quickly readjusts to perceive things as being the right way up again. Various experiments have shown that two people with the *same* retinal impressions can perceive *different* things, while two people receiving *different* retinal impressions can see the *same* thing.[137]

Whose perspective in the above scenario involving Tom and his daughter was the "right" one? Whose perception of "reality" was "better"? Strictly speaking, no one's, but the point here is that no two people experience a given event in precisely the same way—hypnotized or not. What the Thinker thinks, the Prover proves, as R.A. Wilson has pointed out. Tom's daughter was still present (at least in some reference frames), even though he believed and perceived that she wasn't. Everyone else could still see the metaphorical elephant in the room. As Wilson was fond of reminding us, "Reality is plural and mutable."

Cleve Backster achieved a similar feat when he hypnotized a subject to believe that when he awoke he would be unable to perceive Backster for 30 minutes because he wouldn't be in the room. Remaining in the room, Backster (normally a non-smoker) lit a cigarette and smoked it, observing as his subject became increasingly panicky at the levitating cigarette and the smoke being exhaled by an apparently invisible smoker. After the half hour was up, Backster reappeared to his subject as if by magic.[138]

"If the Thinker thinks that the sun moves around the Earth, the Prover will obligingly organize all perceptions to fit that thought; if the Thinker changes its mind and decides the earth moves around the sun, the Prover will reorganize the evidence."[139]

The DIA's 1972 report on "Controlled Offensive Behaviour" disclosed that sanatorium officials in Bulgaria had testified to the effect that "Suggestology," a form of thought repatterning executed on the patient in a state of wakefulness, had cured patients after a few sessions, as well as enabling incisions from surgical operations to heal much faster than normal.[140] The mind was retrained to overwrite the body's normal programming. This sort of thing is an increasingly widely recognized phenomenon. The occultist says that, due to the close interconnection between the mental, astral, and etheric bodies, if someone believes themselves well, their mind may force the body into harmony with their mental state and effect a cure.[141]

The yogi Lahiri Mahasaya once told his then doubtful student, a young Sri Yukteswar, that anything he believed intensely would instantly become so. Yukteswar then asked if he believed he was well and had regained his former healthy weight (he had become unhealthily thin) if it would be so. His guru reassured him that even at that moment it was. Before this exchange, Yukteswar's bodily health had fluctuated drastically in accordance with Mahasaya's verbal insinuations, almost taunting his confused protégé over his consternation and lack of self-awareness.

What Mahasaya was showing his unsuspecting student was that he had the intrinsic power to alter his reality through sheer belief, and that he had indeed been doing it unwittingly all along. He therefore could make himself strong and robust—or sick and feeble—on the basis of belief. Immediately following this exchange, with the revelation having germinated in his mind, Yukteswar weighed himself and found he had gained an incredible 50 pounds of weight—50 pounds that remained on his frame thereafter.[142] How are such phenomena to be explained without acknowledging that we inhabit what Yogananda called an "objectivised dream"?

This case, like the others, is merely a dramatic microcosm of what is happening all the time all around the planet. We are creating our experience of reality *constantly*. Those who hold reductionist beliefs rigidly (Thinker), whether they do it consciously or not, are literally creating, via their Prover (subconscious), a limited perceptual and experiential field for themselves. When you couple that with arrogance and sloppy logic that boils down to "if I can't see it (or do it) then neither can you," you have a recipe for self-induced artificial blindness. This belief is often based on the assumption that everyone perceives the sensory world in the same way, since we all, generally speaking, have sense organs that are designed basically the same. This disregards that fact that anything we perceive (reconstruct) is not perceived directly but "filtered" through the neural network of the brain and our individual information grids (including beliefs) before yielding some sort of impression that we *interpret* as being an objective reality. Any images we perceive are the end result of a lightning-fast but highly sophisticated process of construction, involving various stages, eventually leading (hopefully) to some kind of perception; an *approximation* of reality, not reality itself. In this sense, it is believing that is seeing. As Rudhyar noted in *Culture, Crisis and Creativity*, it is the culture-conditioned mind rather than the eyes that do the seeing.

George Santayana pointed out that we are all much better at believing than seeing. Almost all the time, we see what we believe, and only rarely see what we can't believe.[143] We are less likely to decode into our perceptual reality that which we do not believe in. (We covered these concepts under "The Subjectivity of Experience" in Chapter 7.)

Information grids, or our *models* of the world—also referred to as *schemas*— that lack similar data to what is coming in from the world, will not comprehend or even acknowledge the incoming data, and, as a result, no conscious perception will take place, and this is all the more so when a lack of accurate information is coupled with active disbelief. We don't really see, say, a car; our brain builds a model of it, makes a best guess. Through mental associations and reference to previous experience, we then file our model under *Car* and assess it in relation to other already stored images. We develop a schema that organizes our experience by classifying things and grouping together features and attributes that are typical of, say, cars. This model lets us transcend the limited sense information available to us, in order that we may *perceive* a whole.[144]

As Swann explains,

the "information" that finally comes out as *understanding* will be the sum of the input plus whatever the input gets filtered through in the case of each individual. If matches to the input are found in the memory library, *then* a kind of duplication can take place (which we call "understanding"). But if matches are not found, then the information content probably will be routed through the nearest similarity in the memory library. In this case, we are now one step or more removed from duplication (and removed from "complete understanding"). If no matches are found, then the recipient of the in-put information content will "draw a blank."[145]

These basic principles have been found to extend into activities in the OB/astral state, as well as RV. Both Monroe and Ingo Swann identified the phenomenon of automatic substitution of a nearest match for something that didn't exist in the memory bank. One standout remote viewer at Stanford Research Institute in the 1970s was Hella Hamid, who initially helped bring this recognition problem to the fore and make sense of it. She found that, as her training continued, she began to get a sense of when she was actually missing data and could indicate this *before* her subconscious associative processes took over and replaced whatever the missing data was with the nearest match in her memory.[146]

In *The Structure of Scientific Revolutions*, Thomas Kuhn discussed the research done by the team of Bruner and Postman in the 1940s within the context of how anomalous results in scientific research were first unseen and then ignored, but ultimately precipitated paradigm change. Kuhn notes the way in which the conditioned intellect, when confronted with an anomaly, refers to the memory bank in an attempt to make sense of the anomaly and impose its own contrived order upon it to make it comprehensible. This is largely what science itself is, as well as many of our personal attempts at navigating our familiar everyday worlds: the imposition of a contrived intellectual framework over what merely *is*, a.k.a. an attempt at grasping, seizing, and comprehending what we encounter through our limited human perceptions (which are just approximations anyway).

Bruner and Postman asked experimental subjects to identify, on short and controlled exposure, a series of playing cards, some of which were made to be anomalous, for example, a red six of spades. In each experimental run a single card was displayed in a series of gradually increasing exposures. After each of these, the subject was asked what he had seen, and the test run was terminated by two consecutive correct card identifications. For normal cards most identifications were correct, but the interesting point here is that the *ab*normal cards were almost always immediately identified as one of the *normal* suits.

The anomalous cards were immediately assigned to a pre-existing category in the subject's memory bank (the unfamiliar was replaced with the familiar). As the exposure time for each card increased, however, a sense of anomaly began to creep in. For instance, a subject might have identified a six of spades, except that the black had a red border. Increased exposure caused increased hesitation and confusion until eventually—and sometimes suddenly—most subjects began to correctly identify the anomalous cards without hesitating. After two or three correct identifications the remainder of the anomalous cards presented little difficulty.[147]

This is something we simply refer to as learning or adaptation. We expect to be able to do this, and moreover, we also expect, perhaps unreasonably, that everyone else has the same capacity for it, even when it comes to psi. The next point arising from this compelling study is a small-scale example of what we can observe happening in the world at large within groups of people in relation to data that contradicts the dictates of their semantic circuits and what their memory tells them to expect of reality: a few of Bruner and Postman's subjects were *never* quite able to make the necessary adjustments to their categories to identify the anomalous cards. Even when the average exposure time needed to recognise normal cards was extended by 40 times, over 10% of the anomalous cards could not be correctly named.[148]

It appears that, if sufficiently contrary to conditioned expectation, certain anomalies—even mundane ones such as discrepancies with the appearances of playing cards—are too much for some people and they cannot produce the requisite neurological flexibility or adaptation to facilitate the new experience/data's integration into their minds (at least in the short term). I suspect that for many people, their closed-minded wholesale dismissals of "the paranormal" simply serve to undercut any potential cognitive distress/dissonance caused by contrary data competing for supremacy within their minds (and as I pointed out earlier, all such people know the truth at subconscious levels, so they have to fight to perpetually repress it, especially when the truth is presented to them at the conscious level).

Some of Bruner and Postman's subjects experienced discomfort and distress while viewing anomalous cards at these longer exposure times; their inability to transcend their pre-established categories clearly frustrates and confounds them. No matter what, their conditioned minds would not allow them to perceive accurately what was right in front of their faces—in distress,

473

one subject exclaimed that they weren't even sure what a spade looked like anymore![149]

Thus, we can see how easily our preconceptions from prior conditioning can interfere with our ability to perceive clearly or correctly. Scientists are not immune to this phenomenon because it is a quirk of human psychology—hence the many unscientific opinions wielded by scientists with regard to psi and "the paranormal." (See Chapter 2.)

Believer, Heal Thyself

One of the most spectacular cases of the Thinker being "Proved" is the case of a man named "Wright" who was dying, with cancerous tumors throughout his body, when he tried an experimental new "wonder drug" called Krebiozen, to astonishing effect. He had begged his reluctant doctor, Bruno Klopfer, to let him try it and eventually, due to his dogged determination, Klopfer gave in. He gave Wright an injection of Krebiozen on a Friday, though he barely expected him to last the weekend. Returning the following Monday he found Wright out of bed and walking around. Klopfer reported that his tumors had shrunk dramatically and were half their original size.

Ten days after Wright's first Krebiozen treatment, he left the hospital and was, as far as his doctors could tell, cancer-free. Wright remained well for about two months, that is, until articles began to appear asserting that Krebiozen was powerless against cancer of the lymph nodes. Wright, who was "rigidly logical" and "scientific" in his thinking, "became very depressed, suffered a relapse, and was readmitted to the hospital."

Klopfer now changed tack and told Wright that Krebiozen was indeed as effective as it had seemed, but that some of the initial supplies of the drug had deteriorated during shipping. He explained, however, that he now had a new highly concentrated version of the drug to administer. In reality, the cunning Klopfer simply intended to inject Wright with sterile water. For maximum placebo effect, he even went through an elaborate procedure before injecting Wright, and again the results were dramatic.

Tumor masses melted, chest fluid vanished, and Wright was quickly back on his feet and feeling great—symptom-free for the next two months. But the fairytale ended when the American Medical Association announced that a nationwide study found Krebiozen worthless in the treatment of cancer. His faith completely shattered, Wright's cancer returned with a vengeance and he died two days later.[150]

Welcome to the placebo (and nocebo) effect, or what we might like to call, more plainly, the Belief Effect. It is this sneaky phenomenon that makes life so much more difficult for pharmaceutical companies to get new products into the market. The problem is that control groups often do almost as well as (and sometimes better than) the groups given the new treatment, meaning the drug isn't really working, what is working is the participants' belief!

Hypnosis, which accesses the subconscious (or more specifically, the instinctive mind), is also known to alter our belief structure in similarly profound ways as in the previous examples. Brocq's disease (a form of ichthyosis) develops a thick, horny, reptile-like covering over the skin, which can then harden to the point that even slight movement causes it to crack and bleed. This condition was believed incurable until the early 1950s when a 16-year-old boy with an advanced case was, in a last-ditch attempt at effecting some improvement in his condition, referred to hypnotherapist Dr. Albert A. Mason at the Queen Victoria Hospital in England for treatment.

Mason found the boy to be a good hypnotic subject who was easily inducted into deep trance. With the boy in trance, a confident Mason—thinking he was simply treating a bad case of warts—told him that he was healing and his condition would soon vanish. The scaly layer on the boy's left arm fell off just five days later, and underneath was soft, healthy flesh. After just ten days the arm was completely normal. Mason worked through all areas of his subject's body where scaly skin was present until there was only healthy flesh in its place. For the next five years Mason's young subject remained free of symptoms, until Mason finally lost touch with him—though it is said that he went on to lead a normal life.

This story is considered extraordinary because Brocq's disease is a genetic condition, and getting rid of it means altering the genetic code itself. However, Mason was never able to reproduce this cure of congenital ichthyosis, a fact he attributed to the shattering of his own confidence in the treatment after having been informed he was not treating warts (as he initially thought) but the potentially lethal form of ichthyosis—a condition "known" to be incurable. Following this, he was never able to re-create the prior confidence he held in the hypnosis, and presumably his patients picked up on this at some level. "I was acting."[151]

In a similar vein, a doctor using the path-Oscilloclast device invented by Dr. Albert Abrams, the father of radionics, found himself curing many disease conditions, including cancer. Then one day he realized that the machine had never been plugged in. People were healing unwittingly by the power of suggestion. "You can imprint your thought-forms onto a scalar wave and deliver the 'product' at a distance," writes Bartlett.[152] Or, as Yogi Ramacharaka put it in 1903, "mesmerism or hypnotism is practically the bathing of the person in a flow of thought-forms, kept stimulated and active by a constant supply of Prana."[153]

When you reprogram the subconscious (instinctive) mind's belief structure you can cause the DNA to alter its coding to manifest a new reality—if the method is successful. The body doesn't discriminate, it just does what the encoded information in the holographic auric field (representing various levels of our psyche) is "instructing" it to do. On that basis, much, if not all, illness is psychosomatic or psychogenic[*] and potentially reversible—oftentimes with amazing ease, as EFT and other energy psychology techniques have spectacularly proved so many times.

Gariaev and colleagues' pioneering DNA research accounts for the power of hypnosis (as well as virtually all other psi phenomena, or "hypercommunication"), as outlined by Fosar and Bludorf:

> Since the basic structure of DNA-alkaline pairs and of language are of the same structure . . . [o]ne can simply use words and sentences of the human language! This, too, was experimentally proven! Living DNA substance . . . will always react to language-modulated laser rays and even to radio waves, if the proper frequencies are being used. This finally and scientifically explains why affirmations, autogenous training, hypnosis and the like can have such strong effects on humans and their bodies. It is entirely normal and natural for our DNA to react to language . . . [154]

We can access DNA through light, sound, and the spoken word. When correctly triggered, "jumping DNA," some of the 97–8% of our DNA that does not create the protein codes to build our bodies can move from one location to another (either directly or through an RNA intermediary) and re-code the organism at the physical level, otherwise known as "DNA activation."[155]

The belief effect extends into the surgical realm too. Let's look at a study published in 2002 by Dr. J. Bruce Mosely and colleagues, which compared the

---

[*] Barbara Brennan takes this notion to its logical conclusion—as someone who can see into the different levels of people's psyches—by saying that, in truth, any given physical problem ultimately represents a dissatisfaction of the soul that requires remedy. (Source: Brennan, *Light Emerging*, 49.)

results of sham surgery and real surgery on patients with severe, debilitating knee pain. Study volunteers were divided into three groups: one received lavage (the knee joint was flushed of debris using at least 10 l of fluid), another group received lavage and then debridement (which can include the shaving or removal of damaged cartilage and meniscal fragments), and the third received fake surgery.

In the third group, all the normal procedures were followed: the patient was sedated, three incisions were made in the knee, and the surgeon generally spoke and acted as he would during a debridement procedure. Not only was a saline solution splashed to simulate the sound of a lavage treatment, but the subject was kept in the operating theater for the time it would take to perform a debridement. The incisions were then sewed up in the usual way. All three groups received the same post-operative care treatment, including an exercise program, and recorded their progress over a two year period.

As expected, the two surgery groups improved, BUT—the placebo group improved *at least as much* as the other two. "Indeed, objectively measured walking and stair climbing were poorer in the débridement group than in the placebo group at two weeks, and one year, and showed a trend toward *worse* functioning at two years"[156] (emphasis added). Mosely, who was initially convinced that placebo effects played no role in surgery, courageously admitted afterward that the opposite was the case: the *entire benefit* of this knee surgery lay in the placebo effect. Similarly stunning results have been found in placebo studies on depressed participants as well as in other areas.[157]

The placebo's pharmacomimetic behavior can also imitate a drug's side effects (as opposed to its intended effects). Science historian Anne Harrington put it that placebos are "ghosts that haunt our house of biomedical objectivity and expose the paradoxes and fissures in our own self-created definitions of the real and active factors in treatment."[158] Church reports that placebos cure in about 35% of cases,[159] and medical students are currently taught this interesting fact (thank goodness).[160]

In fact, recent research published in the scientific journal *Public Library of Science* has shown that placebos can be more effective than no treatment at all, *even when the patient is fully informed beforehand that they are being given a placebo—even from a bottle plainly labeled "placebo".*[161] This is probably linked to the fact that the strength of the placebo effect has been increasing for the last 30 years. It seems that we are conditioning or entraining reality, building a sort of parapsychological momentum, accentuating the increasing trend towards mind-over-matter effects.

William Tiller has proposed that the placebo effect and its increasing potency can be attributed to nonlocal informational entanglement between the placebos and the treatments they simulate, which implies the presence of some kind of nonlocal intelligence that must recognize the meaningful similarity and connection between the two: their conceptual bond. Tiller's working hypothesis is that the activated deltron* population has somehow increased at an accelerating rate for the past roughly fifty years, increasing the connectedness between "separate" space-time objects, in particular, between humans and objects.

Put simply, this amplifies the mind-matter interaction so that the reciprocal space aspect of a placebo (or its wave-based quantum aspect in "time-space") assumes dynamic aspects that then produce real effects here in D-space, our electromagnetic space-time frame.[162] This nonlocal information entanglement between meaningfully related entities is not limited to placebos/non-placebos, but is a principle of reality in general, the inevitable result of the operations of a conscious, holofractal universe.

In contrast to the placebo effect, the *nocebo* effect occurs where we engage in negative beliefs that, instead of creating enhanced health and healing, create illness and malfunction. In this light we can see that the "death sentences" so often uttered by doctors to "terminally ill" patients can potentially cause them to create a nocebo effect and ultimately lead to their deaths.[163]

The dire effect of pointing the bone in Australian Aboriginal culture is well known.[164] The physiologist Walter Cannon found by studying cases of voodoo death that some people who believe they are under a spell can die by autosuggestion—even if they are in perfect health.[165] I shudder to think how much voodoo death is being wrought unwittingly within a corporately oriented medical system that gives to *already unwell* people *death sentences* (and arbitrary time lines). Dossey refers to such instances as "medical hexes" and provides some shocking (and all too common) examples of such medical malpractice in *The Dark Side of Consciousness*.[166]

The pendulum of manifestation swings both ways. Lahiri Mahasaya had a famous friend, Trailanga Swami, who was reputed to be over 300 years old. On many occasions, the swami was seen to drink the most deadly poisons with

---

* Deltrons are a form of matter postulated in Tiller's empirical physical theory which allow for the interaction between our D-space reality's matter and the "nonlocal" inverted R-space reality's matter. This facilitates various paranormal phenomena and entanglement in general. In *Psychoenergetic Science* R-space matter is synonymous with aether and Tiller says it is necessary when considering the subtler/occult forces and the origins of known forces and matter in general.

impunity, as well as performing many other miraculous feats.[167] (He also ate very seldom, and yet weighed over 300 pounds, preceding Therese Neumann and her own "inexplicable" combination of inedia and hefty weight.) Thus, we can see that the nocebo and placebo effects have been well known in India for a very long time, because of its traditional spiritual disciplines.

In point of fact, Yogi Ramacharaka emphasized in lessons given in 1903 that pranic/etheric energy is responsible one way or another for virtually all forms of local and distant healing, as well as healing by auto-suggestion and hypnosis (and the rarer form of spiritual healing proper, which also involves higher energies).[168]

Max von Pettendorfer, a critic of one of the co-founders of germ theory (Robert Koch), was so convinced that germ theory was wrong that he publicly drank an entire vial of vibrio cholera, the virulent pathogen Koch discovered in 1884 and believed to cause cholera. To everyone's astonishment, Pettendorfer was completely unaffected.[169]

In 1950 in a clinical study, pregnant women were given a "drug" they were told would remedy their morning sickness. The women found that it "worked," only the substance turned out to be ipecac syrup, something known to actually *induce* vomiting, not prevent it.[170] Belief in a placebo disguised as an analgesic actually produces neuropeptides that fit into pain receptors, thus curing pain.[171] Research at the Common Cold Unit of the Medical Research Council in Salisbury between 1946 and 1989 proved that mere exposure to rhinovirus was not enough on its own to induce illness in volunteers—who did not know whether they were receiving a placebo or the pathogen. It was found instead that emotional distress was linked to greater infection rates.[172] (Stress in general lowers immune function and weakens the etheric body's protection.)

The yogi's understanding of these PK phenomena has far outstripped modern science's—science only fairly recently (in the grand scheme of things) acknowledging the mind–body connection!

The Non-Intention Effect

Many people speak of manifesting a PK intervention by forming a request or intention and then releasing it to the universe. Richard Bartlett's Matrix Energetics utilizes such a method—the art of "doing nothing." A student of his reported to him on a friend who had had a major blockage in her heart identified. As far as the doctors were concerned, she would need surgery, a stent, and a year or more of medication.

Bartlett's student intuitively "checked in" on her friend remotely and was able to see/feel the blockage in her heart. She tracked the reality where her friend would need surgery, a stent, and medication, and then, knowing this was only one possible outcome, she shifted her awareness to view a reality where the doctors could find nothing wrong with her friend's heart. She left it at that and let go, never telling her. Yet, the next medical examination a couple of days later revealed that the blockage no longer existed, much to the woman's bafflement, not to mention her doctor's.[173]

The student had intervened in her friend's reality and selected out of the "quantum soup" of possibility a more favorable reality, which raises an interesting point in itself: we can indeed influence the reality of another person without their consciously knowing about it (I strongly advise taking account of ethical considerations here, however). This suggests to me that practices such as voodoo and black magic, where props are used, are probably utilizing the same principles of consciousness, only in a more indirect manner via the props.

The equipment that is used is not as important as the intention, conviction, and *trust* behind it (non-attachment). Trust (or "faith" enough to let go) is needed to get one's controlling ego-mind out of the way to allow for the larger "cosmic consciousness" to utilize its pool of infinite possibilities, most of which the conscious mind would never conceive of or know how to effect/implement in real time. The unified field is smarter than any one organism immersed in it! It processes the "what" of your intent or desire and provides the "how" of manifesting it—the message is that humans need not try to control the *how* of things because there is a greater transpersonal intelligence to take care of that. ("When your attitude is right the facts don't matter.") The secret lies in the not doing, as Bartlett states.[174]

In laboratory tests with PK in ordinary people, effects often fail to appear *until the subject has their attention diverted*.[175] (Recall the remote healers earlier in this chapter who set their intent and then get out of the way.) This is something that astral traveller Sylvan Muldoon wrote of some 80 years ago, explaining that charging the mind with desire or intent creates "stress" for which the mind seeks an outlet or release via a part of the subconscious he called the crypto-conscious Will: "Then [it] gets a chance to work on the 'stress,' and that which you had given up trying to attain 'materializes'!"[176]

Chakra Connection

In Motoyama's further investigations, the ECG and plethysmograph were employed to attempt to clarify any functional dissimilarities in the cardiovascular systems of yogis and ordinary persons, in relation to the *anahata* (heart) chakra. Motoyama found that in ordinary subjects the baseline fluctuation of the plethysmograph was minimal, indicating constant blood flow, whereas in the case of yogis and other long-term spiritual practitioners, he often noted a significant flux in the basal blood flow as well as anomalies in the heartbeat. This implied to Motoyama that in particular cases the autonomic nerves controlling the cardiovascular system—blood vessels in particular—somehow functioned in an unexpected rhythmic fashion.

In turn, this suggested to Motoyama an abnormally large functional range for the autonomic nerves, as well as the range of dynamic balance between the sympathetic and parasympathetic systems in yogis.[177] It is well known to researchers that yogis often show phenomenal control over bodily functions typically thought to be uncontrollable by the conscious mind (autonomic functions). Motoyama also mentions another yogi who claimed to have awakened his *anahata* chakra and to have achieved voluntary control over his cardiac functions. He was studied at the Lanaula Yoga Institute near Mumbai and was found to have the ability to cause temporary cardiac arrest by holding his breath.[178]

On the basis of his research, Motoyama connected the wider autonomic functionality of yogis with the gradual development of the various chakra centers. Eventually the yogi gains conscious control over the organs governed by a certain chakra.[179] Thus, we can see further bioenergetic roots for mind-over-matter phenomena.

For his research into esoteric human anatomy, Motoyama developed the AMI—Apparatus for Measuring the Functional Conditions of Meridians and their Corresponding Internal Organs—an instrument designed to measure the initial skin current, in response to DC voltage externally applied at special acupuncture points located alongside the base of fingernails and toenails. According to the acupuncture theory, these special points—called "sei (well) points" are ostensibly the terminal points of meridians where the Qi energy either enters or exits the body.

Studies using the AMI and Chakra Machine on subjects who showed clear chakra activity and psi ability led Motoyama to a fascinating conclusion: specific types of psi abilities do seem to be connected to the specific chakras thought to be responsible for them, and people with specific psi abilities do display abnormalities in their meridian systems. Motoyama and his colleagues also found evidence for the idea that psi abilities can be classified into two types: receptive and generative. Motoyama linked receptive powers (remote viewing, for instance) to the lower chakras, and powers of generation (such as PK) to the higher chakras.[180]

It is of interest that one of Kunz and Karagulla's female subjects who possessed moderately developed psi abilities, including high empathy and clairsentience, showed a tendency towards digestive disturbances resulting, apparently, from the increased sensitivity of her solar plexus chakra, through which she connected with people "in terms of feeling quality."[181] According to Motoyama's research, most people whose psi abilities are primarily receptive or "passive" usually show little ability to influence external objects or the thoughts of other people.

On the other hand, strong PK and healing abilities were shown by those subjects with awakened heart chakras. AMI tests showed that subjects whose psi abilities were primarily receptive tended to show functional disorders in specific meridians, including stomach, spleen, kidney and bladder meridians—which all correspond to lower chakras.[182] Subjects whose abilities were mainly of the generative type tended to show energy excesses and instabilities in meridians related to the heart, and, they suspected, the *anahata* chakra. Aside from this, these subjects' ECGs also often showed arrhythmia and patterns characteristic of angina pectoris.[183]

Thus, the ancient metaphysical knowledge handed down by history's greatest yogis and mystics does find a significant degree of scientific support in Motoyama's research. Motoyama also speculates that the transforming function of the chakras may explain the ability of some yogis to remain buried underground for incredible lengths of time (40 days in some cases) and yet remain alive. As detailed already, the chakras receive and convert specific frequencies from each density of the aetheric medium into biologically useful forms (hence the phenomenon of inedia).

New Biological Perspectives on PK: the DNA Phantom Effect

In 1984, Dr. Peter Gariaev discovered a completely unexpected phenomenon linked to DNA, which became known as the "DNA phantom effect." In 1995, quantum biologist Vladimir Poponin and his colleagues, including Gariaev, reported on the research they had been doing at the Russian Academy of

Sciences on this remarkable phenomenon. (It has since been replicated at the Institute of HeartMath and elsewhere.)

Poponin and Gariaev designed their experiment to test the effect of DNA on photons. Removing the air from a specially designed tube, a scattering chamber, they created what's regarded as a vacuum—though photons remained inside, scattered randomly. In the next part of the experiment, samples of DNA were placed inside the closed tube with the photons. The photons did something totally unexpected by conventional knowledge, but which Gariaev would have anticipated based on his original discovery: they created wave patterns. The DNA was somehow influencing and *ordering the photons.* But the most remarkable aspect of the experiment occurred upon removing the DNA altogether: *the light continued to show order and create (spiral) wave patterns*—which persisted for up to a month in some cases.[184]

The DNA sample had "engineered" the vacuum/aether and entrained the local EM environment, supporting the notion that DNA does indeed act as an interface between our space-time reference frame and aether/time-space/implicate order. Was this effect due to the torsion fields accompanying or being harnessed by the DNA? Apparently so: torsion fields are known to be very stable and persistent. Clearly some kind of non-EM field scalar force was somehow organizing the photons in the absence of the DNA.

Crucially, Gariaev discovered that when he "extinguished" the DNA phantom using gaseous nitrogen, it would automatically return within 5–8 minutes,[185] re-emerging from the vacuum. Thus, the idea that the morphogenesis of DNA is essentially initiated and guided by nonlocal forces ("morphic fields") emerging from hyperspace finds a degree of support in these experiments.

More than its astounding implications for the field of biophysics, this experiment has implications for the field of consciousness research. DNA interfacing with the nonlocal and holographic vacuum/implicate order/aether offers a biological mechanism for how a living human being can use intention to influence events nonlocally through time (as per the retrocognition and time-reversed experiments we looked at), as well as nonlocally through space, transcending both linear time and ordinary spatial constraints. The intermediary "between" our biology and the vacuum is apparently the torsion field.

It is also interesting to note that Gariaev and his colleagues have found no other substance that re-creates or emulates the effect of the DNA molecule. Likewise is it interesting to compare the similarities between these experiments revealing DNA's ability to "engineer" the vacuum—and thereby entrain EM energy—with the Phantom Leaf effect and Phantom Limb syndrome. In all three cases it appears that invisible (torsion/scalar) fields retain the form of the physical counterpart generated by the DNA and continue to entrain EM energies coupled to them, for a while at least.

It is interesting, however, to note Tiller's research, which demonstrated that the EM energies in a room can be entrained in the absence of DNA, just by playing a recording of human mental intent. DNA, by harnessing nonlocal torsion fields which couple to and influence local EM energies, also plays a role in the quantum tunneling of photons hypothesized to account for the ability of people such as Geller and Serios who can (or *could* in the case of the late Serios) expose shielded camera film using nothing but deliberate intent.

When you put even just some of the pieces together and acknowledge (for instance) that

- the human "torsion-plasma" fields can be altered by intention and emotional variability
- human intention can alter physical spin states, Van der Waals forces, and molecular structure in physical substances—including metals
- remote/nonlocal interactions between humans and extracted cell and DNA samples have been experimentally established
- isolated human DNA samples can literally engineer the (conscious) holographic vacuum/aether from which our reality emerges,

then it is easy to see that there is no good reason to deny either the conceptual plausibility of mind-over-matter effects, or the many observed and documented instances of it.

Gariaev and Poponin's experiments suggest that in people with extraordinary PK abilities, certain codons in the DNA sequence—which in most people would be inactive—have become operationalized, meaning they can more effectively and predictably project intention into the material world to influence it. "In China a new generation of children is being born now with several codons in their DNA activated which enable them to be extremely psycho-kinetic, clairvoyant, and in other ways able to engage in paranormal activities such as remote viewing almost effortlessly."[186] The increasing number of psychic children being born suggests that humankind is evolving towards an altogether higher, more conscious state of being—a topic I will return to in TGI 2.

Also think back to our discussion of DNA activation using the human voice and Solfeggio frequencies, as well as Gariaev's experiments in re-coding DNA using light and radio frequencies. We established, among other things, that dormant transposons or "jumping DNA"—which comprise about 97% of our DNA—can be operationalized to move around, re-coding the genome to be more functional, with near-immediate physical healing effects.

But, strictly speaking, you do not have to be born with extra codons activated, nor do you have to perform a "DNA Potentiation," in order to become more psychic. We established in Chapter 5 that many, many NDEers have returned from the afterlife to find that they possess incredible psychic abilities they had never before dreamed of having.

Evidently, in these cases, conscious contact with deeper levels of reality (or implicate orders/time-space)—which are all really part of us anyway—causes a transposon burst which operationalizes previously dormant codons; suddenly the NDEer is unintentionally reading minds, healing diseases, and causing unintentional electrical disturbances in their local vicinity. As noted, the other way to precipitate a DNA activation appears to be via kundalini activation, though the two paths may also go hand in hand.[187]

Thus, in principle, there is nothing truly paranormal or bizarre about the ability to, for example, literally manifest a physical object from the aether/time-space/implicate order by using nothing but focused intent. One "merely" organizes the existing undifferentiated (mental, astral, and etheric) consciousness and information around themselves into a desired manifest form. "It from bit." Just remember: you can't spell "it" or "bit" without "I"—and your "I" is fundamentally infinite consciousness. There is nothing else.

I experience what I believe, unless I believe I won't, in which case I don't, which means I did. —Harry Palmer

In short, the testimony has been so abundant and consentaneous that either the facts must be admitted to be such as reported, or the possibility of certifying facts by human testimony must be given up. —Professor Challis, Cambridge, 1863

Epilogue

We have demonstrated beyond all reasonable doubt that the human being not only consists of far more, but is also capable of far more than is believed possible in the materialistic-reductionist philosophy. In linking torsion/scalar fields with consciousness existing in a reciprocal time-space/implicate order (and ultimately enfolded in a completely unified and non-dualistic "holomovement," or infinite consciousness), we have shown that the essence of who we are can never be extinguished, since it was not generated in our brains to begin with, and is indeed not subject to any imagined linear flow of time.

Our formerly formidable fear of "death" can rightfully be seen as a modern and yet outdated superstition. We are, both each and collectively, an infinite, immortal being dreaming "reality" into existence. From this perspective, psi phenomena are not just possible but inevitable and the furthest thing from "paranormal," as mystics and occultists have always known and told those with ears to hear.

Those with eyes to see know that the philosophical postulates of materialistic reductionism are utterly and undeniably untenable, and more to the point, a "dangerous nuisance," as Colin Wilson might say. Why? Because this fragmentary worldview has led—along with certain unfortunate aspects of orthodox organized religion—to corollary perceptions and beliefs that cause us to view seemingly separate and distinct aspects of the planetary ecology and even the human race as expendable.

This is the ego delusion. It allows for the devaluing and marginalization of that perceived by the personality as "not self." What can be perceptually and conceptually separated from oneself can be sacrificed or ignored for one's own convenience or comfort, if need be—this is part of the Darwinian psychopathology of our time.

Within a holistic paradigm of a fundamentally entangled and holographic universe, these conceptualizations can no longer be sustained, and this profound change of perspective can only increase our chances of collective survival—in fact not just survival, but the creation of a paradigm of abundance, compassion, and community, where *real* freedom is a right realized effortlessly in every individual's lifetime. Gone will be the days where predatory and conscienceless tyrants and their banks, corporations, and corrupt governments rule over a scared, submissive, and/or apathetic humankind.

Within the holistic "infinite consciousness paradigm," we can also better conceptualize such out-of-the-box notions as free energy/overunity devices and other alternative and superior energy sources, which are, contrary to misguided popular notions, being widely developed and employed quietly around the globe. They are only "impossible" to the spiritually and conceptually blinded.[1]

Thus far we have taken a glimpse at the monumental human potential for the future, but there has been no space to give certain topics their due. Although much of the material in this volume both directly and indirectly supports the notion of an afterlife, I have not delved deeply into the netherworlds of time-space that souls—for a while at least—call home, and nor have I attempted to comprehensively work such material into the framework presented here. Attempting to deal with such subjects in this limited space would have been an egregious injustice upon such important topics.

Exactly what happens to most people when they "die"? What are the so-called astral and mental planes of occultism actually like, if they exist? Can the living interact with the dead, and if so, to what extent? Is the spirit world all just "love and light," or does it have a darker side? Could occultism and mysticism, working with science, offer us insight into these questions that is undreamt of in orthodox paradigms?

I put it to you that the now irretrievably scientifically proven facts of various siddhis/psi abilities are *not* just cruel mockeries of a naive and futile human yearning to defy what some see as the bleak lacuna that lurks at the end of our fragile existence, for the brain does not create the mind. Should there be any remaining doubts about this, the second volume of this book will put them to rest (in peace).

Widening our scope, we might also ask where exactly humanity is going collectively, and how does this metaphysical knowledge relate? In the story of existence that we are telling ourselves, does 2012 really factor in as the hype suggests, and how will our world look beyond 2012? (In the next volume I will talk about what I call the "2012 window"—a period of time surrounding and including the year 2012—and what it represents.)

Is there meaning behind the madness of the world's accelerating and increasingly confounding events and accumulation of information? Is there the possibility of a mass DNA activation on the horizon? Are we participating in a mass awakening that could transform mankind and life as we know it?

If you think you are ready for the answers to these questions and many more, then in TGI 2 we will go and get them.

Strap in.

ABOUT THE AUTHOR

Brendan is a visionary anchor for the new consciousness, with a compassionate heart, keen intellect, no-bullshit humanitarianism, and genuine loathing for political correctness. He advocates "broad spectrum awareness," meaning a big-picture, well rounded, multi-faceted worldview – the result of years of study "connecting the dots" between the various rabbit holes.

In The Grand Illusion Brendan has attempted what few other authors dare to, making his perspective invaluable to anyone consciously seeking deeper awareness of themselves, the nature of reality, and the challenges of life on earth. Specifically, the TGI books are designed to permanently blow minds and transform human consciousness, and therefore life on earth. TGI 2 and the following titles will continue to push the cutting-edge and raise awareness in order to better the quality of life on Earth for all—that is their raison d'être.

In complement to his writing, Brendan also facilitates very powerful sound-based "DNA activations," offering conscious seekers a trigger point for accelerated evolution and multi-levelled healing. There has been some amazing feedback and lives have indisputably been transformed. That's what it's all about!

For Brendan, in seeking truth, nothing is sacrosanct, no precept too precious, and no dogma unquestionable. The need to understand and deepen consciousness must trump the ego's insecurities, need for control, and fear of change.

On a more personal note, Brendan is a talented musician with a versatile voice and skill on the guitar, and he relishes the opportunity to immerse himself in song-writing. You can find some of his musical work on Youtube (there will eventually be an original album one day down the track).

He invites you to sign up to receive his occasional newsletter and "like" The Grand Illusion Facebook page, as well as joining "The Grand Illusion books dialogue and discussion group."

Follow Brendan on Social Media

Instagram:
instagram.com/brendan.d.murphy/

Gab:
gab.ai/earthbefree

Twitter:
twitter.com/BrendanDMurphy1

Pinterest:
au.pinterest.com/earthbefree/

Facebook:
facebook.com/GrandIllusionBooksScienceSpiritualityConsciousness/

Find me on Youtube – search for:
Exposing The Grand Illusion with Brendan D. Murphy

Global Freedom Movement's Youtube:
youtube.com/user/GlobalFreedomMovemen

DNA Potentiation

"I would like to say a very big, big thank you for potentiating me in the first place, one of the best experiences of my life, a turning point which continues to amaze me everyday. Thank you." –Connie Cauvin

I am certified by Sol Luckman and the Phoenix Center for Regenetics to perform in-person or distance DNA Potentiation, Articulation (the second of the four Regenetics Method activations), Elucidation (the third activation), and the fourth and final activation: Transcension. I perform this healing function as an ordained minister of the Universal Life Church.

The 4 "DNA activations" of the Regenetics Method herald a "return to Source," a personal renaissance for many.

For me personally, I watched as this activation process seemed to turn up the intensity of synchronistic flow in my life, and facilitated things "falling into place" for me along the way. Increased physical robustness and some long overdue healing was also noted, which I write about here: globalfreedommovement. org/diary-dna-potentiator-personal-dna-hack-tivation-saga-continues/

As everyone is unique, so too is each individual's activation and healing unfoldment—predictions are hard to make! I have been truly blown away and humbled by some people's feedback on their experiences. It's my honour to help people access their human potential.

To learn more about these activations and see some testimonials, please visit this page: brendandmurphy.com/dna-activation/

GLOBAL FREEDOM MOVEMENT

Aimee and I created Global Freedom Movement with the input of two good friends on March 1st, 2014, as the result of a confluence of forces and factors synchronistically flowing together, apparently to serve a function and purpose that the collective human unconscious deemed important for us.

In the lead up, we became entangled in a series of bizarre synchronistic events involving an activist expedition to the Aussie outback to connect with some of the original peoples of the land now known as Australia.

You couldn't have planned it if you tried!

We were to broadcast interviews with original Elders from the outback and our group of "co-conspirators" had nominated me in advance as the voice for the job. None of it went quite as planned/expected, but the prospect of a journey to Australia's "red centre" to learn of and try to *do something about* the poverty and marginalizing of the original peoples of these lands is what led to the creation of Global Freedom Movement.

It was immediately clear that Global Freedom Movement was our baby and exactly the kind of vehicle we needed to potentially impact the lives of millions for the better.

From that seminal journey in 2014 Global Freedom Movement has gone from strength to strength. Since then we've been doing our educational and activist work full-time. We started GFM Radio (now GFM Media) broadcasts on a weekly basis and have reached tens of thousands of people with our 60+ interviews. We've reached thousands more through talks, articles, this book, webinars, TV, web, and radio interviews.

Please join our community at globalfreedommovement.org/join. By signing up (it's free), you'll get access to our Resource Library for Truthseekers, our occasional newsletters and important updates and announcements.

GLOBAL FREEDOM UNIVERSITY

Global Freedom Movement (GFM) is really only just getting started. We want you to go "next level" with us. That's why we created the Global Freedom University (a.k.a. the Truthiversity) and social networking community (and more).

Global Freedom University (GFU) is the first of its kind: a truly independent and "alternative," functional, multi-dimensional learning (and social) portal where you will explore broad-spectrum, life-enhancing and myth-busting resources covering the most important subjects for awareness development, healing, and the transformation of life on earth.

This is about more than just information; it's an exposé as well as a "blueprint for living" which explains what has been done to humanity, why it happened, what we can do about it, and the direction we need to move in.

Alternative media interviews and indy news just isn't enough. Through the different faculties, the Truthiversity will pull the broad spectrum of information together into a coherent, accessible whole *so you can truly implement it*. GFM Media will still go on, but as a subset of the Truthiversity, giving "alternative/independent media" its rightful place within a bigger, more coherent picture.

Streamline your awakening. Meet your tribe. Feel alive.

globalfreedommovement.org/university

REVIEWS OF THE GRAND ILLUSION

You've written the best synthesis of modern science and esoteric science that I've seen in 40 years of study in that area. Brilliant! This book is such a perfect introduction for newcomers to the esoteric world and especially for skeptics who need a scientific explanation to make them understand the mystical. You've put in modern language and with up-to-date science what the Theosophist set out to do in the 19th century. I've been waiting for this book for years! P.S. I've signed up for your mailing and... my God, how old are you? You look much too young to have written such a wide-ranging but also very deep book. Again...brilliant! —Michael Wade

———

This book is a must read for anyone desiring the scientific and historical foundation as well as a practical, thorough, logical understanding of all that is mysterious in our world, particularly the relationship between consciousness, energy, and existence. Brendan's incredibly thorough review of the literature as well as his ability to clearly articulate and integrate a wide range of esoteric and scientific concepts is like nothing I have ever seen or read before. He is brilliant to say the least... I HIGHLY recommend this book for all scientists...and anyone who knows there is a way to connect our entire historical knowledge base to an integrated whole of all that is visible and invisible but feels overwhelmed in attempting to put the puzzle together. Brendan has done it for us.

My partner and I have both read *The Grand Illusion* and we were BLOWN AWAY by it. You have the knack for making really sophisticated material easy to understand, and I was grateful in particular for your description of torsion which I could never really understand when others tried to explain it. The whole book was amazing and I am insisting that all of the trainers who teach my model read it as well as putting it on the Must Read list for my classes and telling them about it verbally. It is important. Thank you for this masterpiece. The world needs it. —Lisa Schwarz, developer of the Comprehensive Resource Model

———

TGI was my catalyst. I wasn't seeking anything and it wasn't even recommended. My father phoned me one day and started with "I'm reading this very interesting book..." After the phone call I bought the Kindle version. Then I bought the paper version to loan out to others. I decided after reading that if even 1% of this book was true, what the hell was I doing in my life?

At the end of 2013 I simply got up and turned off my television one night. Within the same week, I was reading TGI with my "extra time." TGI blew open doors and windows and walls and ceilings...and at JUST the right time. During and after reading, I quickly moved into so many different areas of interest and educated myself about so many different topics. I can converse conceptually on a variety of topics and I can understand where people are coming from in their chosen field. NOTHING phases me, no possibility is out of reach and life is even more amazing because the depth available is only ever hinted at for you to discover for yourself and there is NO LIMIT to anything. You go as deep as you want/choose to.

Reality is deeper and higher and wider now. Anything I want it to be. I can, at will, stand myself / perspective back and back and back and then zoom in to peoples' individual perspectives and probe their position in a totally new way. It's a cool conversational skill to have "developed." I'm certainly lighter and happier and it is the baseline I use for each new day. There is a LOT to laugh at—in a genuinely lighthearted way.

There is something about the way TGI is put together...taking you on this adventure ride. Your left brain is satisfied by the science, stats and evidence and your right brain does a little dance with all the possibilities. "If that is true...then that means..."

TGI covers such a wide range of subjects at just the right amount of depth. I had to keep putting the book down to be able to process the possibilities of what I read, which is unusual for me. It is the only book I recommend and I have been recommending it for 3 years now, and counting.

It opens up the world of possibilities, their possibilities, their potential. Historical evidence of human potential in many, many areas. Proven. TGI is an enjoyable read and it is a long read. It took me 3 weeks to get through it on my Kindle and I am a two-to-three-books-a-week person. I totally savoured TGI and even re-read some parts/chapters to glean more juice from each page of treasures.

TGI completely opened up my perspective on life, living and what is humanly possible. TGI has been the impetus and catalyst for exploring my own human potential. I am forever grateful to have had it land in my life at just the perfect time. Thank you. —Tamara Dunn

Brendan, my sole purpose of reaching out to you today is to say THANK YOU. I began my spiritual journey about two years ago and the past five to six months I was lost and tuned out. I asked myself on an almost daily basis "What is it going to take to get back into my meditation, yoga, spiritual practice?" Alongside several life events, negative and positive, I picked up your book which I had ordered almost a year earlier and began to read. I finally just "KNEW" I was ready for change. With your help I was able to get back on the path to my future.

The Grand Illusion is beautifully crafted and well put together...When I reached a time in my life where I felt that people didn't understand me and I should probably conform to those around me, your book was a great assistance to stay true to myself. Thank you. —Taylor Jones

———

A masterpiece. If *The Grand Illusion* were merely paradigm-destroying, which it certainly is for rearguard scientific "Funda-materialists," it would be a satisfying read. Fortunately, for those of us dedicated to establishing a new civilization of consciousness, Brendan Murphy's fascinating, inspiring and seminal work also opens the door to a world of new creative possibilities. If David Wilcock's *The Source Field Investigations* was mind-expanding, *The Grand Illusion* is mind-blowing. —Sol Luckman, author of *Potentiate Your DNA*

———

What a read! [TGI] is a masterful compilation of so-called "paranormal" scientific studies as well as human testimony of psi phenomena. He seamlessly synthesizes occultism with modern science and leaves us wanting even more. After setting a foundation for the reader, he proceeds to utterly dismantle conventional science's eroding framework, giving us a blank slate to work with.

As I read his exposé on conventional science, I found myself frustrated as indoctrinated belief systems within myself were starting to crumble. A few times I even had to put the book down...After the reader and Brendan are on a similar wavelength in regards to the message he is trying to convey, the rocket launches. This book is inundated with interesting studies, human testimony, and a few jaw-dropping photos. TGI is an incredible read through and through. The information [is] put together in an elegant paradigm-smashing fashion. —Bradley

———

I received a copy of the link to your most recent product - this is a really good piece of work, my friend! Good research, well thought out, impeccably reported, a real contribution to the field. I have forwarded it to several others; their reaction is the same as my own. Really well done. Rock on! —David Yurth, scientist, inventor, author of *Seeing Past the Edge*

———

I just wanted to say a big thank you for your work, your writing, sharing your passions and opinions, your dedication and commitment to a better and healthier future for humanity. I first came across an excerpt of your writing about three years ago before your book was published—that fascinating excerpt change my life. It changed my focus. It set me back on a path I had drifted away from. It made my universe make sense. I saw into myself and my world with a sudden "knowing"—I just can't explain it any better than that.

I was utterly awash with a sense of happiness and peace and joy and excitement. It was just one of the most amazing moments of my life—up there with giving birth to my children. I had a moment this evening when I read your name as "The Change Agent" and just wanted to acknowledge that you definitely were my "Change Agent": the beginning spark of a world I am so glad to be finally immersing myself into. —Vanessa P.

———

Thanks to Nexus Newsfeed I found your work. Joy of joys. I have been on this path all my life, so to have found a "Master" is so good. I will be undertaking the Kundalini activation program in the near future, but just wish to express my admiration for your work, now, for the small amount I have read so far. Gnosis is my paradigm. Many thanks. —R.E.

———

I LOVE this book and can't wait for TGI 2. My fascination with the connection between physics and spirituality has spanned the last 44 years and this is the most complete book I've read on the subject (and I've read many). The information is detailed, well researched, yet presented in a format that is understandable. Brendan also includes CURRENT research data missing in many other offerings. If you want to change your life for the better.... this book is a WONDERFUL place to start! —Deborah Lewis

———

Thanks for your work! I've learned a lot on these issues but your research is allowing me to explore and expand my knowledge foundation. Looking forward to learning more! Thank you! —Sue E.

―――――

The reason I purchased TGI is your talk at SYDUFOR exposed a gaping deficit in my knowledge base. I have actually read the first 64 pages and so much was packed into it, I could not believe a solitary human could compile the information (in such an intuitively ordered fashion), less one under age 30... Yes, as I have mentioned before, your book is incredible—beyond your years, a magnificent achievement. —Steve Gilmore a.k.a. Ozzie Thinker, author of *The Beauty of Existence Decoded*, https://ozziethinker.wordpress.com

―――――

I am on a quest to find out the nature of reality. I have read many books that detail aspects of research into the nature of reality and from a limited perception try to establish a theory. This book blows all others away in that the author pulls together research from every field imaginable that in their own way all lead to the same conclusion. He writes about quantum physics, sacred geometry, clairvoyance, the physics of sound and light, shamanic knowledge, ancient Indian mythology, and so much more, and brings it all together to establish a true theory of everything. I have read books that the author draws information from, but none of these books alone can bring together the information that *The Grand Illusion* does. I am looking forward to Book 2. —Racing Ferraris

―――――

What a vast amount of information compiled in one book! Brendan Murphy has pulled together hard evidence from endless sources, from science to mysticism, revealing a common thread that leads essentially to the basis of what consciousness is. The author has a way of presenting the abundance of information in a most captivating way that keeps the reader wanting to know more. This book is an invaluable resource for any seeker of truth. It is by far one of the best single source works I have come across on the topic of the merging of science and spirituality.

This book will serve as a great contribution to our society at a time when so many hunger for truth and knowing beyond the confines of modern science. Now I patiently wait for Book Two. —G. Lalonde

―――――

This impressive, thorough and forward thinking work challenges existing paradigms and explores a wealth of grounded and vetted spiritual scientific research. This information invites us to perceive the illusion of separation and to embrace the truth of Oneness. Truth bomb! —Soulaware

———

Congratulations, brilliant book! When is volume two due out? —S.F.

———

Let me tell you how absolutely grateful I am to have found out about TGI. While I wait for Vol. 2, I'll be re-reading Vol. 1—so much to absorb. I bought my 17-yr-old son his own copy for Christmas. —G.L., Penticton, Canada

———

Brendan, just wanted to say how much I enjoyed your book! Started reading it after my Potentiation, felt like for the first time I could understand physics! Looking forward to the next one. —Julie TwoMoon

———

Thank you so much for producing a fantastic book that covers so much, I am trying to find the second one! —K.G.

———

I just wanted to say thank you for putting together the body of work that you have. I have emphasized for years that the work people like myself do as a psychic and medium is not only natural, but scientifically verifiable, measurable, and documented. I appreciate so much to be able to reference your book to others, so that they too may explore not only how this is possible, but discover the language in which it is described. —Debbie Edwards, psychic and medium, www.debbieedwardsinternational.com

———

...don't want to put it down. The most empowering book I have ever read. It's like going home. Thank you. —Mel Egan

———

Perfectly suited to those with an analytical nature who may find peace in knowing the answers to metaphysics lie in science as much as they do in one's own spirituality. Brendan D. Murphy has written and compiled a thought-provoking and evidentially rich jewel of a book, leaving you in no doubt that science does, most definitely meet spirituality. —Kerrie Wearing, author, soul coach, medium

Well written! Excellent content. You need to be tuned in to really appreciate the information. Once you are finished, you will want to read it again. For deep thinkers. —jcla67

———

A monumental work you will want to take your time with to take it all in. A wonderful compilation of research that should be required reading for the next generation. Brendan makes the mystic and occult compelling and understandable. A work that greatly contributes to the ongoing discussion of the "paradigm shift" from a conservative Newtonian mechanical view of the world to a living, meaningful, and holistic view that resonates with love and intelligence. —Chad Foreman

———

Cannot wait for TGI 2, TGI 1 was excellent from start to finish. —Bruce Verrall

———

I've read *The Grand Illusion* a couple of times and am simply amazed by how you curated all of the material and made some compelling observations about the true nature of reality. Any idea when you are going to release TGI 2? —J. Langley

———

You have recently entered my sphere via your article "Junk DNA: Our Interdimensional Doorway to Transformation." I work with a device called a crystal bed, aka Vogel Photonic Triangulation Unit, created by students of Marcel Vogel. This device sends light through Vogel crystals at different rates of speed (Hz). After a year, intuition screamed at me to incorporate sound so a vibroacoustic sound bed was added. In a nutshell, all of your science is in alignment with all that I have felt intuitively while working with this bed re: DNA activation. I would not claim it, as I could not prove it. Your description of "nested vortices" are exactly what one client has seen during a session. I just want to thank you, for your work, and the essence of who you are. Your article has been shared with Marco Rodin, as well, whom I know personally. —Gisele M. Bonenfant

———

I came across your articles on unexplained-mysteries.com and am extremely impressed with your breadth and depth of subject material. You are obviously an intellectual with a open mind. I like to think of an "open mind" defined as suspending disbelief...In the short time I have perused your articles I have gained much to think about and you have provided extremely helpful knowledge disclosure points I wasn't aware of...Thanks for providing such deep and probing materials. Keep up the explorations. —Bob Debold

————

If you habitually highlight, underline, or make margin notes in books as I do, you'll want to get your marker or sharpened pencil ready when you open this one. Australian Brendan Murphy has begun publishing his long-term research into consciousness and the nature of reality in this first (of many, we hope) volumes to come.

At 29 years of age, he says he's been involved for about 10 years in his studies to come up with this first of two books abbreviated TGI 1 and TGI 2. Reminiscent in my mind of Manly P. Hall who published his great opus at age 28 as part of his life-long pursuit of truth, Murphy appears to be carrying on the tradition.

He presents us with a myriad of both solid scientific and inarguable occult examples of the validity and repeatability of experimental findings linking leading edge physics with paranormal phenomena.

We first investigate the most up-to-date explanations of discoveries in science, from super-string theory to quantum entanglement and beyond. We then compare and analyse more modern day examples of psychic research that are establishing the truth of the "Perennial Philosophy" of mystics, saints, and yogis in light of those scientific findings.

Murphy quotes the late Dr. "Kit" Pedler, Head of Electron Microscopy at the University of London's Institute of Ophthalmology and early unofficial scientific advisor to the Dr. Who TV series: "[A] scientist would have to be either massively ignorant or a confirmed bigot to deny the evidence that the human mind can make connection with space, time, and matter in ways which have nothing to do with the ordinary senses."

One by one, Murphy takes us through chapters on subjects like Consciousness, Quantum Weirdness, Cosmic Oneness, Mystical Experience, the Occult Aether, the Superhologram, Chakras, Dimensional Planes, the Human Aura/Bioplasma/Bio-Field/Torsion-Plasma Field, Thought Forms, Telepathy, Clairvoyance, Psychokinesis, and more.

His references are so varied and so numerous one wonders how this young man had the time and fortitude to tackle such a wealth of information. But, it's all here, and, at least for me, at more than twice Murphy's age, it constitutes a starting point for my own further investigations. "Synthesis" in the subtitle is too modest a word. This is a "compendium," to say the least. As usual, I want to relay some salient quotes from the book to give you its flavour and to encourage you to delve into this most extraordinarily strong and undeniable case for the reality of what is much more than just the everyday 3D world we ordinarily experience:

"[E]vents located in space-time are fundamentally generated by processes outside of it."

"[T]ime itself is holographic in the sense that past, present, and future are simultaneously present at any point in space." "Modern science tells us that the world of supposedly solid matter... is an illusion."

"[T]his reality of ours is just another form of dream...."

"There is always information available that hints of a greater spiritual reality.... We ignore it at our own detriment."

"[T]he human brain is itself a frequency decoder."

"[T]he forces of evolution are fundamentally hyperdimensional."

"[T]he creation of physical reality is directed from and by a subtler level of reality that interacts with and influences DNA, leading to the formation of a physical hologram."

"We are so constantly bombarded by the `powers that be' with false imagery and concepts that are designed to induce... suppression and subversion of the rational mind that it is no wonder so many people never even try to uncover the truth about life on this planet."

"[O]ur reality... is a virtual reality, a giant conglomerate of consciousness software programs interacting."

"[T]he cosmos... is responsive to our beliefs and emotions because it is fundamentally conscious and intelligent."

"[P]si phenomena are not just possible but inevitable and the furthest thing from `paranormal', as mystics and occultists have always known and told those with ears to hear."

And, finally, as good advice and a not-so-subtle warning that is meant to further entice the interested reader:

"This book... is the kind of dangerous and subversive text that can potentially play a civilising or transformative role - as long as one's mind is receptive, curious, and open."

—Alan Glassman, *New Dawn* issue 139, July-August 2013

ENDNOTES

Preface
[1]   Jenkins, *The 2012 Story*, 268.

Introduction
[2]   Rudolf Steiner, *An Outline of Occult Science*, Preface.

Chapter 1
[1]   See Penrose, *Shadows of the Mind*.
[2]   Colin Wilson, *The Occult*, Introduction.
[3]   Rudhyar, *Culture, Crisis and Creativity*, 27.
[4]   <www.abc.net.au/science/news/stories/2006/1791144.htm>.
[5]   Grosso, *Experiencing the Next World Now*, xv–xvi.
[6]   Jones, *PSIence*, 24.
[7]   Atwater, *The Big Book of Near-Death Experiences*, 141.
[8]   See Kaku, *Hyperspace*.
[9]   Jung, *Man and His Symbols*.
[10] Grof, *LSD Psychotherapy*, 261.
[11] Sheldrake, *The Presence of the Past*, 25.
[12] Grof, *LSD Psychotherapy*, 261. See also R.A. Wilson, *Cosmic Trigger*, Part 1, for some fascinating background on Tesla and his insights.
[13] Einstein, *Principles of Research*, 1918. <www.cs.ucla.edu/~slu/on_research/einstein_essay2.html>
[14] See LaBerge & Rheingold, *Exploring the World of Lucid Dreaming*, 8, 9.
[15] Hancock, *Supernatural*, 281–3.
[16] Larry Dossey interview in *New Dawn*, Special Issue No. 9.
[17] Ibid.
[18] Mishlove, *The Roots of Consciousness*, 249–50. Ebook.

19 Targ, Why I Believe in ESP & Why You Should Too, *New Dawn* Special Issue 6(4), 2012.

20 Radin, *The Conscious Universe*, 223.

21 Jones, 205.

22 See White, *Isaac Newton*.

23 Ancient and Modern Science: Psychology: Part VII. *Theosophy*, 83(11), 1995. <www.blavatsky.net/magazine/theosophy/ww/setting/psychology.html>.

24 Weiss, *Many Lives, Many Masters*, 128–9.

25 Quoting from *Man and Science* by W. Heitler. <http://krishnascience.com/5_Higher_Dimensional_Science_2.html>. Taken to its extreme, Darwinian theory was the state-sanctioned science adopted and promoted by Nazi Germany's "Aryan" ruling class. (Lipton & Bhaerman, 117.)

26 Sogyal Rinpoche, *The Tibetan Book of Living and Dying*, 20.

27 Goswami, *The Self-Aware Universe*, 170.

28 Jones, 76.

29 See Kastrup.

30 Blavatsky, *Studies in Occultism*. <www.holybooks.com/wp-content/uploads/Studies-in-Occultism-by-H-P-Blavatsky.pdf>.

31 See Goswami, *The Self-Aware Universe*.

32 Schoch & Yonavjak, *The Parapsychology Revolution*, 114–15.

33 < http://en.wikipedia.org/wiki/Paradigm>.

34 <www.thefreedictionary.com/paradigm>.

35 <www.merriam-webster.com/dictionary/paradigm>.

36 See Lipton & Bhaerman, *Spontaneous Evolution*.

37 Radin, *The Conscious Universe*, xiii.

38 Sogyal Rinpoche, 120.

39 Ibid., 121.

40 See Harrison, *Masks of the Universe*, Preface.

41 Ibid.

42 See Wilson, *Cosmic Trigger*, Preface.

43 See ibid., Part 1.

44 Kaku, *The Physics of the Impossible*, 56–8.

45 Rosenblum & Kuttner, 77–9.

46 Grosso, 151.

47 Sogyal Rinpoche, 20.

48 Blavatsky, *Studies in Occultism*.

49 See *Failed Predictions* at <http://wikibin.org/articles/failed-predictions.html> for most of these with the exception of the last two.

50   Some of My Journeys in Medicine (A Lecture about Science and Reincarnation, 1989). <www.childpastlives.org/library_articles/stevensonlecture.htm>.

51   Sogyal Rinpoche, 55.

52   Harrison, 253.

53   Ibid., 269.

54   Ibid., 270.

55   Pinchbeck, *2012*, 10.

56   Randall, *Psychokinesis*, 12.

57   Kuhn, *The Structure of Scientific Revolutions*, 64.

58   Marrs, *PSI Spies*, 117.

59   Dossey, *The Power of Premonitions*.

60   Humphrey, *UFOs, Psi and Spiritual Evolution*, 17.

61   Quoted in Mossis Kline, *Mathematics and the Search for Knowledge*. <www.informationphysics.com/truth>.

62   Kuhn, 90.

63   See Kuhn.

64   Pearce, *The Biology of Transcendence*, 2.

65   Ibid., 3.

66   See my article *The Newton You Never Knew* at <www.brendandmurphy.com>.

67   Pearce, 125.

68   Ibid., 171.

69   Rudhyar, 107.

70   Ibid., 34.

71   Ibid., 44.

72   Ibid., 26.

73   Ibid., 66–7.

74   Ibid., 180.

75   Ibid., 129.

76   Ibid., 194.

Chapter 2

1   See Eisen, *Suppressed Inventions and Other Discoveries*.

2   See Wilson, *Wilhelm Reich in Hell*, Introduction.

3   Yogananda, Ch. 8.

4   Wilson, *Wilhelm Reich in Hell*, Introduction.

5   Kuhn, 166.

6   Lash, *The Promise of a Lonely Planet*.

7   See Kuhn, Introduction.

8   Wilson, *Prometheus Rising*, 27.

9   *Pathological Disbelief.* Lecture given at the Nobel Laureates' meeting Lindau, June 30, 2004.

10   Carter Hits (another) Home Run! Amazon review by Dr. Larry Dossey (Santa Fe, NM. USA, October 21, 2010). <www.tibetanart.com/Blog/Post.asp?ID=61>.

11   Braude, *Pride and Prejudice in Academia.*

12   Taimni, *The Science of Yoga,* 134 (ebook).

13   See Moody, *Life After Life* (1975).

14   See Moody, *The Last Laugh.*

15   Tiller, *Psychoenergetic Science,* 39.

16   Kuhn, 80.

17   Ibid.

18   McClenon et al., The coverage of parapsychology in introductory psychology textbooks.

19   Van der Leeuw, *The Conquest of Illusion,* 148.

20   Weiss, 11.

21   Yurth, *Seeing Past the Edge,* 142.

22   Blavatsky, *Studies in Occultism.*

23   Atwater, 353.

24   Sogyal Rinpoche, 8.

25   Schoch & Yonavjak, 53.

26   Radin, *Entangled Minds,* 7. Confirmed and elaborated on in private email to author, November 2010.

27   Sogyal Rinpoche, 18.

28   Schoch & Yonavjak, 56.

29   Ibid., 57.

30   Sogyal Rinpoche, 18.

31   DeGracia, *Beyond the Physical,* 261.

32   Pearce, 126.

33   Tiller, *Psychoenergetic Science,* 47.

34   Constable, 32.

35   See Swann, News Item 100.

36   Yurth, *Seeing Past the Edge,* 49–50.

37   Email to author, November 2010.

38   *Aristotle's Logic—Why Aristotelian logic does not work.* <www.abelard.org/category/category.php>.

39   Kuhn, 64.

40   Ibid., 79.

41   Tom Bearden comments on an excerpt from *Stranger than Science* by Frank Edwards. <www.cheniere.org/misc/sparkoflife.htm>.

42   Interview with Larry Dossey, *New Dawn*, Special Issue No. 9.

Chapter 3

1   Quoted in Bazette, *Beyond the Five Senses*, Introduction.

2   Moody, *The Last Laugh*, 65.

3   Ostrander & Schroeder, *Psychic Discoveries Behind the Iron Curtain*, 58.

4   *Aristotle's Logic* (as above).

5   Amit Goswami, *Physics of the Soul*, 229.

6   *Aristotle's Logic* (as above).

7   Wilson, *Quantum Psychology*, 44.

Chapter 4

1   The Soul and Quantum Physics: An interview with Dr. Fred Alan Wolf. <www.fredalanwolf.com/myarticles/Soul%20and%20death%20Q&A.pdf>.

2   See Goswami, *The Self-Aware Universe*.

3   <www.reciprocalsystem.com.>

4   Roebke, *The Reality Tests*.

5   Nehru, *The Wave Mechanics in the Light of the Reciprocal System*.

6   Braden, *Fractal Time*, 188.

7   Goswami, *Physics of the Soul*, 15, 30–1.

8   Capra, *The Tao of Physics*, 78–9.

9   Yurth, *Seeing Past the Edge*, 88.

10   LeShan, *The Medium, The Mystic and The Physicist*, 34.

11   Zeilinger & Aspelmeyer, *A Quantum Renaissance*, <www.physicsworld.com>.

12   Ibid.

13   Peake, *Quantum Entanglement*.

14   Rosenblum & Kuttner, *The Quantum Enigma*, 123.

15   Ibid.

16   See Humphrey, *UFOs, Psi and Spiritual Evolution*.

17   Tiller, 112–13.

18   Q and A page at Fred Wolf's site. <www.fredalanwolf.com/page5.htm>.

19   Ibid.

20   Goswami, *The Self-Aware Universe*, 8–10.

21   Ibid., 46.

22   Jones, 104.

23   Yurth, *Seeing Past the Edge*, 79.

24   Laszlo & Currivan, 29. See also James Glick, Chaos.

25   Quoted by Dr. Bradley Nelson in *The Emotion Code*, 102–3.

26   <www.youtube.com/watch?v=rVWWQKU_-G0>.

27   Leadbeater, *A Textbook of Theosophy*.

28   Hancock, *Supernatural*, 102–3.

29   Williams, *Nothing Better Than Death*, 130.

30   Hancock, *Supernatural*, 103.

31   See Wilson, *The Occult*, 700–1.

32   Montalk, *Astral Physics and Timespace*. See also <http://montalk.net/about>.

33   Bearden, *Excalibur*, 194–5.

34   Strassman, *DMT*, 318.

35   Moberly & Jourdain, *An Adventure*.

36   See Waite, *The Mystic Sciences*, Ch. 1.

37   Braden, *Fractal Time*, 188.

38   Strieber, *The Secret School*, 47.

39   Ibid., 48.

40   Kaku, *Physics of the Impossible*, 244.

41   Jones, 121.

42   Kaku, Physics of the *Impossible*, 244.

43   Ibid., 244–5.

44   Goswami, *The Self-Aware Universe*, 140.

45   Jones, 160–4.

46   Kaku, *Physics of the Impossible*, 180–1.

47   Ibid., 194.

48   See Greene, *The Fabric of the Cosmos*, 339–82.

49   Kaku, *Physics of the Impossible*, 237–8.

50   See Jones & Flaxman, Time Travel & the Multiverse, *New Dawn* Special Issue, 6(4).

51   Ibid., 238.

52   Laszlo & Currivan, 13.

53   Goswami, *Physics of the Soul*, 237.

54   Quoted in Jones, 121.

55   Kaku, *Physics of the Impossible*, 239.

56   See Wilcock, *Shift of the Ages*, Ch. 5.

57   Kaku, *Physics of the Impossible*, 238–40. See also Jones, *PSIence*, Ch. 6.

58   Yurth, *Seeing Past the Edge*, 59.

59   Ibid.

60   Ibid., 276.

61   Alfred, *Our Invisible Bodies*, 25. Kaku details this connection further in *Hyperspace*.

62   Kaku, *Physics of the Impossible*, 60–1.

63   Rosenblum & Kuttner, 150.

64   Jones, 109.

65   See Wilcock, *The Divine Cosmos*, Ch. 4.6.

66 Wilcock, *Hyperdimensional Nebulae.*

67 Rosenblum & Kuttner, 148–9.

68 Ibid., 148.

69 See Greene, *The Fabric of the Cosmos.*

70 Yurth, *Seeing Past the Edge,* 121–2.

71 Wicherink, *Souls of Distortion,* 24. See Wicherink's website: <www.soulsofdistortion.nl>.

72 See Yurth, *Seeing Past the Edge,* 109–10.

73 Yurth, *Y-Bias and Angularity,* 86–7.

74 Yurth, *Seeing Past the Edge,* 236–7.

75 *Contested "faster-than-light" experiment yields same results.* <www.spacedaily.com>. *How Many Neutrinos Does It Take to Screw Up Einstein?* <www.futurenewsnetwork.com>.

76 See Schoch & Yonavjak.

77 Zeilinger & Aspelmeyer, *A Quantum Renaissance.*

78 Ibid. See also Zeilinger, *Dance of the Photons.*

79 See Zeilinger, *Dance of the Photons.*

80 Quoted in Violette, *Extra-Dimensional Universe,* 202.

81 Goswami, *The Self-Aware Universe,* 61.

82 Peat, *Non-locality in Nature and Cognition.*

83 David Pratt, *David Bohm and the Implicate Order.* Reprinted from *Sunrise* magazine, February/March, 1993. <www.theosophy-nw.org/theosnw/science/prat-boh.htm>.

84 Capra, 359.

85 See Brown & Wiegand, *Cosmic Law.*

86 *New York Times,* July 9, 1921. <http://query.nytimes.com/mem/archive-free/pdf?res=F70A11F73D5A1B7A93CBA9178CD85F458285F9>.

87 Stine, 21–22. See also <www.rexresearch.com/russ/russ.htm>.

88 See Payne.

89 <www.sacred-texts.com/nth/elms/elms16.htm>.

90 *Our Amazing Visual Ray!* Compiled and edited by Thomas Joseph Brown. <http://borderlandresearch.com/visual-ray>.

91 Constable, 60–1.

92 R. Schoch & L. Yonavjak, *The Parapsychology Revolution,* 114.

93 Sheldrake, The Sense of Being Stared At, Part 1.

94 Ibid.

95 Ostrander & Schroeder, *Psychic Discoveries Behind the Iron Curtain,* 121–2.

96 Ibid., 139.

97 Sheldrake, The Sense of Being Stared At.

98 Radin, *Entangled Minds,* 127–9.

99 Sheldrake, *Minds Beyond Brains.*

[100] Chalko.

[101] Ibid.

[102] Email communication from David Yurth, February 2012.

[103] Wolf, *Parallel Universes*, 227–8.

[104] Quoted in Wilson, *Quantum Psychology*, 174.

[105] Goswami, *The Self-Aware Universe*, 42.

[106] Rosenblum & Kuttner, 12–13.

[107] Kaku, *Parallel Worlds*, 145.

[108] Talbot, 226.

[109] Schmidt.

[110] McTaggart, *The Intention Experiment*, 164.

[111] Radin, *Time-reversed Human Experience*, 2000.

[112] See RetroPK Database at <www.fourmilab.ch/rpkp/bierman-metaanalysis.html>.

[113] See Brooks. The more technically minded reader might be interested in C. Brukner et al., *Quantum Entanglement in Time*. 2008. <http://arxiv.org/abs/quant-ph/0402127v1>.

[114] See Bem, Feeling the Future.

[115] Peat, *Non-locality in Nature and Cognition*.

[116] Braden, *The Divine Matrix*, 135.

[117] Laszlo & Currivan, 43–4.

[118] Tiller, *Psychoenergetic Science*, 125.

[119] Bearden, *Excalibur Briefing*, 153.

[120] Ibid., 151.

[121] See Jung, *Synchronicity*.

[122] Grof, *The Holotropic Mind*, 178.

[123] Strassman, 322.

[124] Loughlin.

[125] Quoted in Sheldrake, *The Presence of the Past*, 251.

[126] McGuire & Hull, 434.

[127] Ibid., 435.

[128] See Jones, *PSIence*.

[129] Ibid., 91–2.

[130] Laszlo & Currivan, 90–1.

[131] Nelson, *Consciousness and Psi*.

[132] Radin, *Entangled Minds*, 31–3.

[133] Braden, *Fractal Time*, 193.

[134] Ibid., 193–5.

[135] Radin, *Formal Analysis, September 11, 2001*.

[136] See Hoagland, *The Hyperdimensional Election of Barack Obama*, on Google video.

137   Jean E. Burns, *What is Beyond the Edge of the Known World?* (2003). Quoted in Schoch & Yonavjak, 281. See also Spottiswoode.

138   Wilcock, *The Source Field Investigations*, 235.

139   Burns. Quoted in Schoch & Yonavjak, 280.

140   McTaggart, *The Intention Experiment*, 25–6.

141   See Loughlin.

142   See David Wilcock's *The 2012 Enigma* presentation on youtube.com.

143   Ibid.

144   Ibid. For more detail, see: <www.julianvossandreae.com/Work/C60article/c60article.pdf>.

145   Zeilinger & Elitzur, *Shrodinger's Cat*.

146   Wilcock, *The Source Field Investigations*, 266.

147   Shared with me by a "liker" of The Grand Illusion Facebook fan page at <www.facebook.com/The.Grand.Illusion.Books>.

148   See Brooks. McTaggart details these and related experiments extensively in *The Intention Experiment*.

149   Schoch, Time, Entanglement & Consciousness, *New Dawn* Special Issue 6(4).

150   Brooks.

151   Ostrander & Schroeder, *Psychic Discoveries Behind the Iron Curtain*, 33–4.

152   Defence Intelligence Agency, *Soviet and Czechoslovakian Parapsychology Research*, September 1975.

153   Pribram, *Consciousness Reassessed*.

154   Wilson, *Quantum Psychology*, 43.

155   <www.projects.science.uu.nl/igg/jos/foundQM/wigner.pdf>.

156   Wilson, *Cosmic Trigger*, vol. 1.

157   Ibid.

158   Pinchbeck, 49.

159   Yogananda, 228.

160   Hamilton, *Scientific Proof of the Existence of God*.

161   Radin, *The Conscious Universe*, 305.

162   LeShan, 62.

163   Grof, *The Holotropic Mind*, 5.

164   See van der Leeuw, Ch. 5.

165   Narby, 75–6.

166   Kaku, *Physics of the Impossible*, 243.

167   Grof, *LSD Psychotherapy*, 128.

168   DeGracia, *Beyond the Physical*, 16.

169   Ibid., 17.

170   See Capra, *The Tao of Physics*, 339.

171 Underhill, 31.

172 Capra, 338.

173 Taimni, 167–8.

174 LeShan, 34.

175 Ibid., 36.

176 Greene, 139.

177 Tom Bearden comments on an excerpt from *Stranger than Science* by Frank Edwards. <www.cheniere.org/misc/sparkoflife.htm>.

178 See Greene, *The Fabric of the Cosmos*.

179 See LeShan, Appendix D and p. 75.

180 <www.spaceandmotion.com/Physics-Galileo-Galilei.htm>.

181 LeShan, 43.

182 Ibid.

183 Ibid., 56.

184 DeGracia, *Beyond the Physical*, 44–5.

185 Huxley, 116.

186 *Occultism, Semi-Occultism and Pseudo-Occultism*. A lecture by Annie Besant, delivered on Thursday, June 30th, 1898, at the Blavatsky Lodge, London. <www.blavatsky.net/history/besant/essays-and-addresses-vol-III/besant.9.html>.

187 Ibid.

188 Blavatsky, *Studies in Occultism*.

189 Besant, *Occultism, Semi-Occultism and Pseudo-Occultism*.

190 DeGracia, *Beyond the Physical*, 22.

191 Ibid.

192 Radin, *Entangled Minds*, 239.

193 I have to credit Don DeGracia with putting me onto this excellent book.

194 Van der Leeuw, Ch. 3.

195 DeGracia, *Beyond the Physical*, 89.

196 See Randall, 80–1.

197 Radin, *Entangled Minds*, 58.

198 Schoch, What Lives On?

199 Ibid.

200 Ostrander & Schroeder, *Psychic Discoveries Behind the Iron Curtain*, 9.

201 Randall, 151–2.

202 *The Meta Analysis of Research Studies*. <http://echo.edres.org:8080/meta>.

203 Suri.

Chapter 5

1 See Wilber, *The Atman Project*, Ch. 1.

[2]   Ibid.

[3]   Violette, 83.

[4]   Ibid., 90.

[5]   See Greeley.

[6]   Bentov, 175.

[7]   Jung, *On Death and Immortality* (see chapter entitled "On Life After Death").

[8]   Grof, *The Holotropic Mind*, 18.

[9]   Ibid., 19.

[10]   Ibid., 20.

[11]   Ibid., 21.

[12]   Ibid., 202.

[13]   Abhayananda, 1.

[14]   Sabom, 250.

[15]   Schwartz, 116.

[16]   See Jung, *On Death and Immortality*.

[17]   Ibid.

[18]   Ibid.

[19]   Marrs, *PSI Spies*, 27.

[20]   Ibid., 29.

[21]   Ibid., 41.

[22]   Abhayananda, 399–400.

[23]   Lau, *Lao Tzu*, 57.

[24]   Abhayananda, Introduction.

[25]   See the *Conversations With God* series by Neale Donald Walsch.

[26]   Violette, 50. See Bearden for futher exposition of four-law logic.

[27]   Quoted in Yogananda.

[28]   From David Tame, *The Secret Power of Music*. <www.sourcetext.com/hupage/Secular/secular.html>.

[29]   Tim Folger. *News Flash: Time May Not Exist.* <http://discovermagazine.com/2007/jun/in-no-time>.

[30]   Pinchbeck, 50.

[31]   LaBerge & Rheingold, 173.

[32]   LeShan,149.

[33]   Strassman, 234.

[34]   Ibid., 235.

[35]   LaBerge & Rheingold, 6.

[36]   See ibid., Ch. 2.

[37]   Ibid., 174.

[38]   Kaku, *Physics of the Impossible*, 58–9.

39 Ibid., 63.

40 Pearce, *The Biology of Transcendence*, 75.

41 Korotkov, 163.

42 Grof, *LSD Psychotherapy*, 128.

43 Williams, 46.

44 <www.near-death.com/experiences/evidence10.html>.

45 Ibid.

46 Underhill, 110.

47 See Violette, 172–3.

48 Marrs, *Alien Agenda*, 321.

49 Abhayananda, 11.

50 Brown, *Cosmic Explorers*, 231–2.

51 LaBerge & Rheingold, 172.

52 Yurth, *Y-Bias and Angularity*, 128–9.

53 Yurth, *Seeing Past the Edge*, 266.

54 Sogyal Rinpoche, 353.

55 Wilson, *The Occult*, 760.

56 Ring, *Near Death and UFO Encounters as Shamanic Initiations*.

57 <http://blog.enlightennext.org/eeday/?page_id=159>.

58 Grof & Halifax, *The Human Encounter With Death*, 58.

59 See Abhayananda, Preface.

60 Quoted in Abhayananda.

61 Sogyal Rinpoche, 129.

62 Wilson, *The Occult*, 26–7.

63 LaBerge & Rheingold, 177.

64 Underhill, 33.

65 Ibid., 35.

66 Abhayananda, 2–3.

67 Edmond Macaraeg, *The Pope Abandons Limbo! Will Purgatory Follow?* <www.ucg.org/commentary/pope-abandons-limbo-will-purgatory-follow>.

68 Wilson, *The Occult*, 218.

69 Yogi Ramacharaka, *Advanced Course in Yogi Philosophy*.

70 Powell, *The Mental Body*, Ch. 17.

71 Yogi Ramacharaka, *Advanced Course in Yogi Philosophy*.

72 Sri Chinmoy, *Samadhi: The Height of Divine Consciousness*. <www.srichinmoy.org/spirituality/concentration_meditation_contemplation/samadhi/>.

73 Abhayananda, 64.

74 Sogyal Rinpoche, 48.

75 <http://en.wikipedia.org/wiki/Purusha>.

[76] Michael Roll, *The Scientific Proof of Survival After Death*. <www.cfpf.org.uk/articles/background/scientificproof/scientificproof1.html>.

[77] Ron Pearson, Solving the Problem of the Cosmological Constant, *Nexus* 15(1).

[78] Abhayananda, 58–9.

[79] <http://en.wikipedia.org/wiki/Satori>.

[80] Jones, 221.

[81] Abhayananda, 60.

[82] Underhill, 41–2.

[83] Ibid., 40.

[84] See Ring, *The Omega Project*.

[85] See Sutherland, *Transformed by the Light*.

[86] Ibid. Also see Atwater, *The Big Book of Near-Death Experiences*.

[87] See Ring, *Heading Towards Omega*. These trends were marked in Sutherland's worthy study also.

[88] Ibid., 168.

[89] Ibid., 170.

[90] LaBerge & Rheingold, 177.

[91] Ibid., 177–8.

[92] Goswami, *The Self-Aware Universe*, 50.

[93] See Yurth, *Seeing Past the Edge*, 265–6.

[94] Hancock, *Supernatural*, 39–41.

[95] Icke, 191.

[96] Hancock, *Supernatural*, 5–6.

[97] Narby, 69–70.

[98] See Drunvalo Melchizedek.

[99] For the "other things" see Wilcock's brilliant *The Source Field Investigations*.

[100] See Lomas, *The Lost Key*.

[101] Hancock, *Supernatural*, 92.

[102] Ibid., 92–3.

[103] Jenkins, 389.

[104] See Picknett & Prince.

[105] Pinchbeck, 368.

[106] Devereaux.

[107] Quoted in Sheldrake, *The Presence of the Past*, 306.

[108] Ibid., 305.

[109] Ibid., 304.

[110] Luckman, *Potentiate Your DNA*, 79.

[111] Targ & Katra, *The Scientific and Spiritual Implications of Psychic Abilities*. <www.espresearch.com/espgeneral/doc-AT.shtml>.

Chapter 6

[1] Besant & Leadbeater, *Occult Chemistry*, Ch. 2.

[2] See ibid. under "Introduction."

[3] Besant & Leadbeater, *Occult Chemistry*.

[4] DeGracia, *Beyond the Physical*, 109.

[5] Yogi Ramacharaka, *Advanced Course in Yogi Philosophy*, Lesson XII.

[6] Besant & Leadbeater, Ch. 3.

[7] See Blavatsky, *The Secret Doctrine*, Ch. 9.

[8] See Zammit, *A Lawyer Presents the Case for the Afterlife*, Ch. 2.

[9] See Yogananda.

[10] See Besant & Leadbeater, *Occult Chemistry*, Ch. 3.

[11] Yurth, 252.

[12] Besant & Leadbeater, *Occult Chemistry*, 13–1.

[13] LaViolette, *Subquantum Kinetics*.

[14] Haramein.

[15] Email to author, February 24, 2012.

[16] Lipton & Bhaerman, 101.

[17] Besant & Leadbeater, *Occult Chemistry*, Ch. 3.

[18] Ibid.

[19] LaViolette, *Genesis of the Cosmos*, 238–9.

[20] Alfred, *Our Invisible Bodies*, 49.

[21] Ibid., 50.

[22] Wilcock, *Shift of the Ages*, Introduction.

[23] Pratt.

[24] For Haramein's model see <www.theresonanceproject.org/research.html>.

[25] Greene, 215–16.

[26] Rein, *Effect of Conscious Intention on Human DNA*.

[27] <http://library.thinkquest.org/C0118142/norsepan/yggdrasil.php>.

[28] Wilcock, *The Science of Oneness*, Chs 15, 17.

[29] Atwater, *Future Memory*, 140–1.

[30] DeGracia, *Beyond the Physical*, 110.

[31] Ibid. See also Phillips.

[32] Phillips.

[33] DeGracia, *Beyond the Physical*, 110–11.

[34] Ibid., 111.

[35] Phillips.

[36] DeGracia, *Beyond the Physical*, 114.

[37] Yurth, *Seeing Past the Edge*, 255. In 1998 scientists at Fermi Laboratories "validated the discovery of sub-quarks of six specific kinds." Source: D.G. Yurth, *Variations on the*

Maharishi Model: An Integration of Consciousness and the Unified Field. Presented to the 5th Annual International Symposium of the New Energy Society. Salt Palace in Salt Lake City, Utah, August 28, 1999.

38   Ibid., 54–5.

39   Ibid., 55.

40   DeGracia, *Beyond the Physical*, 117.

41   Besant & Leadbeater, *Occult Chemistry*, Ch. 3.

42   LaViolette, *Subquantum Kinetics.*

43   LaViolette, *Genesis of the Cosmos*, 236.

44   Lipton & Bhaerman, 99.

45   LaViolette, *Genesis of the Cosmos*, 237–8.

46   <www.gravitycontrol.org/gravitycontrol.html>.

47   <www.helical-structures.org/einstein_about_ether.htm>.

48   See Leadbeater, *Chakras.*

49   See Leadbeater & Besant, *Occult Chemistry*, 1951. See also Besant & Leadbeater, Appendix—The Aether of Space.

50   Wolinsky, 20.

51   Wilcock, *Shift of the Ages*, Ch. 18.

52   Jones, 144. Henry C. Warren, a former nuclear weapons technician in the US Air Force, has suggested that a mutual gravitational shielding by the plates could play a role in the Casimir effect (analogous to the way massive bodies such as planets partially shield the omnidirectional flow of space/aether from one another), thus linking gravity to this phenomenon. See Warren, *Entrained Spatial Medium…*

53   Kaku, *Physics of the Impossible*, 206–7.

54   Quoted in Blavatsky, *The Secret Doctrine* , referenced by Besant & Leadbeater in *Occult Chemistry.*

55   <www.olypen.com/hcwarren/Background.pdf>.

56   Atwater, *Future Memory*, 157.

57   Wilcock, *The Source Field Investigations*, 273.

58   See Leadbeater, *The Astral Plane.*

59   Luckman, *Conscious Healing*, 106.

60   Wilcock, *The Science of Oneness*, Ch. 8.

61   See LaFreniere.

62   See my article *The Virtual Aether: "Empty Space" Gets an Upgrade* at <www.brendandmurphy.com>.

63   See Yogi Ramacharaka, *Advanced Course in Yogi Philosophy*, Ch. 11.

64   See LaViolette, Ch. 8.

65   Ibid., Ch. 9.

66   Ibid., Ch. 10.

67 See Wilcock, *The Science of Oneness*, Ch. 2.

68 509 McTaggart, *The Field*, 28.

69 Besant & Leadbeater, *Occult Chemistry*, Appendix—The Aether of Space.

70 Wilcock, *The Science of Oneness*, Ch. 2.3.

71 Aspden, *Physics Without Einstein*, 33.

72 See Susskind; see also Greene, *The Fabric of the Cosmos*.

73 R. Waugh & F. Macrae, Higgs boson found, <www.dailymail.co.uk>.

74 See Wilcock, *Shift of the Ages*, Chs 11 and 12. For more on Becker and Hagens' work, see Hatcher Childress, *Anti Gravity and the World Grid*.

75 See Wilcock, *Shift of the Ages*, Ch. 11.

76 Jones, 69.

77 Wilcock, *The Source Field Investigations*, 311–12.

78 Ibid., 314–15.

79 Hoagland, 355–6.

80 Levich.

81 The complete list of "tetrahedral" anomalies on planets from the original "Message of Cydonia" paper by Hoagland and Torun is available in *The Science of Oneness* and also online at <www.jaesonjrakman.com/Cydonia%20101/PAGES/PAGE8sd98fus7d6. htm>, or just find it at <www.enterprisemission.com>.)

82 See Wilcock, *Shift of the Ages*, Ch. 11.

83 Wilcock, Shift of the Ages, Ch. 11. See also C. Munck, Sacred Sites, <www.spiritofmaat. com/archive/nov2/munck.htm>.

84 Hoagland, 354.

85 Adams, *Giant hexagon of clouds*.

86 Hoagland, 356.

87 See ibid., Epilogue.

88 See Frissell, *Nothing in This Book Is True*, Ch. 9.

89 Ibid.

90 Melchizedek, vol. 1, 160

91 Ibid., 79.

92 Ibid., 79–82.

93 Atwater, *Future Memory*, 149.

94 Luckman, *Potentiate Your DNA*, 116.

95 Narby, 100.

96 Pinchbeck, 174.

97 Dust "comes alive" in space, *Sunday Times*. <www.timesonline.co.uk/tol/news/uk/ article2241753.ece>.

98 CBC news, *DNA components made in asteroids, study suggests*. <www.cbc.ca/news/ technology/story/2011/08/09/science-dna-meteorites-asteroids.html>.

[99]   See Braden, *The God Code* for full details of this remarkable discovery.

[100] See Levich and also see Laszlo & Currivan, 49.

[101] Wilcock, *Hypderdimensional Nebulae.*

[102] Email from D. Yurth, January 2012.

[103] Wilcock, *Shift of the Ages*, Ch. 3.

[104] Kaku, *Parallel Worlds*, 239.

[105] Lawlor, 108.

[106] See Melchizedek, vol. 1.

[107] <www.astro.virginia.edu/~mfs4n/sgr>.

[108] Wilcock, *The Science of Oneness*, Ch. 12.3.

[109] Wilcock, *Shift of the Ages*, Ch. 3.

[110] See Bentov, Ch. 1.

[111] Vlad Tarko, *Rotating Water Gives Rise to Geometric Figures.* <http://news.softpedia.com/news/Rotating-Water-Gives-Rise-to-Geometric-Figures-23640.shtml>. See also David Wilcock, *Hyperdimensional Nebulae: Cubes in Space and the 2012 Case.* <www.divinecosmos.com>.

[112] Wilcock, *The Science of Oneness*, Ch. 13.4.

[113] Quoted in Lawlor, Introduction.

[114] Wilcock, *The Science of Oneness*, Ch. 13.4.

[115] See Wikipedia's entry on Chladni: <http://en.wikipedia.org/wiki/Ernst_Chladni>.

[116] Jenny, 64.

[117] Copyright Christine Sterne (2007-8) *Blueprints of the Cosmos, Ocean Geographic*, 2008. email asherah66@gmail.com. To see these yantra images you can also visit: <www.world-mysteries.com/newgw/sci_blueprint4.htm>.

[118] From Tame, *The Secret Power.* <www.sourcetext.com/hupage/Secular/secular.html>.

[119] Watson, *Supernature*, 106.

[120] Quoted in Lawlor, 89.

[121] Wilcock, *Shift of the Ages*, Ch. 7.

[122] Emoto, 4.

[123] Ibid., 12.

[124] Ibid., 46.

[125] Ibid., 13.

[126] Ostrander & Schroeder, *Psychic Discoveries: The Iron Curtain Lifted*, 327.

[127] Wicherink, 101. The holy grail of science. <www.truth-revelations.com/?p=217>. See also <www.divinecosmos.com/index.php?option=com_content&task=view&id=95&Itemid=36>.

[128] See Emoto, Ch. 2.

[129] For more background on this and information regarding the replication and development of Benveniste's work, see McTaggart, *The Field.*

130   McTaggart, *The Field*, 90.

131   Ibid., 90–1.

132   Emoto, 101–2.

133   Rein & McCraty.

134   Wilcock, *The Science of Oneness*, Ch. 2.6.

135   See Emoto.

136   <www.pithemovie.com/gold.html>. To see how to construct a Golden Spiral, see <http://library.thinkquest.org/27890/goldenRatio3.html>.

137   Lawlor, 46.

138   Melchizedek, vol. 1, 208–9.

139   <http://cuip.uchicago.edu/~dlnarain/golden/activity7.htm>.

140   Lawlor, 59.

141   Yurth, *Y-Bias…*, 116–17.

142   Braden, *Fractal Time*, 93–4.

143   <www.goldennumber.net/dna.htm>.

144   Wilcock, *The Divine Cosmos*, Ch. 1.3.

145   Wicherink, 63–4.

146   Laszlo & Currivan, 48.

147   Wicherink, 82–3.

148   Yurth, *Torsion Field Mechanics*.

149   See ibid.

150   Kozyrev, *Possibility of Experimental Study of Properties of Time*. September 1967.

151   Quoted in Levich.

152   Ostrander & Schroeder, *Psychic Discoveries Behind the Iron Curtain*, 160–9.

153   <www.cheniere.org/correspondence/101503.htm>.

154   Wicherink, 101–2.

155   See W.E. Davis, <www.bibliotecapleyades.net/ciencia/ciencia_psycho17.htm>.

156   Wilcock, *The Divine Cosmos*, Ch. 9.7.2.

157   Ibid., 9.6.

158   Yurth, *Torsion Field Mechanics*.

159   See Watson.

160   Wilcock, *Divine Cosmos*, Ch. 9.7.3. See *The Divine Cosmos* and Watson's *Supernature* for further details and other incredible effects of pyramids upon their contents.

161   See Benford.

162   See Watson, *Supernature*, Ch. 3. Ostrander and Schroeder also cover "pyramid power" in *Psychic Discoveries…*

163   Wilcock, *The Source Field Investigations*, 140–1.

164   International Partnership for Pyramid Research. <www.gizapyramid.com/russian/research.htm>.

[165] V. Krasnoholovets, *On the way to disclosing the mysterious power of the Great Pyramid*, <www. gizapyramid.com/drv-article.htm>.

[166] Ibid.

[167] Monroe, 4.

[168] For an introduction to such notions, I suggest reading Hancock, *Fingerprints of the Gods*; Hancock & Bauval, *The Message of the Sphinx*; John Anthony West, *Serpent in the Sky*; John Michell, *The View Over Atlantis*. Drunvalo Melchizedek argues exactly this idea in his *Flower of Life* books. Definitely consult Wilcock's *The Source Field Investigations* for more on what the pyramids are and what they do.

[169] The recently discovered Bosnian pyramid complex features the largest known pyramid on the planet. At 220 m tall, it dwarfs the Great Pyramid by 73 m. Not only that, but physicists have reportedly discovered a beam of energy of 4.5 m radius shooting out of the top at a frequency of 28,000 Hz. Dr. S.S. Osmanagich, Professor of Anthropology at the American University in Bosnia-Herzegovina, reports: "The beam is continuous and its strength grows as it moves up and away from the pyramid. This phenomenon contradicts the known laws of physic [sic] and technology. This is the first proof of non-herzian technology on the Planet. It seems that the pyramid-builders created a perpetual motion machine a long time ago and this 'energy machine' is still working." (<http://piramidasunca.ba/eng/latest-news/item/7778-world-history-and-bosnian-pyramids-2011.html>.) This could be a case of torsion physics in action.

[170] Wilcock, *Shift of the Ages*, Ch. 3.

[171] Yurth, *Torsion Field Mechanics*.

[172] Nachalov & Sokolov.

[173] Luckman, *Conscious Healing*, 52. See also Jones, 183–6, and Levich.

[174] See Constable.

[175] Luckman, *Conscious Healing*, 66.

[176] Morgan, *Scalar Wars*.

[177] See Benford. See also Yurth, *Torsion Field Mechanics*. Wilcock states: "Shipov demonstrated that all electromagnetic fields generate torsion waves." <www.divinecosmos.com/index.php?option=com_content&task=view&id=95&Itemid=36>.

[178] Yurth, *Seeing Past the Edge*, 213.

[179] Korotkov, 148.

[180] [179] Wilcock, *The Divine Cosmos*, Ch. 1.20.

[181] Levich.

[182] A.M. Nowak, *Torsion Fields: Theory of Physical Vacuum*. <www.eioba.com/a/1tzs/torsion-fields-theory-of-physical-vacuum-shipov-and-heim>. "It has been shown that information is conveyed in the Torsion Field at a rate which is at least 1,000,000,000 times the speed of light. This revelation, which is largely due to the ground breaking work of Russian scientist V.A. Dubrovsky up to 1985, has now been confirmed by at

least six other laboratories in the former Soviet states. The group velocity of torsion waves has also independently been shown to be at least 1,000,000,000 times the speed of light." (Yurth, *Variations on the Maharishi Model*.) Also see my article *The Occult Energy Behind the Sense of Being Stared At*, at <www.brendandmurphy.com>.

[183]   <www.divinecosmos.com/index.php?option=com_content&task=view&id=95&Itemid=36>.

[184]   Wilcock, *The Source Field Investigations*, 256.

[185]   Nowak.

[186]   Yurth, *Torsion Field Mechanics*.

[187]   Nowak.

[188]   Korotkov, 148.

[189]   Miller, *Anatomy of the Star Goddess*.

[190]   <http://en.wikipedia.org/wiki/5-MeO-DMT>.

[191]   Peake, Mystery of the Pineal Gland Finally Revealed? *New Dawn* Special Issue 6(4).

[192]   Morgan, *Scalar Wars*.

[193]   Yurth, *Seeing Past the Edge*, 135.

[194]   See Nachalov & Sokolov.

[195]   Yurth, *Seeing Past the Edge*, 136.

[196]   See Hoagland, 354–5.

[197]   Kaku, *Physics of the Impossible*, 232.

[198]   Violette, 6.

[199]   Ibid., 7.

[200]   See Alfred, *Our Invisible Bodies*, 59–62.

[201]   Randall, 215.

[202]   Pinchbeck, 28.

[203]   Sabom, 33.

[204]   Taimni, 308.

[205]   Leadbeater, *Clairvoyance*, Ch. 7.

[206]   McTaggart, *The Field*, 42.

[207]   See Waite, Ch. 1.

[208]   Ibid.

[209]   Ibid., Ch. 35.

[210]   See Bruce, Ch. 29.

[211]   Ibid.

[212]   Wicherink, Ch. 6.

[213]   Wilson, *Cosmic Trigger*, Part 2. For more background on the I Ching, see Colin Wilson, *The Occult*, 97–100.

[214]   Wilcock, *Shift of the Ages*, Ch. 6.

[215]   Kaku, *Parallel Worlds*, 202.

[216] Wilcock, *Shift of the Ages*, Ch. 6.

[217] Ibid., Ch. 21.

[218] Wilcock, *The Science of Oneness*, Ch. 14.22.2.

Chapter 7

[1] <https://en.wikipedia.org/wiki/Pratitya-samutpada>.

[2] <https://en.wikipedia.org/wiki/Indra%27s_net>.

[3] Yurth, *Seeing Past the Edge*, 109.

[4] Laszlo & Currivan, 14.

[5] Susskind, 338.

[6] Laszlo & Currivan, 19.

[7] Farrier.

[8] *The Holographic Principle*. www.scientificamerican.com/article.cfm?id=sidebar-the-holographic-p

[9] Yurth, *Seeing Past the Edge*, 114. See also CERN Courier, Cobalt magnetic resonance forms quantum mirage. <http://cerncourier.com/cws/article/cern/28197>.

[10] Susskind, 338.

[11] Laszlo & Currivan, 49.

[12] Zeilinger, 267.

[13] See Chalko.

[14] Quoted in Yurth, *Seeing Past the Edge*, 156.

[15] Martijn van Calmthout, *The entropy force: a new direction for gravity.* <www.newscientist.com/article/mg20527443.800-the-entropy-force-a-new-direction-for-gravity.html?page=1>.

[16] See Wilson, *The Occult*, Introduction.

[17] Ibid.

[18] Bruce Lipton, "The New Biology: Where Mind and Matter Meet." <www.youtube.com/watch?v=HVECAlT4AXY>; Lipton, "The Biology of Perception." <http://www.youtube.com/watch?v=nU_0BwbNsH4&feature=related>.

[19] See Lipton, *The Biology of Belief*, Ch. 3.

[20] Ibid.

[21] LaBerge & Rheingold, 172.

[22] Dennett, *Out-of-Body Exploring*, 121.

[23] <http://compsci.ca/blog/programming-the-universe-seth-lloyd>.

[24] Greg Ross, *An interview with Seth Loyd.* <www.americanscientist.org/bookshelf/pub/seth-lloyd>.

[25] See Brown, Morphic Resonance and Quantum Biology.

[26] Braden, *Fractal Time*, 83, 93.

[27] Miller & Miller.

28 Talbot, 27.

29 Ibid., 27–8.

30 Wicherink, 31.

31 Gerber, 527.

32 Underhill, 36.

33 Jones, 223.

34 Laszlo & Currivan, 57–8.

35 Prideux, *Comparison*.

36 Grosso, 171.

37 Ibid., 173.

38 Sheldrake, *The Presence of the Past*, 168.

39 See Talbot, 13, 22–3. See also Sheldrake, *The Presence of the Past*, 162–4.

40 Wicherink, 30–1.

41 See Peter Shepherd, *Transforming the Mind*, Ch. 6.

42 Mishlove, *The Holographic Brain*.

43 Ibid.

44 See Shepherd, Appendix.

45 Ibid.

46 See Pearce, Ch. 4.

47 McTaggart, *The Field*, 183.

48 Pearce, 84.

49 Ostrander & Schroeder, *Psychic Discoveries Behind the Iron Curtain*, 146–59.

50 Bentov, 32.

51 Ibid., 157.

52 Pearce, 67.

53 Church, 200. See also McTaggart, *The Field*, for more on Hameroff and Penrose's research.

54 Peake, *New Dawn* Special Issue, 6(4).

55 Wilson, *Quantum Psychology*, 114.

56 Ibid., 114–15.

57 Wolinsky, 17. See my article *Who Thinks Your Thoughts?* (featured in the May 2012 edition of Veritas magazine) at www.brendandmurphy.com for more along these lines.

58 Sogyal Rinpoche, 116.

59 Wilson, *Quantum Psychology*, 91–2.

60 Leadbeater, *Clairvoyance*, Ch. 1.

61 See Watson, *Supernature*, 240–1.

62 Atwater, 108.

63 Ibid., 109, 337–8.

64   Ibid., 334.

65   Hancock, *Supernatural*, 396.

66   Ibid., 397–8.

67   Email to author, February 24, 2012.

68   Van der Leeuw, 47.

69   Grosso, 48–9.

70   See Ostrander & Schroeder, *Psychic Discoveries Behind the Iron Curtain*.

71   Ostrander & Schroeder, *Psychic Discoveries: The Iron Curtain Lifted*, 371–3.

72   Humphrey, 38.

73   See Strassman, *DMT*.

74   For more on this see Wicherink, *Souls of Distortion*; Lipton, *The Biology of Belief*; McTaggart, *The Field*.

75   Watson, *Supernature*, 169.

76   DeGracia, *Beyond the Physical*, Ch. 13.

77   Van der Leeuw, 301.

78   Wolf, *The Soul and Quantum Physics*.

79   Wilson, *Cosmic Trigger*, Preface.

80   Talbot, 159.

81   Pavlina.

82   See Davis.

83   Coleman, *Extraordinary States*. <www.bethcoleman.com>.

84   Gibson, 57–8.

85   Pearce, Ch. 3.

86   Lipton, 132–3.

87   Lipton & Bhaerman, 38–9.

88   Coleman.

89   Lipton, 133.

90   Radford.

91   Lipton & Bhaerman, 32. In *The Genie in Your Genes*, Church offers 50 bits per second for the conscious, versus 11 million bits per second for the subconscious.

92   Bearden. <www.cheniere.org/misc/sparkoflife.htm>.

93   Lipton & Bhaerman, 33.

94   Ibid., 39.

95   Swann. <www.biomindsuperpowers.com/Pages/RealStoryCh7.html>.

96   Bryant & Seebach.

97   Gerber, 227.

Chapter 8

1   Leadbeater, *Man Visible and Invisible*, 16–17.

2   <www.experiencefestival.com/a/Sutratman/id/195150>.

3   Karagulla & Kunz, 30.

4   Brennan, *Hands of Light*, 49, and *Light Emerging*, 19.

5   See Powell, *The Etheric Double*, Ch. 1.

6   Ibid. Karagulla & Kunz are recommended reading along these lines.

7   See Swami Panchadasi, *The Human Aura*.

8   Powell, *The Etheric Double*, Ch. 1.

9   Wilson, *The Occult*, 716.

10 Watson, *Supernature*, 143.

11 Goswami, *Physics of the Soul*, 97.

12 Korotkov, 142.

13 Goswami, *Physics of the Soul*, 97.

14 <www.sheldrake.org/Resources/glossary/index.html>.

15 Montalk, *Astral Physics and Timespace*.

16 Ibid.

17 Ibid.

18 Ibid.

19 Quoted in Bartlett, XII.

20 Steiner, *An Outline of Occult Science*, Ch. 3.

21 Karagulla & Kunz, 160–3.

22 Gerber, 315.

23 Alfred, *Our Invisible Bodies*, 19–20.

24 Leadbeater, *Man Visible and Invisible*, 16–18.

25 See Leadbeater, *The Astral Plane* under "Scenery."

26 See Bruce, Ch. 1.

27 Ibid.

28 Ibid.

29 Ibid.

30 Leadbeater, *The Astral Plane*, as above.

31 Yogi Ramacharaka, *Fourteen Lessons in Yogi Philosophy*, 96.

32 Powell, *The Etheric Double*, Ch. 5.

33 Karagulla & Kunz, 56.

34 See Dennett, Introduction.

35 Ibid.

36 Powell, *The Astral Body*, Ch. 2.

37 Brennan, *Hands of Light*, 51–2.

38 Powell, *The Astral Body*, Ch. 2.

39 Ibid., Ch. 4.

40 Wilcock, *The Source Field Investigations*, 238.

41   Montalk, *Astral Physics and Timespace*. See <http://montalk.net> and <www. bibliotecapleyades.net/ciencia/ciencia_astralplane03.htm>.

42   Alfred, *Our Invisible Bodies*, 18.

43   See Powell, *The Mental Body*, Ch. 20.

44   Ibid., Ch. 4.

45   See Powell, *The Causal Body and the Ego*, Ch. 17.

46   Yogi Ramacharaka, *A Series of Lessons in Raja Yoga*, The Fourth Lesson.

47   Powell, *The Astral Body*, Ch. 7.

48   Ibid., Ch. 8.

49   Powell, *The Mental Body*, Ch. 6.

50   Brennan, *Hands of Light*, 50–1.

51   Powell, *The Mental Body*, Ch. 6.

52   Powell, *The Mental Body*, Ch. 3.

53   Brennan, *Hands of Light*, 51.

54   Collins, 26–7.

55   Leadbeater, *The Inner Life*, 15.

56   Ibid., 107.

57   Powell, *The Mental Body*, Ch. 4.

58   Powell, *The Causal Body and the Ego*, Ch. 15.

59   Brennan, *Hands of Light*, 53–4. For more detail on the causal body of man at various stages of development, see Leadbeater, *Man Visible and Invisible*. Steven Lumiere's website is also a worthy source for material on the subtle bodies and their respective planes: <www.energyreality.com/pgs/7lev.htm>.

60   Powell, *The Causal Body and the Ego*, Ch. 15.

61   Ibid.

62   Leadbeater, *The Inner Life*, 177.

63   See Sogyal Rinpoche, Ch. 18.

64   Ibid., 292–3.

65   Collins, 31.

66   Powell, *The Mental Body*, Ch. 28.

67   Powell, *The Causal Body*, Ch. 31.

68   Ibid., Ch. 32.

69   Ibid.

70   Ibid.

71   See Leadbeater, *Clairvoyance*, Ch. 8.

72   Ibid.

73   Taimni, 370.

74   See DeGracia, *DO_OBE*, Ch. 1.

75   Leadbeater, *The Inner Life*, 75.

76   Powell, *The Causal Body*, Ch. 3.
77   Ibid.
78   Ibid.
79   Goswami, *Physics of the Soul*, 127.
80   Powell, *The Causal Body*, Ch. 26.
81   Ibid., Conclusion.
82   Goswami, *Physics of the Soul*, 95.
83   Bentov, 116.
84   Karagulla & Kunz, 35.
85   See ibid, p. 98.
86   Leadbeater, *The Inner Life*, 311.
87   Karagulla, 146.
88   Motoyama, 260.
89   See Motoyama, 261–5.
90   Church, 126.
91   Gerber, 178.
92   Church, 126.
93   Ibid., 154–5.
94   Gerber, 122–6.
95   Alfred, *Our Invisible Bodies*, 81.
96   Church, 136–7.
97   Alfred, *Our Invisible Bodies*, 87.
98   Brennan, *Hands of Light*, 44.
99   Braden, *The Divine Matrix*, 50.
100   Pearce, 57.
101   See Pearce, Ch. 3.
102   See Brennan, *Hands of Light*.
103   Pearce, 58–9.
104   Motoyama, 183.
105   Leadbeater, *The Chakras*, 10.
106   Ibid., 13.
107   Ibid., Ch. 1.
108   Collins, *How to See and Read the Human Aura*, 80.
109   See Motoyama, Ch. 7.
110   DeGracia, *Beyond the Physical*, 231.
111   See Dennett, Ch. 1.
112   Watson, *Supernature*, 142.
113   Brennan, *Light Emerging*, 29.
114   Ibid., 289–90.

[115] Ibid., 291.

[116] Ibid., 29–30.

Chapter 9

[1] Luckman, *Conscious Healing*, 24–5.

[2] <www.divinecosmos.com/index.php?option=com_content&task=view&id=95&Ite mid=36>.

[3] Payne.

[4] Mutton.

[5] Wilson, *The Occult*, 705–6.

[6] See Waite, Ch. 5.

[7] Powell, *The Etheric Double*, Ch. 11.

[8] Watson, *Supernature*,144.

[9] *Odic Physics Introduction*. <http://odicenergy.com/thescience.htm>.

[10] Ibid.

[11] Rifat, 91.

[12] Farrel, 208.

[13] See Alfred, *Our Invisible Bodies*.

[14] Alfred, *New Dawn*.

[15] Alfred, *Evolution of Dark Plasma Life Forms on Earth*.

[16] Alfred, *Our Invisible Bodies*, 108.

[17] Ibid., 107.

[18] Ibid., 104.

[19] Alfred, *Evolution of Dark Plasma…*

[20] Alfred, *Dark Plasma and the Origin of Angels* ….

[21] Alfred, *Our Invisible Bodies*, 38.

[22] Alfred, *Dark Plasma and the Origin…*

[23] Humphrey, 65, 54.

[24] Ibid., 73.

[25] Payne.

[26] Ibid.

[27] Ibid.

[28] See *The Edinburgh Lectures on Mental Science*, by Thomas Troward, at <www.sacred-texts.com/nth/elms/elms16.htm>.

[29] Swami Panchadasi, *The Human Aura*, Ch. 5.

[30] *The Aura and the Seven Chakras*. <www.mindspring.com/~pmarsh/aura.html>.

[31] Brennan, *Hands of Light*, 31.

[32] Ibid.

[33] See Powell, *The Etheric Double*, Ch. 21.

34   Ibid.

35   Mutton.

36   Korotkov, 80.

37   See Gerber, *Vibrational Medicine*.

38   Yurth, *Torsion Field Mechanics*.

39   Gerber, 55–6.

40   See Ostrander & Schroeder, *Psychic Discoveries Behind the Iron Curtain*.

41   Kirlian Photography Research, <www.kirlian.org/kirlian2.htm>. See also Mishlove, 133–4.

42   Ibid. See also Mutton.

43   See Hunt.

44   Solomon & Soloman, *Harry Oldfield's Invisible Universe*, 74. For more on this topic, see Ostrander & Schroeder.

45   Kirlian Photography Research.

46   Taylor, Kirlian Photography and the New Bioelectrography.

47   Ibid.

48   McTaggart, *The Intention Experiment*, 46.

49   Taylor, *Computerised Bioelectrography*.

50   Chalko.

51   Ibid.

52   Ibid.

53   See Nelson, 111. See also Watson, *Supernature*, Ch. 3.

54   Goswami, *Physics of the Soul*, 179.

55   See Brennan, *Hands of Light*.

56   Gibson.

57   Ibid.

58   Leadbeater, *Man Visible and Invisible*, 115–17.

59   See Swami Panchadasi, *The Human Aura*.

60   Leadbeater, *The Chakras*.

61   Sheldrake, *The Presence of the Past*, 81.

62   Ibid., 99.

63   See McTaggart, *The Field*, 61.

64   Leadbeater, *The Inner Life*, 345–6.

65   Brennan, *Light Emerging*, 184–5.

66   See McTaggart, *The Field*, 61.

67   Backster, 75.

68   Brennan, *Hands of Light*, 49.

69   Harry Oldfield, Energy Fields Revealed, Glastonbury Symposium. <www.youtube.com/watch?v=JNaFjQAykGo&NR=1>.

70   See Solomon & Solomon. See also Oldfield's Glastonbury Symposium presentation.

71   Davis, 20.

72   Ibid.

73   See McTaggart, *The Field*, 57–8.

74   Ibid.

75   Church, 36.

76   Sheldrake, *Morphic Resonance and Morphic Fields.*

77   See Lipton, 80.

78   Ibid., 81.

79   Church, 121–2.

80   Lipton, 81.

81   Church, 158.

82   Ibid.

83   See Miller, Miller & Webb.

84   Church, 159.

85   Uvarov & Agar.

86   Alfred, *Plasma Life.*

87   Mutton.

88   Leadbeater, *The Inner Life*, 209. See also *Chakras*, Ch. 4.

89   Alfred, Plasma Life.

90   Leadbeater, *Chakras*, Ch. 4.

91   Ibid.

92   Bruce, Ch. 28.

93   Leadbeater, *The Astral Plane*, 53.

94   See Powell, *The Etheric Double*, Ch. 16.

95   See Solomon & Solomon, 32.

96   Ibid., 33

97   See Talbot, 177–8.

98   Ibid., 178.

99   Hunt, 20.

100 Ibid.

101 Gibson, 50.

102 Last.

103 Steiner, *An Outline of Occult Science*, Ch. 2.

104 Korotkov, 60.

105 Gori & Firenzuoli.

106 Linsteadt.

107 Hunt, 28–9.

108 Ibid., 29.

109   Ostrander & Schroeder, *Psychic Discoveries Behind the Iron Curtain*, 406.

110   Hamilton, 50.

111   Dakin, *High-Voltage Photography*, 27–30.

112   Lewin.

113   Holewa.

114   Zuger.

115   Hunt, 66.

116   Ostrander & Schroeder, *Psychic Discoveries Behind the Iron Curtain*, 219.

117   McTaggart, *The Field*, 69–70.

118   See McTaggart, *The Field*. See also Linsteadt's article (above) for more on this research.

119   Jeremy Narby, *The Cosmic Serpent*, quoted by Michael Tsarion in his "2012—The Future of Mankind" presentation at the Granada Forum, Los Angeles, 2006.

120   www.fosar-bludorf.com.

121   Narby, 126.

122   Wilcock, *The Source Field Investigations*, 170.

123   See <www.mercola.com>. See also youtube for Oldfield's Glastonbury Symposium presentation.

124   See McTaggart, *The Field*.

125   Motoyama, 279.

126   Gerber, 133.

127   Results of Diagnostic and Healing Tests at Tokyo Denki University, Japan. <www.caroleverett.com/ce-diag.htm>.

128   Yoshio Machi, *Healers Brain Waves*. <www.caroleverett.com/ce-yoshi.htm>.

129   Tiller, *Psychoenergetic Science*, 186.

130   Ibid., 91.

131   The Science of Human Vibrations: Stuart Dawes Speaks to Valerie Hunt. <www.freshmag.com.au/science.html>.

132   See Pearl.

133   Welch, 96.

134   McTaggart, *The Field*, 65–6.

135   See Welch. Lipton explains this lucidly in a seminar presentation you can view at: <www.youtube.com/watch?v=Zcg_ldoU40c&feature=related>.

136   See Brennan, *Hands of Light*, 32–3.

137   Hunt, 31.

138   Ibid., 32.

139   Becker & Selden, 248–9.

140   Ibid., 249.

141   Hunt, 34.

142 See Brennan, *Hands of Light*, 143, and *Light Emerging*, 59.

143 See Gerber.

144 Gerber, 295; McTaggart, 241; Mishlove, <www.williamjames.com/Science/PSIONIC2.htm>.

145 Watson, *Supernature*, 163.

146 See Gerber, 295–7.

147 See Benford.

148 See Brennan, *Hands of Light* for her descriptions of how etheric energy is automatically imparted to physical objects by physical contact (or directed will).

149 See Gerber, 289–93.

150 Rein, *Conformational Changes*.

151 See Levich.

152 *Oldfield Systems* PDF brochure available at <www.electrocrystal.com>.

153 King.

154 See Oldfield's Glastonbury Symposium presentation.

155 Karagulla & Kunz, 154–60.

156 Brennan, *Light Emerging*, 18.

157 King.

158 See Solomon & Solomon.

159 See the plates in Solomon & Solomon.

160 See King's *Nexus* article. See also <www.electrocrystal.com>.

161 Polycontrast Interference Technology. <www.electrocrystal.com/pip.html>.

162 Solomon & Solomon, 153.

163 Ibid., 227–8.

164 See Hunt, Ch. 2.

165 Blavatsky, *Studies in Occultism*.

166 See Schultz, 102.

167 Nelson, 18, 21.

168 Grof, *LSD Psychotherapy*, 156.

169 Ibid., 191.

170 Todeschi, *Edgar Cayce on the Akashic Records*, 95–6.

171 McCraty et al., *Modulation of DNA Conformation by Heart-Focused Intention*. <www.heartmath.org>.

172 See Ostrander & Schroeder, *Psychic Discoveries Behind the Iron Curtain*.

173 See Rein, *Effect of Conscious Intention on Human DNA*. See also McCraty et al., *Modulation of DNA Conformation by Heart-Focused Intention*. <www.heartmath.org>.

174 See above and also Rein, & McCraty, *Structural Changes in Water & DNA Associated with New Physiologically Measurable States*. <www.heartmath.org/research/research-publications/structural-changes-in-water-dna.html>.

175 Luckman, *Conscious Healing*, 100.

176 See Church.

177 Backster, 112–15.

178 Ibid., 131.

179 Braden, *The Divine Matrix*, 48.

180 Defence Intelligence Agency report (1972).

181 Karagulla, 60–2.

182 Ibid., 78–9.

183 Talbot, 172.

184 Karagulla & Kunz, 108.

185 Ibid., 186–7.

186 Karagulla, 133–4.

187 Ibid., 139–40.

188 See Karagulla for more detail.

189 Clarified via email with author.

190 See Hunt, 22–3.

191 Ibid., 23.

192 See Talbot, 169–71.

193 Karagulla & Kunz, 36–7.

194 Hunt, 26–7.

195 Ibid.

196 See Brennan, *Hands of Light*, 33–4.

197 Ibid., 42, 43.

198 Alfred, *Our Invisible Bodies*, 53. Brennan concurs, stating that every second level of the aura is a feeling level, as opposed to the odd-numbered more structured levels which represent concepts. See Brennan, *Light Emerging*, 274.

199 See Brennan, *Hands of Light*, 49–54.

200 Ibid., 42–4, 48.

201 Motoyama, 21.

202 See Vorley, *Metaphysics*.

203 See Powell, *The Etheric Double*, Ch.13.

204 Taimni, 295.

205 See Powell, *The Mental Body*, Ch.14.

206 Leadbeater, *The Inner Life*, 201.

207 Brennan, *Hands of Light*, 48.

208 Bruce, Ch. 14.

209 Brennan, *Light Emerging*, 59.

210 Karagulla & Kunz, 117.

211 Solomon & Solomon, 128.

[212] Ibid., 131.

[213] Luckman, *Conscious Healing*, 59. Note: In *Conscious Healing*, Luckman refers to these energy centres as being electromagnetic, but clarifies in *Potentiate…* that in reality they are torsion centres/vortices. Any light-based/electromagnetic components are secondary effects.

[214] Myss, 166.

[215] Luckman, *Conscious Healing*, 22.

[216] Ibid., 61–2.

[217] Ibid., 63.

[218] Luckman, *Historical & Scientific Overview of Enlightenment*. <http://crowrising.posterous.com/historical-scientific-overview-of-enlightenme>. See also *Conscious Healing*, 131–3.

[219] See Kelleher.

[220] Luckman, *Conscious Healing*, 186.

[221] Dale, 82.

[222] Ibid., 160.

[223] See my series of articles on my experience with the Regenetics method, beginning with *Diary of a DNA Potentiator*. <www.brendandmurphy.com>. An earlier version of this was published in *New Dawn* No. 133, July-August, 2012.

[224] See Linsteadt.

[225] Luckman, *Potentiate Your DNA*, 82–3.

[226] Karagulla, 184.

[227] Laslzo & Currivan, 166.

[228] Strassman, *DMT*, 59.

[229] Becker & Selden, 249.

[230] Strassman, 61.

[231] Ibid., 61.

[232] Wilcock, *The Source Field Investigations*, 40–1.

[233] See *The 2012 Enigma* seminar presentation by David Wilcock on <youtube.com>.

[234] See Bryson, *The Fluoride Deception*.

[235] *Health Effects: Fluoride & the Pineal Gland*. <www.fluoridealert.org/health/pineal>.

[236] Wilcock, *The Source Field Investigations*, 62–3.

[237] Nelson, 126.

[238] Vorley, 50.

[239] See Hall.

[240] 1111 Bill Deagle speaks at the Granada Forum. <http://video.google.ca/videoplay?docid=2221852945040630461&ei=yr0qS8ycJqKAqwK6lZDHBQ&q=bill+deagle&hl=en#docid=-2585664107547943684>.

[241] See Wilcock, *The 2012 Enigma*. (as previous)

[242] Ibid.

[243] Yogi Ramacharaka, *Fourteen Lessons in Yogi Philosophy*, 94.

[244] Strassman, 69.

[245] Wilcock, *The 2012 Enigma*.

[246] Taimni, 295.

[247] Brennan, *Hands of Light*, 163.

[248] Julie Ann Miller, Eye to eye; scientists are taking advantage of unexpected similarities between the eye's retina and the brain's pineal gland. *Science News*, November 9, 1985. <http://findarticles.com/p/articles/mi_m1200/is_v128/ai_4016492/?tag=content;col1>.

[249] Wilcock, *The Source Field Investigations*, 57–61.

[250] See Peake, *New Dawn*.

[251] Wilcock, *The Source Field Investigations*, 57–61.

[252] Welch, 42–3.

[253] Ibid., 42.

[254] See the back cover of Welch's book.

[255] Gerber, 338–9.

[256] See Powell, *The Etheric Double*, Ch.13.

[257] Goswami, *Physics of the Soul*, 246.

[258] Kundalini. <www.crystalinks.com/kundalini.html>.

[259] Bartlett, 153.

[260] See Solomon & Solomon, 208–10.

[261] Alfred, Dark Plasma …

[262] Alfred, *Our Invisible Bodies*, 85.

[263] Ibid., 164–5. See also Alfred, *Dark Plasma Theory – (New) Biology*. <www.dapla.org/subtle_body.htm>.

[264] Eichler.

[265] Lazar et al.

[266] Hamilton, 10.

[267] Church, 256–7.

[268] Pearce, 64.

[269] Yurth, 177.

[270] Vorley, 51.

[271] Brennan, *Hands of Light*, 38.

[272] Ibid.

[273] See Leadbeater, *The Chakras*, Ch. 3.

[274] See Besant & Leadbeater, *Occult Chemistry*, 1951, 94–5.

[275] Leadbeater, *Man Visible and Invisible*, 113.

[276] See Powell, *The Etheric Double*, Ch. 2.

277 Wilson, *Wilhelm Reich in Hell*, Introduction.

278 Atwater, *Future Memory*, 160–1.

279 Kelley.

280 Ibid., 240. See Eisen, 233–46 for more of Jeanne Manning's material on Reich. Also see Wilson, *The Occult*, 708–14 for more background on Reich and his work.

281 Yogananda, 376–7. "Baba" is a term of affection for a saint or holy man. See <www.bible.ca/tongues-dictionary-hindu-yoga.htm>.

282 Ibid., 379, note 1.

283 Yogananda, Ch. 26.

284 Ibid., 378–9.

285 Ibid., 371.

286 Vogl, 12.

287 Ibid., 25.

288 See Yogananda, 300–4.

289 Ibid., 302, note 1.

290 Motoyama, 236.

291 Living on Light Research. <http://home.iae.nl/users/lightnet/health/lightresearch.htm>.

292 http://solarhealing.com/about.

293 Ibid.

294 <http://home.iae.nl/users/lightnet/health/lightresearch.htm>.

295 Ibid.

296 Ibid.

297 Fosar & Bludorf, *The Biological Chip in Our Cells: Revolutionary Results of Modern Genetics*. www.bibliotecapleyades.net/ciencia/ciencia_genetica01.htm

298 Grosso, Padre Pio.

299 Yogananda.

300 Grosso, *Experiencing the Next Life Now*, 200.

301 Sogyal Rinpoche, 270–1.

302 Randall, 50.

303 Sogyal Rinpoche, 274–5.

304 See Yogananda, and see also Sogyal Rinpoche, Ch. 16.

305 Randall, Ch. 4.

306 Montalk, *Astral Physics and Timespace*.

307 Yurth, *Seeing Past the Edge*, 324.

308 Ostrander & Schroeder, *Psychic Discoveries Behind the Iron Curtain*, 225.

309 Karagulla, 46.

310 Korotkov, 39–40.

311 Ibid., 6–4.

[312]   See Kelleher.

[313]   See Gage & Muotri.

[314]   <http://en.wikipedia.org/wiki/Transposon>.

[315]   Brown, Morphic Resonance and Quantum Biology.

[316]   Ibid.

[317]   Besant & Leadbeater, *Thought Forms*, Introduction.

[318]   See Panchadasi, *The Human Aura*.

Chapter 10

[1]   Talbot, 180.

[2]   Prideux, *Comparison*.

[3]   Alfred, *Our Invisible Bodies*, 97.

[4]   Ibid., 100.

[5]   Karagulla & Kunz, 169.

[6]   Taimni, 281.

[7]   Powell, *The Mental Body*, Ch. 8.

[8]   See Bruce, Ch. 35.

[9]   Powell, *The Mental Body*, Ch. 8.

[10]   Yogi Ramacharaka, *Fourteen Lessons in Yogi Philosophy*, 85.

[11]   Powell, *The Mental Body*, Ch. 8.

[12]   Pinchbeck, 165.

[13]   Haughton.

[14]   Powell, *The Mental Body*, Ch. 8.

[15]   Powell, *The Astral Body*, Ch. 7.

[16]   Steiner, *Knowledge of the Higher Worlds*.

[17]   Powell, *The Astral Body*, Ch. 7.

[18]   Ibid.

[19]   Ibid.

[20]   Ibid.

[21]   Ibid.

[22]   Monroe, 28.

[23]   Ibid., 29.

[24]   The page I originally sourced this from can no longer be found. These quotes can be found here instead at <http://setiathome.berkeley.edu/forum_thread.php?id=50439&sort=7>.

[25]   Ibid.

[26]   Hancock, *Supernatural*, 199.

[27]   See Marrs, *Alien Agenda*.

[28]   Swann, Mrs. Zelda Suplee.

29   See Warren, *How to Hunt Ghosts.*

30   Oldfield, Glastonbury Symposium Presentation.

31   See Davis, the *Black Box*, under "Time…The 4th Dimension."

32   Oldfield, Glastonbury…

33   Panchadasi, *Clairvoyance*, Lesson XV.

34   See Leadbeater, *Man Visible and Invisible.*

35   *Encyclopedia of Occultism and Parapsychology*, vol. 2, 1387.

36   Ibid.

37   Wilson, *The Occult*, 717.

38   *Encyclopedia of Occultism and Parapsychology*, vol. 2, 1387.

39   Watson, *Supernature*, 159.

40   Randall, 157.

41   Waite, Ch. 2.

42   Wilson, *The Occult*, 668.

43   Ibid., 717.

44   Watson, 160.

45   Humphrey, 43–4.

46   Ostrander & Schroeder, *Psychic Discoveries: The Iron Curtain Lifted*, 71.

47   Calvi-Parisetti, *21 Days into the Afterlife*. See "Day 17: Picture and music at Scole" for more detail.

48   Solomon & Solomon, 207–8.

49   Oldfield at the Glastonbury Symposium. <www.youtube.com/watch?v=yrj_HiTOxL4&NR=1>.

50   Mishlove, 135–6.

51   Tiller, *Subtle Energy Actions and Physical Domain Correlations.* See also <www.tillerfoundation.com/subtle-energies.html> for sample images.

52   Yogananda, 18–19.

53   See Kubler-Ross.

54   Atwater, *The Big Book of Near-Death Experiences*, 65.

55   Oldfield, Glastonbury Symposium. <www.youtube.com/watch?v=ZbGz6oK87ZQ&feature=related>.

56   See Brennan, *Light Emerging.*

57   Luckman, *Conscious Healing*, 67.

58   Leadbeater, *The Chakras*. See under "Psychic Forces." For the interested reader: Yogi Ramacharaka goes into interesting discussion of exactly why people think like sheep in *Fourteen Lessons in Yogi Philosophy.*

59   Ibid.

60   Steiner, *An Outline of Occult Science*, Ch. 3.

61   DeGracia, *Beyond the Physical*, 287.

62   Ibid.
63   Wilson, *Prometheus Rising*, 97.
64   Ibid.
65   Ibid., 97.
66   Ibid.
67   DeGracia, *Beyond the Physical*, 287–8.
68   Ibid., 288.
69   Korotkov, 170.
70   Wolinsky, 114.
71   See my article *Who Thinks Your Thoughts?* At www.brendandmurphy.com.
72   DeGracia, *Beyond the Physical*, 184.
73   Ibid., 184–5.
74   Sogyal Rinpoche, 78.
75   Goswami, *The Self-Aware Universe*, 162.
76   Ibid., 167–8.
77   See Vesperman.
78   See Brown, Morphic Resonance and Quantum Biology.
79   Jones, 203.
80   See Wilcock, *The Source Field Investigations*, and Brown, *Morphic Resonance and Quantum Biology*.
81   Peat.

Chapter 11

1   Day & Gale, 42.
2   Bazette, Ch. 2.
3   Wilson, *The Occult*, 237.
4   Wilde, *Sixth Sense*, 59.
5   Yogananda, 105.
6   Wilson, *The Occult*, 477.
7   Ostrander & Schroeder, *Psychic Discoveries: The Iron Curtain Lifted*, 354.
8   See Yogananda, 116, note 2.
9   Sheldrake, *Morphic Resonance*.
10   See Schoch & Yonavjak.
11   Swami Panchadasi, *Clairvoyance and Occult Powers*, Lesson III.
12   Ibid.
13   Ibid.
14   Quoted by Cavid Conway in *Secret Wisdom*, 117.
15   Conway, 117–18.
16   See Waite, Ch. 39.

17   Watson, 253.

18   Waite, Ch. 39.

19   Watson, 253.

20   Waite, Ch. 39.

21   Radin, *Entangled Minds*, 86–8; *Encyclopedia of Occultism and Parapsychology*, vol. 2, 1182. An overview of the Pearce-Pratt series of 1850 trials can also be found here: <www.pureinsight.org/node/1271>.

22   J.B. Rhine, *Extra-sensory Perception* (1934), quoted in Schoch & Yonavjak, 136.

23   Venkatasubramanian et al.

24   Frank D. Smith.

25   Goswami, *Physics of the Soul*, 37.

26   See Ostrander & Schroder, *Psychic Discoveries Behind the Iron Curtain*.

27   Standish et al.

28   Goswami, *The Self-Aware Universe*.

29   Reed. Yurth has also linked Gisin's experiments proving nonlocality and entanglement to torsion fields. See Vesperman.

30   Waite, Ch. 21.

31   Watson, 266.

32   Targ & Puthoff, 131–2.

33   Wackermann.

34   Targ & Katra.

35   Ostrander & Schroeder, *Psychic Discoveries Behind the Iron Curtain*, 89. Richard Gerber also provides some coverage of Dean's experiments in *Vibrational Medicine*, 227–8, as does Mishlove in *The Roots of Consciousness*.

36   See Ross.

37   <www.youtube.com/watch?v=Sf9AJCLbaWw&feature=endscreen&NR=1>.

38   <www.rossinst.com/human_eyebeam_detection.html>.

39   Sogyal Rinpoche, 45.

40   Ibid., 43.

41   Radin, *The Conscious Universe*, 68.

42   Radin, *Entangled Minds*, 109–10.

43   Weiss, 153.

44   Grof & Halifax, 69.

45   See Radin, *Entangled Minds*, 120.

46   Bem.

47   Jessica Utts, *Replication and Meta-analysis in Parapsychology*, 1991. Quoted in Schoch & Yonavjak, 187–92. See also Bem for information on these experiments.

48   Wilkins & Sherman.

49   Ibid., 23.

50 Ibid.

51 Ibid., xxi.

52 Ibid., 64.

53 Ibid., 64–5.

54 Ibid., 72.

55 Ibid.

56 Ibid.

57 Ibid., 73.

58 Ibid., 109.

59 Ibid., 113–14.

60 Ibid., 116.

61 Ibid., 128.

62 Ibid.

63 Ibid., 128–9.

64 Ibid., 155.

65 Ibid., 156.

66 Ibid., 184.

67 Ibid., 199.

68 Ibid., 219–20.

69 See Backster, 24–5.

70 Ibid., 29–30.

71 Swann, Cleve Backster.

72 Backster, 40.

73 Powell, *The Astral Body*, Ch. 4.

74 See Yogananda, Ch. 38.

75 See Waite, Ch. 20.

76 See Wilson, *Cosmic Trigger*, Part 1.

77 See Backster, 34–5.

78 Korotkov, 84.

79 Backster, 43–8.

80 Research on the Maharishi Effect. <www.mum.edu/m_effect>.

81 Ibid.

82 Ibid.

83 Ibid. To read the Washington study see <www.mum.edu/m_effect/dc_md.html>. For a list of TM studies see <www.mum.edu/m_effect/charts.html>.

84 McTaggart. *The Intention Experiment*, 183.

85 Email from D. Yurth, February 2012.

86 Powell, *The Mental Body*, Ch. 12.

87 Radin, *The Conscious Universe*, 328.

[88] Bentov, 41–2, 44.

[89] Sheldrake, *Morphic Resonance.*

[90] See Steiner, *An Outline of Occult Science*, Ch. 3.

[91] See Brennan, *Hands of Light*, 52.

[92] See Brown, Morphic Resonance and Quantum Biology.

[93] Conway, 26.

[94] Luckman, *Potentiate Your DNA*, 108.

[95] Lipton & Bhaerman, 117.

[96] Luckman, Metagenetics and DNA Activation, *DNA Monthly*, 7(7). <www.potentiateyourdna.com/resources/dna-monthly/current-issue>.

[97] Hamilton, 140–1. See also Sheldrake, *The Presence of the Past*, 174–81.

[98] Wilcock, *The Science of Oneness*, Ch. 2.6.2.

[99] Grosso, 115.

[100] Schoch and Yonavjak, 89–91.

[101] Brennan, *Light Emerging*, 184–5.

[102] D.G. Yurth, *Variations on the Maharishi Model.*

[103] Sheldrake, *Morphic Resonance.*

[104] See Marrs, *PSI Spies*, 79–80.

[105] Slime Molds Show Surprising Degree of Intelligence. *Discover Magazine* (2009). <http://discovermagazine.com/2009/jan/071>.

[106] Blavatsky, *Studies in Occultism.*

[107] Lipton & Bhaerman, 229.

[108] Wilson, *The Occult*, 125.

[109] Anderson, *The Coincidence File*, 48.

[110] Backster, 31–3.

[111] Schoch & Yonavjak, 49.

[112] See Ostrander & Schroeder (1970 and 1997).

[113] Grosso, *New Dawn* Special Issue No. 9

[114] Bartlett, *The Physics of Miracles*, Introduction.

[115] Leadbeater, *The Inner Life*, 309.

[116] Oldfield at the Glastonbury Symposium. <www.youtube.com/watch?v=R_SDyqfRWO0&feature=related>.

[117] *Soviet and Czechoslovakian Parapsychology Research—Defense Intelligence Agency (DIA)*, Septermber 1975.

[118] Powell, *The Etheric Double*, Ch. 22.

[119] Yogananda, Ch. 218, note 1.

[120] Motoyama, 212.

[121] See Powell, *The Mental Body*, Ch. 9.

[122] Karagulla & Kunz, 171–2.

[123] Ostrander & Schroeder, *Psychic Discoveries Behind the Iron Curtain*, 130–1.

[124] Ibid., 21–2.

[125] Ibid., 23.

[126] Ibid.

[127] These experiments are covered in Ostrander & Schroeder, *Psychic Discoveries Behind the Iron Curtain*, chapter 3.

[128] Dr. Lavrenty S. Shikhobalov, *N.A. Kozyrev's Ideas Today.*

[129] Watson, 262–4.

[130] Ibid., 260.

[131] 1401 [131] Lipton & Bhaerman, 11.

[132] Grosso, 27–8.

[133] See Ostrander & Schroedinger.

[134] Targ & Puthoff, 101.

[135] L.R. Bresmuth, *Unconventional Human Intelligence Support: Transcendent and Asymmetric Warfare Implications of Remote Viewing*, 2001. Quoted in Schoch & Yonavjak, 247.

[136] See Ostrander & Schroeder, *Psychic Discoveries Behind the Iron Curtain.*

[137] Jung, *Synchronicity.*

[138] Targ & Puthoff, 11.

[139] Wilkins & Sherman, 129.

[140] See Bazette, Ch. 10.

[141] Wilson, *The Occult*, 127–8.

[142] Quoted in Atwater, 340.

Chapter 12

[1] Bearden, *Excalibur Briefing*, 151.

[2] Radin, *The Conscious Universe*, 100.

[3] Radin, *Entangled Minds*, 162. This is also detailed in Utts' report (see below).

[4] Jessica Utts, *Replication and Meta-analysis in Parapsychology*, 1991. Quoted in Schoch & Yonavjak, 193–4.

[5] Storm.

[6] The Power of Premonitions: An Interview with Larry Dossey, MD, *New Dawn* Special Issue No. 9, 2009.

[7] ESP Researchers. <www.unexplainedstuff.com/Mysteries-of-the-Mind/ESP-Researchers-Precognition.html>.

[8] Wolf, *Parallel Universes*, 231.

[9] Jung, *Synchronicity.*

[10] Tony Harrington, *Supernatural Warfare.* <http://thespiritseekers.wordpress.com/2011/01/07/supernatural-warfare-how-the-occult-psychics-and-past-lives-affected-the-warfront/>.

11 Bazette, Ch. 4.

12 See Todeschi.

13 Grosso, 181.

14 Humphrey, 46.

15 Radin, *The Conscious Universe*, 125–30.

16 Benjamin Libet. www.informationphilosopher.com/solutions/scientists/libet.

17 Brennan, *Light Emerging*, 182.

18 Is this REALLY proof that man can see into the future? *London Evening Standard.* <www.thisislondon.co.uk>. See also Radin, *The Conscious Universe*, Ch. 7, for Bierman's replications, as well as Bierman and Scholte.

19 Ibid. Radin points out on page 176 of *Entangled Minds* that Bierman has since replicated the presentiment effect "numerous times."

20 McTaggart, *The Intention Experiment*, 171.

21 See Levich. See also Nachalov & Sokolov.

22 McCraty et al. Electrophysiological evidence of intuition: Part 2.

23 Ibid., Part 1.

24 McCraty et al. *The Electricity of Touch.* There are some interesting qualifiers regarding the signal transferrance effect and I suggest consulting the paper in full for the details.

25 Radin, *Entangled Minds*, 142–5.

26 Randall, 152–3.

27 See Targ & Puthoff.

28 Leadbeater, *Clairvoyance*, Ch. 8.

29 Ibid.

30 Swami Panchadasi, *Clairvoyance...*, Lesson XIII. See also Wilson, *The Occult*, 406–7.

31 Ibid.

32 Wilson, *The Occult*, 407.

33 Marrs, *PSI Spies*, 77.

34 Ibid., 163.

35 Ingo Swann, The Second Visit to SRI. Also detailed in Targ & Puthoff, 26.

36 Ibid.

37 Puthoff, *CIA-Initiated Remote Viewing*.

38 Marrs, *PSI Spies*, 117.

39 1451See Targ, *New Dawn* Special Issue, 6(4).

40 Puthoff, *CIA-Initiated Remote Viewing*.

41 Targ & Puthoff, 207–11.

42 See Targ & Puthoff, and see also Marrs, *PSI Spies*.

43 Marrs, PSI Spies, 104. See Marrs, *PSI Spies*, Ch. 4 for more background on SCANATE.

44 Puthoff, *CIA-Initiated Remote Viewing*.

45   Ibid.

46   Ibid.

47   Marrs, *PSI Spies*, 93.

48   Ibid., 94.

49   Leadbeater, *Clairvoyance*, Ch. 4.

50   Rifat, 51.

51   L.R. Bresmuth, Reproduced in Schoch & Yonavjak, 242–3.

52   Excerpt from article from the *Vancouver Courier*, 1996, by Geoff Olson: <www.mceagle. com/remote-viewing/pub/news/96jun02-vc.html>.

53   Psychic's government role revealed. *Nelson County Times* (Dec. 7, 1995): <www.mceagle. com/remote-viewing/pub/news/95dec07-nt.html>.

54   Excerpt from *Newsweek*, December, 1995, by Gregory Vistica: <www.mceagle.com/ remote-viewing/pub/news/95dec11-nw.html

55   Rifat, 54.

56   Ibid.

57   Targ & Puthoff, 47.

58   Rifat, 48–9.

59   Targ, Remote Viewing at Stanford Research Institute.

60   Milton, *The remote viewing experiment that was too successful.*

61   Targ, Remote Viewing …

62   Jahn and Dunne, *Information and Uncertainty* (2003).

63   Dossey, *The Dark Side of Consciousness*. Also see Storm.

64   Hamilton, 107.

65   Jessica Utts, *Replication and Meta-analysis in Parapsychology*, 1991. Quoted in Schoch and Yonavjak, 198.

66   Blavatsky, *Studies in Occultism.*

67   Mishlove, 291–2.

68   Ibid., 292.

69   Targ & Puthoff, 157–8.

70   Superpowers of the Human Biomind (Ingo Swann database). <www. biomindsuperpowers.com/Pages/Superpowers.html>.

71   Rifat, 20.

72   R. Nelson, *Consciousness and Psi.*

73   Rifat, 29–30.

74   McTaggart, *The Intention Experiment*, 75.

75   Alexander et al.

76   McTaggart, *The Intention Experiment*, 106–9.

77   What is the Limbic System? <www.wisegeek.com/what-is-the-limbic-system.htm>.

78   See Bentov.

79   Yurth, *Seeing Past the Edge*, 238–9.

80   Sidorov, *On the possible mechanism of intent in paranormal phenomena.*

81   Grazyna Fosar & Franz Bludorf, *The Biological Chip in our Cells.* <www.fosar-bludorf. com/archiv/biochip_eng.htm>.

82   Sidorov. See also Church.

83   Brennan, *Light Emerging*, 18.

84   Rifat, 95.

85   Swann, A "Communication."

86   Powell, *The Astral Body*, Ch. 16.

87   Leadbeater, *The Inner Life*, 273–4.

88   Alfred, Between the Moon and Earth, 27–9.

89   Monroe, *Journeys Out of the Body*. Quoted in Alfred, *Between the Moon and Earth*, 29.

90   Alfred, *Between the Moon and Earth*, 29.

91   Ibid.

92   Marrs, *PSI Spies*, 207–8.

93   Ibid., 167–8.

94   Dean Radin, *Time-reversed Human Experience*. See also Targ & Puthoff.

95   Brown, *Cosmic Explorers*, 16.

96   Ibid., 19.

97   Ibid., 22.

98   Ibid., 65.

99   See Monroe, *Journeys Out of the Body*.

100 Brown, *Cosmic Explorers*, 252.

101 Ibid., 252.

102 Ibid., 256.

103 Ibid., 89.

104 Mishlove, 245.

105 See Powell, *The Mental Body*, Ch. 28.

106 See Leadbeater, *Clairvoyance*, Ch. 7.

107 Ibid., Ch. 4.

108 Powell, *The Mental Body*, Ch. 28.

109 Talbot, 201.

110 DuBois, *We Are Their Heaven*, 105.

111 Ibid., 102–3.

112 Ibid., 109.

113 Talbot, 201.

114 Rifat, 38–9.

115 Wilson, *The Occult*, 153.

116 Email to author, February 24, 2012.

[117] Hunt, 139.

[118] Yogi Ramacharaka, *Fourteen Lessons in Yogi Philosophy*, 183.

[119] See McTaggart, *The Intention Experiment*, Ch. 10..

[120] See Welch.

[121] McTaggart, *The Intention Experiment*, 158.

[122] See McTaggart, *The Field*. For further verification of the "memory of water" by other scientists, see <www.guardian.co.uk/Archive/Article/0,4273,4152521,00.html>.

[123] Mishlove, 134–5.

[124] Goswami, *Physics of the Soul*, 109.

[125] Rein, *Effect of Conscious Intention on Human DNA*.

[126] Lipton & Bhaerman, 286.

[127] LeShan, 30.

[128] Ibid., 30–1.

[129] Collins, 19.

[130] See Leadbeater, *Clairvoyance*.

[131] See Waite, Ch. 31.

[132] See Denton, *The Soul of Things*.

[133] Karagulla, 215–6.

Chapter 13

[1] <www.uri-geller.com/uri-biography/uribiog3.htm>

[2] See Davis.

[3] Watson, 134–5.

[4] Radin, *Testing Nonlocal Observation*.

[5] See Radin, *The Conscious Universe*, 153–4. In *Cosmos*, Laszlo and Currivan state that bonded couples achieved effects six times greater than when working individually.

[6] Dunne & Jahn, *Experiments in Remote Human/Machine Interaction* (1992).

[7] Jahn et al., Correlations of Random Binary Sequences with Pre-Stated Operator Intention.

[8] Wilcock, *Hypderdimensional Nebulae*.

[9] Tiller, *Subtle Energies*.

[10] Watson, 165.

[11] Wilcock, *Divine Cosmos*, Ch. 9.2–9.3.

[12] Email from Yurth, April 18, 2012.

[13] DIA report (1975).

[14] Ibid.

[15] *Encyclopedia of Occultism & Parapsychology*, vol. 1, 881.

[16] See McTaggart, *The Field*.

[17] DIA report (1975).

18 Ibid.

19 *Encyclopedia of Occultism and Parapsychology*, vol. 1, 567–8.

20 See Randall, 18.

21 Alfred, 194–5.

22 Owen, *The Convulsionists of St. Medard.*

23 Randall, 63.

24 Owen.

25 See Pearce, 12–13.

26 Lipton & Bhaerman, 10.

27 See Powell, *The Astral Body*, Ch. 17.

28 Wilson, *The Occult*, 47.

29 See DIA report.

30 Bearden, *Excalibur Briefing*, 193.

31 Defence Intelligence Agency, *Controlled Offensive Behaviour* (1972).

32 Ibid.

33 Ibid.

34 McTaggart, *The Intention Experiment*, 69–70.

35 Sharon Begley, *Wall Street Journal*, How Thinking Can Change the Brain. <www.dalailama.com/news/post/104-how-thinking-can-change-the-brain>.

36 Church, 99.

37 See Watson, 139–40.

38 Watson, 140–1.

39 Ibid., 152–4.

40 Paul Smith, *Reading the Enemy's Mind.*

41 Ibid.

42 Yurth, *Seeing Past the Edge*, 225–6.

43 Solis.

44 Ibid.

45 Ibid.

46 See Vesperman.

47 Wilcock, *The Source Field Investigations*, 287.

48 Ibid.

49 Marrs, *PSI Spies*, 143–4.

50 Ostrander & Schroeder, *Psychic Discoveries: The Iron Curtain Lifted*, 322–3.

51 Solis.

52 Bearden, *Excalibur Briefing*, 114.

53 See Dakin, 27–30.

54 Bearden, *Excalibur Briefing*, 65.

55 See Randall, 169–74.

56   Ibid., 176–7. See also McTaggart, *The Intention Experiment*, xxviii.

57   See Watson, *Gifts of Unknown Things*.

58   See Violette, 105–8. There is a large excerpt from Dong's book detailing many of Baosheng's varied exploits and his prestigious status in China resulting from them here: <http://sci.tech-archive.net/Archive/sci.physics/2005-02/10684.html>.

59   Humphrey, 38–9.

60   Bartlett, 132.

61   Ibid., 151.

62   Randall, 19.

63   Bruce Cathie, Acoustic Levitation of Stones. Featured in Childress, *Anti-Gravity and the World Grid*.

64   Wilcock, *The Source Field Investigations*, 284, 307–8.

65   Ibid., 307–8.

66   See Luckman, *Conscious Healing*.

67   See Braden, *The Divine Matrix* and *Fractal Time*.

68   Motoyama, 231.

69   Ryhen Satch, *The Power of Levitation (Laghima)*. <www.virtualsynapses.com/2010/09/power-of-levitation-laghima.html#.UINilWex2Sr>.

70   Yoga and Awakening. <www.mysticriveryoga.com/vibhutipada.htm>.

71   <www.brucedepalma.com/n-machine/spinning-ball-experiment/>.   <www.rexresearch.com/depalma/depalma.htm>.

72   Wilcock, *The Source Field Investigations*, 280.

73   Ibid., 279. See also Wilcock's Convergence series, and Levich.

74   Aspden, *Discovery of Virtual Inertia*. See also Wilcock's "Convergence" series.

75   Wilcock, *The Source Field Investigations*, 278.

76   Ibid.

77   Wilcock, *The Source Field Investigations*, 284.

78   See LaViolette, *Genesis of the Cosmos*.

79   Jung, *Psychology and the Occult*, 117.

80   Grosso, 258.

81   Sidorov.

82   Sicher et al.

83   See McTaggart, *The Intention Experiment*, 78–9.

84   Hamilton, 89–90.

85   Leadbeater, *The Inner Life*, 3.

86   Church, 69–70.

87   Sidorov.

88   See Gerber.

89   Hamilton, 54–5.

90   Watson, *Supernature*, 164.

91   Pearce, 199–200.

92   Larry Dossey, *Distance Healing: Evidence*. Printed for the first time in Schoch and Yonavjak, 217–18.

93   Targ & Katra.

94   Dossey, *Distance Healing*

95   Ibid., 221–2.

96   Emoto, 102.

97   Sidorov, *Distant mental interactions, entanglement and energy signatures*. <www.emergentmind.org/proposalsII2.htm>.

98   Hamilton, 84.

99   See Tiller, *Psychoenergetic Science*.

100   Ibid.

101   Radin, *Entangled Minds*, 185–91.

102   Church, 67. See also Dossey, *The Dark Side of Consciousness*.

103   See Walsh, *Conversations With God*, Book 1.

104   Braden, *The Divine Matrix*, 118–20. Braden presents footgage of this "miracle" in seminar presentations. See here: www.youtube.com/watch?feature=player_embedded&v=I2ohSOzV4SQ#!

105   See Yogananda, 20–1.

106   Braden, *The Divine Matrix*, 121.

107   See for example: Mishlove; Hunt; Talbot; Radin, *The Conscious Universe*; Wilson, *The Occult*; McTaggart, *The Intention Experiment*.

108   See Krippner.

109   Braden, *The Divine Matrix*, 145–6.

110   Wilson, *The Occult*, 269.

111   Blavatsky, *Studies in Occultism*.

112   Wilson, *The Occult*, 167.

113   Rob and Trish MacGregor, *The Pauli Effect*. <www.synchrosecrets.com/synchrosecrets/?p=275>.

114   Wilcock, *The Science of Oneness*, Ch. 3.1.

115   See DIA report (1975).

116   Vishita, 141.

117   See Goswami, *Physics of the Soul*, 40.

118   DuBois, 45.

119   Jung, *Synchronicity*, 18.

120   Swann, Dr. Gertrude Schmeidler.

121   See Radin, *Entangled Minds*.

122   *Who is Mario Varvoglis?* <www.parapsych.org/members/m_varvoglis.html>.

[123] Lawrence.

[124] Hamilton, *It's the Thought That Counts*.

[125] Wilkins & Sherman, xx.

[126] Varvoglis.

[127] Swann, Dr. Gertrude Schmeidler.

[128] Mishlove, 297.

[129] Wilkins & Sherman, xxi.

[130] Todeschi, 84–5.

[131] See Pavlina.

[132] See Marrs, *PSI Spies*, 174–5.

[133] Wilson, *Cosmic Trigger*, 78–9.

[134] Honorton.

[135] Talbot, 141.

[136] Ostrander & Schroeder, *Psychic Discoveries: The Iron Curtain Lifted*, 379.

[137] Kuhn, 126–7.

[138] Backster, 14.

[139] Wilson, *Prometheus Rising*, 25.

[140] DIA report (1972).

[141] See Powell, *The Mental Body*, Ch. 11.

[142] Yogananda, 104.

[143] Wilson, *Cosmic Trigger*, 33.

[144] LaBerge & Rheingold, 77.

[145] Swann, Toward Activating…

[146] Swann, Remote Viewing Processes…

[147] Kuhn, 62–3. See also Radin, *The Conscious Universe*, Ch. 14.

[148] Kuhn, 63.

[149] Ibid., 63–4.

[150] Klopfer. See also Wilson, *Quantum Psychology*, Ch. 15.

[151] Sources for this were Talbot, 105 and Lipton, 93–4.

[152] Bartlett, 123.

[153] Yogi Ramacharaka, *Fourteen Lessons in Yogi Philosophy*, 184.

[154] *DNA's Hypercommunication: The Living Internet Inside of Us*. A summary of Grazyna Fosar & Franz Bludorf's *Vernetzte Intelligenz* by Barbel Mohr. <www.bibliotecapleyades.net/ciencia/ciencia_genetica02.htm>.

[155] See Luckman, *Potentiate Your DNA* for more background, as well as the procedure for the first DNA activation (Potentiation) in the Regenetics method. Readers might also want to see my *Diary of a DNA Potentiator* article at brendandmurphy.com.

[156] Moseley et al.

[157] See Lipton, 108–11.

158 Arguriou.

159 Church, 177.

160 Lipton & Bhaerman, 8.

161 *The Guardian,* 22 December 2010, <www.guardian.co.uk/science/2010/dec/22/placebo-effect-patients-sham-drug>.

162 Tiller, *Psychoenergetic Science,* 173–4.

163 See Lipton, 111–12.

164 Sabom, 202–3.

165 Grosso, 39.

166 Dossey, *The Dark Side of Consciousness and the Therapeutic Relationship.* Excerpted from an address to the Sixth Annual Alternative Therapies Symposium and Exhibition, March 2002. <http://media.noetic.org/uploads/files/Dossey.pdf>.

167 Yogananda, 239.

168 See Yogi Ramacharaka, *Fourteen Lessons in Yogi Philosophy.*

169 Church, 67, and Lipton, 95–6.

170 Hamilton, 22–3.

171 Ibid., 30.

172 Leader & Corfield, 15–16.

173 Bartlett, 112.

174 Ibid., 209.

175 Watson, 151–2.

176 Muldoon & Carrington, 275–6.

177 Motoyama, 265–6.

178 Ibid., 266.

179 Ibid., 267.

180 Ibid., 268.

181 Karagulla & Kunz, 218–20.

182 Motoyama, 269.

183 Ibid., 271.

184 Poponin.

185 Gariaev, et al. *Crisis in Life Sciences.*

186 Email communication from D.G. Yurth, February 1st, 2012.

187 See my article *Junk DNA: Doorway to Transformation* at <www.brendandmurphy.com>.

Epilogue

1 For an interesting treatise on this subject, see: <www.cheniere.org/correspondence/041204.htm>.

Selected Bibliography

Abbott, Edwin. *Flatland: A Romance of Many Dimensions*. Little, Brown & Company, 1899.

Abhayananda, S. *History of Mysticism: The Unchanging Testament*. Revised Edition, 2009 (ebook).

Adams, Mike. *Giant Hexagon of Clouds Spins on Saturn while Clouds Disappear from Jupiter*. <www.naturalnews.com/028797_Saturn_hexagon.html>.

Adams, Mike. *Principle of Astrology Proven to be Scientific: Planetary Position Imprints Biological Clocks of Mammals*. <www.naturalnews.com/030698_astrology_scientific_basis.html>.

Alexander, C. et al. EEG and SPECT Data of a Selected Subject during Psi Tasks: The Discovery of a Neurophysiological Correlate. *Proceedings of Presented Papers: The Parapsychological Association 41st Annual Convention*, pp. 3–13.

Alfred, Jay. *Between the Moon and Earth: A Scientific Exploration of Earth-Based Heavens and Hells*. Trafford Publishing, 2006.

Alfred, Jay. Dark Plasma and the Origin of Angels, Aliens, Deities and Ghosts, *New Dawn*, Special Issue No. 7, 2009.

Alfred, Jay. *Evolution of Dark Plasma Life Forms on Earth*. <www.dapla.org/plasma_life_forms.htm>.

Alfred, Jay. *Our Invisible Bodies: Scientific Evidence for Subtle Bodies*. Trafford Publishing, 2005.

Alfred, Jay. *Plasma Life Forms: Spheres, Blobs, Orbs and Subtle Bodies*. <www.dapla.org/plasma_orbs_bodies.htm>.

Anderson, Ken. *The Coincidence File: synchronicity, morphic resonance or pure chance?* Blandford, 1999.

Anderson, Rick. *What is "Scalar Electromagnetics"?* <http://twm.co.nz/Beard_scalem.html>.

Arguriou, Peter. The Placebo Effect, *Nexus*, 14(4) 2007.

Aspden, Harold, Discovery of Virtual Inertia. *New Energy News*, 2, 1995, 1–2.

Aspden, Harold. *Modern Aether Science*. Sabberton Publications, 1972.

Aspden, Harold. *Physics Without Einstein: A Centenary Review*, 2005. <www.aetherscience.org/www-aspden-org/books/pwecent/pwecent2005.pdf>.

Atwater, P.M. H. *Future Memory*. Hampton Roads, 1999.

Atwater, P.M. H. *The Big Book of Near-Death Experiences*. Hampton Roads, 2007.

Backster, Cleve. *Primary Perception: Biocommunication with Plants, Living Foods, and Human Cells*. White Rose Millenium Press, 2003.

Bartlett, Richard. *The Physics of Miracles: Tapping into the Field of Consciousness Potential*. Beyond Words/Atria Books, 2009.

Bazette, L. Margery. *Beyond the Five Senses*. Basil Blackwell, 1946.

Bearden, Tom. *Energy Density of the Vacuum*. <www.cheniere.org/references/energydensityofvacuum.htm>.

Bearden, Tom. *Excalibur Briefing*, 2nd edn. Sydney, 1988.

Becker, Robert O., & Gary Selden. *The Body Electric: Electromagnetism and the Foundation of Life*. Harper Paperbacks, 1998.

Bem, Daryl J. *Ganzfeld Phenomena*. <http://dbem.ws/ganzfeld.html>.

Bem, Daryl J. Feeling the Future. *Journal of Personality and Social Psychology*, *100*, 407–25, 2011. American Psychological Association. <www.apa.org/pubs/journals/psp/index.aspx>.

Benford, M. Sue. "Spin Doctors": A New Paradigm Theorizing the Mechanism of Bioenergy Healing.

<www.journaloftheoretics.com>.

Bentov, Itzhak. *Stalking the Wild Pendulum: On the Mechanics of Consciousness*. Destiny Books, 1988.

Besant, Annie. *Occultism, Semi-Occultism and Pseudo-Occultism*. Lecture given at the Blavatsky Lodge, London, 1898. <www.blavatsky.net/history/besant/essays-and-addresses-vol-III/besant.9.html>.

Besant, Annie, & C.W. Leadbeater. *Occult Chemistry: Clairvoyant Observations on Chemical Systems*. Revised Edition by A.P. Sinnett, Theosophical Publishing House, 1919.

Besant, Annie, & C.W. Leadbeater. *Thought Forms*. Theosophical Publishing House, 1901.

Bierman, Dick J., & H. Steven Scholte. Anomalous Anticipatory Brain Activation Preceding Exposure of Emotional and Neutral Pictures. <www.quantumconsciousness.org/pdfs/presentiment.pdf>.

Blavatsky, H.P. *Studies in Occultism*. A collection of articles from *Lucifer* magazine 1887–91. <www.theosociety.org/pasadena/hpb-sio/sio-hp.htm>.

Blavatsky, H.P. *The Key to Theosophy*. Quest Books, 1992.

Blavatsky, H.P. *The Secret Doctrine*, 1888. Online edition. <www.theosociety.org/pasadena/sd/sd-hp.htm>.

Braden, Gregg. *DNA Report*. <www.bibliotecapleyades.net/mistic/esp_greggbraden_11.htm>.

Braden, Gregg. *Fractal Time: The Secret of 2012 and a New World Age*. Hay House, Inc., Carlsbad, CA, 2009.

Braden, Gregg. *The Divine Matrix*. Hay House, Inc., Carlsbad, CA, 2007.

Braden, Gregg. *The God Code*. Hay House, Inc., Carlsbad, CA, 2004.

Braude, Stephen. *Pride and Prejudice in Academia.* <www.skepticalinvestigations.org/anomalistics/prideandprejudice.htm>.

Brennan, Barbara Ann. *Hands of Light: A Guide to Healing Through the Human Energy Field.* Bantam Books, 1988.

Brennan, Barbara Ann. *Light Emerging: The Journey of Personal Healing.* Bantam Books, 1993.

Brooks, Michael. The Weirdest Link. *New Scientist*, 181(2440) 2004, 32. <http://homepage.mac.com/turder/iblog/B561081935/C1798329063/E1303962906/index.html>.

Brown, Courtney. *Cosmic Explorers.* Dutton Books, 1999.

Brown, William. Morphic Resonance and Quantum Biology, *Nexus*, 19(2) 2012.

Brown, Dean, & Wenden Wiegand. *Cosmic Law: Patterns in the Universe*, 2002. <http://issuu.com/earthcat/docs/cosmic-law-patterns-in-the-universe>.

Bruce, Robert. *Astral Dynamics.* Hampton Roads, 1999.

Bryant, Alice, & Linda Seebach. An Introduction to the Multidimensional Potential of Human Beings. <www.bibliotecapleyades.net/vision_remota/esp_visionremota_23.htm>.

Bryson, Christopher. *The Fluoride Deception.* Seven Stories Press, New York, 2006.

Buchanan, Lyn. *The Seventh Sense: The Secrets of Remote Viewing as Told by a "Psychic Spy" for the US Military.* Paraview Pocket Books, 2003.

Bushby, Tony. *The Bible Fraud.* The Pacific Blue Group Inc., 2001.

Calvi-Parisetti, Piero. *21 Days into the Afterlife.* The Open Mind Site e-Publishing.

Capra, Fritjof. *The Tao of Physics: An Exploration of the Parallels Between Modern Physics and Eastern Mysticism*, 3rd edn. Flamingo, 1982.

Carrington, Hereward. *Modern Psychical Phenomena.* Kegan Paul, Trench, Trubner & Co., Ltd, 1919.

Cathie, Bruce. The *Energy Grid: Harmonic 695: The Pulse of the Universe.* Adventures Unlimited Press, 1997.

Chalko, Thomas J. Is Chance or Choice the Essence of Nature? <http://nujournal.net/choice.html>.

Childress, David Hatcher. *Anti-Gravity and the World Grid.* Adventures Unlimited Press, 1987.

Church, Dawson. *The Genie in your Genes: Epigenetic Medicine and the New Biology of Intention.* Energy Psychology Press, 2009.

Close, Frank. *Antimatter.* Oxford University Press, 2009.

Coleman, Beth. *Extraordinary States.* <www.bethcoleman.com>.

Collins, Judith. *How to See and Read the Human Aura.* Lothian Books, 2003.

Constable, Trevor James. *Sky Creatures: Living UFOs.* Pocket Books, 1978.

Conway, David. *Secret Wisdom: The Occult Universe Revealed.* Vega, 2002.

Croft, Mary Elizabeth. *How I Clobbered Every Cash Confiscatory Agency Known to Man.* 2005. <www.freedomfiles.org/mary-book.pdf>.

Dakin, H.S. *High-Voltage Photography.* H.S. Dakin, 1975.

Dale, Cyndi. *Illuminating the Afterlife.* Sounds True, Inc., 2008.

Davis, W.E. *The Black Box and Other Psychic Generators.* 1987. <www.bibliotecapleyades.net/ ciencia/ciencia_psycho17.htm>.

Day, Peggy, & Susan Gale. *Edgar Cayce On The Indigo Children.* A.R.E. Press, 2005.

DeGracia, Donald J. *Beyond the Physical: A Synthesis of Science and Occultism in Light of Fractals, Chaos and Quantum Theory.* Ebook available at <www.med.wayne.edu/degracialab/ psite/index.html>.

DeGracia, Donald J. *DO_OBE.* Ebook available at <www.med.wayne.edu/degracialab/ psite/index.html>.

Dennett, Preston. *Out-of-Body Exploring: A Beginner's Approach.* Hampton Roads, 2004.

Denton, William & Elizabeth M.F. *The Soul of Things; Or, Psychometric Researches and Discoveries.* Walker, Wise & Company, 1863.

Devereaux, Paul. *Dreaming the Earth.* <www.gothicimage.co.uk/books/symboliclands1. html>.

Dirac, Paul *Is there an Aether?* Extracts from an article by Dirac in *Nature*, 168, 1951, 906–7. <www.mountainman.com.au/aether_8.htm>.

Dossey, Larry. *The Power of Premonitions: How Knowing the Future Can Shape Our Lives.* <www. dosseydossey.com/larry/Interview_Questions-Premonitions.pdf>.

Dossey, Larry. *The Dark Side of Consciousness and the Therapeutic Relationship.* <http://media. noetic.org/uploads/files/Dossey.pdf>.

DuBois, Allison. *We Are Their Heaven: Why the Dead Never Leave Us.* Fireside, 2006.

Dunne, Brenda J. & Robert G. Jahn. Experiments in Remote Human/Machine Interaction. *Journal of Scientific Exploration*, 6(4) 1992, 311–32.

Dunne, Brenda J. & Robert G. Jahn. Information and Uncertainty in Remote Perception Research. *Journal of Scientific Exploration*, 17(2) 2003, 207–41.

Eichler, John B. A New Mechanism for Matter Increase within the Earth, *Nexus* 18(3) 2011.

Eisen, Jonathan. *Suppressed Inventions and Other Discoveries.* Perigee Trade, 2001.

Emoto, Masaru. *The True Power of Water: Healing and Discovering Ourselves.* Atria Books and Beyond Words Publishing. 2005.

Encyclopedia of Occultism and Parapsycholog, 2 vols, ed. J. Gordon Melton. Gale Group, Inc., 2001.

Farrel, Joseph P. *Reich of the Black Sun: Nazi Secret Weapons and the Cold War Allied Legend.* Adventures Unlimited Press, 2005.

Farrier, John. *Scientific Evidence that the Entire Universe Is a Holographic Projection around the Earth*, Feb. 7, 2010. <www.neatorama.com>.

Frissell, Bob. *Nothing in This Book Is True, But It's Exactly How Things Are.* Frog Limited, 1994.

Gage, Fred H., & Alysson R. Muotri. What Makes Each Brain Unique. *Scientific American*, March 2012, 20–5.

Gariaev, P.P. et al. *Crisis in Life Sciences. The Wave Genetics Response.* <www.emergentmind. org/gariaev06.htm>.

Gariaev, P.P. et al. Principles of Linguistic-Wave Genetics. *DNA Decipher Journal*, 1(1) 2011, 11–24.

Gariaev, P.P. et al. *The DNA-Wave Biocomputer.* <www.laserponcture.net/anglais/gariaev. pdf>.

Gerber, Richard. *Vibrational Medicine: The #1 Handbook of Subtle-Energy Therapies.* Bear & Company, 2001.

Gibson, Suzanne S. *The Effect of Music and Focused Meditation on the Human Energy Field as Measured by the Gas Discharge Visualisation (GDV) Technique and Profile of Mood States.* <http://holosuniversity.net/pdf/Gibson_Diss.pdf>.

Gleick, James. *Chaos: Making a New Science.* Penguin Books, 1988.

Gori, Luigi, & Fabio Firenzuoli. *Ear Acupuncture in European Traditional Medicine.* <www. ncbi.nlm.nih.gov/pmc/articles/PMC2206232>.

Goswami, Amit. *Physics of the Soul: The Quantum Book of Living, Dying, Reincarnation and Immortality.* Hampton Roads, 2001.

Goswami, Amit. *The Self-Aware Universe: How Consciousness Creates the Material World.* Jeremy P. Tarcher/Putnam Books, 1995.

Greeley, A. The Impossible: It's Happening. *Noetic Sciences Review*, Spring 1987, 7–9.

Greene, Brian. *The Fabric of the Cosmos.* Penguin Books, 2005.

Griffin, G. Edward. *World Without Cancer*, 2nd edn. American Media, 1997.

Grof, Stanislav. *The Holotropic Mind: The Three Levels of Human Consciousness and How They Shape Our Lives.* HarperCollins, 1993.

Grof, Stanislav. *LSD Psychotherapy.* Hunter House, 1980.

Grof, Stanislav, & Joan Halifax. *The Human Encounter With Death.* E.P. Dutton, 1977.

Grosso, Michael. *Experiencing the Next World Now.* Paraview Pocket Books, 2004.

Grosso, Michael. Padre Pio, Paranormal Man, *New Dawn*, Special Issue No. 9.

Hagelin, J. S., D.W. Orme-Johnson, M. Rainforth, K. Cavanaugh & C.N. Alexander. Results of the National Demonstration Project to Reduce Violent Crime and Improve Governmental Effectiveness in Washington, D.C. *Social Indicators Research*, 47 1999, 153–201.

Hall, Manly Palmer. *The Secret Teachings of All Ages.* H.S. Crocker Company, Inc., 1928.

Hamilton, Craig. *Scientific Proof of the Existence of God: An interview with Amit Goswami.* <www. enlightennext.org/magazine/j11/goswami.asp?page=1>.

Hamilton, David. *It's the Thought that Counts: Why Mind Over Matter Really Works.* Hay House, Inc., Carlsbad, CA, 2009.

Hancock, Graham. *Fingerprints of the Gods.* Three Rivers Press, 1995.

Hancock, Graham. *Supernatural: Meetings with the Ancient Teachers of Mankind*, rev. edn. Disinformation Company Ltd, 2007.

Hancock, Graham, & Robert Bauval. *The Message of the Sphinx.* Three Rivers Press, 1996.

Haramein, Nassim. What is the Origin of Spin? <www.theresonanceproject.org/pdf/origin_of_spin.pdf>.

Harrison, Edward. *Masks of the Universe*. Macmillan, 1985.

Hatcher Childress, David. *Anti-Gravity and the World Grid*. Adventures Unlimited Press, 1987.

Haughton, Brian. A Mystic in Tibet, *New Dawn*, Special Issue No. 3, 2007.

Hoagland, Richard. *The Monuments of Mars*. North Atlantic Books, 1987, 1992.

Holewa, Lisa. *Boy without a Cerebellum Baffles Doctors* (February 12, 2011). <www.aol.com>.

Honorton, Charles. Rhetoric over substance: the impoverished state of scepticism. *The Journal of Parapsychology*, June, 1993. <http://findarticles.com/p/articles/mi_m2320/is_n2_v57/ai_14890637/pg_3/>.

Hughes, Jeff. Occultism and the Atom: The Curious Story of Isotopes. *Physics World*, September 2003. <http://physicsworldarchive.iop.org>.

Humphrey, Christopher. *UFOs, PSI and Spiritual Evolution: A Journey through the Evolution of Interstellar Travel*. Adventures Unlimited Press, 2004.

Hunt, Valerie. *Infinite Mind*, 2nd edn. Malibu Publishing Co., 1996.

Huxley, Aldous. *The Perennial Philosophy*. Chatto & Windus, 1947.

Icke, David. *Tales from the Time Loop*. Bridge of Love Publications, 2003.

Jahn, R.G., B.J. Dunne, R.D. Nelson, Y.H. Dobyns, and G.J. Bradish. Correlations of Random Binary Sequences with Pre-Stated Operator Intention: A Review of a 12-Year Program. *Princeton Engineering Anomalies Research (PEAR) School of Engineering and Applied Science, Princeton University*.

Jenkins, John Major. *The 2012 Story*. Jeremy P. Tarcher/Penguin, 2010.

Jenny, Hans. *Cymatics: A Study of Wave Phenomena and Vibration*, rev. edn. New Market, 2001.

Jones, Marie D. *PSIence*. New Page Books, 2007.

Jones, Marie D. & Larry Flaxman. Time Travel and the Multiverse. *New Dawn* Special Issue 6(4) 2012.

Jung, C.G. *Man and His Symbols*. Laurel, 1968.

Jung, C.G. *On Life After Death*. <http://ebookbrowse.com/c-g-jung-on-life-after-death-pdf-d19086894>.

Jung, C. G. *Psychology and the Occult*. Routledge Classics, 2008.

Jung, C.G. *Synchronicity: An Acausal Connecting Principle*. First Princeton/Bollingen Paperback Edition, 1973.

Kaku, Michio. *Hyperspace: A Scientific Odyssey Through Parallel Universes, Time Warps, and the 10th Dimension*. Oxford University Press, 1994.

Kaku, Michio. *The Physics of the Impossible: A Scientific Exploration Into the World of Phasers, Force Fields, Teleportation and Time Travel*. Doubleday, 2008.

Kaku, Mickio. *Parallel Worlds: A Journey Through Creation, Higher Dimensions, and the Future of the Cosmos*. Doubleday, 2005.

Karagulla, Shafica. *Breakthrough to Creativity*. DeVorss & Co., Inc., 1968.

Karagulla, Shafica & Dora Van Gelder Kunz. *The Chakras and the Human Energy Fields.* Quest Books, 1998.

Kasten, Len. How "Rogue Scientists" Discovered Free Energy. *New Dawn* Special Issue 6(4).

Kastrup, Bernardo. A New Call to Lift Nature's Veil. *New Dawn* Special Issue 6(4) 2012.

Kehr, R. Webster. *The Detection of Ether,* 2002. <www.teslaphysics.com/files/Detection.pdf>.

Kelleher, Colm. Retrotransposons as Engines of Human Bodily Transformation. *Journal of Scientific Exploration* 13(3), 1999, 9–24.

Kelly, Charles R. *What Is Orgone Energy?* <www.orgone.org/articles/ax9kelley1a.htm>.

King, Evy. Harry Oldfield's Amazing Imaging Technologies, *Nexus* 14(3) 2007.

Klopfer, Bruno. Psychological Variables in Human Cancer, *Journal of Prospective Techniques* 31, 1957. Quoted at <http://mindhacks.org/miraculous-healing-with-the-mind>.

Korotkov, Dr. Konstantin. *Light After Life: A Scientific Journey into the Spiritual World.* Backbone Publishing, 1998.

Krippner, Stanley. *Possible Geomagnetic Field Effects in Psi Phenomena.* <www.urigeller.com/content/research/kripp1.htm>.

Kübler-Ross, Elisabeth. *The Wheel of Life: A Memoir of Living and Dying.* Bantam Books, 1998.

Kuhn, Thomas. *The Structure of Scientific Revolutions.* University of Chicago Press, 1962.

LaBerge, Stephen, & Howard Rheingold. *Exploring the World of Lucid Dreaming.* Ballantine Books, 1990.

LaFreniere, Gabriel. *Matter is Made of Waves.* <www.glafreniere.com/matter.htm>.

LaMoth, John D. (Defence Intelligence Agency). Controlled Offensive Behaviour—USSR, 1972.

LaMoth, John D. & Louis F. Maire III (Defence Intelligence Agency). Soviet and Czechoslovakian Parapsychology Research, 1975.

Lash, John Lamb, *The Promise of a Lonely Planet. Three: Stalking the Anthropos.* <www.metahistory.org/gnostique/archonfiles/PlanetPromise3.php>.

Last, Walter. The Holistic Solution to Overcoming Cancer, *Nexus* 16(1) 2008–09.

Laszlo, Ervin, & Jude Currivan. *CosMos: A Co-creator's Guide to the Whole World.* Hay House, Inc., Carlsbad, CA, 2008.

Lau, D. C. *Lao Tzu: Tao Te Ching.* Penguin Books, 1963.

LaViolette, Paul A. *Genesis of the Cosmos: The Ancient Science of Continuous Creation.* Bear & Company, 2004.

LaViolette, Paul A. *Subquantum Kinetics (a non-technical summary).* <www.etheric.com/LaVioletteBooks/ether.html>.

Lawlor, Robert. *Sacred Geometry: Philosophy and Practice.* Thames & Hudson Ltd, 2002.

Lawrence, Tony. Gathering in the Sheep and Goats: A Meta-analysis of Forced Choice Sheep-Goat ESP Studies, 1947–1993. Proceedings of Presented Papers: Parapsychological Association 36th Annual Convention, 75–86.

Lazar, Sarah W., et al. Meditation Experience is Associated with Increased Cortical Thickness. *Lippincot, Wilkins and Williams NeuroReport*, 16(17) 2005, 1893–97.

Leadbeater, C.W. *A Textbook of Theosophy*. <www.anandgholap.net/Textbook_Of_Theosophy-CWL.htm>.

Leadbeater, C.W. *Clairvoyance*. Theosophical Publishing House, 1899.

Leadbeater, C.W. *Man Visible and Invisible*. Adyar, 1902.

Leadbeater, C.W. *The Astral Plane: Its Scenery, Inhabitants, and Phenomena*, 3rd edn. Revised Theosophical Manuals No. 5, 1900.

Leadbeater, C.W. *The Chakras*, 1st edn. Theosophical Publishing House, 1927.

Leadbeater, C.W. *The Inner Life*. Theosophical Publishing House, 1978.

Leadbeater, C.W., & Annie Besant. *Occult Chemistry: Investigations into Clairvoyant Magnification into the Structure of the Atoms of the Periodic Table and Some Compounds*, 3rd edn, 1950. <www.subtleenergies.com/ormus/oc/ocindex.htm>.

Leader, Darien, & David Corfield. *Why Do People Get Ill?* Penguin Books, 2008.

LeShan, Lawrence. *The Medium, The Mystic and The Physicist: Toward a General Theory of the Paranormal*. Penguin/Arkana, 1995.

Levich, A.P. On the Way to Understanding the Time Phenomenon: the Constructions of Time in Natural Science. Part 2. The "Active" Properties of Time According to N.A. Kozyrev. *World Scientific*, 1996, 1–42.

Lewin, Roger. Is Your Brain Really Necessary? *Science*, December 12, 1908, 1232–34.

Linsteadt, Stephen. *Frequency Fields at the Cellular Level*. <www.soulsofdistortion.nl/dna3a.html>.

Lipton, Bruce. *The Biology of Belief*. Hay House, Inc., Carlsbad, CA, 2009.

Lipton, Bruce & Steve Bhaerman. *Spontaneous Evolution*. Hay House, Inc., Carlsbad, CA, 2009.

Loder, Theodore C. *"Outside the Box" Space and Terrestrial Transportation and Energy Technologies for the 21st Century*. <www.theorionproject.org/en/documents/STAIF03Loder.pdf>.

Lomas, Robert. *The Lost Key: The Supranatural Secrets of the Freemasons*. Hodder & Stoughton, 2012.

Loughlin, Charles D. Archetypes, Neurognosis and the Quantum Sea. *Journal of Scientific Exploration*, 10(3) 1996, 375–400.

Luckman, Sol. *Conscious Healing: Book One on the Regenetics Method*. Booklocker Publishing, 2006.

Luckman, Sol. *Potentiate Your DNA*. Crow Rising Transformational Media, 2010.

Manning, Jeanne. Wilhelm Reich: Scientist With an Attitude. In Eisen, *Suppressed Inventions and Other Discoveries*. Penguin Group, 2001.

Marrs, Jim. *Alien Agenda: Investigating the Extraterrestrial Presence among Us*. HarperPaperbacks, 1998.

Marrs, Jim. *PSI Spies: The True Story of America's Psychic Warfare Program*. New Page Books, 2007.

Machi, Yoshio. *Healers Brain Waves*. <www.caroleverett.com/ce-yoshi.htm>.

McClenon et al. The Coverage of Parapsychology in Introductory Psychology Textbooks: 1990–2002. *Journal of Parapsychology*, 2003.

McCraty R., et al. Electrophysiological Evidence of Intuition: Part 1. The Surprising Role of the Heart. *The Journal of Alternative and Complementary Medicine*, 10(1) 2004, 133–43.

McCraty, R., et al. Electrophysiological evidence of intuition: Part 2: A System-wide Process? *Journal of Alternative and Complementary Medicine*. 10(2) 2004, 325–36.

McCraty R., et al. *Modulation of DNA Conformation by Heart-Focused Intention.* <http://www.vitality-living.com/resources/Modulation_of_DNA.pdf>.

McCraty R., et al. *The Electricity of Touch: Detection and Measurement of Cardiac Energy Exchange between People.* <www.reiki.org/Download/electricity_of_touch1.pdf >.

McClenon et al., The coverage of parapsychology in introductory psychology textbooks: 1990–2002. *Journal of Parapsychology*, 2003. <http://findarticles.com/p/articles/mi_m2320/is_1_67/ai_104657315/?tag=content;col1>.

McGuire, William, & R.F.C. Hull (eds). *C.G. Jung Speaking: Interviews and Encounters.* Princeton/Bollingen, 1993.

McTaggart, Lynne. *The Field.* Element, Hammersmith, 2003.

McTaggart, Lynne. *The Intention Experiment: Using Your Thoughts to Change Your Life and the World.* Free Press, 2007.

Melchizedek, Drunvalo. *The Ancient Secret of the Flower of Life*, 2 vols. Light Technology Publishing, 1998, 2000.

Michell, John. *The View Over Atlantis.* Abacus, 1975.

Miller, Iona. *Anatomy of the Star Goddess.* <http://zero-point.tripod.com/stargoddess/anatomy.html>.

Miller, Frank & Iona. From Helix to Hologram. *Nexus* 10(5) 2003.

Miller, Richard Alan, Iona Miller & Burt Webb. *Quantum Bioholography: A Review of the Field from 1973 – 2002.* <http://spywhisperer.iwarp.com/whats_new_11.html>.

Milton, Richard. *The Remote Viewing Experiment that was Too Successful.* <www.ecognosis.org/show_news.php?n=5888>.

Mishlove, Jeffrey. *The Roots of Consciousness.* <www.williamjames.com/Intro/CONTENTS.htm>

Mishlove, Jeffrey, with Karl Pribram. *The Holographic Brain.* <http://twm.co.nz/pribram.htm>.

Moberly, C.A.E., & E.F. Jourdain, *An Adventure.* <http://ebook.lib.hku.hk/CADAL/B31417310>.

Monroe, Robert A. *Far Journeys.* Main Street Books, Doubleday, 1985.

Montalk, Tom. *Astral Physics and Timespace.* <http://montalk.net/notes/astral-physics>.

Montalk, Tom. *Longitudinal Waves.< http://montalk.net/notes/longitudinal-waves>.

Moody, Raymond. *Life After Life.* Mockingbird Books, 1975.

Moody, Raymond A. *The Last Laugh.* Hampton Roads, 1999.

Morgan, Bill. *Scalar Wars: The Brave New World of Scalar Electromagnetics.* <www.prahlad.org/pub/bearden/scalar_wars.htm>.

Moseley, J.B., K. O'Malley, et al. A Controlled Trial of Arthroscopic Surgery for Osteoarthitis of the Knee. *New England Journal of Medicine*, 347(2) 2002, 81–8.

Motoyama, Hiroshi. *Theories of the Chakras*. Quest Books, Theosophical Publishing House, 1995.

Muldoon, Sylvan, & Hereward Carrington. *The Projection of the Astral Body*. Rider Books, 1992.

Mutton, Karen. Exploring the Aura, *New Dawn*, No. 103.

Myss, Caroline. *Sacred Contracts: Awakening Your Divine Potential*. Bantam, 2001.

Nachalov, Y.V. & A.N. Sokolov. Experimental Investigation of New Long-Range Actions. <www.geocities.co.jp/Technopolis/1228/torsion_field/doc17/doc17.html>.

Narby, Jeremy. *The Cosmic Serpent: DNA and the Origins of Knowledge*. Phoenix, 1999.

Nehru, K.V.K. *The Wave Mechanics in the Light of the Reciprocal System*. <www.reciprocalsystem. com/rs/cwkvk/wavemech.htm>.

Nelson, Bradley. *The Emotion Code*. Wellness Unmasked Publishing, 2007.

Nelson, Roger. Consciousness and Psi: Can Consciousness be Real? *Utrecht II: Charting the Future of Parapsychology*. October 2008, Utrecht, The Netherlands. <http://noosphere. princeton.edu/papers/pdf/consciousness.real.pdf>.

Novak, Gary. *The Truth About Relativity*. <http://nov47.com/eins.html>.

Nowak, A.M. *Torsion Fields: Theory of Physical Vacuum*. <www.eioba.com/a/1tzs/torsion-fields-theory-of-physical-vacuum-shipov-and-heim>.

Ostrander, Sheila, & Lynn Schroeder. *Psychic Discoveries Behind the Iron Curtain*. Bantam Books, 1970.

Ostrander, Sheila, & Lynn Schroeder. *Psychic Discoveries: The Iron Curtain Lifted*. Souvenir Press, 1997.

Owen, Robert Dale. *The Convulsionists of St. Medard*. <www.spiritwritings.com/ ConvulsionistsStMedard.html>.

Pavlina, Steve. *The Death of Skepticism*. <www.stevepavlina.com/blog/2006/08/the-death-of-skepticism>.

Payne, Buryl. *The Biofield: A Different Type of Magnetism?* Nexus 15(4) 2008.

Peake, Anthony. *Quantum Entanglement: A Primer*. <www.anthonypeake.com/forum/ viewtopic.php?f=5&t=718>.

Pearce, Joseph Chilton. *The Biology of Transcendence*. Park Street Press, 2002.

Pearl, Eric. *The Reconnection*. Hay House, Inc., Carlsbad, CA, 2001.

Pearson, Ron. Solving the Problem of the Cosmological Constant, *Nexus* 15(1) 2007–8.

Peat, F. David. *Non-locality in Nature and Cognition*. <www.fdavidpeat.com/bibliography/ essays/nat-cog.htm>.

Penrose, Roger. *Shadows of the Mind: A Search for the Missing Science of Consciousness*. Oxford University Press, 1994.

Pinchbeck, Daniel. *2012: The Return of Quetzalcoatl*. Jeremy P. Tarcher/Penguin, 2007.

Pnym, Gary. *Recent Paranormal Observations of the Atomic Structure of Orbitally Rearranged Monoatomic Elemental forms of the Transition Metals.*
<www.life-enthusiast.com/education/ormus/ormus_spiritual.htm>.

Powell, Arthur E. *The Astral Body.* Theosophical Publishing House, 1927.
<http://ebookbrowse.com/powell-the-astral-body-pdf-d39291430>.

Powell, Arthur E. *The Causal Body and the Ego.* Theosophical Society, 1928. <www.theosophical.ca/books/CausalBodyAndTheEgo,The_AEPowell.pdf>.

Powell, Arthur E. *The Etheric Double.* Originally published 1925. <www.4shared.com/document/yjRtXQKK/The-Etheric-Double-Arthur-e-Po.html>.

Powell, Arthur E. *The Mental Body.* First published by the Theosophical Society, 1927.
<http://ezosource.com/_en/books/Arthur_E_Powell_-_The_Mental_Body.pdf>.

Phillips, Stephen M. Extrasensory Perception of Subatomic Particles, *Journal of Scientific Exploration*, 9(4) 1995, 489–525. <www.scientificexploration.org/journal/jse_09_4_phillips.pdf>.

Poponin, V. *The DNA Phantom Effect: Direct Measurement of A New Field in the Vacuum Substructure.* <www.bibliotecapleyades.net/ciencia/ciencia_genetica04.htm>.

Pratt, David, *David Bohm and the Implicate Order.* <www.theosophy-nw.org/theosnw/science/prat-boh.htm>.

Pribram, Karl. *Consciousness Reassessed.* <www.paricenter.com/library/papers/pribram02.php>.

Prideux, Jeff. *Comparison between Karl Pribram's "Holographic Brain Theory" and More Conventional Models of Neuronal Computation.* <http://acsa2000.net/bcngroup/jponkp>.

Puthoff, Harold. *CIA-Initiated Remote Viewing At Stanford Research Institute,* <www.biomindsuperpowers.com/Pages/CIA-InitiatedRV.html>.

Putterman, Seth J. Sonoluminescence: Sound into Light. *Scientific American,* 1995, 33–7.

Radford, Gary P. *Scientific Knowledge and the Twist in the Tail.* <www.theprofessors.net/sublim.html>.

Radin, Dean. *Entangled Minds: Extrasensory Experiences in a Quantum Reality.* Paraview Pocket Books, 2006.

Radin, Dean. *Formal Analysis, September 11, 2001.* <http://noosphere.princeton.edu/911formal.html>.

Radin, Dean. *Testing Nonlocal Observation as a Source of Intuitive Knowledge.* <www.alice.id.tue.nl/references/radin-2008.pdf>.

Radin, Dean. *The Conscious Universe: The Scientific Truth of Psychic Phenomena.* HarperOne, 1997.

Radin, Dean. *Time-reversed Human Experience: Experimental Evidence and Implications.* Boundary Institute, Los Altos, CA, 2000. <www.emergentmind.org/PDF_files.htm/timereversed.pdf>.

Ramacharaka, Yogi. *Fourteen Lessons in Yogi Philosophy and Oriental Occultism.* Digital Version 1.00 by www.arfalpha.com, created April 2003. Original version published in 1903 by Yogi Publication Society.

Ramacharaka, Yogi. *Advanced Course in Yogi Philosophy and Oriental Occultism.* Yogi Publication Society, 1904.

Randall, John. *Psychokinesis: A Study of Paranormal Forces Through the Ages.* Souvenir Press Ltd, 1982.

Reed, Donald. *Torsion Field Research.* <www.padrak.com/ine/NEN_6_1_6.html>.

Rein, G. *Conformational Changes in Human DNA Characterize the Radiated Energy from the Aulterra Formulation™.* <www.aulterra.com.tr/QBResearchCopper.pdf>.

Rein, G. *Effect of Conscious Intention on Human DNA.* Published in the Proceeds of the International Forum on New Science, Denver, CO. October, 1996. <www.shamarie.com.au/pdf/wellness/Cons-dna.pdf>.

Rein, G., & Rollin McCraty. Structural Changes in Water and DNA associated with New Physiologically Measurable States. *Journal of Scientific Exploration,* 8(3) 1994, 438–39.

Rifat, Tim. *Remote Viewing: The History and Science of Psychic Warfare and Spying.* Century, 1999.

Ring, Kenneth. *Heading Toward Omega: In Search of the Meaning of the Near-Death Experience.* Quill/William Morrow, 1985.

Ring, Kenneth. *The Omega Project: Near-Death experiences, UFO Encounters, and Mind at Large.* Quill/William Morrow, 1992.

Ring, Kenneth. *Near Death and UFO Encounters as Shamanic Initiations: Some Conceptual and Evolutionary Implications.* <www.near-death.com/experiences/articles011.html>.

Roebke, Joshua. The Reality Tests, *Seed,* June 2008. <http://seedmagazine.com/content/article/the_reality_tests/P3/pdf>.

Roll, Michael. *The Scientific Proof of Survival After Death.* <www.cfpf.org.uk/articles/background/scientificproof/scientificproof1.html>.

Rosenblum, Bruce, & Fred Kuttner. *The Quantum Enigma.* Oxford University Press, 2006.

Ross, Colin A. Hypothesis: The Electrophysiological Basis of Evil Eye Belief. *Anthropology of Consciousness,* 21(1) 2010, 47–57.

Rudhyar, Dane. *Culture, Crisis and Creativity.* Theosophical Publishing House, 1977.

Sabom, Michael B. *Recollections of Death.* Corgi Books, 1982.

Schmidt, Helmut. Observation of a Psychokinetic Effect Under Highly Controlled Conditions. *Journal of Parapsychology,* 57 (December) 1993. <www.fourmilab.ch/rpkp/observ.html>.

Schoch, Robert. What Lives On? Investigating Life after Death, *New Dawn,* Special Issue No. 7, 2009.

Schoch, Robert M., & Logan Yonavjak. *The Parapsychology Revolution: A Concise Anthology of Paranormal and Psychical Research.* Jeremy P. Tarcher/Penguin, 2008.

Schoch, Robert. Time, Entanglement and Consciousness. *New Dawn* Special Issue 6(4) 2012.

Schwartz, Gary E. *The Truth About Medium.* Hampton Roads, 2005.

Schultz, Mona Lisa. *Awakening Intuition.* Three Rivers Press, 1998.

Sheldrake, Rupert. *Minds Beyond Brains: Recent Experimental Evidence.* <www.selfdiscoveryportal.com/Conquest.htm>.

Sheldrake, Rupert. *Morphic Resonance and Morphic Fields: An Introduction,* <www.sheldrake.org/Articles&Papers/papers/morphic/morphic_intro.html>.

Sheldrake, Rupert. *The Presence of the Past.* HarperCollinsPublishers, 1994.

Sheldrake, Rupert. The Sense of Being Stared At, Part 1. *Journal of Consciousness Studies,* 12(6) 2005, 10–31.

Shepherd, Peter. *Transforming the Mind,* 2005. <www.trans4mind.com/transformation>.

Sherwood, Jane. *The Country Beyond: The Doctrine of Re-Birth.* The C.W. Daniel Company Ltd, 1991.

Sicher, R., et al. A Randomized Double-Blind Study of the Effect of Distant Healing in a Population With Advanced AIDS Report of a Small Scale Study 246–51. *Western Journal of Medicine,* 169(6) 1998, 356–63.

Sidorov, Lian G. *On the Possible Mechanism of Intent in Paranormal Phenomena.* <www.journaloftheoretics.com/links/papers/intent.pdf>.

Sidorov, Lian. *Distant mental interactions, entanglement and energy signatures.* <www.emergentmind.org/proposalsII2.htm>.

Smelyakov, Sergey, & Yuri Karpenko. *The Auric Time Scale and the Mayan Factor: Demography, Seismicity and History of Great Revelations in the Light of the Solar-planetary Synchronism. Kharkov, 1999 Corrections, 2004.* <www.scottmandelker.com/TGS/Science/AMCC.pdf>.

Smith Jr., Frank D. *Penrose-Hameroff Quantum Tubulin Electrons, Chiao Gravity Antennas, and Mead Resonance,* 2002. <www.valdostamuseum.org/hamsmith/QM03.pdf>.

Smith, Paul. *Reading the Enemy's Mind: Inside Star Gate: America's Psychic Espionage Program.* <http://readingtheenemysmind.com/Excerpt.html>.

Sogyal Rinpoche. *The Tibetan Book of Living and Dying.* Rider Books, 2002.

Solis, Mark A. *The Hutchison Effect: An Explanation.* <www.world-mysteries.com/hutchison_e.htm>.

Solomon, Jane, & Grant Solomon. *Harry Oldfield's Invisible Universe.* Thorsons, 1998.

Spottiwsoode, S.J.P. Apparent association between effect size in free response anomalous cognition experiments and local sidereal time. *Journal of Scientific Exploration,* 11(2) 1997.

Standish, L.J. et al. Electroencephalographic Evidence of Correlated Event-related Signals between the Brains of Spatially and Sensory Isolated Human Subjects. *Journal of Alternative and Complementary Medicine,* 10(2) 2004, 3007–14.

Steiner, Rudolf. *An Outline of Occult Science,* 1972. <www.astroccult.net/AnOutlineofOccultScience_by_RudolfSteiner.pdf>.

Steiner, Rudolf. *Knowledge of the Higher Worlds,* 1918. <http://stopnwo.com/docs2/KnowledgeoftheHigher%20Worlds.pdf>.

Sterne, Christine. *Blueprints of the Cosmos,* 2008. <http://fliiby.com/file/840118/amwypfcl26.html>.

Stine, Harry C. *Mind Machines You Can Build*. Top of the Mountain Publishing, 1992.

Storm, Lance. Meta-Analysis in Parapsychology: II. Psi Domains other than Ganzfeld. *Australian Journal of Parapsychology*, 6(2) 2006, 135–55.

Strassman, Rick. *DMT: A Doctor's Revolutionary Research into the Biology of Near-Death and Mystical Experiences*. Park Street Press, 2001.

Strieber, Whitley. *The Secret School: Preparation for Contact*. Simon & Schuster, 1997.

Suri, H. A Critique of Contemporary Methods of Research Synthesis. *Post-Script*, 1(1) 2000. <www.edfac.unimelb.edu.au/research/resources/student_res/postscriptfiles/vol1/vol1_1_suri.pdf>.

Susskind, Leonard. *The Cosmic Landscape: String Theory and the Illusion of Intelligent Design*. Back Bay Books, 2006.

Sutherland, Cherie. *Transformed by the Light: Life After Near-Death Experiences*. Bantam Books, 1995.

Swami Panchadasi. *Clairvoyance and Occult Powers*, 1916. <www.astroccult.net/clairvoyance_and_occult_powers_by_panchadasi.pdf>.

Swami Panchadasi. *The Human Aura: Astral Colours and Thought Forms*. Project Gutenburg Ebook. Produced by Michael Ciesielski, Annika Feilbach and the booksmiths at <www.eBookForge.net>. First published by the Yoga Publication Society, 1912.

Swann, Ingo. A "Communication" from the Hard Drive Faculties of Our Species. <www.biomindsuperpowers.com/Pages/RealStoryCh19.html>.

Swann, Ingo. Cleve Backster, 1971. <www.biomindsuperpowers.com/Pages/RealStoryCh6.html>.

Swann, Ingo. Dr. Gertrude Schmeidler. <www.biomindsuperpowers.com/Pages/RealStoryCh9.html>.

Swann, Ingo. Mrs. Zelda Suplee, 1971. <www.biomindsuperpowers.com/Pages/RealStoryCh5.html>.

Swann, Ingo. News Item 100: Particles Moving Faster Than the Speed of Light! *News Items and Updates*, 1(August) 1997. <www.biomindsuperpowers.com/Pages/8-1.html>.

Swann, Ingo. Remote Viewing Processes and Layers of Meaning (June 2002). <www.biomindsuperpowers.com/Pages/rvandlayers.html>

Swann, Ingo. The Second Visit to SRI. <www.biomindsuperpowers.com/Pages/RealStoryCh53.html>.

Swann, Ingo. Toward Activating the Superpowers of the Human Biomind (March, 1997). <www.biomindsuperpowers.com/Pages/TowardActivating-4.html>.

Taimni, I.K. *The Science of Yoga: The Yoga Sutras of Patanjali*. Theosophical Publishing House, n.d.

Talbot, Michael. *The Holographic Universe*. HarperCollins, 1996.

Targ, Russel. Remote Viewing at Stanford Research Institute in the 1970s: A Memoir. *Journal of Scientific Exploration*, 10(1) 1996, 77–88.

Targ, Russel, Why I Believe in ESP and Why You Should Too, *New Dawn* Special Issue 6(4), 2012.

Targ, Russel, & Jane Katra, *The Scientific and Spiritual Implications of Psychic Abilities.* <www.espresearch.com/espgeneral/doc-AT.shtml>.

Targ, Russel, & Harold E. Puthoff, *Mind-Reach: Scientists Look at Psychic Abilities.* Hampton Roads, 2005.

Taylor, Roger. *Computerised Bioelectrography: Kirlian Photography Brought Up to Date.* <http://korotkov.org/file/computerised_bioelectrography.pdf>.

Taylor, Roger. Kirlian Photography and the New Bioelectrography, *Nexus* 14(3) 2007.

Tennenbaum, Jonathon. *Russian Discovery Challenges Existence of Absolute Time.* <www.21stcenturysciencetech.com/articles/time.html>.

Thomson, David. *Aether in Space is Fluid.* <http://softaether.blogspot.com/2009/05/aether-in-space-is-fluid.html>.

Tiller, William. Subtle Energies. *Science & Medicine*, 6(3) 1999. <www.tillerfoundation.com/subtle-energies.html>.

Tiller, William A. *Subtle Energy Actions and Physical Domain Correlations* <www.biomindsuperpowers.com/Pages/SubtleEnergyActions.html>.

Tiller, William. *Psychoenergetic Science: A Second Copernican-Scale Revolution.* Pavior Publishing, 2007.

Todeschi, Kevin J. *Edgar Cayce on the Akashic Records.* A.R.E. Press, 1999.

Underhill, Evelyn. *Man and the Supernatural.* E.P. Dutton & Company, 1928.

Uvarov, Valery, & Carl Agar, Synchronizing the Energy Bodies, *New Dawn*, No. 93, 2005.

Van der Leeuw, J. J. *The Conquest of Illusion.* Theosophical Publishing House, 1928.

Varvoglis, Mario *The Sheep/Goat Effect.* <www.parapsych.org/sheep_goat_effect.htm>.

Vayro, Ian Ross. *God Save Us from Religion.* Joshua Books, 2007.

Vayro, Ian Ross. *Tears in Heaven.* Joshua Books, 2008.

Vayro, Ian Ross. *They Lied to Us in Sunday School.* Joshua Books, 2006.

Venkatasubramanian G. et al. Investigating Paranormal Phenomena: Functional brain imaging of telepathy. <www.ahealthymind.org/library/Telepathy%20Venkatasubramanian%2009.pdf>.

Violette, John R. *Extra-Dimensional Universe.* Hampton Roads, 2001.

Vishita, Swami Bhakta. *Genuine Mediumship, or, The Invisible Powers.* Advanced Thought Publishing Co., 1919.

Vogl, Adalbert Albert. *Therese Neumann: Mystic and Stigmatist 1898–1962.* Tan Books and Publishers, Inc., 1987.

Vorley, Ethan. *Metaphysics.* Alchemy Realm Publications, 2006. <www.alchemyrealm.com/Metaphysics.pdf>.

Wackermann, J. Dyadic Correlations between Brain Functional States: Present Facts and Future Perspectives. *Mind and Matter*, 2(1), 105–122.

Waite, Margaret. *The Mystic Sciences.* Apollo Books, 1971.

Walsch, Neale Donald. *Conversations with God: An Uncommon Dialogue*, Books 1 & 2. Hodder & Stoughton, 1996.

Walsch, Neale Donald. *Conversations with God: An Uncommon Dialogue*, Book 3. Hampton Roads, 1998.

Warren, Henry C. *The Entrained Spatial Medium Gravitational Sink Model.* <www.olypen.com/hcwarren/SpatialFlow.pdf>

Warren, Joshua P. *How to Hunt Ghosts.* Fireside (Simon & Schuster), 2003.

Watson, Lyall. *Gifts of Unknown Things: A True Story of Nature, Healing and Initiation from Indonesia's "Dancing Island."* Destiny Books, 1991.

Watson, Lyall. *Supernature.* Coronet Books, Hodder Paperbacks Ltd, 1974.

Weiss, Brian. *Many Lives, Many Masters.* Fireside books, Simon & Schuster, 1988.

Welch, Robyn Elizabeth. *Conversations With the Body.* Hodder Mobius, 2002.

Werblin, Frank, & Botond Roska. The Movie in Our Eyes. *Scientific American* 296(4).

West, John Anthony. *Serpent in the Sky: The High Wisdom of Ancient Egypt.* Quest Books, 1993.

White, Michael. *Isaac Newton: The Last Sorcerer.* Basic Books, 1997.

Wicherink, Jan. *Souls of Distortion: A Convergence of Science and Spirituality*, ed. Neil Haddon. 14th edn, 2008. <www.soulsofdistortion.nl/SODA_toc.html>.

Wilber, Ken. *The Atman Project*, New Edition. Quest Books, 1996.

Wilcock, David. *Hyperdimensional Nebulae: Cubes in Space and the 2012 Case.* <http://divinecosmos.com/index.php?option=com_content&task=view&id=325&Itemid=30>.

Wilcock, David. *Shift of the Ages.* 2002. <www.divinecosmos.com/index.php?option=com_content&task=category&sectionid=6&id=18&Itemid=36>.

Wilcock, David. The Aether Science of Dr. N.A. Kozyrev, *Nexus*, 14(3) 2007.

Wilcock, David. *The Divine Cosmos.* 2001(?). <http://divinecosmos.com/start-here/books-free-online/20-the-divine-cosmos>.

Wilcock, David. *The Source Field Investigations.* Dutton, 2011.

Wilcock, David. *The Ultimate Secret of the Mayan Calendar: An Imploding Cycle of Energy Increase, Culminating in 2012–2013.* <http://divinecosmos.com/index.php?option=com_content&task=view&id=45&Itemid=30>.

Wilcock, David. *The Science of Oneness.* 2001(?). <http://divinecosmos.com/start-here/books-free-online/19-the-science-of-oneness>.

Wilde, Stuart. *Sixth Sense.* Hay House, Inc., Carlsbad, CA, 2000.

Wilkins, Hubert, & Harold M. Sherman. *Thoughts Through Space: A Remarkable Adventure in the Realm of Mind.* Hampton Roads, 2004

Williams, Kevin R. *Nothing Better than Death.* Xlibris Corporation, 2002. <www.near-death.com>.

Wilson, Colin. Mediums and Mystics, *New Dawn*, Special Issue No. 7, 2009.

Wilson, Colin. *The Occult.* Watkins Publishing, 2004.

Wilson, Robert Anton. *Cosmic Trigger.* New Falcon Publications, 1977.

Wilson, Robert Anton. *Prometheus Rising.* New Falcon Publications, 1983.

Wilson, Robert Anton. *Quantum Psychology.* New Falcon Publications, 1990.

Wilson, Robert Anton. *Wilhelm Reich in Hell.* New Falcon Publications, 1990.

Wolf, Fred Alan. *Parallel Universes: The Search for Other Worlds.* Simon & Schuster, 1988.

Wolf, Fred Alan. *The Soul and Quantum Physics,* <www.fredalanwolf.com/myarticles/Soul%20and%20death%20Q&A.pdf>.

Wolff, Milo. *The Origin of Instantaneous Action in Natural Laws.* <www.quantummatter.com/articles/the_origin_of_instantaneous.html>.

Wolinsky, Stephen. *Quantum Consciousness: A Guide to Experiencing Quantum Psychology.* Bramble Books, 1993.

Yogananda, Paramhansa. *Autobiography of a Yogi.* Self-Realization Fellowship, 2006.

Yurth, David G. *Seeing Past the Edge.* 1997/2002.

Yurth, David G. *Torsion Field* Mechanics: Verification of Non-local Field Effects in Human Biology, 2000. <www.clayandiron.com/news.jhtml?method=view&news.id=1509>.

Yurth, David G. *Y-Bias and Angularity: The Dynamics of Self-Organizing Criticality From the Zero Point to Infinity.* 2007.

Zammit, Victor. *A Lawyer Presents the Case for the Afterlife.* 2006. <www.victor zammit.com>.

Zeilinger, Anton. *Dance of the Photons: From Einstein to Quantum Teleportation.* Farrar, Straus & Giroux, 2010.

Zeilinger, A., & M. Aspelmeyer. *A Quantum Renaissance.* <www.physicsworld.com>.

Zeilinger, A., & A.C. Elitzur, *Shrodinger's Cat: Quantum versus Classical World?* 2003. <http://a-c-elitzur.co.il/site/siteArticle.asp?ar=36>.

Zuger, Abigail. Removing Half of Brain Improves Young Epileptics' Lives. *New York Times,* Aug. 19, 1997. <www.nytimes.com/1997/08/19/science/removing-half-of-brain-improves-young-epileptics-lives.html?src=pm>.

INDEX

CPSIA information can be obtained
at www.ICGtesting.com
Printed in the USA
BVHW03s1704090518
515756BV00031B/528/P